D1206093

Researches in Geochemistry

A seminar series conducted at the Department of Geology

The Johns Hopkins University

Researches in Geochemistry

Edited by

PHILIP H. ABELSON

Director, Geophysical Laboratory
Carnegie Institution of Washington

NEW YORK • JOHN WILEY & SONS, INC.

London • Chapman & Hall, Limited

Library of Congress Catalog Card Number: 59-6755

PRINTED IN THE UNITED STATES OF AMERICA

Contributors

PHILIP H. ABELSON, *Director, Geophysical Laboratory, Carnegie Institution of Washington, Washington, D. C.*

GUSTAF O. S. ARRHENIUS, *Associate Professor of Biogeochemistry, Scripps Institution of Oceanography, La Jolla, California*

WAYNE U. AULT, *Chemist, U. S. Geological Survey, Washington, D. C.*

PAUL B. BARTON, Jr., *Geologist, U. S. Geological Survey, Washington, D. C.*

FRANCIS R. BOYD, *Staff Member, Geophysical Laboratory, Carnegie Institution of Washington, Washington, D. C.*

FELIX CHAYES, *Staff Member, Geophysical Laboratory, Carnegie Institution of Washington, Washington, D. C.*

SYDNEY P. CLARK, Jr., *Staff Member, Geophysical Laboratory, Carnegie Institution of Washington, Washington, D. C.*

GORDON L. DAVIS, *Staff Member, Geophysical Laboratory, Carnegie Institution of Washington, Washington, D. C.*

EGON T. DEGENS, *Visiting Assistant Professor of Geochemistry, The Pennsylvania State University, University Park, Pennsylvania (now at Geologisches Institut der Universität, Würzburg, Germany)*

HESSEL DE VRIES, *Professor of Biophysics, University of Groningen, Groningen, Netherlands*

SAMUEL EPSTEIN, *Associate Professor of Geochemistry, Division of Geological Sciences, California Institute of Technology, Pasadena, California*

HANS P. EUGSTER, *Staff Member, Geophysical Laboratory, Carnegie Institution of Washington, Washington, D. C. (now at Department of Geology, The Johns Hopkins University, Baltimore, Maryland)*

ROBERT M. GARRELS, *Professor of Geology, Harvard University, Cambridge, Massachusetts*

JULIAN R. GOLDSMITH, *Professor of Geology, University of Chicago, Chicago, Illinois*

WILLIAM E. HANSON, *Administrative Fellow, Gulf Research and Development Company, Mellon Institute, Pittsburgh, Pennsylvania*

HERBERT E. HAWKES, *Professor of Mineral Exploration, University of California, Berkeley, California*

MACKENZIE L. KEITH, *Professor of Geochemistry, The Pennsylvania State University, University Park, Pennsylvania*

KONRAD B. KRAUSKOPF, *Professor of Geochemistry, Stanford University, Stanford, California*

GUNNAR KULLERUD, *Staff Member, Geophysical Laboratory, Carnegie Institution of Washington, Washington, D. C.*

WILLARD F. LIBBY, *Commissioner, U. S. Atomic Energy Commission, Washington, D. C.; Research Associate, Carnegie Institution of Washington, Washington, D. C.*

GORDON J. F. MACDONALD, *Associate Professor of Geophysics, Massachusetts Institute of Technology, Cambridge, Massachusetts (now at Institute of Geophysics, University of California, Los Angeles, California)*

CHARLES MILTON, *Geologist, U. S. Geological Survey, Washington, D. C.*

GEORGE W. REED, *Associate Chemist, Argonne National Laboratory, Lemont, Illinois*

JAMES B. THOMPSON, JR., *Associate Professor of Mineralogy, Harvard University, Cambridge, Massachusetts*

GEORGE R. TILTON, *Staff Member, Geophysical Laboratory, Carnegie Institution of Washington, Washington, D. C.*

Preface

A major revolution in research activity in earth science has been going on for the past decade. It is reflected in the strong and increasing emphasis on laboratory findings in the papers presented at the annual meetings of the Geological Society of America, and it is underlined by the establishing in 1955 of the Geochemical Society, an organization which continues to grow.

The characteristic pattern of present-day research is one of intensive individual efforts, only partly correlated, as investigators singly or in small groups pursue their separate interests. Their findings are published in literally hundreds of highly diversified journals. Faced by this outpouring of new information, the earth scientists, both the professionals and those in training, can scarcely keep abreast with the developing frontier of geochemistry.

As a contribution toward the alleviation of this situation, the Geophysical Laboratory of the Carnegie Institution of Washington organized a seminar series in geochemistry, held at the Laboratory and at the Johns Hopkins University during the academic year 1957–1958. The shared enthusiasm of the participants in the lectures and discussions, their enlarged perspectives over their field and their own orientation within it, are communicated in these essays, assembled at the conclusion of the series, and similarly entitled, *Researches in Geochemistry.*

Topics were chosen to provide a cross section of current research activity in numerous areas of inquiry. New developments in nuclear geology are presented by Libby (tritium), Epstein (use of oxygen isotopes in geothermometry), Ault (isotopic sulfur), and Reed (activation analysis). Geochronology is treated by Tilton and Davis (dating of ancient rocks) and de Vries (C^{14} developments). Chemical considerations pertaining to ore solutions, deposits, and prospecting are set forth by Krauskopf (composition of a magmatic gas phase), Barton (chemical environment of ore deposition), Kullerud (sulfide geothermometry), and Hawkes (geochemical prospecting). Geochemistry of organic substances, including petroleum, is discussed by Abelson (organic geochemistry) and Hanson (petroleum). Some processes occurring at low temperatures, including sedimentation, are examined by Arrhenius (deep-sea sedimentation), Garrels (reactions at low temperatures), Keith and Degens (criteria of marine versus nonmarine environments), and Milton and Eugster (minerals in the Green River shale). Some of the reactions occurring during metamorphism are considered by Thompson (metasomatism), Boyd (amphiboles), and Eugster (iron minerals). The geochemistry of carbonates is treated by Goldsmith, and short-range ordering by Chayes. Considerations important to our view of the interior of the earth are presented by MacDonald (constitution of the earth) and Clark (high-pressure phenomena).

Each essay reviews the present status of research in its specific area, describes the author's recent contributions, and contains an extensive selected bibliography.

Limitations on time and space restricted the number of contributions that could be included. This volume does not pretend to embrace all or even a major fraction of the activity in geochemistry. I hope, however, that the essays will interest and stimulate, and serve as a valuable reference source, both for graduate students and for all who are interested and active in earth science.

I am indebted to many colleagues for advice in the choice of participants and reviewers. The cooperation of Professor Aaron C. Waters of the Johns Hopkins University and of Professor Gordon J. F. MacDonald of the University of California at Los Angeles is especially appreciated. The members of the staff at the Geophysical Laboratory gave generous and able assistance in editing the manuscripts. The office staff was most helpful and efficient, particularly Dolores M. Thomas, the editor, and Marjorie E. Imlay, stenographer. A. D. Singer can be credited with a superb job of expediting. Final editing for style was the responsibility of Lucile B. Stryker of the Office of Publications of the Carnegie Institution of Washington.

PHILIP H. ABELSON

Geophysical Laboratory
Washington, D. C.
December 3, 1958

Contents

Sedimentation on the Ocean Floor

GUSTAF O. S. ARRHENIUS

Scripps Institution of Oceanography

Minerals accumulating on the ocean floor from suspension or solution in sea water have their origin in all the geospheres and in outer space. Owing to differences in physicochemical processes involved in the formation of solids in the lithosphere, the hydrosphere, the biosphere, the atmosphere, and extraterrestrial space, the source of sedimentary minerals can often be determined from their isotopic or elemental composition, crystal structure, or other characteristic properties. Variations in the rate and type of contribution from these different sources can be traced in the sedimentary record, and they yield information on the geological history of the earth. Events that have a global or wide regional effect and a duration in time of the order of 10^3 years or more are particularly well registered in the pelagic deposits, and in favorable cases can be quantitatively reconstructed.

Lithogenous Components

The lithogenous components of pelagic sediments are chemically unaltered debris of igneous and metamorphic rocks, mechanically disintegrated by weathering, transport processes, or volcanic eruptions, and transported into the ocean by wind or water. Some of the components of igneous and metamorphic rocks are unstable in sea water and transform rapidly into stable hydrous minerals, especially when present in a finely divided state. Quartz, feldspar, and mica are the most common relatively stable lithogenous minerals found in ocean sediments.

The rate of lateral transport by ocean currents is low in comparison with the sinking rate in water of sand- and silt-sized mineral grains, and of the flocs formed by coagulation of the fine-grained fraction of silicate minerals. As a result, the bulk of water-borne detrital matter from continents and islands is deposited in a zone with a width of a few hundred kilometers or less, surrounding the source areas. The rate of accumulation in areas of continuous deposition within this zone varies between the order of 10^{-1} cm·millennium^{-1} in the peripheral part and several orders of magnitude higher in the inner part. Thus, continents, islands, and seamounts are surrounded by sedimentary and volcanic aprons, ending in smooth plains, which border the low-relief areas typical of very low rates of deposition (Menard, 1956) (fig. 1).

Owing to submarine slumping, solifluction, and discharge of rivers with a high sediment load into the ocean, high-density suspensions are generated, which can be propagated along the ocean bottom over long distances (Kuenen and Migliorini, 1950). The marginal zone of rapid deposition around continents and islands is broadened by these processes, especially where, as in the Atlantic Ocean, the submarine channels perpendicular to the coast feed the suspension beyond the continental shelf into the deep ocean. Troughs and ridges parallel to the coast, as in parts of the Indo-Pacific Ocean, impede the spreading of sediments by turbidity flow into the ocean basins.

The lowest rates of contribution of lithogenous and other continental minerals accordingly are found in ocean basins far from land and protected against turbidity flow by trenches and ridges. Examples of such areas are shown in figures 1 and 2. The contribution of lithogenous minerals to sedimentation in such protected areas appears to be of the order 10^{-2} to 10^{-1} cm·millennium^{-1} and to consist mainly of wind-borne material. The rate of supply of this material consequently reflects the distribution over the earth of arid source areas and of strong, persistent air currents. This is exemplified by the occurrence of atmospheric dust around the continents (fig. 3) and by the high quartz content of Pacific sediments below the tropical jet stream in the northern hemisphere (Goldberg and Rex, 1958).

Hydrogenous Components

Hydrogenous minerals are formed from solutes in the ocean or in the continental part of the hydrosphere. It has been demonstrated (Correns and von Engelhardt, 1938) that the components of igneous silicates are ionically dissolved in weathering, and hydrogenous minerals like the clays appear to be formed largely by precipitation from such solutions. It is not known to what extent the clay minerals of pelagic deposits are precipitated from solution in the ocean, or to what

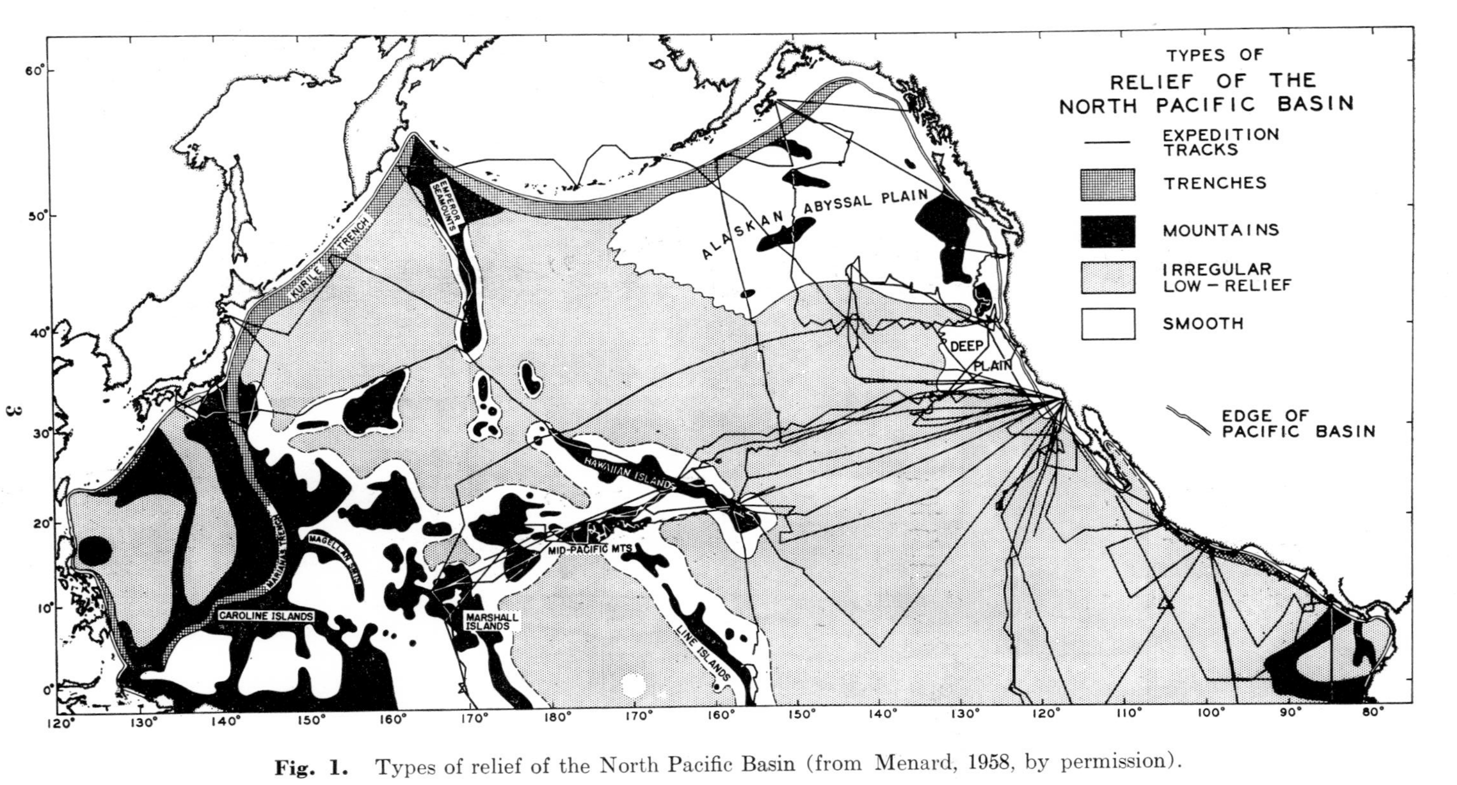

Fig. 1. Types of relief of the North Pacific Basin (from Menard, 1958, by permission).

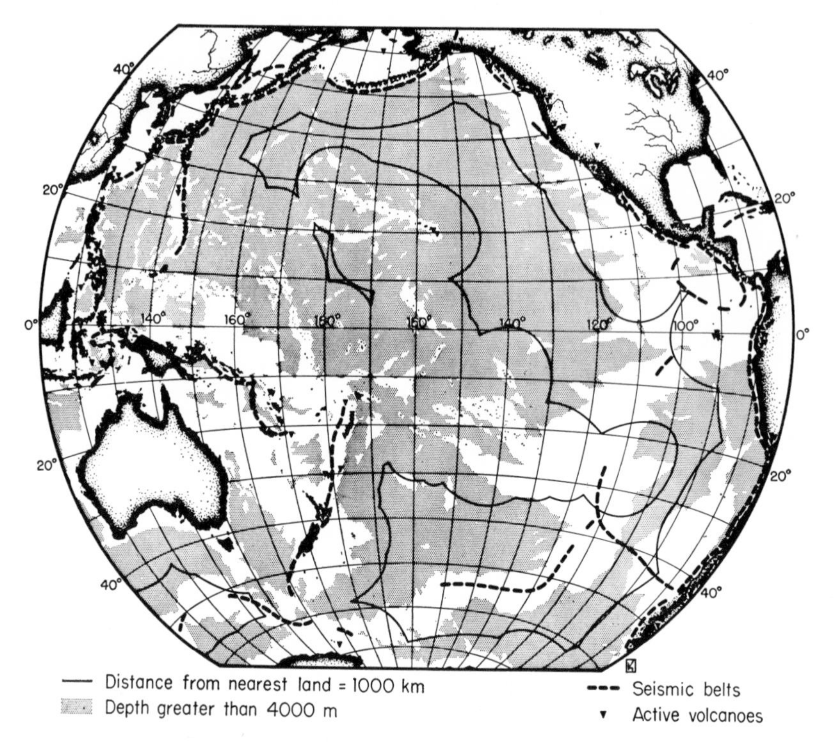

Fig. 2. Main topographic, seismic, and volcanic features of the Pacific (from Revelle, Bramlette, Arrhenius, and Goldberg, 1955, by permission).

proportion they represent precipitates formed shortly after dissolution of the continental igneous source minerals and subsequently transported into the ocean by water or wind (Arrhenius, 1954; Goldberg and Arrhenius, 1958). There is good evidence that montmorillonite is formed by decomposition of volcanic glass on the ocean floor. The problem of the site of formation of clay minerals is of interest from a general geochemical and petrological as well as from a historical-geological point of view, as variations in time of the composition of any clay minerals of marine origin would reflect variations in the composition of the ocean. Such a gradual change from Cambrian to Recent is indicated by the composition of the clays on the Siberian shield (Vinogradov and Ronov, 1956). Other workers, however, suggest that most of the clays are formed at the site of weathering and subsequently transported to the sea (Weaver, 1958). Evidence for a continental or marine origin of hydrous silicate minerals of the ocean

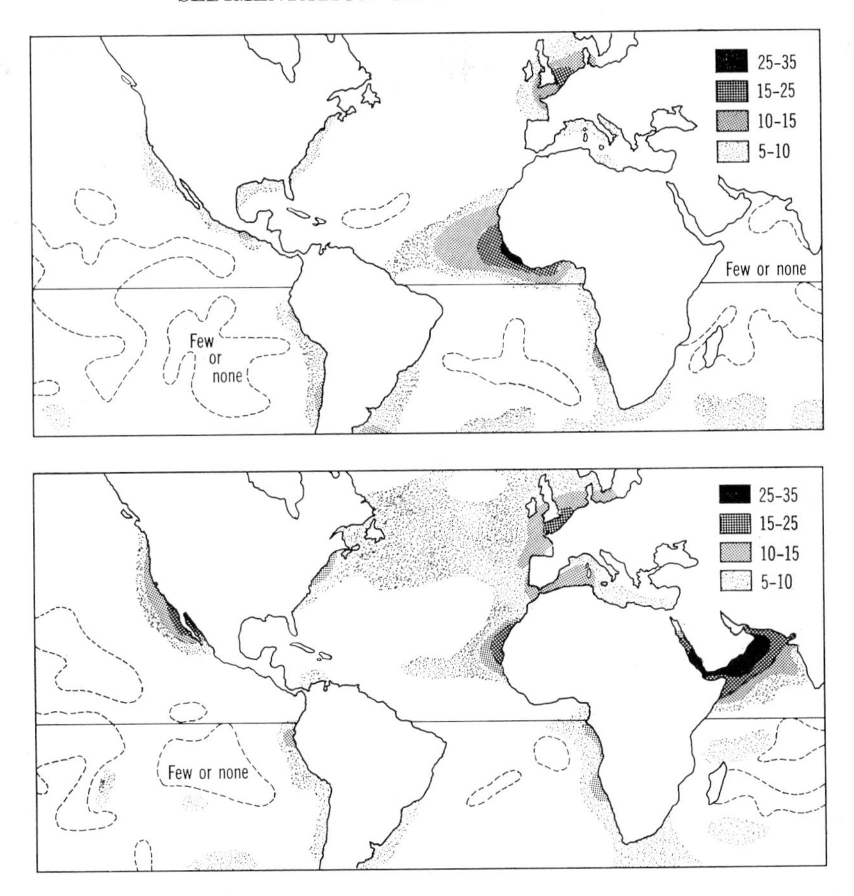

Fig. 3. Average frequency of haze during northern winter (upper graph) and summer season (lower graph). The figures indicate reported cases of haze in percentage of total number of observations. Haze is defined as generally due to microscopic particles in the atmosphere, such as smoke, dust, or salt, with visibility 1 to 2 km, as distinguished from mist and fog, caused by droplets of water.

The extensive transport of eolian sand and dust by the harmattan in winter and by the southwest monsoon in summer is indicated by the high corresponding frequencies of haze. This transport is also evident from the content of silt-sized rounded calcite and quartz, the quartz frequently with blistered surface and ferric hydroxide coating of the grains, in the sediments below the areas of high haze frequency in the equatorial Atlantic and Indian Ocean (Correns, 1953; Radczewski, 1939; Arrhenius, 1950). Similar evidence is found in the Mediterranean (Norin, 1958).

The haze area in northwestern Europe is probably due to industrial smoke production. Forest fires are believed to contribute to the Atlantic high-latitude haze during the northern summer. (Redrawn from McDonald, 1938.)

floor could be derived from their oxygen isotope composition and from studies of the distribution and turnover of dissolved species of aluminum in sea water.

A frequently occurring component of slowly depositing pelagic sediments is the zeolite phillipsite. The relatively large size of the crystals, and their occurrence, make it clear that this silicate mineral is definitely of marine hydrogenous origin, but little is known so far about its mode of formation. Owing to its high ion-exchange capacity phillipsite appears to play an important role in the sorption of ions diffusing through the sediment. As a result, variations in concentration of this zeolite markedly influence the ultimate distribution of radium in the sediment as described below.

Another hydrogenous component of importance in pelagic deposits is a group of hydrated manganese–iron oxide minerals that constitute microscopic aggregates distributed through the sediment. In places where the micronodules remain at the sediment surface for a considerable length of time, they grow to macroscopic dimensions, and finally cover parts of the ocean bottom as a pavement. Such pavements are estimated to extend over 10 per cent of the ocean floor (Menard, personal communication), and constitute high-grade manganese ores of potential usefulness (Goldberg and Picciotto, 1955; Dietz, 1955). The rate of growth appears to vary between the order of 10^{-2} and 10^{-3} $cm \cdot millennium^{-1}$. The crystal structure is strongly disordered and has recently been demonstrated (Buser and Grütter, 1956) to be a double layer consisting of MnO_2 alternating with $Mn(OH)_2$ together with $Fe(OH)_3$ and varying amounts of other heavy metals like Pb, Mo, Co, Cu, Zn, Th, and the rare-earth elements. It has been suggested that the manganese nodules are formed by catalytic oxidation of the manganous ion in sea water by a gel film of ferric oxide hydrate, formed at the bottom surface by discharge of the ferric oxide hydrate colloid in sea water (Goldberg and Arrhenius, 1958). Heavy-metal ions are scavenged from sea water by this process, and by similar ones referred to below. Coprecipitation and sorption thus appear to be the most important mechanisms regulating the concentration of these ions in the ocean.

The solubility relations of apatite in sea water are not well known, although it is evident that apatite is unstable in present-day deep water which has a low temperature and a high CO_2 tension; the apatite of skeletal remains thus slowly goes into solution on the ocean floor. In shallow water, hydrogenous apatite appears to form today from phosphate ion in solution, largely by isomorphous replacement of calcite, which is also sometimes found to be altered into dolomite (Bramlette, personal communication). The widespread occurrence of hydrogenous apatite in the Lower and Middle Tertiary sediments, outcropping on seamounts and other topographic highs in the Pacific Ocean, suggests that the replacement process was operative over a greater depth range in pre-Pleistocene time, when the deep water had a temperature higher than the present one by 10° or more. Such a temperature differential is indicated by oxygen-isotope measurements on benthonic foraminifera (Emiliani and Edward, 1953).

Owing to its peculiar structure, biogenous apatite dissolving on the deep sea floor offers a suitable surface for the adsorption and fixation as phosphates of the rare-earth elements and of thorium isotopes (Arrhenius, Bramlette, and Picciotto, 1957). Rare-earth contents up to a few per cent of the aggregate weight are thus accumulated, and a large part of the thorium, including ionium (Th^{230}), is transferred from the sea water to the biogenous apatite. The apatite-bearing skeletal debris also contains an organic component consisting chiefly of alteration products of collagen. Heavy-metal ions, mainly Zn, Cu, Pb, Sn, and Ag, are transferred from sea water to these organic phases. The zinc concentration may amount to 5 per cent or more of the organic phase, and the element appears to occur as salts of higher fatty acids.

Marine hydrogenous barite is not common in most parts of the ocean, but in deposits below areas of high organic productivity it occurs in concentrations of several per cent, more than twenty times above the level found in adjacent areas (fig. 4). The barite occurs as euhedral

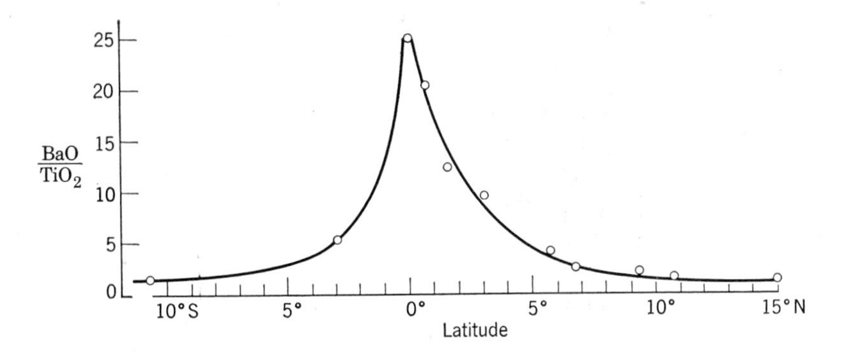

Fig. 4. Relative rate of accumulation of barium as a function of latitude, across the equatorial zone of high organic productivity. The rate is represented by the ratio BaO/TiO_2 in Postglacial sediments. (Redrawn from Goldberg and Arrhenius, 1958.)

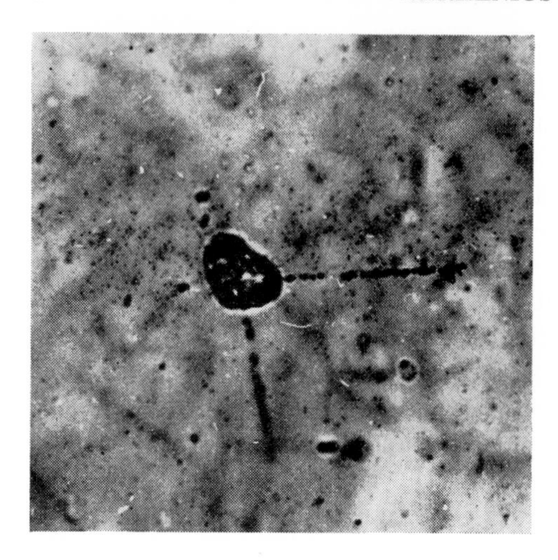

Fig. 5. Radioautograph showing α tracks emerging from fecal pellet with inclusions of barite. Track length, approximately 20 microns. The pellet is immersed in the nuclear photographic emulsion (from Picciotto and Arrhenius, unpublished).

crystals, mostly 3 to 20 microns in size, free or growing as inclusions in fecal pellets from mud-eating animals (fig. 5). The high rate of accumulation of barite in high-productivity areas and especially inside fecal pellets is believed to depend on an increased sulfate-ion concentration due to the decomposition of proteins and the subsequent oxidation of sulfide to sulfate ion by dissolved oxygen.

Biogenous Components

Skeletal remains of plants and animals form a large part of ocean sediments. Most abundant are remains of unicellular planktonic organisms with skeletal structures consisting of calcite or opaline silica. These, as well as other biogenous solids, are unstable under the conditions prevailing at the sediment-water interface in the deep ocean, with the order of decreasing solubility: aragonite, calcite, opal, apatite. The rates of accumulation of these components thus vary between wide limits: calcite, for example, from zero to the order of 5 $cm \cdot millennium^{-1}$. Calcite does not accumulate in areas where the dissolution rate outweighs the production rate, as at great ocean depths or below areas with moderate or low productivity of plankton having carbonate skeletons.

The highest rates of accumulation of calcite are found in tropical areas with high organic productivity in the surface layer of the ocean, as below the zone of upwelling along the equator in the East Pacific Ocean. In this zone diatoms form an important part of the phytoplankton, but the rate of accumulation of diatomaceous silica on the bottom reaches values only about one-fifth that of calcium carbonate. In the temperate and polar areas of high organic productivity, planktonic organisms with calcareous skeletons resistant enough to withstand dissolution are relatively rare, and diatomaceous silica is the most important biogenous component accumulating on the ocean floor.

Phosphatic debris of scales, bones, and teeth of fish forms a geochemically important component of ocean sediments, responsible for all the phosphorus now depositing on the deep ocean floor. The structure is typical of phosphatic skeletons in higher animals: a fibrous aggregate consisting of parallel-aligned apatite crystallites, elongated along the *Z* axis and with an interstitial matrix of alteration products of original collagen. The size of the apatite crystallites varies in different groups of organisms; average lengths of 300 to 400 Å were found in bone fragments of bathypelagic fish and 600 to 1200 Å in ear bones of whales, one of the few mammal remains found on the ocean floor. The internal surface of the apatite of fish debris, computed from the crystallite size, amounts to 100–200 $m^2 \cdot g^{-1}$, which partly explains the efficiency of the fish debris in scavenging heavy metals from sea water.

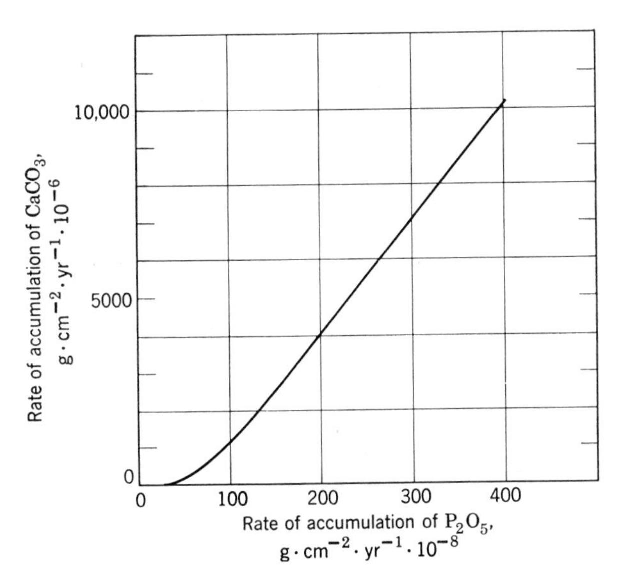

Fig. 6. Average relation between the rates of accumulation of calcium carbonate and of phosphate in sediments from the east equatorial Pacific (from Arrhenius, 1952, by permission).

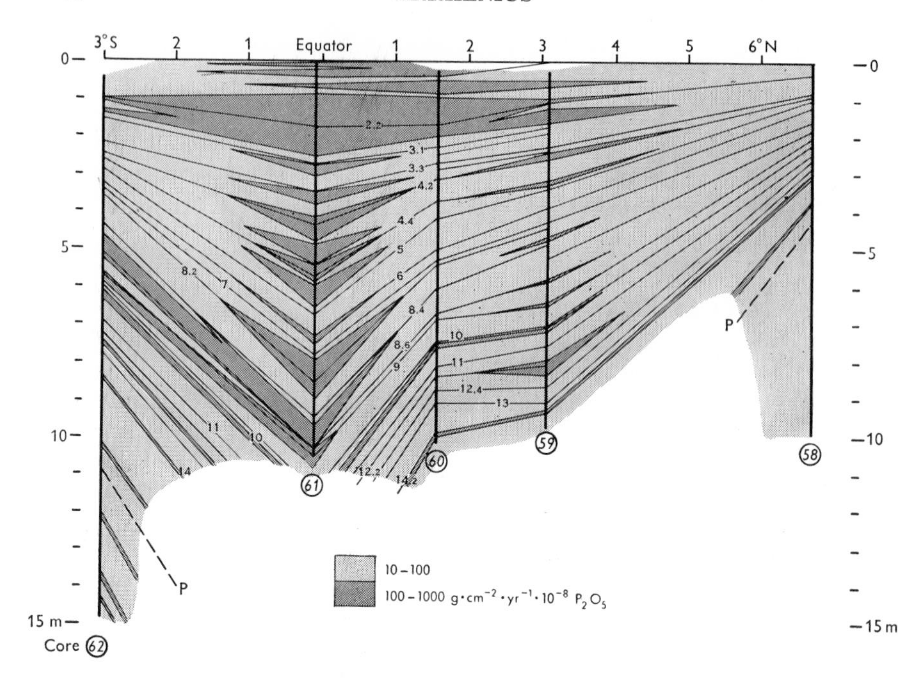

Fig. 7. Rate of accumulation of phosphate in a meridional section through the sediments of the east equatorial Pacific at about longitude 130° W. Vertical lines mark the sampling locations. The numbers in the figure indicate stratigraphic units. The highest rate of accumulation of phosphate is found below the equatorial zone of high productivity, and in the even-number stages and substages, which also show the highest rates of accumulation of biogenous calcite and opal. These units are interpreted as corresponding to ages and subages of an increased trade-wind intensity, and therefore of intensified upwelling and organic productivity in the equatorial divergence (from Arrhenius, 1952, by permission).

The concentration of fish debris is generally low and of the order of 0.1 to 5 per cent. The higher values in this range are found mostly in clay sediments laid down during Tertiary time, when the rate of transport of detrital material from the continents into the ocean was lower than in the Pleistocene, and consequently marine hydrogenous and biogenous components were less diluted by detrital minerals.

The rate of accumulation of fish debris is highly variable, and closely proportional to the rate of accumulation of calcium carbonate (figs. 6, 7, and 8). The rate of accumulation of biogenous apatite is another parameter reflecting organic productivity in the ocean, and the populations of fish responsible for the main part of the debris are stationary

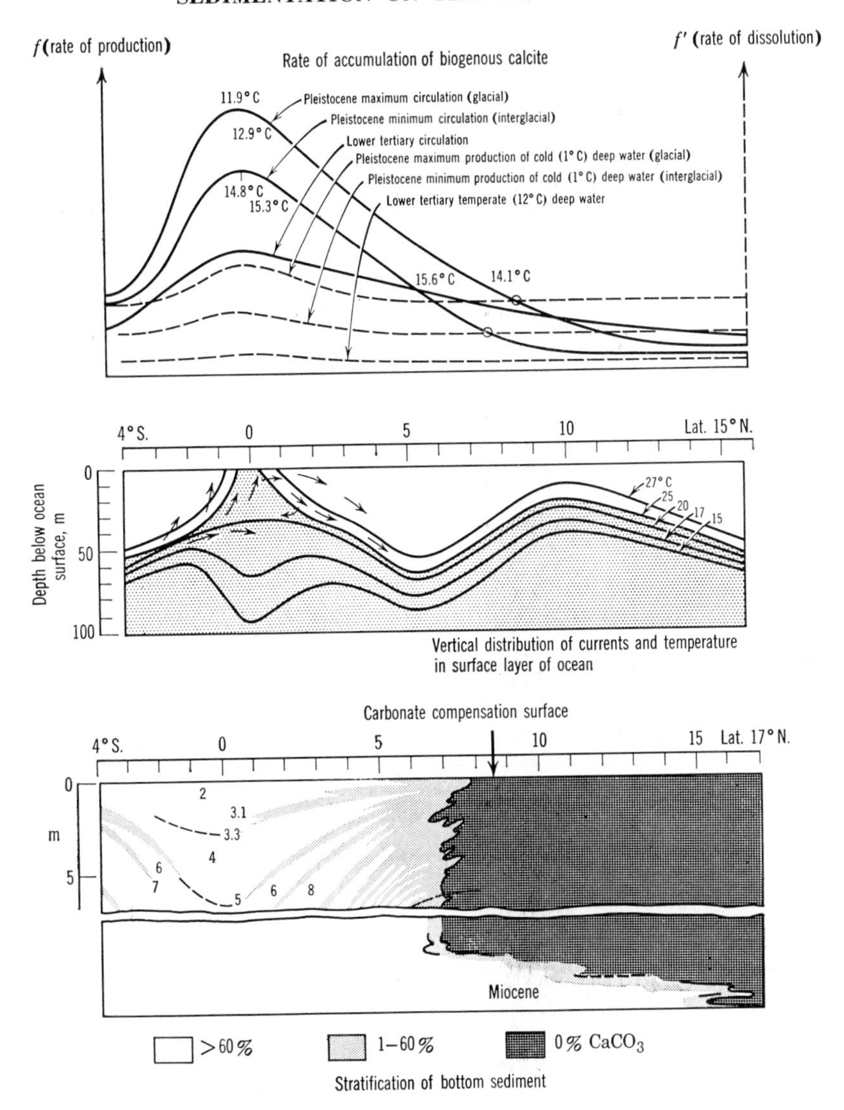

Fig. 8. Meridional profile at approximately longitude 130° W. in the Pacific Ocean, showing the distribution of properties in the surface layer of the ocean (middle graph), the stratification of the bottom sediment (lower graph), and interpretation of the sedimentary record in terms of rates of production, dissolution, and accumulation of calcium carbonate from planktonic organisms (upper graph).

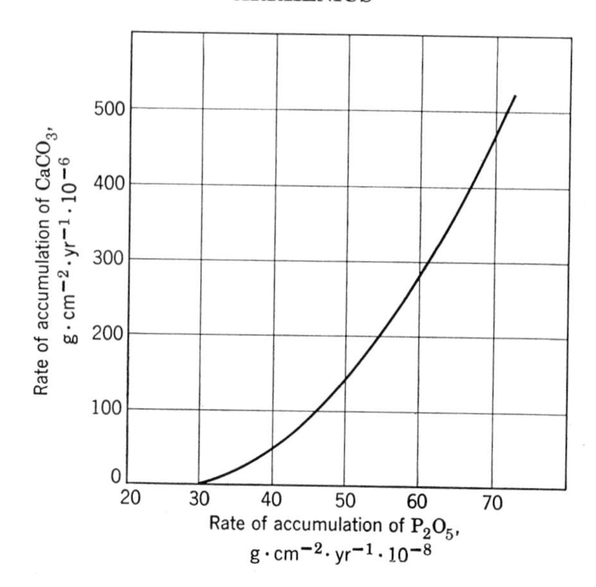

Fig. 9. Lower part of curve shown in figure 6, showing nonlinearity. This part of the distribution is based on approximately 300 samples (from Arrhenius, 1952, by permission).

below the zones of productivity. The characteristics of teeth, bone, and scale debris indicate that it is derived mostly from small species of bathypelagic fish.

In the range of accumulation rate of calcium carbonate below a few hundred $mg \cdot cm^{-2} \cdot millennium^{-1}$ the fraction of carbonate lost by dissolution on the ocean floor is large, and owing to the lower rate of dissolution of apatite as compared with calcite the sediments are left relatively richer in phosphate (fig. 9).

Cosmogenous Components

The accretion of solids from outer space occurs at such a low rate that cosmogenous objects of small size cannot be readily recognized in the rapidly accumulating terrestrial and epicontinental sediments. In slowly growing oceanic deposits, however, microscopic spherical droplets of nickel-iron are found, which are most probably of cosmic origin. The rate of accumulation of these objects appears to be of the order of $4 \cdot 10^{-8}$ $g \cdot cm^{-2} \cdot millennium^{-1}$ (Laevastu and Mellis, 1955), but the total rate of accretion of meteoritic dust may be higher. The nickel-iron droplets that have been found are approximately 15 to 230 microns in diameter. Smaller spherules could have formed a considerable proportion of the original distribution and might later have been decomposed by oxidation. An error of a factor of 2 in the estimate is possible from this effect. Further, cosmogenous silicates certainly accompany the nickel-iron dust reaching the earth, and it seems probable that the mass ratio of the two components is of the same order as the frequency ratio of observed falls of stone meteorites to those of iron meteorites, i.e. around 14. The total rate of accretion of unvaporized cosmogenous matter on the earth may thus be at least of the order of 10^{-6} $g \cdot cm^{-2} \cdot millennium^{-1}$, or 5000 tons over the surface of the earth per year.[1] A more accurate estimate of the accretion rate of unvaporized cosmogenous silicate dust and its variation with time might be obtained from a study of the distribution in pelagic clay sediments of the monoclinic magnesium-iron pyroxenes clinoenstatite-clinohypersthene, which occur in meteorites but are rare in tellurian igneous rocks.

Chronology of Ocean Sediments

The pelagic deposits provide a unique record of the general geological evolution of the earth during the Cenozoic era. Hence it is of interest to devise accurate methods for determination of the age of the strata that make up this system. The application of such methods further provides information on the rate of geological processes both in the past and at present.

The radiocarbon of biogenous calcite has been used to date late Glacial and Postglacial strata (Arrhenius, Kjellberg, and Libby, 1951; Arrhenius, 1952; Emiliani, 1955). These correspond to the top meter or less of the sediment, and the limitations of the method prevent dating of the deeper parts of the sequences. Attempts have been made to calibrate by radiocarbon some other property of the sediment believed to be time dependent, and to extrapolate the age in older strata from the distribution of this property. Depth in the core (Emiliani, 1955) has been chosen as such a property, on the basis of the fact that the thickness of individual strata is very uniform in certain profiles from the Atlantic Ocean and on the assumption that this indicates

[1] This computation uses values for density, water content, and rate of deposition of the sediment based on more recent work and slightly different from those employed by Laevastu and Mellis.

approximate constancy in time of the total rate of deposition, including biogenous, lithogenous, and hydrogenous solids.

In another case (Arrhenius, 1952) the variation in space of the rate of deposition of different components was investigated; it was found that in a topographically protected area distant from land in the east equatorial Pacific the rate of accumulation of titanium showed only little variability in space in spite of variations of the total rate of deposition by more than a factor of 10. It was also found that in those parts of this area where the biogenous contribution did not vary markedly with depth in the top few meters of sediment, i.e., with time throughout Upper Pleistocene, the titanium content remained nearly constant. These facts were taken to indicate that the rate of accumulation of titanium has remained constant within narrow limits during Upper Pleistocene over the area in question. A certain mass of titanium in a column of unit cross section would under these conditions approximately correspond to a definite length of time. This time span was determined by the radiocarbon age of the lower boundary of a column with a known titanium content.

Extrapolations based on this method, and on the one mentioned previously, give reasonable results, with agreement between the Atlantic and Pacific climatic records to an estimated age of about 100,000 years. For strata older than this, extrapolation in the Atlantic and the Pacific has given divergent results, leading to an estimate of about half a million years for the total length of the Pleistocene from the Atlantic record as compared with the order of a million years from the Pacific record. Efforts are therefore being made to determine the age of the Upper Pleistocene strata directly by a method involving the specific activity of ionium, described later.

Attempts have recently been made (Arnold, 1956; J. Merrill, M. Honda, and J. R. Arnold, unpublished; Goel et al., 1957; Peters, 1955, 1957) to use radioactive Be^{10} for age determination of marine sediments. This nuclide is formed in the upper atmosphere by the action of cosmic-ray particles on nitrogen and oxygen, and has a half-life of $2.7 \cdot 10^6$ years, which makes it quite suitable for work on Upper Pliocene and Pleistocene strata. One difficulty, however, is the short residence time (a few hundred years) of beryllium in sea water, preventing complete mixing through the oceans before precipitation takes place.

The refinement of the potassium-argon method has made it possible to measure sediments in the age range 10^7 to 10^8 years in cases where hydrogenous minerals occur with a satisfactory retentivity for argon (Wasserburg, Hayden, and Jensen, 1956). The hydrous mica glauconite has been used for this purpose. Further advantages may be offered by use of potassium-bearing hydrogenous apatite, which has a dense structure and thus possibly a high gas retentivity. Leakage of argon can be controlled by checking the amount of helium derived from uranium in the mineral.

The recent development of a method for age determination by rhenium 187, decaying into osmium 187 with an estimated half-life of $6.2 \cdot 10^{10}$ years (Herr and Merz, 1958), is of potential usefulness for ocean sediments older than about $25 \cdot 10^{6}$ years, i.e. Lower and Middle Tertiary and older. The application of this method to marine sediments would require an investigation of the aqueous geochemistry of rhenium and osmium, as the accuracy in this case depends on a high specific concentration of the radiogenic osmium isotope.

The earliest attempts to develop an absolute method for age determination in pelagic sediments made use of the distribution of the members of the U^{238}-series elements. Pettersson in 1938 made the important discovery that the high radium content of young pelagic sediments is supported by the parent element Th^{230} (ionium), which is separated from its predecessor, uranium, by precipitation from solution in sea water. For technical reasons Pettersson and his co-workers (Pettersson, 1938, 1953; Kröll, 1955), as well as other workers in the field, chose to measure radon in equilibrium with radium, assuming that the radium in the sediment would be in equilibrium with ionium. It was soon found that in many sedimentary sequences radium is more irregularly distributed than would be expected from decay of regularly distributed ionium. In some Pacific sequences with strata containing much of the zeolite phillipsite, radium has been found to be concentrated in the phillipsite (Arrhenius and Goldberg, 1955). In the absence of indications of a corresponding concentration of ionium, it appears that, upon decay of ionium in the sediment, part of the radium formed goes into solution and diffuses through the sediment, and part is resorbed in minerals with high ion-exchange capacity. Another trap for migrating radium is provided by hydrogenous barite growing in the sediment, which thus becomes one of the most strongly α-active components of the sediment (Arrhenius, Bramlette, and Picciotto, 1957; Picciotto and Arrhenius, unpublished) (fig. 5). A considerable amount of the dissolved radium appears to be returned to the ocean by this diffusion process, and a corresponding increase of the radium content of sea water with increasing depth in the ocean has been demonstrated (Koczy, 1956).

It thus appears doubtful that the radium content of the sediment can in any case be interpreted in terms of geological age; also the lack of a specific activity in radium makes the results sensitive to variations in the rate of accumulation of the parent element and of other sedimentary components. A way out of this difficulty was indicated by Picciotto, who devised a method for the direct determination of the specific activity of ionium, using as a reference isotope Th^{232}. Goldberg and Koide (1958), who developed an α-spectrometric method for the simultaneous determination of ionium and thorium, carried out a number of determinations of the ratio Io/Th in sediment cores from the Pacific; they found a regular exponential decrease of the ratio with depth in the sediment, indicating that ionium is not redistributed after deposition. The ionium-thorium method thus appears promising as a tool for age determination in the Upper and Middle Pleistocene, and offers the special advantage of being independent of variations in the rate of deposition.

Uranium is also transferred, though at a very low rate, to the oxidized deep-sea sediments, giving rise to a small amount of supported ionium. Especially in strata with an age of several ionium half-lives, uranium-supported ionium becomes a significant fraction of the total ionium content, and the Io/Th ratio has to be duly corrected.

The assumptions on which the ionium-thorium method rests are that the two isotopes are in chemical equilibrium with each other in sea water, that the ratio Io/Th has remained constant over the period of time involved in a given water mass, and that the contribution of thorium and uranium in detrital minerals is negligible or can be checked. Similar assumptions are made when other radionuclides are employed for the chronology of ocean sediments. Hence, information on the path of the elements in question through the hydrosphere is a prerequisite for their use for geochronological purposes. Studies of the amounts and distribution of uranium and thorium in sea water have been made (Pettersson, 1953; Koczy et al., 1957; Sackett et al., 1958), but our knowledge of the relative distribution of ionium and thorium is still not conclusive. For the transfer of the thorium isotopes from the ocean to the sediment several mechanisms have been suggested, for example coprecipitation with ferric oxide hydrate (Pettersson, 1938) and absorption on clay minerals (Holland and Kulp, 1954). Studies of the distribution of these nuclides in the different solid phases of the sediment have demonstrated, however, that they are concentrated in the ferromanganese oxide–hydrate double-layer minerals (Goldberg and Picciotto, 1955)

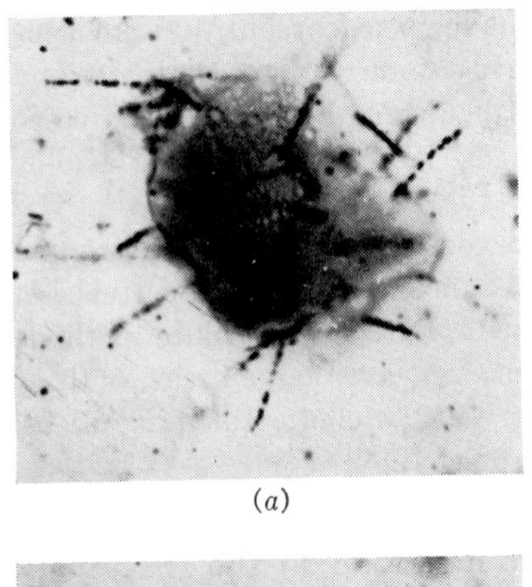

(*a*)

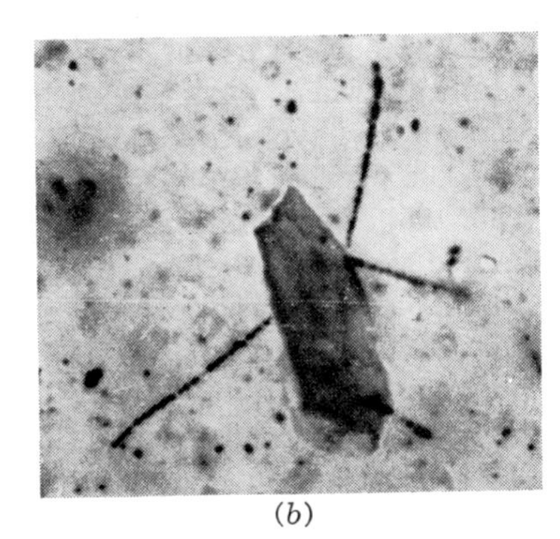

(*b*)

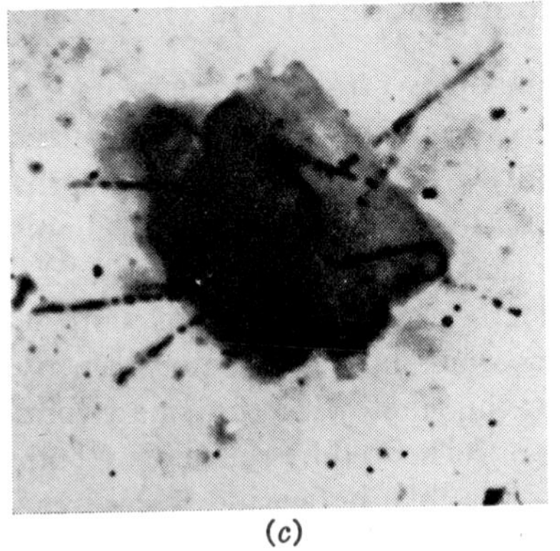

(*c*)

Fig. 10. High α activity of fossil skeletal fish debris as indicated by radioautographs (from Picciotto and Arrhenius, unpublished).

and in the apatite crystallites of skeletal debris of fish (Arrhenius, Bramlette, and Picciotto, 1957; Picciotto and Arrhenius, unpublished) (fig. 10), whereas the clay minerals appear inactive. Living bathypelagic fish do not display the remarkable concentration of heavy metals typical of the skeletal debris in the sediment, and it thus appears that the transfer takes place during or after deposition and before burial of the fossil debris. The ionium in the ferromanganese minerals might be located in the ferric oxide hydrate part of the structure, which would support Pettersson's suggestion of ferric precipitates as scavengers of ionium from sea water. The concentration of ionium and thorium by identical processes in identical minerals provides a proof that the assumption of chemical equilibrium between species of thorium isotopes in sea water is justified, at least as far as the last phase of the transfer process is concerned.

Relative age determinations based on the evolutionary change of fossil-forming organisms have been made in calcareous and siliceous sediments, where fossil coccolithophorids, foraminifera, diatoms, and radiolarians have proved useful in distinguishing between the different Cenozoic epochs (Bramlette and Riedel, 1954; Riedel, 1957; Kolbe, 1955, 1957; Lohman, 1942; Phleger, Parker, and Peirson, 1953). The marked vertical variation in chemical composition of the Pleistocene strata, due to climatic change, provides a means for detailed correlation of stages and substages. Different strata, dated by absolute methods at one or a few localities, can thus be traced over large areas, both in the Atlantic (Bramlette and Bradley, 1942; Schott, 1935; Emiliani, 1955) and in the Pacific Ocean (Arrhenius, 1952).

The Geological Record of Sedimentation in the Ocean

Owing to difficulties in sampling sedimentary strata to greater depths than about 15 meters, most sediment cores from undisturbed parts of the ocean bottom so far studied contain only Recent and Plio-Pleistocene deposits. In numerous cases, however, short cores and dredge hauls from topographic highs have revealed that older, mostly Tertiary deposits outcrop or are covered unconformably by thin strata of younger sediments. Specimens older than Cretaceous have so far not been reported, and it is interesting to couple this fact with the small total thickness of sediments (200 to 300 meters) observed by seismic methods over large areas of the Pacific Ocean, possibly indicating widespread effusion of lava over the bottom in Cretaceous time (Revelle, Bramlette, Arrhenius, and Goldberg, 1955).

Oxygen-isotope data indicate that the temperature of the deep and bottom water during Early and Middle Tertiary was about 10° C higher than now, a value in accordance with the vaster expanse of calcareous sediments during these times due to lower rate of dissolution of calcium carbonate. The high ratio of hydrogenous to lithogenous minerals makes it probable that mechanical weathering on the continents was less extensive during Tertiary than at the present time. The cooling of the deep water body to the near-zero temperatures now prevailing is recorded at the Pliocene-Pleistocene transition (Emiliani, 1955), and strata with glacial drift in the middle latitudes indicate the penetration far south of icebergs during the glacial ages (Arrhenius, 1950). Simultaneous periods of cooling of the equatorial surface water are recorded by the oxygen-isotope ratio in the calcareous tests of planktonic foraminifera. The cooling is probably mainly due to invasion of cold water from higher latitudes in the Atlantic and to increased upwelling of deep water along the equatorial divergence in the Pacific.

The changes in time of biogenous deposition in the equatorial zone of high productivity in the Pacific are of particular interest, as there is a direct relation between the rate of organic productivity and the rate of upwelling of deep water, which, in turn, is determined by the intensity of the trade winds. The sedimentary stratification in this area thus provides a record of the low-latitude atmospheric circulation through Tertiary and Quaternary time. A condensed illustration of these conditions is presented in figure 8. The central diagram of this figure shows a meridional cross section through the surface layer of the ocean in the east equatorial Pacific at longitude 120–130° W., where the features of the vertical circulation are well developed, and where the regularity in lithogenous sedimentation makes possible a quantitative study of variations in time of the biogenous components.

The temperature distribution in this middle diagram is indicated by the isotherms for 15°, 17°, 20°, 25°, and 27° C. The cold, nutrient-rich intermediate water is marked by a dotted surface, and the vertical circulation pattern is shown by arrows. The Equatorial Counter-current, running eastward, is limited by the South Equatorial Current at about 5° N., and by the North Equatorial Current at about latitude 10° N., both moving westward. Divergence of these wind drift currents produces upwelling along the equator. The rise of the intermediate water, which is rich in nutrient salts, into the surface layer, where most of the sunlight is absorbed, leads to a greatly increased production of algae, sustaining a corresponding production of other members of the food chain. At higher tropical latitudes the absence of a mechanism for enriching the euphotic layer keeps the productivity low. The resultant rate of production of skeletal calcium carbonate from coccolithophorids and foraminifera is illustrated in the upper diagram, where the full-line curve marked "Pleistocene minimum circulation (interglacial)" corresponds to present conditions. The scale of the abscissa axis is the same as in the middle graph. The inferred rate of dissolution of calcium carbonate before final burial of the fossils is indicated by the curve marked "Pleistocene minimum production of cold (1° C) deep water (interglacial)," which shows a flat maximum under the equatorial productivity maximum, due to the effect of carbon dioxide produced by the respiration of bottom-living animals feeding on the rain of organic detritus.

The resultant rate of accumulation of calcium carbonate corresponds to the ordinate difference between the two curves. At the intersection of these curves between latitude 7° and 9° N., carbonate accumulation accordingly drops to zero. Siliceous clays cover the bottom of the ocean north of the present loci of this intersection, the carbonate compensation line.

The temperature figures in the graph, referring to oxygen-isotope measurements (Emiliani and Edward, 1953; Emiliani, 1955) at latitude 0°, 2°, and 7° N., demonstrate qualitatively the increase in temperature away from the equator.

Before discussing the other curves in the upper graph, representing the conditions in the past, the lower diagram in figure 8 will be explained. This diagram is a generalized cross section through the bottom deposits along the same meridian as in the upper graphs. The ordinate has arbitrarily been chosen = 0 for the present sediment surface. The lower, detached half of the graph, showing the stratification of the Middle Tertiary sediments, is deficient in detail because of the paucity of observations. The shading indicates the carbonate concentration, which in a rough way reflects the rate of accumulation of carbonate.

The profile demonstrates the main features of the marked stratification of the calcareous deposits. Below the surface layer, which is characterized by relatively low carbonate concentrations, lies a stratum (2) high in carbonate, and coinciding in time with the last glaciation in higher latitudes. This stratum is preceded by another low-carbonate stratum (3) and a high-carbonate stratum (4), the last indicating extraordinarily high rates of accumulation of biogenous carbonate and silica. Altogether about nine major carbonate maxima occur in the Pleistocene part of the sequence. The underlying Pliocene sediments are characterized by less variability of the carbonate content with time. The Pliocene-Pleistocene transition, indicated by a rapid drop in bottom-water temperature (Emiliani, 1955) and by a marked change in the fossil assemblages of coccolithophorids (Bramlette, personal communication; Bramlette and Riedel, 1954), is shown as a dashed line crossing over the carbonate compensation surface near the break in the profile.

From measurements in stratum 4 the full-line curve marked "Pleistocene maximum circulation (glacial)" in the top diagram and the dashed curve marked "Pleistocene maximum production of cold (1° C) deep water (glacial)" have been constructed. The productivity appears to have been largely increased, especially in the equatorial divergence, and probably to some extent also the dissolution due to respiration of benthonic animals, although not enough to counterbalance the greatly

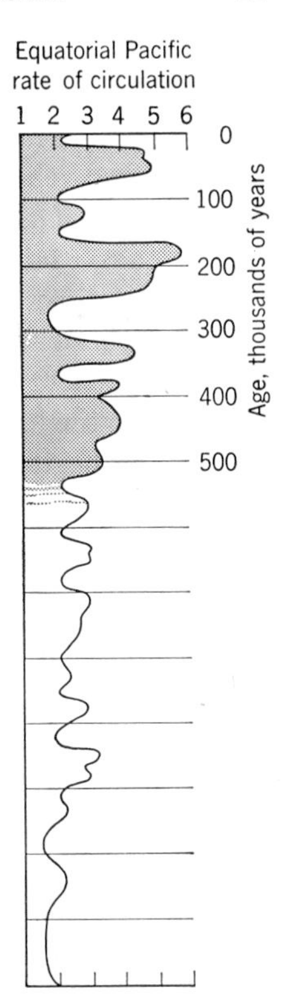

Fig. 11. Relative rate of low-latitude atmospheric circulation during the Pleistocene, estimated from the rate of accumulation of biogenous solids below the Equatorial Current system. The time scale is obtained by extrapolation based on the cumulative titanium content of the sediment, and should probably be considered as applicable only to the upper half million year part of the sequence (shaded). The Pliocene-Pleistocene boundary falls within the lowest two sections of the graph (from Arrhenius, 1952, by permission).

increased rate of deposition of calcareous skeletal remains. As a result the over-all rate of accumulation of calcium carbonate reaches a maximum during this time. The greatest increase occurs at the equator, where values of the order of 3 to 10 $g \cdot cm^{-2} \cdot millennium^{-1}$ of calcium carbonate are found. The paleotemperature data in the same graph indicate a steepening of the temperature gradient from the equator, which is taken as additional evidence for an increased rate of upwelling in the divergence as the cause of the increased productivity. The reason for this intensified vertical circulation occurring during the glacial ages is probably an increase in the tropical atmospheric circulation depending on a displacement toward the equator of the high-pressure centers now located between latitude 20° and 35°. Under these conditions the stratification of biogenous components in the equatorial Pacific provides a direct and undisturbed record of the climatic evolution of the earth during the last few million years. A reconstruction of the variations in trade-wind intensity on the basis of the sedimentary record is given in figure 11.

The examples cited above may serve to illustrate the advantages for quantitative geological studies offered by sediments from the water hemisphere. The properties of these sediments yield information on the physical, chemical, and biological reactions which regulate the composition of the ocean. The rates of the reactions have changed in the past, and these changes, recorded in the sedimentary strata, indicate world-wide modifications of the intensity of such processes as atmospheric circulation, volcanic activity, weathering, glaciation, and accretion of cosmic matter.

Owing to the low rates of accumulation, and the continuous, thorough mixing of the top stratum of the sediments by mud-eating animals, the oceanic record is smoothed, with a time factor estimated to vary between a few thousand and a few ten thousand years. This effect makes it difficult to resolve events of short duration, such as the post-glacial climatic oscillations. Most of the history recorded in pelagic sediments can be traced with a better time resolution in the sediments accumulated on and around the continents; local effects, however, frequently obscure or distort the record in these cases. The sedimentary record in protected areas of the ocean floor, far away from the continents, thus offers distinct advantages for a wide regional or global integration of geological processes and for their interpretation on a quantitative basis.

References

Arnold, J. R. 1956. Beryllium-10 produced by cosmic rays, *Science, 124,* 584–585.

Arrhenius, G. 1950. The Swedish deep sea expedition: The geological material and its treatment, *Geol. Fören. i Stockholm Förh., 72,* 185–191.

Arrhenius, G. 1952. Sediment cores from the East Pacific, *Rept. Swed. Deep Sea Expedition, 5,* Göteborg.

Arrhenius, G. 1954. Origin and accumulation of aluminosilicates in the ocean, *Tellus, 6,* 215–219.

Arrhenius, G., M. N. Bramlette, and E. Picciotto. 1957. The localization of radioactive and stable heavy nuclides in ocean sediments, *Nature, 180,* 85–86.

Arrhenius, G., and E. D. Goldberg. 1955. Distribution of radioactivity in pelagic clays, *Tellus, 7,* 226–231.

Arrhenius, G., G. Kjellberg, and W. F. Libby. 1951. Age determination of Pacific chalk ooze by radiocarbon and titanium content, *Tellus, 3,* 222–229.

Bramlette, M. N., and W. H. Bradley. 1942. Geology and biology of North Atlantic deep sea cores between Newfoundland and Ireland, I, Lithology and geologic interpretations, *U. S. Geol. Survey Profess. Paper 196a.*

Bramlette, M. N., and W. Riedel. 1954. Stratigraphic value of discoasters and some other microfossils related to recent coccolithophores, *J. Paleontol., 28,* 385–403.

Buser, W., and A. Grütter. 1956. Über die Natur der Manganknollen, *Schweiz. mineral. petrog. Mitt., 36,* 49–62.

Correns, C. W. 1953. Der Anteil des Staubes an der Bildung der Sedimentgesteine, *Z. Ver. deut. Ing., 95,* 293–296.

Correns, C. W., and W. von Engelhardt. 1938. Neue Untersuchungen über die Verwitterung des Kalifeldspates, *Chem. Erde, 12,* 1–22.

Dietz, R. 1955. Manganese deposits on the northeast Pacific sea floor, *Calif. J. Mines Geol., 51,* 209–220.

Emiliani, C. 1955. Pleistocene temperatures, *J. Geol., 63,* 538–578.

Emiliani, C., and G. Edward. 1953. Tertiary ocean bottom temperatures, *Nature, 171,* 887–889.

Goel, P. S., D. P. Kharkar, D. Lal, N. Narsappaya, B. Peters, and V. Yatirajam. 1957. The beryllium-10 concentration in deep sea sediments, *Deep Sea Research, 4,* 202–210.

Goldberg, E. D., and G. Arrhenius. 1958. Chemistry of Pacific pelagic sediments, *Geochim. et Cosmochim. Acta, 13,* 153–212.

Goldberg, E. D., and M. Koide. 1958. Ionium-thorium chronology in deep sea sediments of the Pacific, *Science, 128,* 1003.

Goldberg, E. D., and E. Picciotto. 1955. Thorium determinations in manganese nodules, *Science, 121,* 613–614.

Goldberg, E. D., and R. W. Rex. 1958. Quartz contents of pelagic sediments of the Pacific Ocean, *Tellus, 10,* 153–159.

Herr, W., and E. Merz. 1958. Zur Bestimmung der Halbwertszeit des ^{187}Re, Weitere Datierungen nach der Re/Os Methode, *Z. Naturforsch., 13a,* 231–233.

Holland, H. D., and J. L. Kulp. 1954. The transport and deposition of uranium, ionium, and radium in rivers, oceans, and ocean sediments, *Geochim. et Cosmochim. Acta, 5,* 197–213.

Koczy, F. 1956. Vertical eddy diffusion in deep water, *Nature, 178,* 585.

Koczy, F., E. Picciotto, G. Poulaert, and S. Wilgain. 1957. Mesure des isotopes du thorium dans l'eau de mer, *Geochim. et Cosmochim. Acta, 11,* 103–129.

Kolbe, R. W. 1955. Diatoms from equatorial Atlantic cores, *Rept. Swed. Deep Sea Expedition, 7,* 3.

Kolbe, R. W. 1957. Diatoms from equatorial Indian Ocean cores, *Rept. Swed. Deep Sea Expedition, 9,* 1.

Kröll, V. 1955. The distribution of radium in deep-sea cores, *Rept. Swed. Deep Sea Expedition, 10,* 1, Göteborg.

Kuenen, Ph. H., and C. I. Migliorini. 1950. Turbidity currents as a cause of graded bedding, *J. Geol., 58,* 91–127.

Laevastu, T., and O. Mellis. 1955. Extraterrestrial material in deep sea deposits, *Trans. Am. Geophys. Union, 36,* 385–389.

Lohman, K. 1942. Geology and biology of North Atlantic deep sea cores between Newfoundland and Ireland, 3, Diatomaceae, *U. S. Geol. Survey Profess. Paper 196b.*

McDonald, W. F. 1938. Atlas of climatic charts of the oceans, *U. S. Dept. Agr., Weather Bureau, no. 1247.*

Menard, H. W. 1956. Archipelagic aprons, *Bull. Am. Assoc. Petrol. Geologists, 40,* 2195–2210.

Menard, H. W. 1958. La topographie et la géologie des profondeurs océaniques, *Coll. Intern. Centre natl. recherche sci., 83.*

Norin, E. 1958. The sediments of the central Tyrrhenian Sea, *Rept. Swed. Deep Sea Expedition, 3,* 1.

Peters, B. 1955. Radioactive beryllium in the atmosphere and on the earth, *Proc. Indian Acad. Sci., 41,* 67–71.

Peters, B. 1957. Über die Anwendbarkeit der Be-10 Methode für Messung kosmischer Strahlungsintensität und der Ablagerungsgeschwindigkeit von Tiefseesedimenten vor einigen millionen Jahren, *Z. Physik, 148,* 93.

Pettersson, H. 1938. *Mitt. Inst. Radiumforschung, 400a.*

Pettersson, H. 1953. Radium and the deep sea, *Am. Scientist, 41,* 245–255.

Phleger, F., F. Parker, and J. Peirson. 1953. North Atlantic Foraminifera, *Rept. Swed. Deep Sea Expedition, 7,* 1.

Radczewski, O. E. 1939. Eolian deposits in marine sediments, *Recent Marine Sediment Symposium* (P. D. Trask, ed.), pp. 496–502, American Association of Petroleum Geologists, Tulsa, Oklahoma.

Revelle, R., M. N. Bramlette, G. Arrhenius, and E. D. Goldberg. 1955. Pelagic sediments of the Pacific, *Geol. Soc. Am., Spec. Paper 62,* 221–236.

Riedel, W. 1957. Radiolaria: A preliminary stratigraphy, *Rept. Swed. Deep Sea Expedition, 6,* 3.

Sackett, W., H. Potratz, and E. D. Goldberg. 1958. Thorium content of ocean water, *Science, 128,* 204–205.

Schott, W. 1935. Die Foraminiferen in dem äkvatorialen Teil des atlantischen Ozeans, *Wiss. Ergeb. deut. atl. Exped. Meteor, 1925–1927, 3,* 3.

Vinogradov, A. P., and A. B. Ronov. 1956. Composition of sedimentary rocks of the Russian platform in relation to the history of their tectonic movements, *Geokhimiya, 6,* 3–24 (in Russian).

Wasserburg, G., R. Hayden, and K. Jensen. 1956. A^{40}-K^{40} dating of igneous rocks and sediments, *Geochim. et Cosmochim. Acta, 10,* 153–165.

Weaver, C. E. 1958. Geologic interpretation of argillaceous sediments, *Bull. Am. Assoc. Petrol. Geologists, 42,* 254–271.

Rates of Geochemical Reactions at Low Temperatures and Pressures

ROBERT M. GARRELS
Harvard University

Introduction

The major aim of geology is to re-create the environments of the past. But the problem of interpreting conditions at the time of deposition of sedimentary rocks, for example, depends first of all upon a knowledge of the relation of modern sediments to their environments plus an ability to recognize the effects of changes resulting from the processes of diagenesis and metamorphism.

From the standpoint of the geochemist it thus becomes important to attempt to find out, by experiment, on theoretical grounds, and by field observation, the equilibrium relations between minerals and their environments as well as the rate of attainment of equilibrium. Which minerals can be relied upon to equilibrate rapidly and thus be guides to the last solution to which they were subjected? Which can persist through conditions that would destroy them if they had reacted freely?

The geologic and chemical literature on this important subject has not been summarized with any thoroughness. The following discussion, by assembling a small amount of the available data, may perhaps be suggestive of the kinds of relations that need investigation. The relations considered are those at standard temperature and pressure in inorganic aqueous environments, and thus include only environments at or near the earth's surface.

Ionic Reactions in Solution

In general, reactions among dissolved species are rapid. Dissolved inorganic substances are present in solution chiefly as simple ions, and interactions among these charged particles usually take place so fast as to be instantaneous from the geologist's viewpoint. Typical of such reactions are the oxidation of U^{+4} to UO_2^{++} by ferric ion in acid solution, or the change of $CO_3^{=}$ to HCO_3^{-} by the addition of hydrogen ion. Many standard laboratory procedures in organic chemistry are based on the high rates of such changes.

A major exception to this generalization is related to the formation and breakdown of polymerized ionic species. Most notable offenders are anionic complexes of vanadium, molybdenum, and arsenic. Their behavior is similar in that they tend to form relatively simple anions in strongly alkaline solution, but with increasing acidity complexes with molecular weights of more than 1000 can be formed. For vanadium the sequence of anions is (Evans, 1956, p. 5)

$$2VO_4^{-3} + 2H^+ = V_2O_7^{-4} + H_2O$$

$$2V_2O_7^{-4} + 4H^+ = V_4O_{12}^{-4} + 2H_2O$$

$$5V_4O_{12}^{-4} + 8H^+ = 2V_{10}O_{28}^{-6} + 4H_2O$$

For molybdenum (Jenkins and Tyree, 1956, p. 25) the sequence is

$$7MoO_4^{-2} + 8H^+ = Mo_7O_{24}^{-6} + 4H_2O$$

$$8Mo_7O_{24}^{-6} + 20H^+ = 7Mo_8O_{26}^{-4} + 10H_2O$$

The vanadium anions form relatively rapidly on acidification, but the depolymerization process is much slower, so much so that the rate is a serious deterrent to experimental work on the system. Weeks or months may be necessary for equilibration. Thus the time involved begins to be of importance geologically.

The uncharged dissolved species of general geologic interest are few, but of major importance. They include water itself, H_2CO_3, H_2S, and H_4SiO_4. Of these only H_4SiO_4 is recalcitrant in terms of reactions in homogeneous solution. It tends to polymerize and to grade imperceptibly from true dissolved monomeric H_4SiO_4 into polymerized dissolved complexes and finally into solid polymers. H_2O, H_2S, H_2CO_3, and monomeric H_4SiO_4 react rapidly to give equilibrium amounts of ionic species according to reactions of the type

$$H_2X = H^+ + HX^-$$

But the reaction

$$(H_4SiO_4)_x = xH_4SiO_4$$

is generally slow and is catalyzed positively or negatively by numerous agents. The time necessary for equilibrium may again be weeks or months.

Several geologically important dissolved species are so slow to equilibrate that reactions involving them may not be completed in hundreds of years, or perhaps even longer. Foremost perhaps is dissolved oxygen, which does not exert the oxidizing potential predicted for it. Studies by Cooper (1937, p. 305) have shown that the observed oxidation potential of atmospheric oxygen as measured by its effect on iron dissolved in sea water is about half a volt below that predicted. In other words, the effect (at least the short-term effect) of the atmosphere on systems apparently in equilibrium with it is not that of a partial pressure of oxygen of $1/5$ atmosphere but that of a gas with an incredibly minute oxygen pressure.

A second important species is sulfate ion, which is reducible at a measurable rate in aqueous solutions at low temperature only under conditions more stringent than those encountered in nature. If zinc is allowed to react with dilute sulfuric acid, hydrogen is released from the water, but the sulfate (or bisulfate) ion remains unchanged, even though the potential required to release hydrogen from water is far below that calculated to be necessary to reduce sulfate ion to sulfur or sulfide.

In summary, simple ions in solution generally react swiftly, and equilibrate in seconds or minutes; polymerized ions may require periods of days or weeks for condensation or disaggregation; simple molecular species react rapidly. Consequently, with a few noteworthy exceptions, it is a fair generalization that natural aqueous solutions are in internal equilibrium. Thus, measurements of oxidation potential of natural waters can be used to calculate the ratios of oxidation-reduction pairs such as Fe^{+++}/Fe^{++}, VO^{++}/V^{+++}, Pb^{+4}/Pb^{++}, or Cu^{++}/Cu^{+}, and the results are confirmed by other experiments.

Precipitation from Aqueous Solution

The formation of precipitates from homogeneous solution is ordinarily a rapid process. If a solution of a ferric salt is titrated with sodium hydroxide, equilibrium with a precipitate is apparently obtained within a few minutes after addition of each portion of hydroxide. Similar results are obtained with most oxides, hydroxides, hydroxyoxides, basic salts, and sulfides. On the other hand, carbonates and silicates are slow to form; experiments on these compounds require days or weeks for the formation of a precipitate.

The first precipitate formed, however, although it is in equilibrium with the solution, is seldom stable with respect to other solid phases. When a precipitate is formed, either in the laboratory or in nature, the change in solution characteristics leading to the formation of the precipitate is usually rapid. Perhaps a bubble of H_2S rises through a bottom mud, or a change in atmospheric pressure changes the amount of dissolved CO_2 in sea water. The result of this sudden change is to supersaturate the system with respect to more than one solid. The first solid to appear is the one that relieves supersaturation with respect to its components at a greater rate than other solids do.

Several kinds of metastability of the first precipitate can be recognized. In the simplest, the composition of the precipitate remains fixed, but the precipitate increases in stability with time because of increase in grain size, probably largely through a complex process of solution of small particles and growth of larger ones. Second, the first precipitate may be more highly hydrated than the stable phase, and reconstitution may take place through "splitting-out" of water, with little change in composition otherwise. The mechanisms by which this change may occur are probably numerous. Third, the metastable phase may be dimorphous with the stable phase, in which event composition remains the same but a structural rearrangement is required. Fourth, the metastable phase may be markedly different in composition from the stable species, and the paths by which readjustment may take place are endlessly varied.

Thus it can be said that, whereas a change in a natural solution commonly tends to produce a precipitate almost instantaneously, a substantial time interval, which may range from a few hours to millions of years, elapses before true equilibrium with the surrounding solution is achieved.

Much detailed information on the rates of these various kinds of processes is undoubtedly available scattered through the chemical literature. Here, a few examples familiar to the author are discussed.

Simple aging

As far as simple aging is concerned—growth in particle size—a few days or weeks at room temperature is generally sufficient to produce a stable solid from the mother solution. For example, brochantite requires about 2 weeks when precipitated from copper sulfate; malachite, somewhere between 3 weeks and 3 months (J. Silman, personal communication).

Relations among slightly soluble hydrates

When the aging process involves splitting-out of water, equilibrium may not be reached, even in geologic time. The precipitation of iron oxides is an excellent and important example of this phenomenon. An attempt is made to show some of the possible complications related to the iron oxides in figure 1. The relations portrayed are somewhat speculative, as will emerge from the following discussion.

It is known that the first iron precipitate from solution is a highly hydrous oxide, probably represented best by the formula $Fe_2O_3 \cdot nH_2O$. It has a fairly well defined solubility product (Cooper, 1937, p. 303):

$$(Fe^{3+})(OH^-)^3 = 10^{-37}$$

The solubility product of crystalline Fe_2O_3 is approximately 10^{-42} (Latimer, 1952, p. 221), and that of crystalline $Fe_2O_3 \cdot H_2O$ is of the same

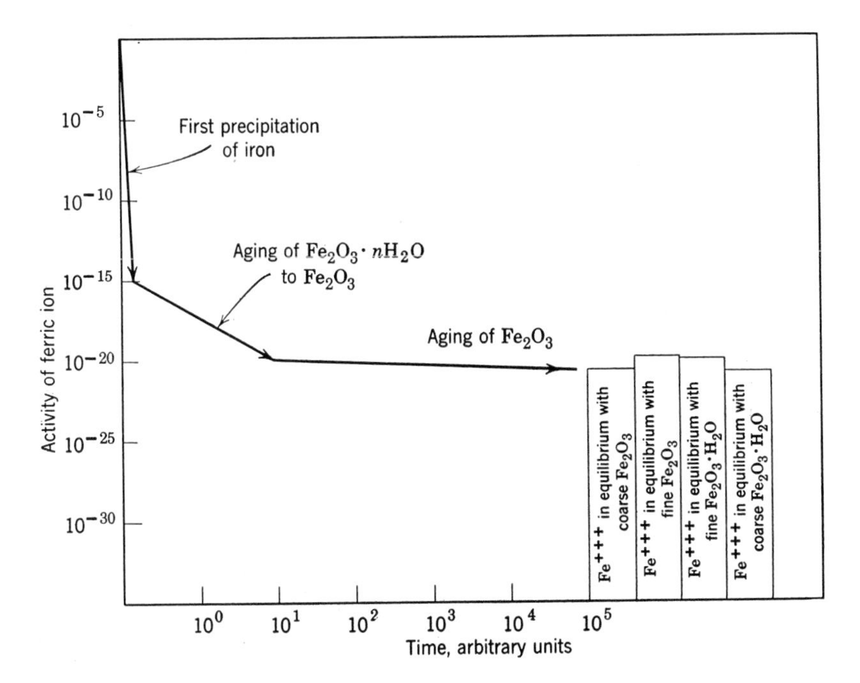

Fig. 1. Schematic diagram showing possible changes of ferric oxide precipitate with time at *p*H 7 in aqueous solution. Fe_2O_3 is shown persisting metastably with respect to $Fe_2O_3 \cdot H_2O$. The numbers used in the ordinate are for illustrative purposes only. They are of the right order of magnitude, but their absolute values are not accurately known.

order of magnitude, but it is not definitely known which is smaller. The problem is complicated by polymorphism; there are three structures of $Fe_2O_3 \cdot H_2O$ and two of Fe_2O_3. The observed aging product of $Fe_2O_3 \cdot nH_2O$ may be either $Fe_2O_3 \cdot H_2O$ or Fe_2O_3 (Mackenzie, 1952, p. 75; and Milligan, 1952, p. 232), and each, once formed as a crystalline precipitate, apparently can persist indefinitely. For purposes of discussion it is assumed that α-Fe_2O_3 (hematite) and α-$Fe_2O_3 \cdot H_2O$ (goethite) are the stable polymorphs at low temperature and furthermore that goethite is stable relative to hematite in nearly pure water.

As shown in figure 1, the first precipitate from a solution containing dissolved ferric iron is the hydrous oxide of indefinite water content. At pH 7, the concentration of ferric iron in equilibrium with the precipitate is only about 10^{-16}. As the precipitate ages and splits out water the resultant structure, hematite or goethite, apparently is dictated by minor compositional differences in the solution, resulting in catalysis of the rate of recrystallization to one or the other. As shown, hematite appears first, and recrystallizes, with concomitant drop in the concentration of ferric ion in the solution. At this stage the relatively coarse hematite has a lower activity of ferric ions in equilibrium with it than finer crystalline goethite, so that in the absence of nuclei goethite cannot form, even though coarsely crystalline goethite is more stable than coarsely crystalline hematite. This energy barrier may indefinitely prevent transformation of hematite to goethite.

Furthermore, if recrystallization has to take place by solution of hematite and recrystallization of goethite, the low concentration of ferric ion in the solution would tend to make transfer of iron slow. As shown in figure 1 the difference in concentration of ferric iron in equilibrium with the two phases is a factor of 10, but the concentration difference is

$$10^{-21} - 10^{-22} \cong 10^{-21}$$

Such a small concentration difference does not constitute much of a driving force, even though the distance of transport from one phase to the other is small.

Thus a series of slightly soluble hydrates, in dilute aqueous solution, may form and coexist, because the initial precipitation of a given species is catalyzed and after formation the rate of losing or gaining water is so slow that equilibrium is not achieved.

The aluminum oxide hydrates behave in much the same way as the iron oxides. In lateritic soils the monohydrate and the trihydrate occur intimately intermixed, yet the chance that conditions are such that both are in equilibrium is slight. The trihydrate is stable in dilute aqueous solution, and the monohydrate in humid air. Thus, when the soil is water-saturated, the trihydrate is stable; when the soil dries out and the humidity is low, the monohydrate is stable. It is reasonable, therefore, that the rate of conversion is so slow that each persists through the periods during which the other is stable.

Dehydration of silica $(H_4SiO_4)_x$ is another example of the slow change related to water loss. Many natural waters are supersaturated with respect to quartz. According to Siever (1957, p. 826), "Solutions undersaturated with respect to amorphous silica (<140 ppm) but supersaturated with respect to quartz are stable over a period of years. . . . clear crystalline quartz, by methods so far known, cannot be formed directly from solution at anywhere near room temperatures and atmospheric pressure. . . . several thousand years may be needed to either precipitate or convert amorphous silica to quartz." Krauskopf (1956) considers the rate of attainment of equilibrium between $(H_4SiO_4)_x$ and quartz so slow that solubility control by quartz can be neglected in discussing the transport of silica in fresh waters. In passing, it must be noted that, whereas the inorganic process is slow, intervention of organisms frequently causes rapid equilibration. The role of organisms as catalysts is to speed many of the inorganic reactions here listed as geologically slow.

A fourth example is the uranium oxide hydrates. Many specimens of oxidized uranium ores contain several hydrates of UO_3.

Dimorphs

The occurrence of the metastable species of a dimorphous pair, such as aragonite instead of stable calcite, or marcasite instead of pyrite, may also be related to the kinetics of recrystallization of a rapidly formed primary phase. If sea water suddenly becomes enriched in carbonate ion, perhaps through diurnal variations in organic activity, the system may well be highly supersaturated with respect to both calcite and aragonite, which differ in solubility by a factor of 1.5 to 2 (Latimer, 1952, p. 319). If aragonite grows faster in the particular medium, the precipitate may be almost entirely aragonite. Once aragonite is formed, the rate of its conversion to calcite is slow.

As far as pyrite and marcasite are concerned, relations are complex; studies of the kinetics of sulfide precipitation indicate that there may be a precursor to both. When simple sulfides are precipitated in acid or even in neutral solution, the sulfide-ion activity is so low that the mechanism is

$$Me^{++} + 2HS^- = Me(HS)_2 = MeS + H_2S$$

Again a "splitting out" is involved, in this instance of H_2S instead of H_2O. There is no similar information on pyrite or marcasite, but, inasmuch as the $S_2^=$ ion activity in natural solution at low temperature is always low, the mechanism must follow some devious path, such as

$$Fe^{++} + 2HS^- = Fe(HS)_2 = FeS_2 + H_2$$

or

$$2Fe^{++} + 4HS^- = 2Fe(HS)_2 = 2FeS + 2H_2S$$

$$2FeS + \tfrac{1}{2}O_2 + H_2O = FeS_2 + Fe^{++} + 2OH^-$$

At any rate, inasmuch as the solubilities of marcasite and pyrite are probably similar and both are stable relative to the medium, either may form and persist.

Metastability related to marked compositional change

The final category of reactions considered is not at all clearly defined, and is used as a catchall to bring attention to other reactions in which approach to equilibrium is hindered by the interpolation of some readily precipitated solid between the solution and its stable solid products. (The three reactions cited are chosen for special interest geologically.)

If a ferrous salt is neutralized by a hydroxide, in the absence of oxygen, a white crystalline precipitate of ferrous hydroxide with a well defined and reproducible solubility product is formed. This precipitate reacts to form magnetite, hydrogen, and water:

$$3Fe(OH)_2 = Fe_3O_4 + H_2 + 2H_2O$$

The rate is highly variable from experiment to experiment; the reaction as shown is much simpler than the one that occurs, for the white precipitate changes slowly through light green to dark green to black. Usually the rate is measurable experimentally in that the presence of hydrogen can be detected within a few hours after precipitation of the ferrous hydroxide.

On the other hand, if a ferrous salt in solution is treated with H_2S, the first precipitate is an amorphous black precipitate, FeS or $Fe(SH)_2$. Except in strongly alkaline solution, the FeS-water mixture is unstable with respect to pyrite, magnetite, and hydrogen.

Under natural conditions the reactions producing pyrite following precipitation of FeS are complicated, but the slowness of the reaction to pyrite is attested by the recognition of FeS in many natural precipitates. Again it appears that the eventual change to pyrite or marcasite is governed by the mechanism of the reaction of FeS with its aqueous environment.

The third reaction of interest is the precipitation of normal ordered dolomite. It may be that, usually, when solution characteristics change from those under which dolomite is soluble to those under which it is stable, the system also becomes supersaturated with respect to calcite. If calcite precipitates more rapidly, it becomes a metastable intermediate and conversion to dolomite can take place only by dissolution and reprecipitation. If the calcite crystals are removed from the mother liquid by settling, the new environment may be one in which dolomite is not stable or perhaps one in which the quantity of magnesium in the pore liquid is not sufficient to convert an appreciable portion of calcite to dolomite. Thus in a sense the mechanics of the system is such that the metastable intermediate is removed from the environment in which it was metastable and becomes a stable phase in the new surroundings. We can guess that the original advantage in rate of calcite over dolomite results from rapid precipitation that does not permit time for ordering of alternate layers of Ca^{++} and Mg^{++}.

Summary

Although ionic reactions to form precipitates are rapid, it is probably exceptional that the precipitate formed is stable (except for grain enlargement). Instead, the changes in composition that resulted in the first precipitate cause the solution to be supersaturated with respect to one or more solids in addition to the first to appear. The mechanisms involved in the change from first precipitate to final stable solid are highly varied and complex, but a general rule can be formulated. If the solubility of a given phase is small, and if the solubility difference between the phase and a more stable phase is also small, then the metastable phase may persist long enough to be significant geologically. If the first and second phases are dimorphs, persistence of the metastable phase may be of the order of geologic eras.

Solution of Solids

Now the reverse question can be asked: how fast does a solid in equilibrium with a given solution respond to a change in the solution? Two main cases can be considered: congruent and incongruent solution.

Congruent solution

Many solids dissolve to equilibrium with a given solution rapidly, but the exceptions are so numerous as to prevent satisfactory generalization. Total solubility is an important control; if a solid is in equilibrium with a solution containing dissolved solid of the order of 0.1 mole per liter or more, a change in the solution can be expected to be followed by rapid dissolution of the solid. The rate of response tends to drop off as the total solute diminishes. The rate, of course, increases with the surface available and the amount of stirring. The following remarks are qualitative and apply to the typical occurrences of the minerals in a restricted volume of solution.

Evaporites can be expected to dissolve rapidly when put into contact with fresh water. Ten grams of fine (<100 mesh) gypsum dissolves to equilibrium in a liter of water within hours. Its solubility in pure water is about 0.01 mole per liter. If fine-grained calcite or aragonite is subjected to an increase in the CO_2 pressure of its marine environment, resaturation occurs locally within minutes. For these minerals also the solubility is in the vicinity of 0.01 mole per liter. Quartz, on the other hand, with a pure water solubility of about 0.0001 mole per liter, requires months to come to equilibrium as opposed to minutes for a comparable surface area of calcite under the same conditions.

Crystalline hematite, even with a large surface area, and exposed to conditions in which it has a high equilibrium solubility, is extremely recalcitrant. Crystalline gibbsite behaves similarly.

Probably the best generalization to make for geologic purposes is that fine-grained precipitates of all kinds approach equilibrium through congruent solution within a few weeks, and that coarse-grained (silt size or larger) minerals do so only if their solubility is large (0.01 mole per liter). If solubility is less than 0.01, behavior is not generally predictable.

Incongruent solution

In the complex fluids of natural environments incongruent solubility is far more prevalent than congruent solution. When environmental conditions change so that a mineral tends to dissolve, it almost always reacts to a new solid plus solution. When this occurs, the possibility of prediction of the rate of achievement of equilibrium, even in the most qualitative terms, is negligible.

Some of the reactions that have been studied show why this is so. If crystals of sodium sulfate are placed in solutions of calcium chloride, the results of successive apparently identical experiments may be different. In one experiment the sodium sulfate may armor with a thin film of gypsum, after which reaction apparently ceases. In a second, the sodium sulfate crystal may disintegrate entirely into a fine-grained powder of gypsum. In a third, most of the crystal may armor with gypsum but a gypsum spire may grow from a small area.

Thus in incongruent solution the possibility of armoring of the original phase by the new one is always present, but whether it will in fact take place depends on the volume relations of the two phases, whether the new phase is porous, whether it is adherent, and whether it forms a continuous coating. If armoring does take place, then the original phase may persist indefinitely beyond its range of stability.

One of the most important geologic examples of armoring involves the preservation of feldspars. Feldspars react with aqueous solutions to form a thin surface coat of H-silicate (Correns and von Engelhardt, 1938). According to Nash and Marshall (1956), the outer layers of the feldspar become disordered, but beneath the broken-up zone hydrogen ions occupy K^+ or Na^+ sites to form an H-feldspar.

After this coating develops, further reaction of the feldspar is slow, and is controlled by the rate of diffusion of K^+ ions outward through the H-occupied zone. Because solid diffusion rates are low at room temperature, the feldspar may exist almost indefinitely if the environment is not too far removed from its field of stability. The presence of tremendous volumes of arkose in the geologic column can thus be attributed to this armoring effect. If equilibrium were attained between most stream waters and feldspars, the feldspars would be destroyed and their place taken by H-silicates such as kaolinite or halloysite.

The presence of abundant magnetite in placer deposits is probably another example of armoring. Magnetite is markedly unstable relative to hematite in stream environments, but is presumably protected by a thin film of hematite.

The armoring phenomenon has been investigated at length by metallurgists interested in the protection of metals against corrosion, but little has been done in the obvious extension to minerals. Our understanding of weathering phenomena would undoubtedly be advanced by studies from this viewpoint, for alteration of silicates takes place through whole sequences of incongruent solutions.

Summary and Conclusion

It should be evident that attempts to generalize concerning rates of reaction of minerals inevitably run into difficulties because of the numerous variables. Some of these factors can be assessed qualitatively; others cannot. In a sense, our qualitative knowledge of rates has to be used to estimate whether a given mineral disequilibrium falls entirely beyond the range of time expected for equilibrium or whether it is of the kind that can persist indefinitely.

On the other hand, although generalization is difficult and dangerous, it does emerge that studies of rates and mechanisms of selected reactions can be of much help to the geologist. The work on feldspars by Correns and von Engelhardt and by Nash and Marshall is a fine example of the development of the kind of information that permits us to understand the metastable persistence of feldspar, and it prevents us from making the error of using the composition of waters that have been in contact with arkose as guides to the composition of an equilibrium fluid. Similarly, persistence of clay minerals in nonequilibrium depositional environments, a thesis advocated by some students of the problem from studies of the relation of the minerals of source areas to the minerals of sediments, emerges as a likely conclusion by analogy with the behavior of feldspar. But if it could be demonstrated in terms of rates and mechanisms in the way that feldspar metastability has been worked out, the conclusions from studies of provenance would be strengthened. At present, it can be said only that metastable persistence of clay minerals is reasonable in terms of what is known about rates of reaction of silicates at low temperatures in aqueous solution.

In conclusion, an attempt has been made to classify reaction types, and to express them in terms of those likely to result in reaction rates so slow as to be of importance in maintaining metastability through times of geologic importance (months, years, millions of years). From the geologic standpoint, slow rates are largely related to conversion of solids to more stable solids, whether the approach be through precipitation or through dissolution. Several slow reactions of geologic importance are correlated with the difficult process of the "splitting out" or acceptance of water by slightly soluble phases such as Fe_2O_3, Al_2O_3, UO_3, or SiO_2. In the dissolution of minerals, the protection of the original phase by armoring with a new phase is of major importance. This mechanism is especially characteristic of the rock-forming silicates.

References

Cooper, L. H. N. 1937. Some conditions governing the solubility of iron, *Proc. Royal Soc. London, B, 124,* 303.

Correns, C. W., and Wolf von Engelhardt. 1938. Neue Untersuchungen über die Verwitterung des Kalifeldspates, *Chem. Erde, 12,* 1–22.

Evans, H. T., Jr. 1956. Some crystal chemical studies of iso- and heteropoly complexes, *Symposium on Structure and Properties of Heteropoly Anions,* Annual Meeting of Am. Chem. Soc., Div. Phys. Inorg. Chem., pp. 5–7.

Jenkins, L. H., and S. Y. Tyree. 1956. Light scattering of isopolymolybdates, *Symposium on Structure and Properties of Heteropoly Anions,* Annual Meeting of Am. Chem. Soc., Div. Phys. Inorg. Chem., pp. 25–34.

Krauskopf, K. B. 1956. Dissolution and precipitation of silica at low temperatures, *Geochim. et Cosmochim. Acta, 10,* 1–26.

Latimer, W. M. 1952. *Oxidation Potentials,* Prentice-Hall, New York, 392 pp.

Mackenzie, Robert C. 1952. Investigations on cold-precipitated hydrated ferric oxide and its origin in clays, A. I. M. E. Symposium, *Problems of Clay and Laterite Genesis,* New York, pp. 65–76.

Milligan, W. O. 1952. Hydrous and hydrated ferric oxides, A. I. M. E. Sym posium, *Problems of Clay and Laterite Genesis,* New York, pp. 232–233.

Nash, V. E., and C. E. Marshall. 1956. The surface reactions of silicate minerals, II, Reactions of feldspar surfaces with salt solutions, *Missouri Univ. Agr. Expt. Sta. Research Bull. 614,* 36 pp.

Siever, Raymond. 1957. The silica budget in the sedimentary cycle, *Am. Mineralogist, 42,* 821–842.

Geochemical Indicators of Marine and Fresh-Water Sediments[1]

M. L. KEITH
and
E. T. DEGENS[2]
Pennsylvania State University

Knowledge of the environment of deposition of sedimentary rocks is fundamental to investigations of geologic history; it has a number of applications to coal and petroleum geology and to studies of the distribution of economic concentrations of minerals or elements associated, on the one hand, with marine basins, or, on the other hand, with areas of continental weathering and deposition. The problem is to determine the limits of the ocean and its advances and retreats during the earth's history.

Fossils are the most useful indicators, particularly those that are abundant and widespread and that have related modern forms restricted either to marine or to fresh-water environments. Confusion may arise because some species that originally inhabited fresh water may have adapted themselves to marine conditions, and, conversely, some marine species may have become adapted to fresh-water conditions. A serious limitation on the diagnostic use of fossils is encountered in areas where considerable sequences of sedimentary rocks are nonfossiliferous or sparsely fossiliferous.

Petrographic studies may provide useful criteria in some areas, but most of the features of clastic sedimentary rocks that can be seen in hand specimen or under the microscope are related primarily to source area and mechanical processes of sedimentation, and supplementary

[1] Contribution number 57–98, Mineral Conservation Series, from the College of Mineral Industries, Pennsylvania State University.

[2] Present address: Geologisches Institut der Universität, Würzburg, Germany.

chemical tests are desirable for environmental studies. Within recent years the use of geochemical criteria has been proposed, some of which show promise of widespread application. The purpose of the present paper is to record some examples of geochemical features of sedimentary rocks which result from the environment of deposition and can be used as indicators of the chemistry of that environment.

Previous Work

Studies of the geochemistry of sedimentary rocks pertinent to the specific question at hand include the investigations of boron by Goldschmidt and Peters (1932*a* and *b*) and by Landergren (1945);[3] the studies of Goldschmidt (1937), Wickman (1944), Krauskopf (1955, 1956), and others on the concentration of rare metals in sediments; those of Adams and Weaver (1958) on the thorium/uranium ratio; and those of Degens et al. (1957, 1958) and of Keith and Bystrom (1959) dealing with measurable differences between marine and fresh-water sedimentary rocks. Literature on variation of the isotopic composition of carbon and oxygen is summarized in the review of Ingerson (1953); recent papers with data necessary to interpretation of isotopic differences between marine and fresh-water sediments include those of Landergren (1953), Craig (1953), Epstein and Mayeda (1953), Epstein and Lowenstam (1953), Jeffrey et al. (1955), Epstein (1956), Wickman (1956), and Silverman and Epstein (1958).

There are a number of both specialized and general works on various phases of marine geochemistry; of these it is appropriate to mention the work of Harvey (1945, 1949), Hutchinson (1947), Rubey (1951), Sverdrup et al. (1952), Goldberg and Arrhenius (1958), and the valuable collection of papers in the recent G. S. A. memoir on marine ecology, edited by Hedgpeth (1957). Data on the geochemistry of the various types of continental sediments are widely scattered in the literature; a recent monograph and source reference on limnology is that by Hutchinson (1957).

Geochemical Indicators

Sediments are deposited in widely different environments. The chemical environment varies in the kind and amount of the ions present as well as in temperature, pressure, and organic activity. Resulting de-

[3] Summarized in Goldschmidt (1954), p. 286.

pendent variables include the *p*H and redox potential at or near the sediment-water interface. All these parameters influence the chemical and mineralogical composition of the sediment. Most important and potentially most useful among chemical characteristics are those which are greatly dominant in one environment, which become fixed in the sediment, and which are not appreciably changed by diagenesis or weathering.

The term "geochemical facies" has previously been used by Teodorovich (1947), who defined different sedimentary environmental facies by means of specific mineral indicators of oxidation-reduction potential and *p*H. Adams and Weaver (1958) propose that geochemical facies of sedimentary rocks be defined in terms of the thorium/uranium ratio. A similar term, *chemofacies*, somewhat analogous to the term biofacies as used to refer to the fossil assemblage of a rock, might be used to designate all the chemical elements that are collected, precipitated, or adsorbed from the aqueous environment or fixed by chemical reactions within the bottom muds. It is generally difficult to make a clear-cut separation between elements associated with detrital material and those of nondetrital origin, and "chemofacies" is intended only as a convenience in discussing chemical differences among environmental groups of sediments.

Current studies, summarized herewith, are aimed at determining which features of the marine chemofacies are measurably different from those of the fresh-water chemofacies. In order to determine significant differences it is necessary to compare groups of sedimentary rocks of the same age and from the same general area, so that as many as possible of the variables due to different source areas and climates can be eliminated. If a criterion does not work under these sampling conditions, it cannot be expected to be useful for general application.

Partition of Elements during Sedimentation

The paths that chemical elements follow during cycles of weathering, transportation, and deposition are governed by their chemical properties as well as by the physical and chemical properties of minerals. Major and minor elements can be grouped according to their tendencies to be concentrated in specific sedimentary rock fractions. Excluding the resistates and evaporites, the most important fractions with their contained major elements are as follows: (1) clay minerals (Al, Si, K, Mg); (2) oxidates (Fe, Mn); (3) organic material (C,

N, H); (4) sulfides (Fe, S); (5) carbonates (Ca, Mg, C); and (6) phosphates (P, Ca, F).

In the following sections each sedimentary rock fraction and the elements associated with it will be considered in turn. Discussion will be centered on the suitability of particular elements as indicators of marine versus fresh-water deposition.

All the above fractions are deposited in both marine and fresh-water environments, but the proportions vary, and some of the associated trace elements are characteristically different in marine and the corresponding fresh-water fractions. In general, chemical analysis of the total sample of a sedimentary rock is much less significant for environmental studies than analyses of separated fractions, because interpretation requires that similar materials be compared. Quantitative measurement and separation of the fractions is often difficult, however, particularly if the fractions are intimately intermixed in fine-grained rocks.

The separated fractions, of course, represent only a partial sample of a rock in its present form; as pointed out by Krauskopf (1955) for rare metals in sediments, the particular form of combination of an element in a sedimentary rock may be different from the form in which the element was first deposited.

Elements in the Clay Fraction and in Shales

The clay fraction in sedimentary rocks probably is mainly detrital, and therefore the clay minerals very likely owe their composition in large part to the rocks, soils, and climate of the source area, although some modifications may take place by adsorption, recrystallization, and reaction in the basin of deposition. Authigenic clay minerals would be expected to reflect the chemistry of the environment of deposition more closely; as a practical matter, however, it is not possible to separate authigenic and detrital clay minerals.

Attempts have been made to use clay mineral ratios for environmental interpretation; as examples may be mentioned the work of Millot (1949, 1952), Grim and Johns (1954), Murray (1954), Keller (1956), and Degens et al. (1957). It is found in some areas that marine shales have a higher proportion of illite than fresh-water shales, but the environmental significance of this observation has been questioned by Weaver (1958) on the grounds that the source area effect is dominant. In more porous rocks, like sandstones, the contained clay minerals are subject to post-depositional leaching and alteration (Glass et al., 1956; Milne and Earley, 1958), and therefore clay mineral ratios probably have limited application, if used alone, as indicators of depositional environment of sediments. Nevertheless, the proportion of different clay minerals in a sediment is one of the factors that control the trace-element assemblage and therefore may be expected to assist in interpreting and using geochemical criteria. Development of improved methods of quantitative clay mineral determination is desirable.

For simplicity and ease of sample treatment, preliminary geochemical studies by Degens et al. (1957) and Keith and Bystrom (1959) were made on unseparated shale samples, in spite of the realization that more specific chemical data and probably more generally applicable interpretations could be obtained by analyzing the separated clay fraction.

Table 1, from the data of Keith and Bystrom (1959), shows the

TABLE 1. Average Composition of 15 Marine Shales and 15 Fresh-Water Shales of Pennsylvanian Age

	Per Cent					PPM			
	Marine		Fresh-Water			Marine		Fresh-Water	
	$\overline{X}$	s	$\overline{X}$	s		$\overline{X}$	s	$\overline{X}$	s
SiO_2	**54.53**	3.33	**57.29**	3.30	B	**115**	34	**44**	28
TiO_2	**0.92**	0.05	**0.94**	0.10	Ga	**8**	7	**17**	4
Al_2O_3	**20.89**	1.54	**21.24**	1.43					
MnO	**0.80**	0.05	**0.12**	0.07	Li	**159**	26	**92**	24
CaO	**0.54**	0.49	**0.31**	0.16	F	**817**	182	**642**	121
MgO	**1.65**	0.29	**1.73**	0.15	Sr	**250**	52	**205**	52
Na_2O	**0.22**	0.03	**0.21**	0.04					
K_2O	**3.71**	0.37	**3.53**	0.34					
P_2O_5	**0.23**	0.12	**0.17**	0.06					
Fe	**6.67**	3.34	**5.82**	2.13					
S	**0.92**	0.68	**0.15**	0.13					
Wt. loss (750° C)	**8.73**	1.46	**7.27**	1.53	Wt. loss (140° C)	0.9%	0.5	0.5%	0.3

$\overline{X}$ = mean.
s = standard deviation.

Analyses (in large part) by A. M. Bystrom and M. Grender. No determinations were made of organic material, or of the relative proportions of Fe^{2+} and Fe^{3+}. Therefore, totals of the $\overline{X}$ columns are not significant.

average composition of 15 marine shales and 15 fresh-water shales of the Allegheny series (Pennsylvanian) from the northern part of the Appalachian coal basin. The fresh-water shales are from the Freeport formation, and the marine shales from the Kittanning and upper Clarion formations. Unpublished cross-bedding data of E. G. Williams and E. T. Degens indicate that the source area for all the analyzed shales is probably the same, that is, to the south of the Appalachian basin. Diagnostic fossils used to classify the shales as marine or fresh-water in origin are listed by Degens et al. (1957, p. 2431).

The most striking observation about the major constituents (those in amounts greater than 0.1 per cent), which are listed on the left-hand side of table 1, is that only sulfur and manganese are different in the two groups; both are more abundant in the marine than in the fresh-water shales. It is apparent that none of the other major elements offers any promise as a diagnostic element for differentiating between marine and fresh-water shales in the area investigated.

The observed similarity in bulk composition of the marine and fresh-water shales sampled is in accord with the contention of Weaver (1958) that the clay minerals in shales are mainly detrital rather than authigenic. Perhaps one should not expect the bulk composition of detrital material contributed by rivers to be radically changed as a result of composition of the water in the basin of deposition.

Some of the trace elements are significantly different in the two groups, however. Trace elements found concentrated in the marine shales include boron and lithium (appreciably higher in the marine samples), and fluorine and strontium (slightly higher). A preliminary spectrochemical study of shale samples (Degens et al., 1957) indicated that nickel and rubidium [4] may also be slightly higher in the marine group, but not vanadium, although Goldschmidt (1954, p. 494) suggests that a higher vanadium content is to be expected in marine shales than in corresponding fresh-water deposits.

Some of the above trace elements may be incorporated in clay mineral structures: for example, fluorine and chlorine, in addition to their occurrence in sedimentary phosphates, can substitute for the

[4] Current re-evaluation of methods of determining rubidium in shales shows good correspondence between a flame photometer method (Horstman, 1956) and an X-ray fluorescence method, but the data obtained by optical emission spectroscopy are not in good agreement with results of the other two methods. Therefore, the previously reported rubidium abundance data cannot be considered reliable, and further work will be necessary to determine rubidium abundance in the marine and fresh-water shales.

hydroxyl ion in clay minerals; nickel and lithium can proxy for magnesium in illite and chlorite. The probable form of combination of boron is an interesting problem. It has been shown by Degens et al. (1957, 1958*a*) that the boron in shales is not removed by treatment with hydrochloric acid. Boron is, in part, in similarly insoluble form in modern marine muds (Goldberg and Arrhenius, 1958; Degens, Keith, Williams, and Kanehiro, 1959). Goldberg and Arrhenius, finding that the boron is released upon boiling in strong alkali, concluded that it probably is proxying for silicon in the tetrahedral sheets of clay minerals. An alternative suggestion (Degens et al., 1958) is that tourmaline may form by reaction between ocean water and clay minerals, boron and sodium (or lithium) being supplied from the sea solution, alumina and silica from the clays. This reaction has recently been demonstrated in the laboratory (Frondel and Collette, 1957) for higher temperatures, and it may well operate at ocean temperatures. The occurrence of authigenic tourmaline in coarser-grained sedimentary rocks is well established (Krynine, 1946).

Trace elements found to be more abundant in the fresh-water shales than in the marine ones include gallium (table 1) and chromium. A preliminary spectroscopic investigation showed a mean chromium content of 110 ppm (median 100 ppm) in a group of 11 fresh-water shales, a mean of 62 ppm (median 60) in 11 marine shales. Other elements that tend to remain behind in continental sediments in insoluble form include titanium, niobium, zirconium, and thorium (Goldschmidt, 1937). Recent data on thorium and thorium/uranium ratios are given in a paper by Adams and Weaver (1958).

Some of the above-listed elements may be useful indicators of fresh-water sedimentary rocks, but they will probably be less useful than marine indicators because their distribution must be expected to be more strongly affected by the composition of the source area rocks than by the composition of the depositional environment.

Examples of environmental diagrams for the Pennsylvanian shales examined are shown in figures 1 and 2, based upon analytical data of Degens et al. (1957) and of Keith and Bystrom (1959), with some added lithium determinations by M. Grender. It will be noted that there is some overlap of marine and fresh-water samples, but that either one of the diagrams can probably be used for marine versus fresh-water diagnosis of Pennsylvanian shales in the area studied. Brackish-water shales (fig. 1) do not appear to be distinguishable as a separate group.

For elements like boron and gallium, which appear to be related to

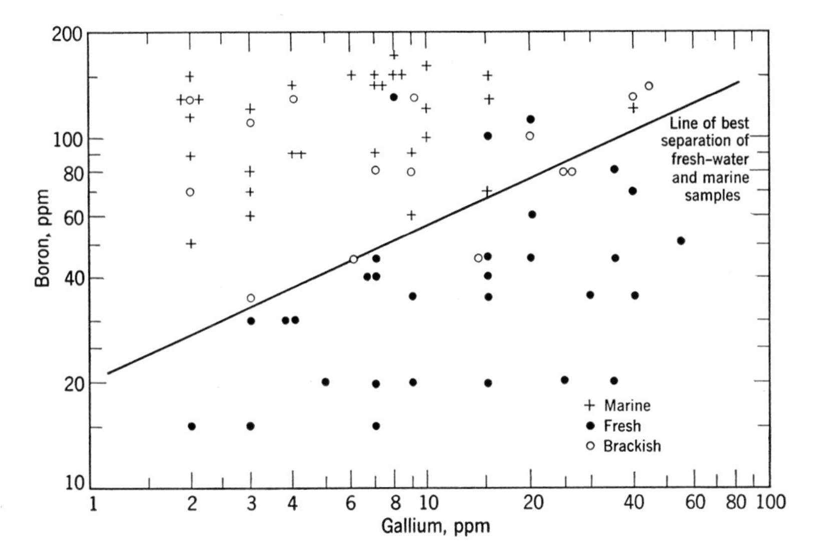

Fig. 1. Boron versus gallium content of a group of Pennsylvanian shales of marine, brackish, and fresh-water origin (after Degens et al., 1957, by permission).

the clay fraction (Degens et al., 1957, 1958), there probably would be an advantage for general application in plotting the trace-element abundance data against the clay mineral ratio (e.g., the illite/kaolinite ratio) as independent variable.

Application of environmental diagrams like figures 1 and 2 to other areas remains to be demonstrated. It is to be expected that the absolute amounts of trace elements will vary from one sedimentary province to another. For example, the boron content of sedimentary rocks in parts of the western United States is known to be higher than in the eastern states. It is likely, however, that the boron content of marine shales will generally be higher than that of comparable fresh-water shales from the same area and sedimentary sequence.

In order to confirm the hypothesis that each marine cycle of sedimentation adds an increment of boron to the sedimented material (Landergren, 1945), analyses were made on a series of modern muds from Hawaii. Results are reported in detail in a paper that has been submitted to the *Journal of Geology*.

The boron content of recent marine muds from the island of Oahu is consistently higher than that of fresh-water stream and lake muds from the same island. Detailed comparison and interpretation must

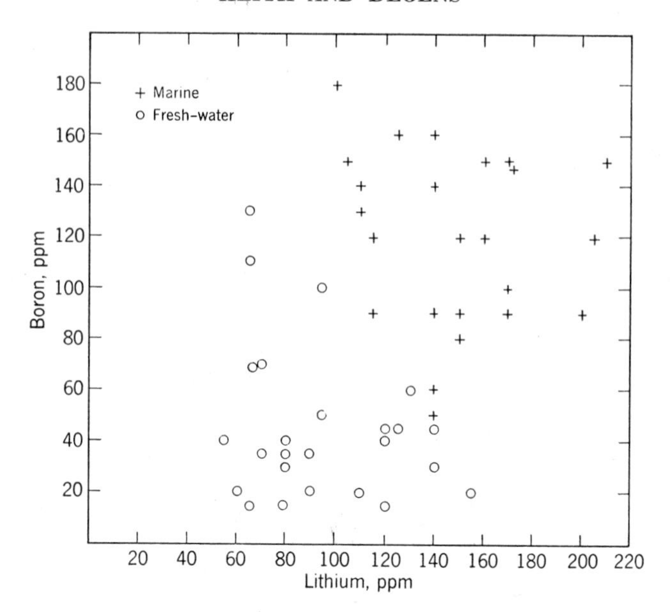

Fig. 2. Boron versus lithium content of a group of Pennsylvanian shales of fresh-water and marine origin (after Keith and Bystrom, 1959).

await completion of a current investigation of the boron content of the carbonate fraction and of the effect of acid treatment used to remove carbonates. Present results, however, show that the boron/gallium ratio of original samples as well as of samples treated with 2 *N* HCl serves to differentiate the marine muds and the fresh-water muds; the average boron/gallium ratio is higher in the marine muds by a factor of more than 5.

Lithium is similarly concentrated in the marine muds relative to the fresh-water muds of the Hawaiian suite. The observations on boron and lithium in a suite of recent muds are therefore similar to those recorded for the Pennsylvanian shales examined (figs. 1 and 2) and add weight to the conclusion that boron and lithium are suitable as indicators of the environment of deposition of shales.

Oxidate Fraction

Manganese and iron may be closely associated in igneous rock minerals but tend to be separated by low-temperature inorganic processes. Under weathering and sedimentation conditions, both iron and manganese are dissolved to some extent, but iron tends to remain behind. Except in the most acid surface waters, or under reducing conditions, iron is oxidized to Fe^{3+} and forms hydrated ferric oxide, whereas manganese tends to be more stable in ionic solution and may be carried long distances. A large proportion of the iron that reaches the ocean is probably in suspended form, whereas much of the manganese may reach the ocean in dissolved (divalent) form or adsorbed on clays (Murata, 1939).

Because of the above difference in behavior, the Mn/Fe ratio may be found useful as a criterion for differentiating marine from fresh-water sediments. The available data for shales are insufficient to justify a decision. Goldschmidt (1954, p. 639) quotes data of Steiger, Revelle, and Correns which show a higher Mn/Fe ratio in deep-sea muds than in terrigenous muds, whereas river muds analyzed by Murata (1939) contained more manganese than shallow-water ocean muds but less than deep-sea muds. Our results (table 1) show more manganese in the marine than in the fresh-water shales analyzed. The potential usefulness of the Mn/Fe ratio is limited by the changes in relative manganese and iron content that may take place under reducing conditions in bottom muds (Goldschmidt, 1954, p. 638), and also by the changes in manganese and iron content that result from subsequent weathering of exposed rocks. Degens (1958) found a significant difference between the Mn/Fe ratios of unweathered marine and fresh-water shales of the Ruhr district in Germany.

Factors that have been considered in attempting to explain the trace-element assemblages associated with the hydrated iron and manganese oxide fractions include adsorption and a reported difference in the charge on the colloids (Goldberg, 1954); hydrous manganese oxide in colloidal form is reported to have a negative charge with a consequent affinity for cations, whereas iron oxide colloids reportedly have a positive charge under most conditions in natural surface waters and consequently a tendency to attract anions. This subject has recently been reviewed by Krauskopf (1955), who concludes that the available data are insufficient to establish a distinction. It appears likely that such a distinction can be demonstrated only by controlled laboratory studies and by comparative trace-element analyses of coexisting iron and manganese oxide minerals, with due consideration of the mineralogy. A current study of residual limonite deposits in central Pennsylvania provides some data on trace-element assemblage as a function of manganese content. In these deposits, barium, calcium, zinc, cobalt, and nickel, and less certainly silver and cadmium, show a positive correlation with manganese, whereas chromium, and less certainly arsenic, show a positive correlation with iron. Minerals identified include cryptomelane, psilomelane, goethite, and poorly crystallized hydrous ferric oxide. Probably barium is largely combined in the psilomelane in the limonites referred to. The other trace-element relations noted are consistent with a preferential affinity of cations for manganese oxides and a contrasting affinity of chromate and arsenate anions for iron oxide, but ionic substitution is probably at least as important as adsorption and may be more important. B. L. Sreenivas (personal communication) has shown recently that cryptomelane (normally potassium-bearing) can alternatively incorporate divalent and trivalent cations in its structure, with resultant changes in structure and cell dimensions. Ions of a wide range of ionic size can be accommodated, from Ni^{2+} to Ba^{2+} and from Cr^{3+} to La^{3+}.

Whatever the mechanism involved, it appears, as pointed out by Goldberg (1954), that the hydrous iron and manganese oxides are important primary collectors of trace elements during weathering and sedimentation.

The widespread occurrence of titanium in sediments and its relationship to iron have received some study. Our results on shales of Pennsylvanian age (table 1) show no difference in the titanium content of marine and fresh-water shales, in agreement with the data summarized by Goldschmidt (1954, p. 411). A reconnaissance study of fresh-water and marine muds from Hawaii showed a high titanium content (from weathered basalts), gradually decreasing in a downstream direction (fig. 3), probably owing mainly to fractional separation of the heavy TiO_2 minerals from the lighter clays.

Organic Fraction

Extensive investigations have been made on the organic material in sedimentary rocks, much of the work being motivated by the problem of the origin of petroleum. Marine and brackish-water sedimentary rocks appear to have been emphasized, and information about the organic fraction of fresh-water sedimentary rocks is more limited. An up-to-date summary of investigations dealing with lake muds is given by Hutchinson (1957). Recent papers dealing in part with the trace-element assemblages of the organic fraction include those of Black and Mitchell (1952), Krauskopf (1955, 1956), and Goldberg (1957).

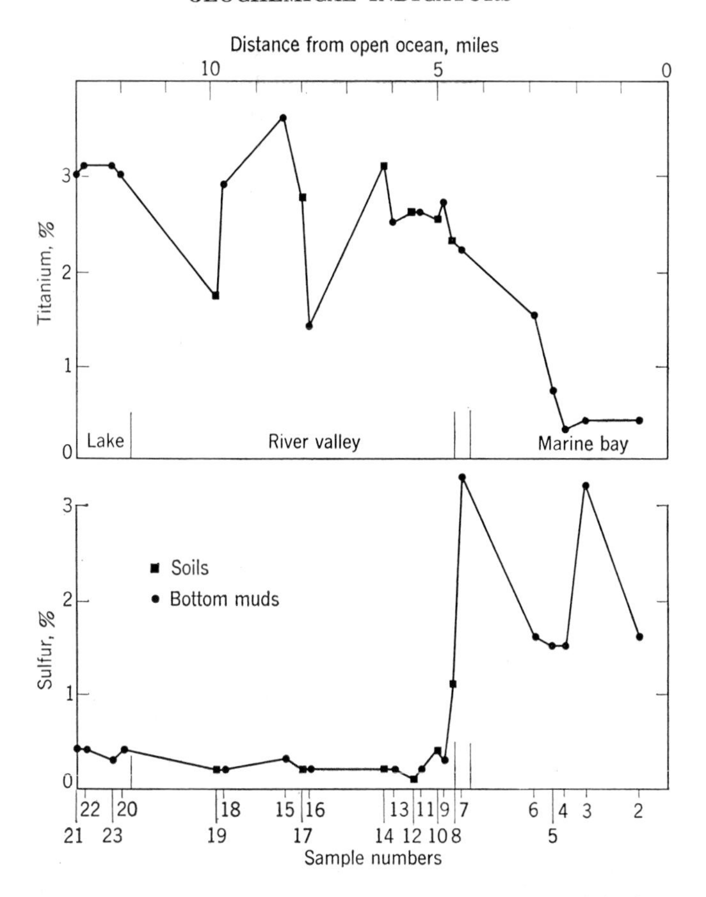

Fig. 3. Variation in sulfur and titanium content in untreated fresh-water and marine muds from Oahu, Hawaii.

It is well established that trace elements can be enriched in organic matter by several processes, including the life processes of plants and animals, adsorption and precipitation effects during sedimentation, and the formation of metallo-organic complexes.

The effects of these processes cannot usually be separated, but the total effect apparently produces some characteristic differences between organic debris of continental and that of marine origin. Characteristic differences were found (Degens et al., 1957) in a preliminary study of the organic fraction separated from Pennsylvanian shales by froth flotation (table 2). Differences probably deserving further study are the suggested relative concentration of copper, lead, and tin in the or-

TABLE 2. Trace Elements Concentrated in the Organic Fraction of Marine and Fresh-Water Shales

(Data of Degens et al., 1957)

Element	Fresh-Water Shales, ppm			Marine Shales, ppm				Lower Limit of Detection
Sample No.	*110*	*114*	*135*	*291*	*297*	*299*	*302*	
Pb	400	150	100	40	50	40	150	(10)
Ni	20	25	20	150	100	70	80	(5)
Sn	30	40	20	7	5	5	10	(2)
Cu	500	1500	1000	150	100	150	800	(1)
Zn	400	600	1500	400	300	500	1000	(200)
Ag	2	5	2	2	8	...	2	(1)
Co	40	10	20	20	20	...	40	(10)
Mo	4	4	3	6	2	...	5	(2)
V	100	100	80	150	150	100	200	(10)

Other trace elements found (B, Ba, Be, Cr, Ga, Mn, Rb, and Sr) are not concentrated in the organic fraction relative to the raw shale.

ganic fraction of fresh-water shales and of nickel and possibly vanadium in the organic fraction of marine shales. The enrichment of nickel and vanadium may be due in part to the formation of stable nickel and vanadium porphyrins. More detailed investigations of metallo-organic complexes and of incorporation of trace elements in specific hydrocarbons of marine and fresh-water sedimentary rocks would probably be fruitful.

The isotopic composition of carbon in the organic fraction appears to be one of the most promising indicators of the environment of deposition of sedimentary rocks. Silverman and Epstein (1958) analyzed a group of petroleums and organic extracts, finding that those derived from marine sediments contain carbon with a higher C^{13}/C^{12} ratio [5] ($\delta = -22.2$ to -29.4) than that of comparable organic materials derived from nonmarine sediments ($\delta = -29.9$ to -32.5).

[5] δ in parts per thousand (‰) $= \left(\frac{(C^{13}/C^{12})_{\text{sample}} - (C^{13}/C^{12})_{\text{standard}}}{(C^{13}/C^{12})_{\text{standard}}}\right) \times 1000.$

Sulfide Fraction

A number of sulfides occur in sedimentary rocks in a manner compatible with the hypothesis that they were formed more or less contemporaneously with the sedimentation. Probably pyrite and marcasite are quantitatively most important, and it is therefore desirable to investigate their trace-element assemblage. As noted by Krauskopf (1955), the available data regarding syngenetic sedimentary sulfides are very limited.

Frequently there may be a genetic connection between sedimentary sulfides and organic material. The principal sources of available sulfur for sulfide formation are the decomposition of proteins and the action of anaerobic bacteria which use sulfate ions in their life processes and liberate H_2S. The processes have been studied and referred to by a number of authors, among them Galliher (1933), Rittenberg (1941), and Caspers (1957).

Bacteria are most active in the presence of abundant organic material in bottom muds. The amount of H_2S produced is also a function of the amount of sulfur available as sulfate ion. For this reason, more H_2S should be formed and more sulfides precipitated under marine conditions, where sulfate is abundantly available, than under otherwise similar conditions of deposition in a fresh-water basin. This conclusion is supported by sulfur analyses of marine and fresh-water shales of Pennsylvanian age (table 1) as well as by analyses of modern fresh-water and marine muds from Oahu, Hawaii (fig. 3).

Goldschmidt (1954, p. 530) suggests that the first-formed sulfide is mainly hydrotroilite, $FeS \cdot nH_2O$. The iron sulfides probably are formed mainly within the bottom muds rather than precipitated directly from the overlying water layer. As is pointed out by Hutchinson (1957, p. 726), dissolved iron in ionic form is in extremely small amount in the epilimnetic waters of most lakes; it is in even smaller concentration in sea water. In deeper waters, wherever there is an oxygen deficiency and the mud surface is reduced, ferrous iron tends to diffuse into the water. Therefore, the conditions for precipitation of iron sulfide, requiring the presence of both H_2S and dissolved iron, would normally be developed only within or immediately above the bottom muds. The fact that the trace-element assemblage in sedimentary pyrite is similar in some respects to that in the organic fraction may support the inference that some of the trace elements were initially collected by organic material and subsequently released by decay processes and incorporated in the sulfide fraction. Elements notably concentrated in both organic and sulfide fractions in a group of Pennsylvanian shales include nickel, cobalt, copper, and lead. Arsenic is concentrated in the sulfide fraction (fig. 4) but is below

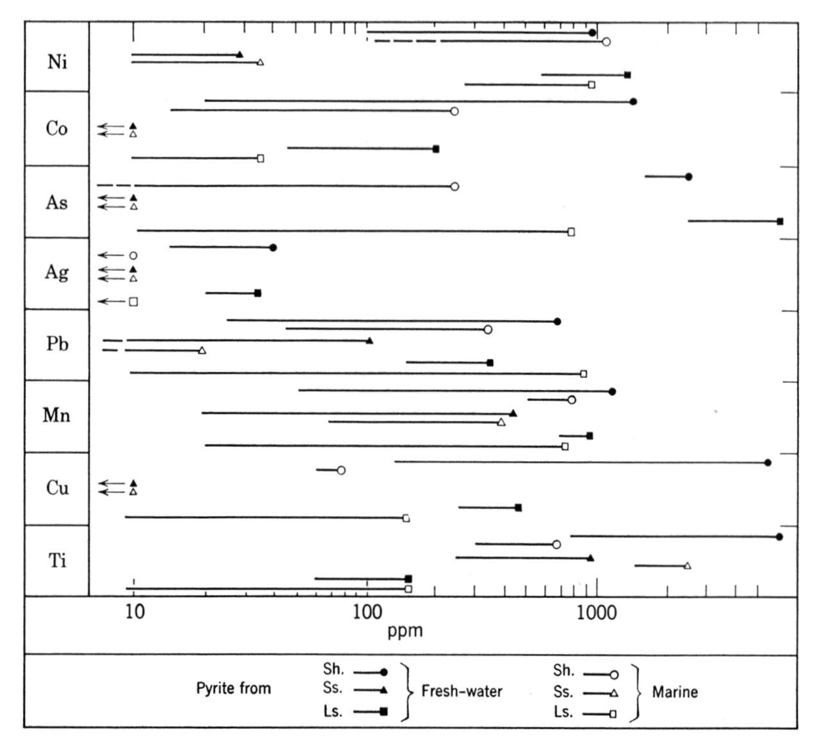

Fig. 4. Range in trace-element content of sedimentary pyrite and marcasite based on preliminary spectrochemical analysis of sulfides from the following rocks.

Marine (or brackish water): Vanport limestone (Pennsylvanian) at Parkers City, Pa.; Vanport limestone, 1 mi E. of Mercer, Pa.; Trenton limestone (Ordovician), near Wagner Bank limonite pit, 0.7 mi N.E. of Centre Hill, Pa.; black shale above Upper Clarion coal (Pennsylvanian), 3 mi S.E. of Clearfield, Pa.; Gatesburg sandstone (Cambrian), 3 mi S.E. of Tyrone, Pa.; Chattanooga shale, probably brackish (Mississippian), at Smithville, Tenn.; black shale, probably brackish, above Lower Clarion coal (Pennsylvanian), 3 mi S.E. of Clearfield, Pa. (contains marcasite rather than pyrite).

Fresh water: Johnstown limestone beneath Upper Kittanning coal (Pennsylvanian), 1 mi S.E. of Clearfield, Pa. (contains pyrite plus minor marcasite); black Catskill shale (Devonian) at First Fork Dam, Pa.; black shale above Upper Freeport coal (Pennsylvanian), 2 mi S. of Clearfield, Pa.; Oswego sandstone (Ordovician), 7 mi W. of State College, Pa.

the limit of detection in the organic fraction of sedimentary rocks from the same region. Therefore, it seems likely that arsenic was initially collected by some other process (nonorganic), for example by the hydrous oxides of iron and manganese, as concluded by Goldschmidt (1954, p. 473) and by Goldberg (1954).

It is possible that much of the iron in sulfide form in sedimentary rocks was first brought to the bottom muds as hydrous ferric oxide. Fine-grained hydrous ferric oxide probably is unstable under the reducing conditions developed in bottom muds high in organic matter, and some Fe^{2+} ions may be released and made available for reprecipitation as sulfides or as iron carbonate.

Pyrite from a few samples of fresh-water shale (fig. 4) contains higher amounts of cobalt, arsenic, silver, and copper than pyrite from a small group of marine shales; pyrite from a few limestone samples shows a similar contrast in the abundance of the same four trace elements. Pyrite from a few sandstones examined has a very sparse content of trace elements, except for manganese and titanium.

Further work on a large number of samples will be required in order to confirm the observed differences. Possibly the differences between marine and fresh-water pyrite are due to differences in the trace-element assemblage initially collected by organic material, hydrated ferric oxide, etc. On the other hand, a "dilution" effect is possible, as a result of the more abundant formation of sulfides under marine conditions. Abundant sulfide formation in an environment of limited trace-element availability would be expected to produce sulfides with a sparse content of trace elements.

Some of the above-noted characteristics, including the abundance of sulfur in shales and in the clay fraction of other sediments, as well as the trace-element assemblage of the separated sulfide fraction, offer promise as criteria for environmental studies.

Carbonate Fraction

Trace elements. Many studies have been made of the composition and trace elements of limestones and dolomites and of fossils composed of carbonates. A summary and complete bibliography for marine carbonates is provided by a paper of Revelle and Fairbridge (1957). The list of trace elements incorporated in appreciable amounts in sedimentary carbonates is rather limited; the principal cations incorporated are, of course, those whose ionic size and charge make them suitable deputies for calcium and magnesium.

A possible indicator element is strontium, the distribution of which in limestones and calcareous fossils has been studied in some detail, but most of the work has been done on marine sediments and fossils (Kulp, Turekian, and Boyd, 1952; Lowenstam, 1954; Thompson and Chow, 1955; and Revelle and Fairbridge, 1957).

Strontianite is isostructural with aragonite, and very much larger amounts of strontium can be incorporated in aragonite than in the calcite structure—facts that have an important bearing on investigations of strontium distribution and on potential use of strontium content to differentiate between marine and fresh-water limestones.

Strontium has been found in approximately equal amount (about 600 ppm) in marine and fresh-water limestones of Pennsylvanian age, and therefore does not appear to be promising as an indicator element for environmental studies. Other possible indicator elements deserving investigation include cadmium, tin, and manganese, suggested by Goldberg (1957). Current studies in our laboratory are aimed at a re-examination of differences in the trace-element assemblages of fresh-water and marine limestones.

Carbon and oxygen isotopes. The search for an indicator for general application to environmental studies of sedimentary carbonates leads to an examination of the relative abundance of the isotopes of carbon and oxygen. Pertinent investigations of the isotope geology of oxygen include those of McCrea (1950), Urey et al. (1951), Silverman (1951), Epstein and Mayeda (1953), and Epstein (1956); pertinent studies on carbon include those of Craig (1953), Landergren (1953), Jeffrey et al. (1955), Wickman (1952, 1956), and Silverman and Epstein (1958).

A large proportion of previously investigated samples were of marine origin; very little study appears to have been devoted to the isotopic composition of fresh-water limestones or the carbonate fraction of other fresh-water sedimentary rocks.

Comparison of the isotopic composition of a group of marine limestones and fossils and a group of fresh-water limestones and fossils (fig. 5) shows that the heavier isotope, C^{13}, is enriched in marine carbonate samples and relatively depleted in the fresh-water samples. Figure 5 is plotted from unpublished data of R. N. Clayton and E. T. Degens. The abundance of the heavier isotope in each sample is plotted as difference in parts per thousand, from an arbitrary standard, a marine belemnite from the Peedee formation (Cretaceous), of South Carolina, which was used as a reference sample by University of Chicago investigators (Urey et al., 1951). Samples with isotopically light

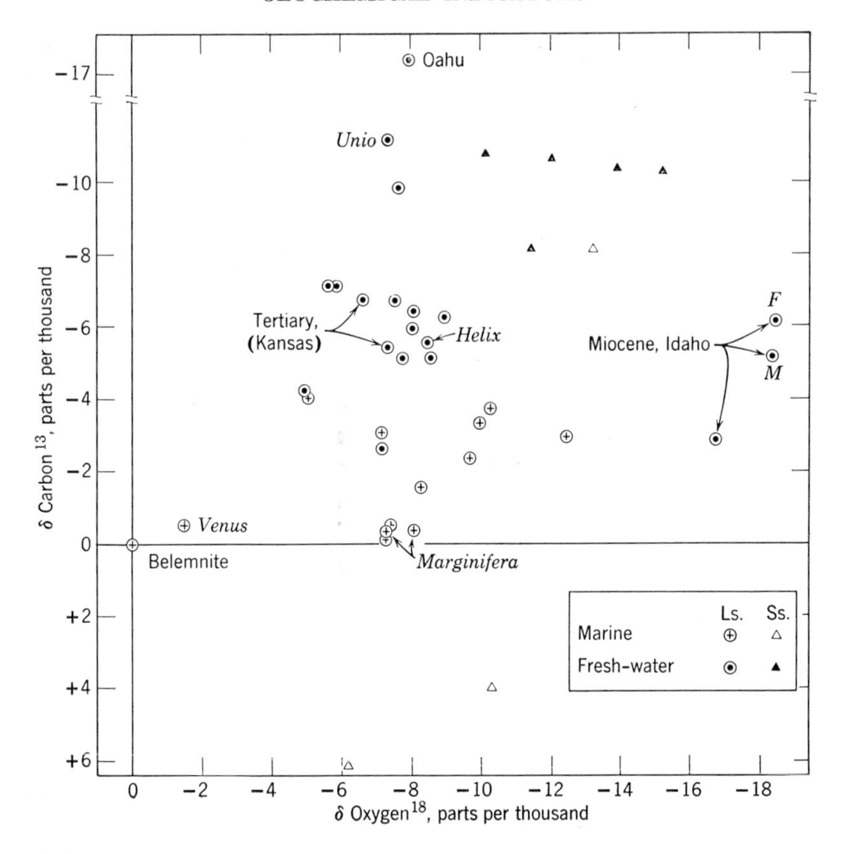

Fig. 5. Variation in C^{13} and O^{18} content of carbonates in a group of fresh-water and marine limestones, fossils, and sandstones (from unpublished data of R. N. Clayton and E. T. Degens).

carbon are toward the top of the diagram; those with isotopically heavier carbon, toward the bottom. Similarly, samples represented by points toward the left-hand side of the diagram contain a higher proportion of isotopically heavy oxygen than samples represented by points farther to the right.

Marine fossils measured, in addition to the belemnite standard, have nearly the same carbon isotope ratio; they include *Venus mercenaria* (a recent marine pelecypod) and two specimens of *Marginifera muricatina,* a marine brachiopod from the Pennsylvanian (two different formations represented).

Fresh-water fossils measured include *Unio* (a recent fresh-water pelecypod), *Fructicola* (*Helix*) (a recent fresh-water gastropod), and an unidentified gastropod (point *F* on the diagram) from fresh-water limestone of probable Miocene age from Idaho. Point *M* and the unlettered point below it represent samples from a thick limestone horizon of the same formation but collected at localities in different counties, and about 20 miles apart. Also represented are two fresh-water limestones of Tertiary age from Kansas and one recent mud from a lake on the high plateau of Oahu, Hawaii. The remaining points represent limestones of Pennsylvanian age plus a few preliminary determinations on the carbonate fraction of sandstones.

It will be noted that the isotopic composition of oxygen does not appear to be a consistently useful criterion for differentiating the marine and the fresh-water carbonate in samples of older sediments, probably because of isotopic exchange of oxygen, which is known to take place between carbonates and water with which they are in contact after their original deposition. The Miocene samples from Idaho seem to have escaped modification due to isotopic exchange of oxygen.

The isotopic composition of carbon appears to be more diagnostic in the samples studied; there is some overlap of the points representing marine and fresh-water limestones, but the separation is good enough to justify the conclusion that measurement of the isotopic composition of carbonate carbon offers a promising criterion for environmental study of limestones. Clayton and Degens made only a few preliminary measurements on the carbonate fraction of shales and sandstones; many more will be needed before the possible extension of the technique to those rock types can be evaluated. Preliminary isotopic analyses on the carbonate carbon of shales do not show a consistent difference between those of marine and those of fresh-water origin. With one exception, however, the few marine sandstones measured differ from the fresh-water sandstones (fig. 5), and the direction of the difference is consistent with the data for limestones; i.e., the carbonate fraction of sandstones of fresh-water origin contains carbon isotopically lighter than that of comparable marine sandstones.

Consideration of probable causes of the observed differences suggests a need for some caution in making environmental interpretations based on isotopic analyses of only a few samples. In general, inorganic carbonate and most of the organic carbonate in nondetrital sediments probably formed in thermodynamic equilibrium with the water of the specific basin of deposition. Differences between the isotopic composition of oxygen of ocean water and that of oxygen of continental waters are attributed to the effects of evaporation and precipitation, which tend to concentrate O^{18} in the ocean and O^{16} in rain, ice, and snow; variation within one environment probably is due mainly to temperature effects (Epstein and Mayeda, 1953).

The parallel enrichment of C^{13} in the bicarbonate ion of the ocean and C^{12} in atmospheric carbon dioxide and continental waters is attributed to processes of photosynthesis and organic decay. Variation in the relative proportions of atmospheric carbon dioxide washed down by rain, and carbon dioxide from oxidation of organic material, can produce wide variation in the isotopic composition of carbon in dissolved carbon dioxide. As a result, some overlap is to be expected between the isotopic composition of carbon in continental and marine waters and consequently between continental and marine carbonates. The cited preliminary data on Pennsylvanian limestones and sandstones encourage the belief that measurements of the isotopic composition of carbonate carbon will be found generally useful in spite of the above-noted limitations. Improved diagnosis of sedimentary environments can be expected from the use of several geochemical criteria, and it is suggested that isotopic criteria can be used advantageously in conjunction with trace-element criteria.

Conclusions

1. Trace-element analyses of sedimentary rocks may provide a number of criteria for differentiating rocks of marine origin from those of fresh-water origin. The most promising are elements of the marine chemofacies, such as boron, lithium, sulfur, and fluorine.

2. An element like boron, which is in a relatively insoluble form of combination in the sedimentary rocks studied, has some advantage over fluorine and sulfur, which are more susceptible to post-depositional removal and are therefore less satisfactory for environmental study of weathered rocks.

3. Trace-element data for the separated fractions of sedimentary rocks are more easily interpreted than data for untreated rock samples, and they permit comparison of rocks of different bulk composition. For example, data on the trace-element content of sandstones are almost meaningless because of the wide variability in proportions of grains and matrix material, and in the relative amounts of clay minerals, carbonates, organic material, etc., in the matrix. The trace-element assemblage of the clay fraction, however, can usefully be compared from one sandstone to another. Trace-element analyses of raw samples probably are significant only for rocks in which one

fraction (for example, the clay fraction in shales) is greatly predominant.

4. The general utility of the proposed criteria remains to be demonstrated for rocks of other ages and geographic areas. Very likely environmental diagrams will have to be constructed for different sedimentary basins, by initial analyses of a group of known marine and fresh-water samples.

5. For the Pennsylvanian stratigraphic sequence studied, it appears possible to differentiate marine and fresh-water shales, or sandstones, by means of two of the selected criteria, for example by boron and lithium analyses. Environmental diagnosis by trace elements can be more generally applied and can be improved (in the sense of increasing the percentage of correct determinations) if a number of trace elements are used in conjunction, either in a multivariant plotting model or in an equation derived from a multivariant analysis of the trace-element data.

6. If detrital and post-depositional carbonates can be avoided or allowed for, the C^{13}/C^{12} ratio of carbonate carbon in limestones and sandstones appears to offer an environmental criterion that may be widely applicable to studies of stratigraphy and paleogeography.

Acknowledgments

Most of the Pennsylvanian samples used were collected and identified by E. G. Williams; the Hawaiian samples were collected by Y. Kanehiro, of the University of Hawaii. Chemical analyses of the shales and muds were made by A. M. Bystrom, M. Grender, and W. W. Mills. Isotopic analyses of the carbonate samples were made by R. N. Clayton, using a mass spectrometer constructed under a National Science Foundation grant to M. L. Keith and J. A. Hipple.

The assistance of the above colleagues and associates, and the support of the National Science Foundation, are gratefully acknowledged.

References

Adams, J. A. S., and C. E. Weaver. 1958. Thorium to uranium ratios as indicators of sedimentary processes: Example of concept of geochemical facies, *Bull. Am. Assoc. Petrol. Geologists, 42,* 387.

Black, W. A. P., and R. L. Mitchell. 1952. Trace elements in the common brown algae and in sea water, *J. Marine Biol. Assoc. United Kingdom, 30,* 575.

Caspers, H. 1957. Black Sea and Sea of Azov, *Geol. Soc. Am., Mem. 67,* vol. 1, p. 801.

Craig, H. 1953. The geochemistry of the stable carbon isotopes, *Geochim. et Cosmochim. Acta, 3,* 53.

Degens, E. T. 1958. Geochemische Untersuchungen zur Faziesbestimmung im Ruhr-Karbon, *Glückauf, 94,* 513.

Degens, E. T., E. G. Williams, and M. L. Keith. 1957. Environmental studies of carboniferous sediments, I, Geochemical criteria for differentiating marine and fresh-water shales, *Bull. Am. Assoc. Petrol. Geologists, 41,* 2427.

Degens, E. T., E. G. Williams, and M. L. Keith. 1958. Environmental studies of carboniferous sediments, II, Application of geochemical criteria, *Bull. Am. Assoc. Petrol. Geologists, 42,* 981.

Degens, E. T., M. L. Keith, E. G. Williams, and Y. Kanehiro. 1959. Environmental study of some recent sediments from Hawaii, *J. Geol.* (in press).

Epstein, S. 1956. Variations of the O^{18}/O^{16} ratios of fresh waters and ice, *Natl. Acad. Sci.–Natl. Research Council, Publ. 400,* 20.

Epstein, S., and H. A. Lowenstam. 1953. Temperature-shell growth relations of recent and interglacial Pleistocene shoal-water biota from Bermuda, *J. Geol., 61,* 424.

Epstein, S., and T. K. Mayeda. 1953. Variation of O^{18} content of waters from natural sources, *Geochim. et Cosmochim. Acta, 4,* 213.

Frondel, C., and R. L. Collette. 1957. Synthesis of tourmaline by reaction of mineral grains with $NaCl–H_3BO_3$ solution, and its implication in rock metamorphism, *Am. Mineralogist, 42,* 754.

Galliher, E. W. 1933. The sulfur cycle in sediments, *J. Sediment. Petrol., 3,* 51.

Glass, H. D., P. E. Potter, and R. Siever. 1956. Clay mineralogy of some basal Pennsylvanian sandstones, clays and shales, *Bull. Am. Assoc. Petrol. Geologists, 40,* 750.

Goldberg, E. D. 1954. Marine geochemistry, I, Chemical scavengers of the sea, *J. Geol., 62,* 249.

Goldberg, E. D. 1957. Biogeochemistry of trace metals, *Geol. Soc. Am., Mem. 67,* 345.

Goldberg, E. D., and G. O. S. Arrhenius. 1958. Chemistry of Pacific pelagic sediments, *Geochim. et Cosmochim. Acta, 13,* 153.

Goldschmidt, V. M. 1937. Principles and distribution of chemical elements in minerals and rocks, *J. Chem. Soc., 1937* (pt. 1), 655.

Goldschmidt, V. M. 1954. *Geochemistry,* Clarendon Press, Oxford.

Goldschmidt, V. M., and C. Peters. 1932*a*. Zur Geochemie des Bors, *Nachr. Ges. Wiss. Göttingen, Math.-physik. Kl., III,* 402.

Goldschmidt, V. M., and C. Peters. 1932*b*. Zur Geochemie des Bors, II, *Nachr. Ges. Wiss. Göttingen, Math.-physik. Kl., III,* 528.

Grim, R. E., and W. D. Johns. 1954. Clay mineral investigation of sediments in the northern Gulf of Mexico, *Clays and Clay Minerals, Proc. 2nd Natl. Conf. 1953, Natl. Acad. Sci.–Natl. Research Council Publ. 327,* 81–103.

Harvey, H. W. 1945. *Recent Advances in the Chemistry and Biology of Sea Water,* Cambridge University Press.

Harvey, H. W. 1949. On manganese in sea and fresh water, *J. Marine Biol. Assoc. United Kingdom, 28,* 155.

Hedgpeth, J. W. (ed.). 1957. Treatise on marine ecology and paleoecology, *Geol. Soc. Am., Mem. 67,* vol. 1.

Horstman, E. L. 1956. Flame photometric determination of lithium, rubidium and cesium in silicate rocks, *Anal. Chem., 28,* 1417.

Hutchinson, G. E. 1947. The problems of oceanic geochemistry, *Ecol. Monographs, 17,* 299.

Hutchinson, G. E. 1957. *A Treatise on Limnology,* John Wiley & Sons, New York.

Ingerson, E. 1953. Nonradiogenic isotopes in geology: A review, *Bull. Geol. Soc. Am., 64,* 301.

Jeffery, P. M., W. Compston, D. Greenhalgh, and J. de Laeter. 1955. On the carbon-13 abundance of limestones and coals, *Geochim. et Cosmochim. Acta, 7,* 255.

Keith, M. L., and A. M. Bystrom. 1959. Comparative analyses of marine and fresh-water shales, *Penn. State Univ., Mineral Inds. Expt. Sta. Bull.* (in press).

Keller, W. D. 1956. Clay minerals as influenced by environments of their formation, *Bull. Am. Assoc. Petrol. Geologists, 40,* 2689.

Krauskopf, K. B. 1955. Sedimentary deposits of rare metals, *Econ. Geol., Fiftieth Anniv. Vol.,* pt. 1, p. 411.

Krauskopf, K. B. 1956. Factors controlling the concentration of thirteen rare metals in sea water, *Geochim. et Cosmochim. Acta, 9,* 1.

Krynine, P. D. 1946. The tourmaline group in sediments, *J. Geol., 54,* 65.

Kulp, J. L., K. Turekian, and D. W. Boyd. 1952. Strontium content of limestones and fossils, *Bull. Geol. Soc. Am., 63,* 701.

Landergren, S. 1945. Contribution to the geochemistry of boron, II, The distribution of boron in some Swedish sediments, rocks, and iron ores; the boron cycle in the upper lithosphere, *Arkiv Kemi, Mineral. Geol., 19a,* 26.

Landergren, S. 1953. Carbon isotopes in marine sediments, *Deep-Sea Research, 1,* 98.

Lowenstam, H. A. 1954. Factors affecting the aragonite:calcite ratios in carbonate-secreting marine organisms, *J. Geol., 62,* 284.

McCrea, J. M. 1950. On the isotopic chemistry of carbonates and a paleotemperature scale, *J. Chem. Phys., 18,* 849.

Millot, G. 1949. Relations entre la constitution et la genèse des roches sédimentaires argileuses, *Géol. appl. et prospect. minière, 2,* 352.

Millot, G. 1952. Prospecting for useful clays in relation to their conditions of genesis, A. I. M. E. Symposium: *Problems of Clay and Laterite Genesis,* p. 107.

Milne, I. H., and J. W. Earley. 1958. Effect of source and environment on clay minerals, *Bull. Am. Assoc. Petrol. Geologists, 42,* 328.

Murata, K. J. 1939. Exchangeable manganese in river and ocean muds, *Am. J. Sci., 237,* 725.

Murray, H. H. 1954. Genesis of clay minerals in some Pennsylvanian shales of Indiana and Illinois, *Clays and Clay Minerals, Proc. 2nd Natl. Conf. 1953, Natl. Acad. Sci.–Natl. Research Council Publ. 327,* 47.

Revelle, R., and R. Fairbridge. 1957. Carbonates and carbon dioxide, *Geol. Soc. Am., Mem. 67,* 239.

Rittenberg, S. C. 1941. Studies on marine sulfate-reducing bacteria, Ph.D. Dissertation, University of California.

Rubey, W. W. 1951. Geologic history of sea water; an attempt to state the problem, *Bull. Geol. Soc. Am., 62,* 1111.

Silverman, S. R. 1951. The isotope geology of oxygen, *Geochim. et Cosmochim. Acta, 2,* 26.

Silverman, S. R., and S. Epstein. 1958. Carbon isotopic compositions of petroleums and other sedimentary organic materials, *Bull. Am. Assoc. Petrol. Geologists, 42,* 998.

Sverdrup, H. U., M. W. Johnson, and R. H. Fleming. 1952. *The Oceans: Their Physics, Chemistry, and General Biology,* Prentice-Hall, Inc., New York.

Teodorovich, G. L. 1947. (Sedimentary *geochemical facies*), *Biulleten moskovskogo obschestva ispytalelei prirody, Geol. Div. 22,* no. 1. (Reviewed by G. V. Chilingar, *Bull. Am. Assoc. Petrol. Geologists, 39,* 764, 1955.)

Thompson, T. G., and T. J. Chow. 1955. The strontium-calcium atom ratio in carbonate secreting marine organisms, *Papers in Marine Biol. and Oceanog., Deep-Sea Research,* Suppl. to vol. 3, p. 20.

Urey, H. C., H. A. Lowenstam, S. Epstein, and C. R. McKinney. 1951. Measurement of paleotemperatures and temperatures of the upper Cretaceous of England, Denmark and the southeastern United States, *Bull. Geol. Soc. Am., 62,* 399.

Weaver, C. E. 1958. Geologic interpretations of argillaceous sediments, I, Origin and significance of clay minerals in sedimentary rocks, *Bull. Am. Assoc. Petrol. Geologists, 42,* 251.

Wickman, F. E. 1944. Some notes on the geochemistry of the elements in sedimentary rocks, *Arkiv Kemi, Mineral. Geol., 19* (pt. B), 1.

Wickman, F. E. 1952. Variations in the relative abundance of the carbon isotopes in plants, *Geochim. et Cosmochim. Acta, 2,* 243.

Wickman, F. E. 1956. The cycle of carbon and the stable carbon isotopes, *Geochim. et Cosmochim. Acta, 9,* 136.

Geochemical Prospecting

H. E. HAWKES

University of California

Geochemical prospecting for minerals may be defined as mineral exploration based on the systematic measurement of one or more chemical properties of a naturally occurring material. Early work in geochemical prospecting emphasized the analysis of soil for traces of the ore metals. Recent developments emphasize the importance of studies of geochemical patterns in all natural materials—rock, soil, ground and surface water, vegetation, stream and lake sediments, and even air. The elements measured are most commonly the commercially important metals.

Geochemical Anomalies

The development of geochemical prospecting methods has given rise to a number of words and ideas that are not familiar to the geochemical profession as a whole. Many of these hinge around the concept of the geochemical *anomaly,* an example of which is illustrated in figure 1. A geochemical anomaly is an area where unusually high metal content, or some other chemical characteristic of a naturally occurring material, such as soil, indicates the presence of a mineral deposit in the vicinity.

Not all areas of high metal content, however, contain ore. Some anomalies result from special features of the environment that cause local enrichments of an element from source material of normal composition. A spectacular example of a geochemical pattern of no economic significance is provided by the Arctic dwarf birch, in which the ash normally contains in the order of 0.5 per cent zinc. This is considerably more than the zinc content of most other species of plants even where they are rooted directly in zinc-rich soil overlying a base-metal deposit. The concentration of zinc in the dwarf birch

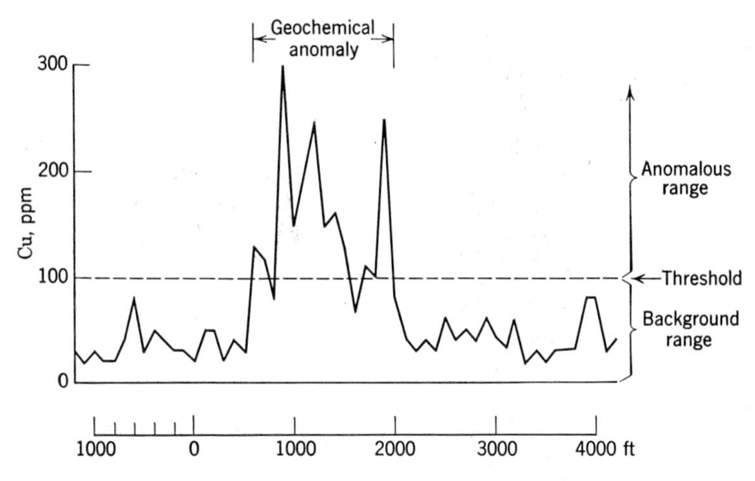

Fig. 1. A geochemical soil anomaly, Blackbird District, Idaho. Data from plate 20, Canney, Hawkes, Richmond, and Vhay (1953).

is not a commercially important anomaly, as it does not help in prospecting. One of the principal problems in interpreting geochemical prospecting data is distinguishing enrichments of metal of no economic significance from the anomalies that are indicative of ore.

The task of recognizing anomalies has led to a number of other concepts. Before an area showing abnormal properties can be identified, we must know what the normal situation is. In geochemical prospecting work, the normal concentration of a given element in a given material is known as the *background.* This is a familiar idea to geochemists, as the first task of geochemistry as set forth by Goldschmidt was the determination of the average composition of the earth's crust. To the prospector, however, the idea of background involves more than a single value; it suggests also a range of composition throughout which he does not need to worry about ore deposits. Geochemical background is therefore somewhat analogous to noise in a radio signal or in an electronic amplifier.

Threshold. In studying the data of a geochemical field survey, it is usually possible to select a value below which the variations represent only normal background effects, and above which they have significance in terms of ore. This value has been called the *threshold* value. Sketching a threshold contour on a geochemical map can be extremely helpful in interpretation, as it emphasizes the parts of the area surveyed where further exploration should be carried out.

Contrast. Consideration of the *contrast* of a geochemical anomaly, or ratio of anomalous to background values, can be very helpful in interpreting geochemical prospecting data. The contrast of an anomaly must exceed about 2 to 1 if the anomaly is to stand out above normal background variations. Experience has shown, however, that contrasts of 10 to 1 are common, and contrasts of as much as 100 to 1 are not unknown. The high contrast of most geochemical anomalies permits the use of relatively less precise and hence more economical methods of sampling and chemical analysis.

Primary Geochemical Anomalies

Geochemical anomalies can be classified into two groups, depending on whether they were formed at depth by processes of petrogenesis, metamorphism, and hydrothermal activity, or whether they are the effect of weathering, transportation, and sedimentation at the surface of the earth. The anomalies of deep-seated origin are called *primary,* and the ones of surficial origin are *secondary.*

Primary anomalies can be further classified according to their size and genesis. Very large areas of anomalous chemical properties, such as the tin-rich areas of Indonesia and Malaya, are called *geochemical provinces.* Where the feature embraces only a mining district or a group of deposits, we speak of an *areal geochemical anomaly.* Geochemical patterns resulting from the deposition of material along the channels followed by ore-bearing solutions are known as *leakage halos.* Finally, the most local of the primary geochemical anomalies is the dispersion pattern of metals in the wall rocks of ore bodies, formed presumably by the diffusion of ions through aqueous solutions in the pore spaces of the rock at the time the ore minerals were deposited.

Secondary Geochemical Anomalies

Secondary anomalies can be conveniently classified according to whether the weathering products comprising them have been transported from their source, and if so whether the principal transporting agency was ice or water. Elements such as silicon and aluminum that occur characteristically with the insoluble products of weathering, and that move slowly away from their source in the bedrock, may be thought of as relatively immobile; conversely, elements that tend to be soluble in subsurface and surface water, such as sodium and chloride, are the mobile elements. The relative mobility of substances comprising the different kinds of secondary geochemical anomalies is indicated in table 1. In general, immobile elements are dispersed by mechanical agencies, whereas the mobile elements are carried as suspensions and aqueous solutions in subsurface or surface waters.

TABLE 1. Relative Mobility of Elements Comprising Secondary Geochemical Anomalies

	Relative Mobility of Elements Comprising Anomaly		
Secondary Geochemical Anomalies	Low	Medium	High
No appreciable transport			
Leached outcrops	x		
Gossans	x		
Residual-soil anomalies	x		
Glacial transport			
Boulder trains	x		
Anomalies in fine-grained till	x	x	
Transport by subsurface water			
Ground-water anomalies			x
Plant anomalies		x	
Superimposed halos		x	
Transport by surface water			
Stream-water anomalies			x
Stream-sediment anomalies		x	
Heavy-mineral patterns	x		

With table 1 as a guide, let us now review the various kinds of secondary geochemical anomalies, from the point of view of the agencies of transport responsible for their formation.

No appreciable transport. Residual geochemical patterns reflect materials left behind by the weathering of ore deposits. They consist mostly of primary minerals such as quartz that survive weathering and insoluble secondary products such as the clay minerals and iron oxides. Weathered base-metal sulfide deposits ordinarily have a substantially higher ore metal content than the leached outcrops and gossans derived from barren pyrite.

The metal content of residual soils has been the most commonly used of all the determinations in geochemical prospecting. Systematic sampling and analysis of residual soil lends itself especially well to routine, large-scale operation both in the field and in the laboratory, and relatively untrained personnel can do a satisfactory job. Furthermore, the method is reasonably reliable. So far, no residual soil known positively to have been developed from a metal-rich parent rock has failed to show anomalous metal values. Apparent failures appear if the soil is not residual, or if parent rock was locally not mineralized. Systematic soil analysis of metals is finding its place beside geologic mapping and geophysical methods as a routine method of metal exploration. In the Rhodesian Copper Belt, for example, roughly a million soil samples per year were being collected and analyzed by the operating companies as of early 1957. It is difficult to say how many discoveries should be attributed to geochemical soil surveys, for this work is commonly done in conjunction with other kinds of prospecting methods as part of well balanced exploration programs. It has, however, contributed materially to the discovery of at least four base-metal deposits that subsequently have been brought into production.

Glacial transport. Glacially transported ore boulders have been traced to their source, resulting in numerous important discoveries in Sweden and Finland. Within the last few years, chemical analysis of the fine-grained fraction of till has shown considerable promise, and led to at least one discovery. Systematic glacial prospecting has not been widely adopted in North America.

Transport by subsurface water. The analysis of ground water for the soluble weathering products of ores probably shows as much promise as any other geochemical method. The metal content of water descending through fissures exposed in mine workings has been used as a guide to possible ore in the rocks overhead. In Western areas of low water table and moderate relief the metal content of laterally moving ground water can be easily sampled in ranchers' wells, and may reveal indications of metalliferous deposits up the slope of the water table from the sampling point. In areas of higher water table, the metal content of spring water may also be a very useful ore guide.

Plants concentrate many elements both toxic and nontoxic from salts dissolved in the ground water and soil moisture. In general, these are deposited within the living tissue of the plants, commonly in the leaves, buds, blossoms, twigs, or other outer parts where evaporation is rapid. Chemical analysis of the outer parts of plants can under favorable conditions provide a useful guide to ores buried at considerable depth (Warren, Delavault, and Irish, 1952).

The mineral nutrients available to the plants may also control the distribution of plant species. Certain plants grow only on soil containing large concentrations of selenium (Cannon, 1957). Inasmuch as selenium invariably accompanies uranium in the ores of the Colorado Plateau, these so-called selenium "indicator" plants have become useful ore guides. Other plants are indicators of calcium, sulfate, and perhaps other elements or ions. In Northern Rhodesia, a species of plant has been noted that grows only on copper-rich soil derived from the weathering of copper ore. This plant is now used as one of the principal ore guides in the Rhodesian Copper Belt, and all prospecting parties are trained in its recognition.

Metal-rich ground water generally leaves part of its load of dissolved metal in the clastic material through which it filters, either as adsorbed ions or as minerals that can be readily broken down by leaching with weak chemical solvents. Patterns of this kind have been called "superimposed" halos, inasmuch as they have been superimposed on whatever dispersion patterns were originally present in the matrix. A familiar example of a superimposed geochemical pattern may be seen in some kinds of desert caliche, where calcium carbonates and sulfates have been brought in by the soil moisture and precipitated by evaporation.

Chemical analysis has revealed patterns of metals in transported cover overlying sulfide deposits in the bedrock. Figure 2 shows the pattern of zinc and lead in alluvium overlying bedrock sulfides in the anaerobic environment of a swamp in Nigeria. Here the time necessary for the development of the pattern can be fairly well determined, inasmuch as the alluvium that forms the matrix was almost certainly deposited during a period of catastrophic erosion following the first clearing of the forest about 400 years ago. Similar patterns are observed in glacial till as much as 60 feet above bedrock and in the organic matter of peat bogs overlying mineralized bedrock (Salmi, 1955). Presumably patterns of this kind in transported cover have been formed by the upward movement of material either by diffusion or by convection of the soil moisture.

Transport by surface water. All weathering products, both solid and soluble, funnel through surface drainage channels before they reach their ultimate resting place in a sedimentary basin. Analysis of the various components of surface waters thus provides an extremely powerful reconnaissance method of exploration. Ideally, a chemical

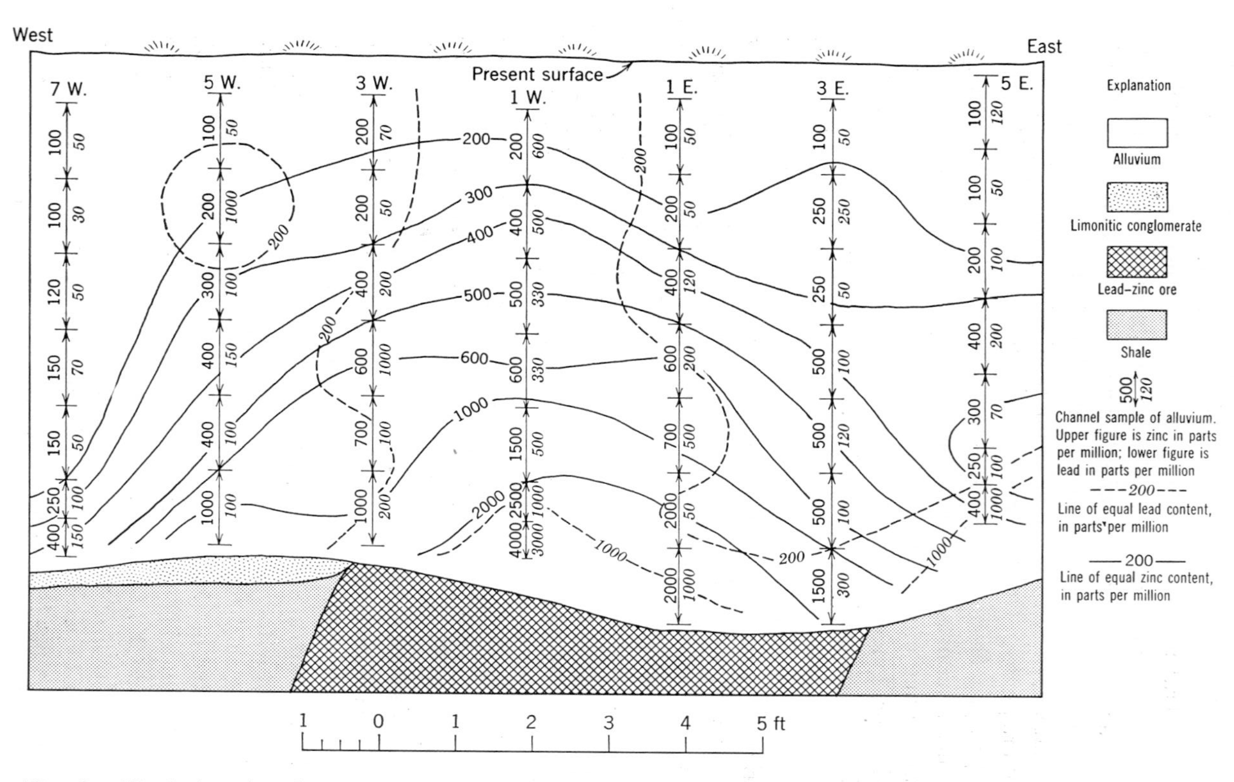

Fig. 2. Vertical section showing distribution of lead and zinc in alluvium over Ameri lode, Nyeba District, Nigeria; from Hawkes (1954).

determination on a single sample taken from a stream will tell whether there is a chance for ore in the area drained by the stream.

Trace analysis of stream water was one of the earliest methods of geochemical prospecting to be widely used. To be fully effective, prospecting by analysis of natural water, or "hydrogeochemistry," must concern itself with the more mobile elements, like zinc (Huff, 1948) and uranium (Fix, 1956). Unfortunately, the trace content of many metals in stream water tends to be relatively unstable, varying unpredictably with variations in rainfall, sunlight, time of day, and time of year. Thus it was found that determinations of trace metals in surface waters were not readily reproducible, and the data of surveys were not always easy to interpret.

The content of readily soluble or adsorbed metal in the stream sediments constitutes a fairly dependable measure of the metal content of the stream water, averaged over a substantial period of time (Hawkes and Bloom, 1956). The copper or zinc leached from stream sediment by a cold solution of ammonium citrate is an indication of the average metal content of the water and serves as a guide to ore deposits in the basin drained by the stream. This relationship is extremely useful in practical work because it is convenient to collect and analyze sediments. A substantial number of important discoveries have resulted from prospecting surveys based on analysis of stream sediment for readily extractable metals.

The Blackbird Cobalt District—A Case History

A good example of the mechanics of operation of a geochemical prospecting survey and of the kind of results that may come from it is provided by the work of the U. S. Geological Survey in the Blackbird Cobalt District of central Idaho. Development of this district has established it as one of the outstanding cobalt deposits of the world and by far the greatest in the United States. The early geochemical prospecting effort has been summarized in an unpublished U. S. G. S. open-file report (Canney, Hawkes, Richmond, and Vhay, 1953).

The geology of the Blackbird District has been studied over a period of years by J. S. Vhay. According to him, the rocks of the District consist mostly of interbedded quartz-biotite schist and fine-grained quartzite, which are metamorphosed sedimentary rocks of the Precambrian Yellowjacket formation (Belt series). A part of the Cretaceous Idaho Batholith and associated paragneisses occur in the northern part of the District. The principal cobalt deposits are located in a north-trending structural block bounded on the east and west by faults and consisting of relatively highly contorted and schistose rocks.

This structural block is cut by a number of shear zones, many of which are mineralized by chalcopyrite, cobaltite, pyrite, and pyrrhotite. Apparently, the cobaltite was emplaced before the chalcopyrite, so that in places one may be present without the other. Weathering of the sulfide minerals is commonly deep. Where cobaltite is accompanied by either chalcopyrite or pyrite, all the minerals are destroyed to a great depth. If only one of these minerals is present alone, however, it may be found fairly near the surface.

The topography of the area consists of an ancient, gently rolling erosion surface at an elevation ranging from 7000 to 8000 feet. The area is dissected by Blackbird Creek and its tributaries with steep-walled slopes ranging from 15° to over 35°. Although no evidence of glaciation was seen in the area, all the upland area shows evidence of mixing of the mantle by frost action during at least two widely separated periods. This frost activity is probably associated with periods of Pleistocene glaciation elsewhere in North America. The mixed material appears to be derived quite locally from the weathered rock, with only a minor amount of downslope creep. Thus a sample of the frost-mixed material, as far as geochemical prospecting work is concerned, is essentially a sample of the weathered bedrock.

Soil samples were collected at intervals of 100 feet along traverses, as shown in figure 3. A number of different systems were used in laying out these traverses, as follows: (1) rectangular coordinate system oriented N. 60° E., or approximately at right angles to the trend of the mineralized structure; (2) traverses on ridge crests, where the samples represent material that is essentially in place; (3) traverses at the base of slopes, where the samples represent material derived from upslope. The majority of samples were collected by two-man teams. On reconnaissance traverses the head man would keep the compass line, dig the sample hole, and mark the station number on a tree with weatherproof crayon. The rear man would collect the sample and record the notes. In a full day of uninterrupted work two men could cover 5000 feet in very rugged and heavily timbered terrain, and as much as 15,000 feet where the traverse lay along roads or open ridge-crests.

Experiment showed that samples taken at a depth of 6 to 9 inches gave satisfactory results. The samples were dried and sieved to minus

80 mesh. Chemical analysis was by the methods described by Stevens and Lakin (1949), Almond and Bloom (1951), and Almond (1953).

Figure 3 summarizes the results of the regional geochemical prospecting work in the Blackbird District. The analytical values for copper and cobalt in the soil samples have been smoothed by using running averages of three adjoining samples. It was found after plotting these figures that smooth threshold contours could be drawn at 30 ppm cobalt and 80 ppm copper. Within the threshold contour for cobalt, the average cobalt content of the soil is 100 ppm; outside this line it is 20 ppm. Inasmuch as none of the soil samples represented

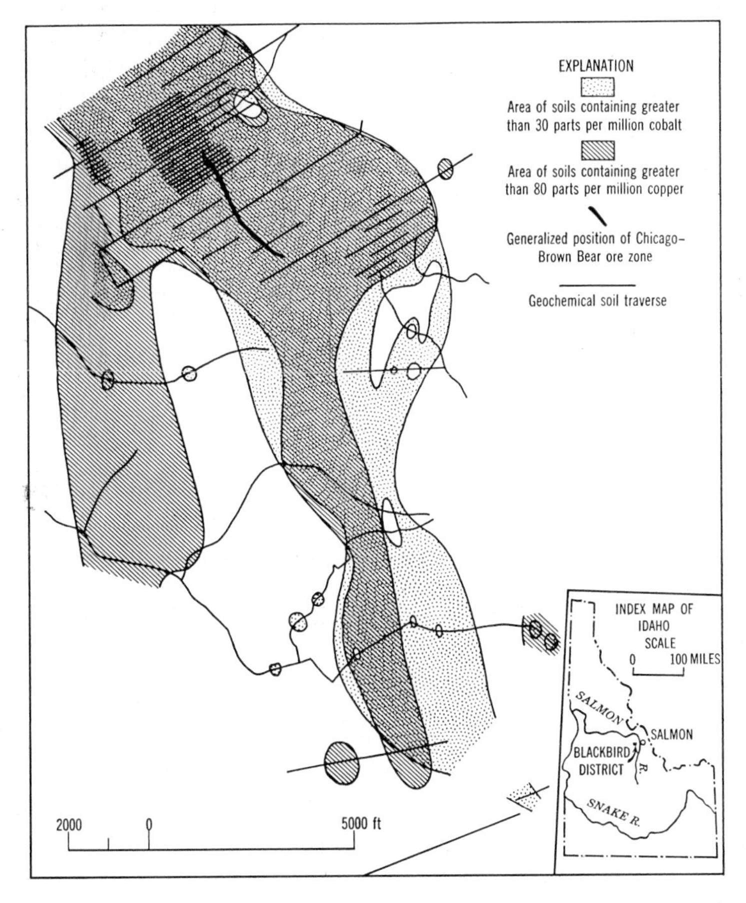

Fig. 3. Geochemical soil survey, Blackbird Cobalt District, Idaho. Adapted from plate 1 of Canney, Hawkes, Richmond, and Vhay (1953).

in this pattern has been transported for any great distance, it seems reasonable to suppose that this contour also represents a geochemical feature of the unweathered bedrock, in which a very large volume of rock is diffusely mineralized with copper and cobalt.

This point of view, if correct, leads to some rather interesting correlations and conclusions of a general nature. In the first place, all the cobalt prospects that lie within the 30 ppm threshold contour for cobalt are characterized by cobaltite as the principal cobalt mineral, whereas outside this contour all but two of the prospects have cobaltiferous arsenopyrite as the principal cobalt mineral.

Another interesting aspect of this large area of high cobalt content is the absolute quantity of metal introduced. If we assume that this area of 3 square miles contains an excess over normal background of 50 ppm cobalt, then 250 tons of cobalt per foot of depth have been introduced. Expressed in equivalent units, this is several hundred times as much cobalt as has been found in all the known deposits of the District. In other words, the emplacement of the ore bodies was only a minor aspect of a far larger mineralizing event.

The implication of this pattern is that a reconnaissance soil sampling survey in which samples were taken on 1-mile centers would have led to the discovery of the Blackbird District if its existence had not already been known.

Problems in Geochemical Prospecting

Geochemical prospecting surveys accumulate vast quantities of data relating to the distribution of elements in near-surface geologic materials. The analysis of these data presents a number of problems of wide interest to geochemistry. A brief review of these problems follows.

Geochemical provinces. In a geochemical province, the chemical composition is significantly different from the average. In mineral exploration, geochemical provinces are important if they are coincident with metallogenetic provinces or areas where certain kinds of ore deposits are more abundant than normal. Thus, it has been reported that normal granitic rocks in the tin fields of Indonesia and Malaya contain more tin than similar igneous rocks outside the tin fields. Tin-rich igneous rocks in unexplored areas might therefore be used as guides in finding new tin fields. Although quite a number of reports of this kind are in the literature, none of them is very convincing, largely because not enough samples were studied to make the conclusions statistically valid. This general subject of geochemical provinces certainly deserves the attention of geochemists in both the applied and the basic aspects of their profession.

Channels for hydrothermal solutions. Economic geologists commonly assume that the mineralizing solutions came either up the vein system or up the most conspicuous fracture system. Geochemical studies of primary anomalies strongly suggest that leakage halos represent metals deposited by the mineralizing solutions as they pass through the access channels either before they reach the site of deposition or after they leave it. Studies of the geometric distribution of trace elements in the country rock surrounding an ore deposit, therefore, may help in unraveling the history of formation of the deposit, and may indicate the channels used by the solutions during ore transport.

Fixation of trace elements in rocks. Scattered experiments on the leaching of igneous rocks and minerals with weak chemical reagents have indicated that very large proportions of many of the trace elements can be removed without attacking the crystal lattices of the primary minerals (Brown et al., 1953; Tausson, 1956). The implication is that these trace elements are situated either at the intercrystal boundaries in relatively soluble form or are distributed along parting surfaces in minerals exposed by normal grinding. Further work on this phenomenon would be of extreme interest in geochemical prospecting, particularly if the abundance of the readily soluble trace elements was found to correlate in any way with mineralization.

Fixation of trace elements in soils and sediments. A great deal of geochemical prospecting work is involved with determining the content of an element that can be removed from the soil or sediment sample by treatment with various kinds of chemical extractants. With stream sediments, for example, the pattern formed by copper that can be dissolved by treatment with cold citric acid bears a much closer relation to the copper content of the water than the copper extracted by hot acetic acid. In the mature, leached soils of the southern Appalachians, the zinc removed by a fusion with potassium bisulfate gives a more pronounced geochemical pattern than the zinc removed by hot nitric acid. Observations of this kind suggest that the trace elements are held in the soil by very specific mechanisms. Depending on the individual problem, the following mechanisms have been suggested: adsorption, occlusion with precipitated iron or manganese oxides, fixation within the lattice of clay minerals, immobile metallo-organic complexes, and minerals containing the trace element as a major constituent. It would be very interesting, and unquestionably very helpful in interpreting geochemical prospecting data, to know definitely how the trace elements are fixed in the soil or sediment.

Conduction of electricity. The problem of the development of superimposed halos by the migration of ions of ore metals upward into transported overburden has led to speculation that the ions were impelled by an electric field resulting from the oxidation of sulfides. The same electric field has been studied by exploration geophysicists as the self-potential effect. The measured polarity of the electric field as observed in nature, however, is precisely the opposite of what is suggested by the theory of oxidation of sulfide minerals at the upper end of an electronic conductor. Curiously enough, this paradox has received virtually no attention in the geophysical literature. The general subject of the mechanics of flow of electricity within the upper mile of the earth's crust has been sadly neglected. When do electric charges move as ions, when as electrons, and when as electron holes?

Theodore Madden (personal communication) at M. I. T. has conducted experiments on samples containing both electronically and electrolytically conductive material. He has found that an ion moving through the water in the pore spaces of a rock under the influence of a steady electric field cannot in general discharge at the interface between the electrolyte and a metallic mineral unless the potential drop across that interface is far greater than is commonly found in nature. This observation leads to some interesting speculations. Do earth materials, and in particular minerals, have two parameters for electric conductivity, one that gives its conductivity for electrons and the other for ions? If electrolytic and electronic conductivity are not interchangeable, can we have two semi-independent patterns of natural current flow in the ground, the one carried by electrons and the other by ions? Is it possible for the direction of flow and current density of electronic electricity to be quite different from that of the electrolytic current in the same material and at the same time?

Mobility in the cycle of weathering. Of all the basic problems in geochemistry that have a bearing on the practical issues faced by the geochemical prospector, the most important is the question of mobility in weathering. The rate at which the various elements move in the cycle of erosion depends on whether they occur most commonly as resistant primary minerals, stable secondary minerals, relatively unstable precipitates from solution, or water-soluble ions. The immobile elements will be found hanging behind in the gossan and residual soil, while the mobile ones move out rapidly in solution in ground and surface water. Thus, in prospecting for lead-zinc deposits, the first step is to look for the relatively mobile zinc in stream water and sediment. After the mineralized area has been localized by a geochemical reconnaissance of zinc in the drainage pattern, residual soils would be systematically sampled and analyzed for the immobile lead, which should define the bedrock source of metals most closely. Knowledge of which elements are mobile, and under what conditions, is necessary in selecting the elements to be used respectively for reconnaissance and for detailed geochemical exploration.

An estimate of the relative mobility of the elements may be arrived at in several ways. One approach is to consider the relative effect on a given element of all the factors that influence its solubility in the weathering environment. For each element, this series of factors would include first the stability of the common primary minerals when exposed to the environment of abundant space, oxygen, water, and carbon dioxide. Then, once the element is in solution, all manner of chemical traps can remove it from the mobile phase. Changes in *p*H may precipitate it as a hydroxide or basic salt. Changes in composition of the containing solution may precipitate it as an insoluble mineral. Other minerals undergoing precipitation may occlude the element and take it out of solution. It may be adsorbed to the active surfaces of particles, or find a niche within the crystal lattice of some mineral in contact with the solution. Changes in oxidation potential may change its ionic species and cause it to precipitate as an insoluble mineral. It may be taken out of solution by some living organism and incorporated into a living structure. It may be precipitated by dead organic matter. To offset the tendency to be precipitated, there are also mechanisms that tend to keep material in the aqueous phase; these include the tendency under some conditions to form soluble organic or inorganic complexes, or to be dispersed as colloidal suspensions. Suffice it to say that the factors controlling the mobility of an element in the cycle of weathering are numerous and extremely complex. They are so complicated, in fact, that after all of them have been considered it is still difficult to say on theoretical grounds whether a given element is likely to be mobile or immobile.

A more rewarding approach to the problem of mobility, therefore, might be to consider not whether an element *should* be mobile, but whether it *is*. Two empirical ways of evaluating the mobility of an element in the weathering cycle have been discussed in the literature. One involves a comparison of the composition of residual soils (what has been left behind in weathering) with the composition of the unweathered rock; the other, a comparison of the mineral residue of surface water (what has been dissolved out) with the composition of the unweathered rock.

The residual-soil approach was used by Goldich (1938) in evaluating mobility. As a result of his computations, he concluded that sodium and calcium are lost early in the process of weathering, and potassium and barium are lost later; that is, sodium and calcium are more mobile than potassium and barium.

The mineral residues of surface waters have been used in estimates of mobility by Smyth (1913) and Polynov (1937). Smyth computed the relative mobility of the common elements by comparing the average

TABLE 2. Specific Estimates of Relative Mobility of Common Elements in Weathering

After Anderson and Hawkes (1958)

		Littleton Schist		Oliverian Granite		Black Mountain Granite	
		Per Cent	Ratio W/R	Per Cent	Ratio W/R	Per Cent	Ratio W/R
Ca	Water	25.37	5.55	42.64	18.07	27.61	12.84
	Rock	4.57		2.36		2.15	
Na	Water	11.30	4.85	17.35	4.29	22.33	5.67
	Rock	2.33		4.05		3.94	
Mg	Water	29.44	15.41	15.09	35.92	12.80	49.22
	Rock	1.91		0.42		0.26	
K	Water	7.44	0.88	3.03	0.59	3.19	0.53
	Rock	8.45		5.11		6.05	
Si	Water	23.99	0.37	21.49	0.29	32.62	0.45
	Rock	65.14		73.32		72.28	
Al	Water	2.07	0.18	0.14	0.01	1.20	0.09
	Rock	11.32		12.12		13.25	
Fe	Water	0.39	0.06	0.26	0.10	0.25	0.12
	Rock	6.28		2.62		2.07	
Total	Water	100.00	1.00	100.00	1.00	100.00	1.00
	Rock	100.00		100.00		100.00	

composition of the mineral residue of all rivers with that of all crustal rocks as presented by Clarke. Polynov compared figures for the average composition of igneous rocks with figures for the composition of the residue of river waters from catchment basins underlain largely by massive igneous rocks. Both investigators found that the common elements could be arranged in order of increasing mobility as follows: iron-aluminum, silica, potassium, magnesium, sodium, and calcium.

More recently, Anderson and Hawkes (1958), working in the glaciated areas of New England, have made determinations of the composition of the mineral residues of surface water draining areas of relatively homogeneous igneous and metamorphic rocks of known composition. As shown in table 2, computations of relative mobility of the major elements based on these figures are the same as those of Smyth and Polynov except for the position of magnesium, which now appears as the most mobile element.

If computations of this kind have any validity at all, it should be legitimate to extend them to include minor elements as well as the seven major ones. A comparison of the minor-element content of stream water draining an area underlain exclusively by a homogeneous rock of known minor-element composition would provide a valuable empirical measure of mobility. For a complete perspective on the subject of mobility, studies of this kind should be conducted in a wide variety of rock types, climates, and topographies. Such an investigation could be augmented by a study of the movement of spike solutions added to a natural drainage channel.

In any event, the question of the mobility of the minor elements in the weathering cycle is of extreme importance in geochemical prospecting and deserves the attention of the geochemical profession at large.

References

Almond, Hy. 1953. Determination of traces of cobalt in soils, *Anal. Chem., 25,* 166–167.

Almond, Hy, and Harold Bloom. 1951. A semimicro method for the determination of cobalt in soils and rocks; a field test using the chromograph, *U. S. Geol. Survey Circ. 125.*

Anderson, D. H., and H. E. Hawkes. 1958. Relative mobility of the common elements in weathering of some schist and granite areas, *Geochim. et Cosmochim. Acta, 14,* 204–210.

Brown, Harrison, et al. 1953. Geochemical aspects of interstitial material in igneous rocks (Abstract), *Bull. Geol. Soc. Am., 64,* 1400.

Canney, F. C., H. E. Hawkes, G. M. Richmond, and J. S. Vhay. 1953. A preliminary report of geochemical investigations in the Blackbird District, *U. S. Geol. Survey Open-File Rept.*

Cannon, Helen L. 1957. Description of indicator plants and methods of botanical prospecting for uranium deposits on the Colorado Plateau, *U. S. Geol. Survey Bull. 1030M,* 399–516.

Fix, P. F. 1956. Hydrogeochemical exploration for uranium, *U. S. Geol. Survey Profess. Paper 300,* 667–671.

Goldich, S. S. 1938. A study in rock weathering, *J. Geol., 46,* 17–58.

Hawkes, H. E. 1954. Geochemical prospecting investigations in the Nyeba lead-zinc district, Nigeria, *U. S. Geol. Survey Bull. 1000-B.*

Hawkes, H. E., and Harold Bloom. 1956. Heavy metals in stream sediment as an exploration guide, *Mining Eng., 8,* 1121–1126.

Huff, L. C. 1948. A sensitive field test for heavy metals in water, *Econ. Geol., 43,* 675–684.

Polynov, B. B. 1937. *The Cycle of Weathering,* Thos. Murby & Co., London, 220 pp.

Salmi, Martti. 1955. Prospecting for bog-covered ore by means of peat investigations, *Bull. comm. géol. Finlande, 169.*

Smyth, C. H., Jr. 1913. The relative solubilities of the chemical constituents of rocks, *J. Geol., 21,* 105–120.

Stevens, R. E., and H. W. Lakin. 1949. The chromograph, a new analytical tool for laboratory and field use, *U. S. Geol. Survey Circ. 63.*

Tausson, L. V. 1956. Geochemistry of Pb and Zn in granitoids (Abstract), *XX Geol. Congr. Abstr.,* p. 377.

Warren, H. V., R. E. Delavault, and Ruth I. Irish. 1952. Biogeochemical investigations in the Pacific Northwest, *Bull. Geol. Soc. Am., 63,* 435–484.

Additional Selected Bibliography

Hawkes, H. E. 1957. Principles of geochemical prospecting, *U. S. Geol. Survey Bull. 1000-F,* 225–355.

Lakin, H. W., Hy Almond, and F. N. Ward. 1952. Compilation of field methods used in geochemical prospecting by the U. S. Geological Survey, *U. S. Geol. Survey Circ. 161.*

Geochemistry of Organic Substances

PHILIP H. ABELSON

Geophysical Laboratory
Carnegie Institution of Washington

Organic chemicals or graphitic carbon are found in fine-grained sedimentary rocks formed throughout most of the history of the earth and on the average constitute about 0.7 per cent of the weight of such rocks. Rubey (1951) has estimated that this reduced carbon amounts to 68×10^{20} grams. The economic importance of oil, coal, and oil shale is enormous, and expanding uses of these raw materials in petrochemistry make it desirable to evaluate more accurately occurrences of organic substances in sediments. Such knowledge also is essential to our understanding of past life and indeed to our concepts of origins of life. This chapter will present highlights of the chemical constitution of present-day creatures. It will discuss factors that determine destruction or long-time survival of organic compounds and will review some of the natural occurrences of these substances.

The composition and principal chemical mechanisms of most of the creatures living today are relatively well known and have led to some important generalizations governing the common denominators of life. One striking feature is the large proportion of water, which constitutes two-thirds or more of the total weight of most organisms. Another is the ubiquitous presence of such elements as potassium, magnesium, and phosphorus. Most important here are the great similarities in composition of the organic-carbon-containing compounds which usually constitute the major fraction of the dry weight of soft parts of animals (Florkin, 1949; Baldwin, 1949).

Some typical data for a variety of organisms are given in table 1. The animal values are in relatively close agreement and do not differ much from those of *Chlorella* grown in a favorable environment rich in nitrogen salts. More detailed examination of the constituent groups is even more revealing. Many of the lipides are formed on the

TABLE 1. Major Constituents of Living Forms

Data on animals from Florkin (1949); data on algae from Milner (1953)

Living Form	Per Cent of Dry Weight		
	Protein	Lipide	Carbohydrate
Sea urchin			
Unfertilized egg	66.9	31.2	5.4
40-hour larva	60.6	17.4	3.4
Oyster	51.2	11.1	28.2
Silkworm			
Larva	55.5	13.3	1.8
Imago	63.4	24.3	6.5
Alga (ash-free)			
Chlorella (favorable environment)	46.4	20.2	33.4
Chlorella (unfavorable environment)	13.1	63.4	23.5

familiar triglyceride pattern (fig. 1); the principal carbohydrate is glucose, either alone, as a polymer, or in combinations such as glucose-phosphate; the proteins though individually widely divergent in properties are principally composed of only about twenty amino acids. Some of these are more abundant than others, glumatic acid, for example, constituting 10 per cent or more of the total protein of some organisms and accordingly 5 per cent of the dry weight.

Other constituents though not always quantitatively abundant are evidently of great importance in the patterns of living things. Nucleic acids (combined with proteins) in both plants and animals universally participate in duplication and cell division. Various of the B vitamins are indispensable components. Porphyrins participate as essential constituents of most forms of living matter. Cytochromes, which contain porphyrins, are found in all aerobic organisms. Chlorophyll, the green pigment of leaves and algae, also possesses the porphyrin structure.

Deep-seated reasons lie behind these basic patterns, in the functions for which the various substances are used. Proteins are employed as enzymes or catalysts. By speeding up certain sequences of reactions they actually regulate many of the living processes. The carbohydrate glucose, for example, can be oxidized chemically in numerous non-specific ways. In the inorganic world comparatively high temperatures are required if reasonable rates of reaction are to be attained. Through the use of enzymes in living systems sugar is oxidized rapidly in a sequence of reactions at ordinary temperatures, and the energy is released in an orderly way. One of the products of carbohydrate metabolism is adenosinetriphosphate (ATP). Supplies of this energy-rich compound are stored by all animals and most microorganisms. Almost every type of energy requirement, including mechanical, electrical, and chemical, is met by ATP. The actual release of the energy is mediated by protein catalysts.

This universality is particularly important in the functioning of the musculature of most of the phyla. In these organisms the protein myosin is involved in combination with ATP. In the clam *Mercenaria mercenaria,* as well as in most shelled animals, scars on the shell show the points of muscle attachment, and these are preserved in fossil specimens. The shape of the shell of 25-million-year-old specimens is identical to those of today, including the muscle scar. It seems quite likely that the old clams had musculature

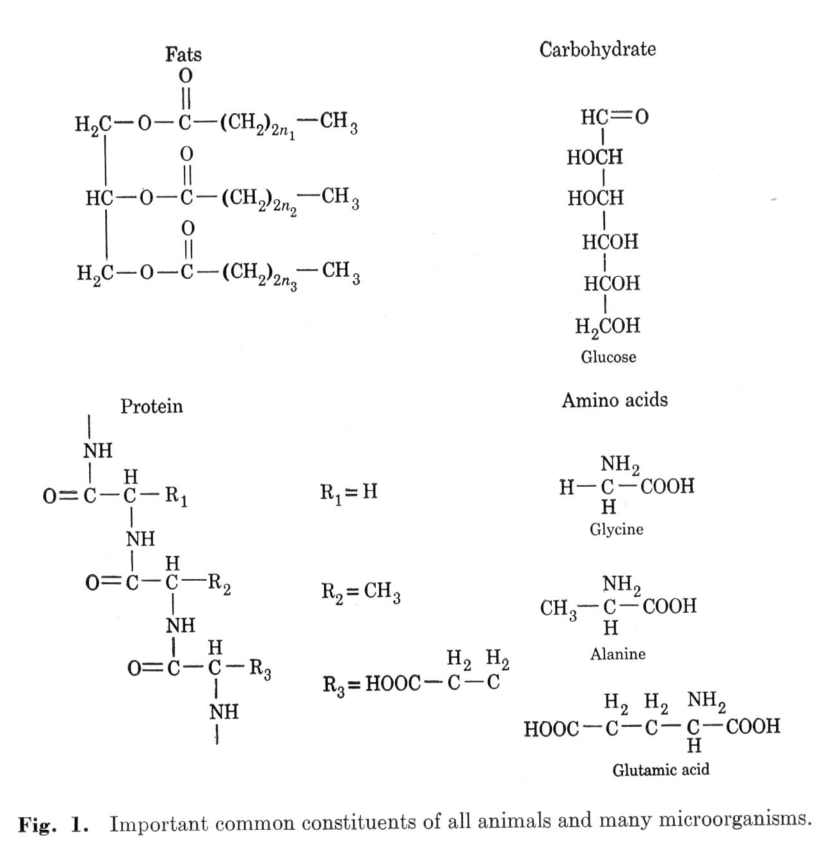

Fig. 1. Important common constituents of all animals and many microorganisms.

exactly like that of the modern species and that the conventional myosin, ATP system was employed. Similar arguments are applicable to other invertebrates and to vertebrates. In reconstructing extinct forms paleontologists implicitly and almost instinctively assume that muscle processes have not changed in major degree since early Cambrian times 550 million years ago. One may speculate further that other soft parts also contained proteins employed in their familiar roles as catalysts. Organic geochemistry has already provided evidence supporting this speculation and as we shall see promises more.

A few of the great universal patterns having been illustrated, it is appropriate to consider briefly a few differences. A mere glance at the various types of living forms would lead one to expect differences of some kind. An interesting example, quoted by Florkin (1949) and summarized in table 2, shows the relative methionine and cystine

TABLE 2. Amino Acid Composition of Globins

From Florkin (1949)

	Per Cent	
Globin	Methionine	Cystine
Human	1.35–1.48	1.05–1.35
Monkey (rhesus)	1.34–1.43	1.15–1.21
Cow	1.71–1.79	0.45–0.67
Horse	0.89–1.03	0.65–0.94
Dog	0.54–0.58	1.56–1.89
Fox	0.53–0.55	1.69–1.71
Jackal	0.59	1.62

content of protein globin derived from hemoglobin of a number of mammals. All the animals used the amino acids methionine and cystine, but the amounts employed were variable though bearing a close relation to phylogenetic patterns.

Another example involves the lipides. It is well known that the fats of various animals have different melting points, reflecting differences in degree of saturation and chain length. Bergmann (1949) has pointed out other important differences in the lipides of various phyla, particularly in the relative proportions of fats and waxes. The more primitive animal phyla contain relatively less fats and more waxes and sterols than higher animals.

Other examples of biochemical differences include variations in biosynthetic capacities. Thus, the vertebrates have a thyroid gland which can synthesize thyroxin while most lower animals lack this capacity. Further illustrations could be cited, and doubtless there are also many yet unknown but equally crucial differences in qualitatively important though quantitatively minor constituents. It is unlikely, however, that any new findings will substantially modify the earlier picture of the great biochemical similarities in all animals and many microorganisms.

Fate of Organic Substances in Geologic Environments

Having indicated the probable nature of the chemicals synthesized by past living organisms, we shall next examine the fate of these substances and the conditions favorable for their survival. Although annual production of organic matter is enormous, most of it is metabolized, mainly by microorganisms. Aerobic environments are particularly unfavorable for the preservation of organic chemicals. In the presence of oxygen and moisture, biochemical substances are rapidly consumed by microorganisms, which may multiply with generation times shorter than an hour. Aerobic conditions are, of course, also favorable for the growth of multicellular organisms. In lake and ocean bottoms scavengers consume large quantities of organic matter; they also accelerate microbial destruction of the remainder by providing stirring action, and by opening holes for better aeration.

Anaerobic conditions are favorable to the preservation of organic material. No multicellular organism can exist under truly anaerobic conditions. Anaerobic microorganisms are relatively inefficient. They multiply only slowly and are not very effective as chemical operators. Perhaps the most favorable environment for preservation is an anaerobic one having the additional feature of protection from bacterial attack.

In sediments, which are rich in organic material, available oxygen dissolved in water is often consumed. In some anaerobic environments sulfate is an important factor, for this anion can be used by some bacteria as a source of oxygen in the metabolism of organic chemicals. After the exhaustion of available oxygen the E_h of the sediment may decline to low values, and ultimately chemical action even by anaerobes ceases, leaving much original material unaltered or only slightly changed.

Thermal Stability of Organic Compounds

Organic substances that escape biological attack are subject to a variety of chemical hazards, including reaction with other materials in the environment. The most fundamental limitation is, of course, the intrinsic instability of almost all organic substances.

Many compounds decompose with rates given by the relation

$$dc/dt = -kc$$

where c is concentration, t is time, and $k = Ae^{-E/RT}$; E is activation energy, R the gas constant, and T is absolute temperature. Kinetic studies (see Daniels and Alberty, 1955) have shown that for a large number of substances A, the frequency factor, has values of about 10^{13} per second. In figure 2 are displayed time-temperature curves representative of the degree of stability found in organic substances. Thus, a value of $E = 58{,}000$ cal/mole corresponds to the activation energy needed to break a C—C bond in straight-chain hydrocarbons. These substances are among the most stable of organic compounds. Activation energy for degradation of some porphyrins amounts to about 53,500 cal/mole. Values for amino acids lie in the range 30,000 to 44,000 cal/mole. The measurement of these constants will be discussed in more detail later. An important feature of the time-temperature relation shown in figure 2 is the sharp dependence of reaction rates on thermal conditions. Therefore, the possible depths of burial and geothermal gradients must be especially considered in seeking ancient organic substances.

Another type of reaction involves two components having concentrations c_1 and c_2. Here c_1 might refer to an organic substance and c_2, for instance, to oxygen, water, or sulfur;

$$dc_1/dt = -kc_1c_2$$

where $k = se^{-E/RT}$; s is again a frequency factor and has values about 10^9. In many cases activation energies for second-order reactions such as those mentioned fall in the range 15,000 to 25,000 cal/mole. Some curves for these reactions are shown in figure 3, corresponding to reactions of oxygen with organic substances. Again there is a pronounced temperature dependence, though not as striking as that displayed in figure 2.

Before making extensive tests on geologic samples for organic substances it is desirable to establish some criteria for indicating whether

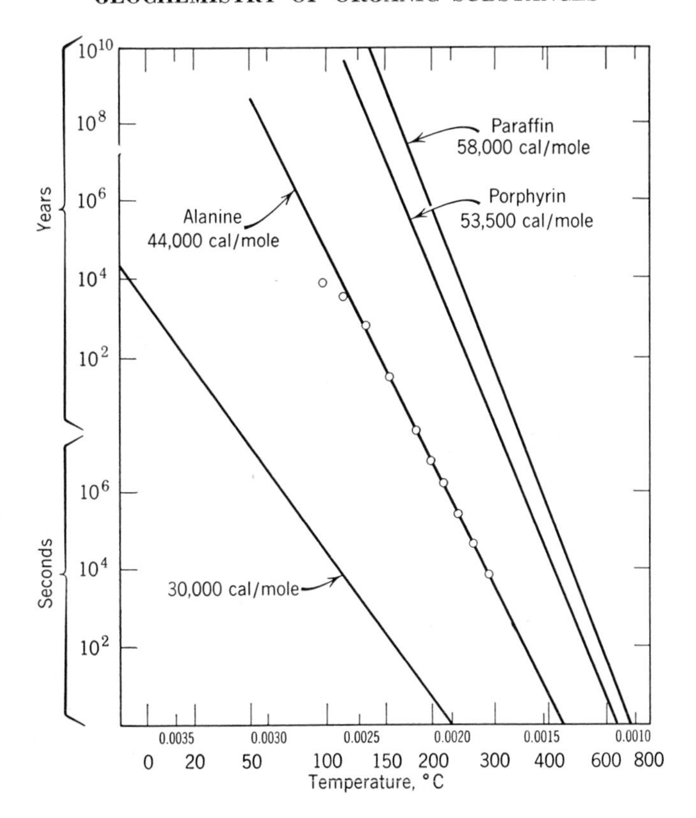

Fig. 2. Temperature-time curves (log time versus $1/T$) for degradation of organic substances—first-order reaction rates calculated for straight-chain hydrocarbons and porphyrins with $A = 10^{13}$. Curve for alanine experimentally determined, $A = 3 \times 10^{13}$.

the sought-for materials have sufficient thermal stability to survive under the presumptive environmental conditions. Often an approximate thermal history can be estimated, leaving the activation energy E as the principal unknown.

Considerable insight concerning stability can be gained merely by determining the temperature at which a substance begins to decompose at an appreciable rate. For instance, benzene may be heated to about 500° C before much reaction occurs. It is not surprising that benzene is found in petroleum taken from Ordovician (~450-million-year-old) reservoir rocks. In contrast, a substance like pyruvic acid which decomposes rapidly at 165° C could not be expected to survive for long periods at room temperature.

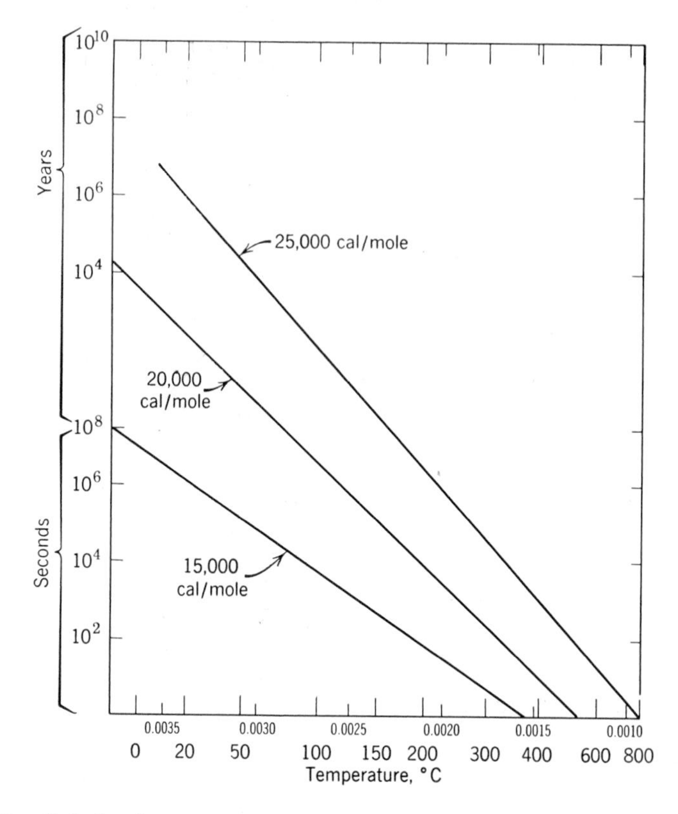

Fig. 3. Calculated temperature-time curves (log time versus $1/T$) for second-order reaction rates. Curves applicable to oxidation of organic substances by oxygen in ground water, oxygen concentration assumed 10^{-4} M.

The situation is not always simple, as the following description of some studies on the stability of amino acids will indicate. Initial experiments evaluated the thermal stability of amino acids in the form of pure solids. Alanine held at 250° C for an hour becomes a thick, viscous brown syrup which yields colloidal solutions when dissolved in water. Ninhydrin tests on the material before and after hydrolysis indicate that polymerization has occurred. Fox (1957) has shown that peptides of a variety of amino acids are formed under similar conditions. An attempt to test the stability of an amino acid thus became instead a test of the thermal stability of a polymer. In actual geological environments such as in a fossil amino acid concentrations are often very low, ~0.01 per cent. It would appear that individual amino acid molecules ordinarily have little opportunity to react with one another. A test, to be representative, should preferably be performed by heating actual fossil materials in the presence of water. As a substitute, dilute solutions were employed. The degradation reaction for alanine is one of decarboxylation:

$$\begin{array}{ccccccccc} H_3 & & NH_2 & & & H_3 & & NH_2 & \\ C & — & C & — COOH & \rightarrow & C & — & C & + CO_2 \\ & & H & & & & & H_2 & \end{array}$$

Water does not appear to take part in the reaction and should not influence the rate of degradation.

Results of a series of experiments are shown in figure 2. The data are in accord with those generally found in first-order reactions with values of $A = 3 \times 10^{13}$ and $E = 44{,}000$ (Abelson, 1954; Vallentyne, 1957*a*). The four points shown at the top of the line are taken from the work of Conway and Libby (1958). They were obtained by studying the degradation of C^{14}-tagged alanine; the tracer isotope was in the carboxyl carbon. In their experiments reaction rates of the order of 10^{-11} per second were measured. The degradation of alanine was thus studied at reaction rates differing by eleven orders of magnitude and including rates approaching those characteristic of times available for geologic processes. The C^{14}-tagging method that made such studies possible is, of course, widely applicable to other organic substances. The desirability of avoiding great extrapolations in degradation rates should be obvious intuitively. New reaction mechanisms that are masked at high temperatures may suddenly appear at lower ones. An example of this arose in the alanine study. Tests were conducted in sealed tubes containing some air over the dilute solution. Somewhat erratic results were obtained when the experiments were conducted at temperatures below 200° C. The difficulty was traced to oxygen. At low temperatures the predominating event was a second-order reaction involving oxygen. Conway (1958) estimated that at room temperatures the oxidative reaction proceeds about 10^6 times as fast as the decarboxylation.

This type of experience indicates the danger of complete confidence in studies made at very high temperatures involving short reaction times and requiring extrapolations of 10^{13} or 10^{14} for use in geologic situations. At present, only a few experiments have been performed with organic substances in which the incubation times have been longer than a day.

Abelson (unpublished data) has surveyed the stability of some of the other amino acids and classified them into three groups on the basis of thermal stability of solutions at temperatures in the range 200° to 250° C.

Relatively stable: Alanine; glycine; glutamic acid; leucine, isoleucine; proline; valine. $E \sim 44{,}000$ cal/mole.
Moderately stable: Aspartic acid; lysine; phenylalanine.
Relatively unstable: Serine; threonine; arginine; tyrosine.

Tests on aqueous solutions of aspartic acid are of doubtful value since this compound is hydrolyzed by water to malic acid plus ammonia. Otherwise, however, the laboratory findings agree very well with observations on fossil materials. Alanine, glycine, glutamic acid, the leucine family, proline and valine, and small amounts of aspartic acid are the common constituents of old fossils (Abelson, 1954). On the other hand, serine and threonine are not seen even in late Tertiary materials. Indeed, if these two were found in an old fossil, suspicion of contamination would be justified.

Correlation between laboratory stability tests and field occurrences has been shown in at least two other examples. McNab et al. (1952), who studied the stability of a Venezuelan crude oil containing bound oxygen and sulfur, obtained a value of 49,000 cal/mole. They quote also a value of 58,000 cal/mole for gas and oil. Montgomery (personal communication) has conducted experiments on porphyrins incorporated in tars, obtaining a value for activation energy of 53,500 cal/mole. These examples can be correlated with actual occurrences in nature of these types of compounds. Hydrocarbons have been recovered in large quantities from Ordovician reservoir rocks. Treibs (1936) has identified porphyrins in Ordovician shales.

The value of 58,000 cal/mole for degradation of straight-chain hydrocarbons represents an upper limit for straight-chain carbon-to-carbon binding in general. The presence of substituent groups for hydrogen such as OH or the presence of COOH in place of CH_3 results in compounds more subject to fragmentation.

Carbon-to-carbon bonds in ring structures such as benzene or naphthalene are very stable. At elevated temperatures cyclohexane, however, loses hydrogen:

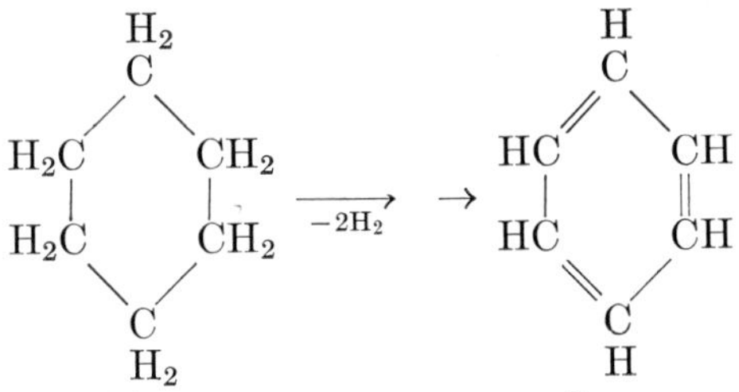

```
        H2                              H
        C                               C
      /   \                           //  \
  H2C       CH2                    HC       CH
   |         |      ------->  →     |       ||
  H2C       CH2      -2H2          HC       CH
      \   /                           \\  /
        C                               C
        H2                              H
   Cyclohexane                      Benzene
```

All such ring compounds are subject to dehydrogenation tending ultimately toward graphite.

Reactions with Other Molecules

Organic substances do not always survive as long as intrinsic stability might allow. A rather dramatic illustration is the well known effect of a combination of oxygen and sunlight on porphyrins. If a dilute solution of the substance is exposed to strong sunlight, the original color, characteristic of the intact molecule, fades and may disappear in less than a day. This quick degradation contrasts with survival of porphyrins for 450 million years in proper environments. Oxygen itself reacts with all organic substances, and the heats of activation involved are considerably less than those for the simple breakage of the organic molecules.

Water is present in sedimentary rocks, which are the usual habitat of organic substances. Many hydrolytic reactions have relatively low activation energies. In the presence of water, proteins are degraded into their constituent amino acids. Fats are split into glycerin and fatty acids. In geologic environments the time required for this reaction to occur is only a few hundred years.

Free sulfur is found in association with organic matter in many sedimentary rocks. Reaction of the sulfur apparently occurs at appreciable rates at low temperatures, for many sulfur-bearing compounds are found in petroleums.

Evidence of hydrogenation of a compound in sediments seems valid in at least one example, namely, the reduction of the vinyl side group of a porphyrin to an ethyl radical noted by Treibs (1936). Schönbrunner (1940) described hydrogenation of oleic and sorbic acids by anaerobic bacteria. Another study (Blanchard and MacDonald, 1935) demonstrated hydrogenation of fatty acids to corresponding alcohols.

Some Occurrences of Organic Substances in Nature

Proteins and their constituent amino acids may be found in a wide variety of environments including soils, sediments, bogs and peat beds, and Recent bones and shells. These ubiquitous occurrences are not substances that have been extracted from soil humus, humic acid, and surprising in view of the universal participation of proteins in living matter.

With time, proteins originally present in these environments probably are metabolized and partly incorporated in growing organisms. Only in situations in which proteins are inaccessible to biological attack could one expect original protein to be preserved. Most environments of preservation are accessible to water, and hydrolysis of proteins to peptides and ultimately free amino acids could be expected in a million years or less.

In a review of the occurrence of nitrogen in coal Kirner (1945) listed peat. Among the materials named were proteins, proteoses, peptones, and the amino acids alanine, leucine, aspartic acid, isoleucine, proline, asparaginic acid, glutamic acid, tyrosine, histidine, arginine, and lysine.

Erdman, Marlett, and Hanson (1956) have made an interesting comparative study of the amino acid content of a typical Recent shallow-water, marine deposit and that of a similar sediment laid down approximately 30 million years ago. The Recent sample, collected on the inner continental shelf of the Gulf of Mexico, represents a narrow sedimentary layer at a depth of 120 cm; this is below the zone of major bacterial activity. The age of the sediment is probably not more than a few thousand years. The older sample was a section of a marine shale core cut from the Anahuac formation in Fort Bend County, Texas, at a depth of 5000 feet. Examination of these materials showed that the modern and ancient marine samples selected for study are quite similar with respect to concentrations of carbonate carbon, organic carbon, and fixed nitrogen. The concentrations of free or combined amino acids were less in the Oligocene sample by a factor of 6. The Recent sediment contained 3.0 micromoles per gram (μM/g). The nature of the amino acids present was also studied with results shown in tables 3 and 4. It may be noted that the surviving amino acids were the same ones that were found (Abelson, 1954) in studies on fossils.

TABLE 3. Comparison of a Recent and an Oligocene Marine Mud

From Erdman, Marlett, and Hanson (1956)

Content	Recent	Oligocene
Carbonate carbon, %	0.71	1.49
Organic carbon, %	0.53	0.27
Organic nitrogen, %	0.044	0.032
Amino acids, μM/g	3.0	0.51

TABLE 4. Principal Amino Acids in Recent and Oligocene Sediments *

From Erdman, Marlett, and Hanson (1956)

Recent	Oligocene
Valine	Alanine
Leucines	Glutamic acid
Alanine	Glycine
Glutamic acid	Proline
Aspartic acid	Leucines
Glycine	Aspartic acid
Proline	
Tyrosine	
Phenylalanine	

* Arranged in order of decreasing abundance.

Amino Acids in Fossils

Some of the most interesting occurrences of proteins and amino acids are in fossils. Within calcareous structures such as shells, the substances are protected from bacteria and often are not completely leached away by ground water. If the $CaCO_3$ of a fossil recrystallizes, soluble amino acids are, of course, lost. Many shells consist mainly of aragonite, which on recrystallizing changes to calcite, usually coarsely crystalline. Recrystallization of calcitic fossils can often be detected by noting the appearance of the specimen.

Recent shells and calcareous materials of biological origin have been examined (Abelson, 1954) as a guide to the understanding of occurrences of organic materials in fossils. The presence of proteins in bones has long been established, but virtually nothing was known about

TABLE 5. Amino Acid Content of Various Recent Tropical Calcium Carbonate Shells

Specimen	Description	Mineral Composition	Amino Acid Content *
Porites lichen	Reef-building coral	Aragonite, 10 to 20 per cent calcite	6.7
Porolithon onkodes	Coralline alga	Calcite with $MgCO_3$ in solid solution	17.6
Chama lazarus	Reef-dwelling clam	Aragonite	16.4
Codakia punctata	Ribbed clam	Aragonite	8.4
Atactodea glabrata	Intertidal clam	Aragonite	42.7
Cymatium muricinum	Thick-shelled snail	Aragonite	20
Tridacna maxima	Man-eating clam	Aragonite	26.6
Cypraea mauritiana	Tropical snail	Aragonite	6.2

The materials were furnished by Preston Cloud, U. S. Geological Survey. The *Porites lichen* and *Porolithon onkodes* were collected at Saipan. The other specimens were collected at Onotoa Atoll in the Gilbert Islands.

* In micromoles per gram; 1 μM/g is approximately equal to 1 part per 10,000.

the nature of organic constituents in shells. In table 5 [1] are shown results of examination of some tropical shells. It will be noted that all specimens listed contained amino acids in amounts ranging from 6 to 40 micromoles per gram. Forty other Recent, arbitrarily chosen shells were surveyed; all were found to contain protein. The amino acids appearing were those typically found in protein hydrolyzates, with occasional specimens showing additional unidentified components.

Abelson (1955) has reported some observations bearing on the rate of hydrolysis of proteins in shells. The shell of the clam *Mya myarenaria* was employed to check the effect of relatively short exposures to geological environments. Recent specimens of this shell and items dated at 1000 years were compared. Solution of the Recent shell in dilute hydrochloric acid left a residue of filamentous light-colored protein. The 1000-year-old specimen yielded protein which was amber-colored and had only a relatively limited mechanical strength. Tests showed that protein content and amino acid content were identical in the two types of specimen. In another experiment, shells were dissolved in a mixture of dilute hydrochloric acid and trichloroacetic acid. Insoluble protein was removed from the mixture by centrifugation.

[1] Tables 5, 7, and 8 are from *Carnegie Institution of Washington Year Book 53;* table 6 is from *C. I. W. Year Book 54.*

The clear supernatant solution was examined as to its content of free amino acids, peptides, or soluble protein. A negligible amount was found in each case, a fact which shows that the proteins of the 1000-year-old shell had not been broken into fragments of low molecular weight.

For studying older materials the clam *Mercenaria mercenaria* was a convenient object. This edible hard-shell clam, which lives today, is represented by fossil specimens dating back at least 25 million years. Specimens of Pleistocene age were tested which on geologic evidence are thought to be in the range 100,000 to 1 million years old. Comparison of Recent and older specimens revealed that marked changes had occurred in the fossil proteins. The material isolated by the usual protein precipitants was a black, tarry substance that could scarcely be called a protein, although it yielded amino acids on hydrolysis. The clear supernatant solution contained peptides and free amino acids. The total amino acid content of the Pleistocene shell was only 18 per cent of that found in Recent shells. When Miocene (25-million-year-old) shells were examined, amino acids were found, but no traces of proteins or peptides could be detected. These results are summarized in table 6.

TABLE 6. Amino Acid Content of *Mercenaria mercenaria*

	Amino Acid Content, μM/g		
Age	Protein Bound	Soluble Protein or Peptide	Free
Recent	33.0	1.5	<0.35
Pleistocene	2.1	2.25	1.0
Miocene	0	0	0.75

Initially most of the protein of the shell is evidently present in water-insoluble layers. For thousands of years only moderate changes occur, which do not affect the solubility of the protein. By the time 1 to 5 per cent of the peptide bonds are broken (10,000 to 100,000 years), the protein fragments are much more soluble and some can be leached out of the shell. Some of the amino acids or peptides are probably entrapped in the aragonite structure. Ultimately in the presence of water these peptide bonds are broken, leaving only free amino acids in the shell. It is of interest to note in table 6 that the free amino acid content of the shell changed only moderately in the period from 1 million to 25 million years.

Examination of bones from the La Brea tar pit in Los Angeles yielded an interesting result. These fossils were preserved in an asphalt matrix for perhaps 15,000 years (Flint, personal communication). Total amino acid content of several specimens of bone was 10 to 12 per cent. Studies of the peptide linkage showed that there were virtually no free amino acids and that the amino acids remained linked together. Apparently the asphalt provided an essentially sterile, anaerobic environment in which the concentration of water was very low.

Abelson (1954) studied the amino acid content of a series of fossil materials. In table 7 are shown results obtained from a series of 25-

TABLE 7. Amino Acid Content of Fossils from One Locality

Specimen	Description	Mineralogy	Amino Acid Content, μM/g
Glycymeris parilis	Clam	Aragonite	0.80
Mercenaria mercenaria	Clam	Aragonite	0.75
Melosia staminea	Clam	Aragonite	0.90
Lyropecten madisonius	Scallop	Calcite	1.10
Eucrassatella melina	Bivalve	Aragonite	0.60
Turritella variabilis	Snail	Aragonite	0.40
Ecphora tricostata	Snail	Inner aragonite, outer calcite	1.20
Turritella indenta	Snail	Aragonite	0.50

Fossils collected at Plum Point, Zone 10, Calvert Formation, Maryland, by Wendell Woodring, Kenneth Lohmann, and Philip H. Abelson. Age of shells, about 25 million years.

Amino acids present included alanine, glycine, leucine, valine, glutamic acid, and aspartic acid.

million-year-old shells. All specimens examined were found to contain amino acids.

In table 8 results of examination of a wide variety of fossils may be noted. Specimens were chosen from formations likely to have had a mild thermal history. These results show no trend with time, which is not too surprising, since different burial histories were involved.

Actually the oldest fossil in this group was richest in amino acids. By means of radioactive tracers amino acids from fossils have been shown to be identical with present-day compounds.

TABLE 8. Amino Acid Content of Various Fossils

Name	Approximate Age, years	Formation	Amino Acid Content, μM/g	Principal Constituents
Plesippus (prehistoric horse)	Late Pliocene 5×10^6	Hagerman Lake Beds, Ida.	0.6	Ala, gly
Plesippus (prehistoric horse, tooth)	Late Pliocene 5×10^6	Hagerman Lake beds, Ida.	1.5	Gly, ala, leu, val, glu
Mesohippus (prehistoric horse, tooth)	Oligocene 40×10^6	White River, Nebr.	0.31	Ala, gly
Mosasaurus (dinosaur)	Cretaceous 100×10^6	Pierre Shale, S. Dak.	1.8	Ala, gly, glu, leu, val
Anatosaurus (dinosaur)	Cretaceous 100×10^6	Lance, Lance Creek, Wyo.	2.8	Ala, gly, glu, leu, val, asp
Stegosaurus (dinosaur)	Jurassic 150×10^6	Morrison, Como Bluff, Wyo.	0.26	Ala, gly, glu
Dinichthys (fish)	Devonian 360×10^6	Ohio Black Shale	3.0	Gly, ala, glu, leu, val, asp

Specimens were furnished from the U. S. National Museum by C. Lewis Gazin and David H. Dunkel.

Ala, alanine; asp, aspartic acid; glu, glutamic acid; gly, glycine; leu, leucine; val, valine.

The amino acids found in the fossils listed in tables 7 and 8 are those which laboratory tests have shown to be most stable. They are precisely those amino acids that could survive if a modern protein were to be stored in a fossil for similar periods of time. It therefore seems likely that the fossils originally contained proteins which played an important role in the lives of ancient creatures just as they do in today's organisms.

Lipides

Fatty acids, waxes, and hydrocarbons have been found in soils, peats, brown coals, and petroleum. Schreiner and Shorey (1908) isolated dihydroxystearic acid, $CH_3(CH_2)_7CHOHCHOH(CH_2)_7COOH$ from soils of low fertility. These included a Tennessee soil, classified as a Clarksville silt loam containing 3.26 per cent organic matter. As much as 0.05 gram of the dihydroxy acid was found per kilo of soil. Subsequently, the same authors (Schreiner and Shorey, 1910) identified α-hydroxystearic acid, $CH_3(CH_2)_{15}CHOHCOOH$, and lignoceric acid as constituents of a Maryland soil—the Elkton silt loam. In a review of the products obtained from peat Kiebler (1945) lists additional examples of organic acids. Shabarova (1954) isolated salts of oleic acid from a Black Sea ooze.

Tanaka and Kuwata (1928) found palmitic ($C_{16}H_{32}O_2$), myristic ($C_{14}H_{28}O_2$), stearic ($C_{18}H_{36}O_2$), and arachidic ($C_{20}H_{40}O_2$) acids in petroleums from Japan, California, and Borneo.

Lochte (1952) reviewed extant knowledge about petroleum acids and bases and summarized the position in the early 1930's. On the basis of studies of mixtures of acids obtained from refinery products and in some cases from crude, a number of generalizations could be made, some of which are presented here:

1. Phenols and carboxylic acids are found in all acid mixtures.
2. The carboxylic acids consist of a mixture of the lower liquid and a few higher solid aliphatic acids and alicyclic acids which are known as naphthenic acids.
3. Acids with less than 8 carbons are almost entirely aliphatic (straight chain) in nature.
4. Monocyclic acids start at C_6, range to C_{20}, and predominate between C_9 and C_{13}.
5. Bicyclic acids start at C_{12} and predominate above C_{14}.

Williams and Richter (1935) isolated isovaleric, *n*-heptylic, *n*-octylic, and *n*-nonylic acids from a West Texas distillate. Hancock and Lochte (1939) fractionated 70 liters of crude acids obtained from Signal Hill crude petroleum. They found a series of substances including acetic, propionic, isobutyric, *n*-butyric, isovaleric, and *n*-valeric acids.

Later investigations by Lochte and collaborators (Quebedeaux, 1943, and Ney, 1943) resulted in identification of 2- and 3-methylpentanoic and *n*-hexanoic acids; 2-, 3-, 4-, and 5-methylhexanoic and *n*-heptanoic acids; *n*-octanoic and *n*-nonanoic acids. In addition a series of naphthenic acids were found.

Isolation of these organic acids attests to their long-time stability in geologic environments and raises the expectation that examples of their occurrence could be multiplied if further search were made.

Because of the enormous economic interest attaching, petroleum is the best studied of the naturally occurring substances. Rossini (1953), who has conducted the most exhaustive investigation, has isolated more than two hundred compounds from a Ponca City, Oklahoma, crude. The oil was produced from the uppermost part of the Wilcox sand formation of the Simpson Group, Middle Ordovician in age (450 million years), at a depth of about 3870 feet. Temperature in the well was 70° C. Some of the hydrocarbons isolated are shown in table 9.

TABLE 9. Some Hydrocarbons Isolated from Gas-Oil Fractions of Ordovician Crude

Formula	Compound	Type	Estimated Amount in Crude Petroleum, volume %
C_7H_{16}	*n*-Heptane	Normal paraffin	2.3
C_7H_{14}	Methylcyclohexane	Cyclohexane	1.6
C_7H_8	Toluene	Benzene	0.51
C_7H_{14}	1,*trans*-3-Dimethylcyclopentane	Cyclopentane	0.87
C_7H_{14}	1,*trans*-2-Dimethylcyclopentane	Cyclopentane	0.48
	Derivable from fatty acids (total)		7.00
C_7H_{16}	2-Methylhexane	Branched paraffin	0.73
C_7H_{16}	3-Methylhexane	Branched paraffin	0.51
	Other types (total)		1.55

Data abstracted from Rossini, Mair, and Streiff (1953).

The relationship between these hydrocarbons and fatty acids (saturated and unsaturated) is treated by Hanson in this volume. The conversion of the naturally occurring even-numbered carbon containing fatty acids to odd-numbered straight-chain hydrocarbons can be explained by chemical decarboxylation. The problem of genesis of even-numbered hydrocarbons is more puzzling. One interesting possible mechanism has been suggested by Shabarova (1954), who postulates the reduction of the fatty acids by hydrogen and hydrogen sulfide. The existence of cyclic acids and hydrocarbons is probably related to internal rearrangements of unsaturated fatty acids. Substantial quantities of straight-chain hydrocarbons are present in petroleums from source rocks formed in every period of geologic time between the present and the Ordovician. Since large quantities of such compounds are produced from Ordovician rocks, one is led to infer that organisms were producing straight-chain fatty acids 450 million years ago.

Carbohydrates

Most of the annual production of carbohydrates is, of course, synthesized by plants, much of it in the form of polymerized sugars, notably cellulose. Since the tonnages involved are enormous it is not surprising that Recent peats, bogs, soils, and muds contain carbohydrates in various forms. Waksman (1936) listed some of the carbohydrates that have been identified in humus, including cellulose, mannan, galactan, levulan, and pentosan.

Vallentyne (1957*b*) has reviewed occurrences of sugars in lake waters and in lake seston. He and his co-workers identified sucrose, maltose, glucose, fructose in seston. Free sugars were found in fresh-water sediments by Vallentyne and Bidwell (1956) and Whittaker and Vallentyne (1957) in amounts of 10 to 3000 milligrams per kilogram of organic matter present. Sugars identified included glucose, fructose, galactose, arabinose, ribose, xylose, sucrose, and maltose.

Carbohydrates in Fossils

Cellulose, which is a polymer of glucose, appears to be much more stable than the monomer. The reactive aldehyde group is involved in the formation of the polymer and is thus not available for other reactions. In any event, cellulose is the principal carbohydrate that has been isolated from fossils.

Gothan (1922) appears to have been the first investigator to isolate cellulose from an ancient environment—the Niederlauswitz (Miocene) formation in Germany. Others isolated and characterized it from a number of middle Tertiary environments. One of the more important investigations was that of Staudinger and Jurisch (1939), who measured the specific viscosities of some Miocene preparations and found that the degree of polymerization had fallen from an original value of perhaps 2000 to 3000 to about 200—an indication that, on the average, original polymer molecules had been severed into about ten smaller units.

Barghoorn (1948) and Barghoorn and Spackman (1950) also found relatively low degrees of polymerization in cellulose fractions isolated from early Tertiary lignites and fossil fruits. Barghoorn (1949*a* and *b*) considered that the degradation of cellulose was due to chemical hydrolysis rather than to bacterial decomposition.

Porphyrins

Occurrence of porphyrins in natural environments and in petroleums has been extensively investigated, owing in part to the ease with which these substances may be detected. Porphyrins are a source of many difficulties in the refining of oil, and the petroleum industry has supported studies on them.

Structural formulas for the two most important porphyrin pigments are shown in figure 4. It can be noted that both hematin, the porphyrin of hemoglobin, and chlorophyll have the inner tetra pyrrole ring. They differ in their substituent groups and in the metal that is bound to them. When these pigments are exposed to geologic environments, both iron and magnesium are relatively quickly lost, metal-free porphyrins being formed. In time these combine with vanadium and nickel ions, which occupy sites formerly filled by iron or magnesium, to yield very stable complexes, and it is in this form that most porphyrins are found in old sediments and petroleums. In only a few instances have metal-free porphyrins been isolated. Blumer (1950) isolated free porphyrin from Swiss bitumens, but found that they were only one-hundredth as abundant as the metal-porphyrin complexes.

As the complexes are very soluble in petroleums and almost completely hydrophobic, it is not surprising that they are commonly found in crude oils. Metal-free porphyrins, on the contrary, are relatively

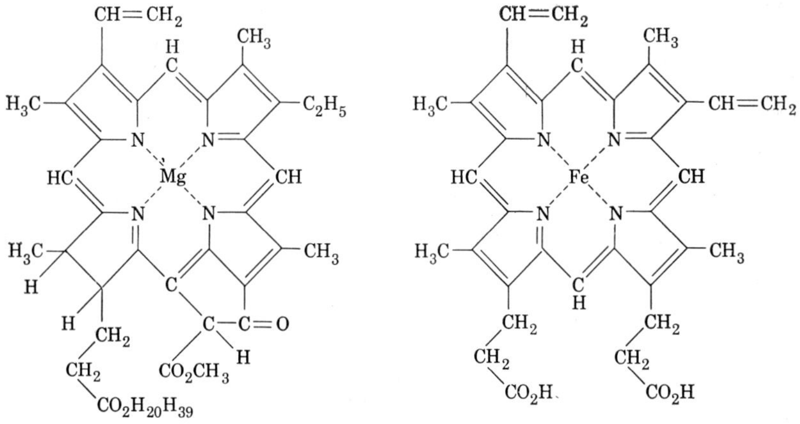

Chlorophyll

Hemin

Fig. 4. Structures of important porphyrins.

more hydrophilic and have not been found in petroleum. Dunning (1954) and Blumer (1956) have been particularly active recently in studies of naturally occurring porphyrins.

The major pioneering work and perhaps the major contributions, however, were made by Treibs (1934*a* and *b*, 1935*a* and *b*, 1936). He devised useful procedures for isolating these pigments and found them in about a hundred specimens from a wide variety of geological environments, some as much as 500 million years old.

In a review of his work, Treibs (1936) reported finding metal porphyrins in 66 crude oils, 9 asphalts, 4 earth waxes, and 5 asphaltites. Seventy bituminous oil shales, 8 phosporites, 1 guano, 7 cannel coals, and 17 coals contained both metal porphyrin complexes and green pigments. A Swiss oil shale was richest in porphyrin complex, containing 4000 parts per million. The oldest occurrence was in "Eastern burning shales" of Cambrian age.

Treibs was also aware of the importance of laboratory tests on the stability of porphyrins. He observed that, when pheophytin was heated to 250–320° in petroleum, phylloerythrin was formed. Further heating resulted in a decarboxylated form of desoxophyllerythrin. He found carboxylated porphyrins in only a few tests.

The impressive body of findings by Treibs came at an important juncture. The controversy was still raging between proponents of the inorganic and the organic hypotheses of the origin of petroleum. The discovery of porphyrin pigments in oil almost identical to those being formed in sediments today provided crucial evidence for the organic origin of oils, and gradually this point of view has become accepted.

The isolation of porphyrins from a series of geologic environments of ages dating back to the Cambrian is important to our views about the nature of past living things. These findings, added to earlier discussion of the ancient synthesis of fatty acids and proteins, helps build a fairly impressive structure of evidence indicating the long duration of important features of the present-day comparative biochemical plan.

Precambrian Occurrences

Discussion about ancient chemicals is necessarily speculative. Majority opinion agrees that life existed in Precambrian times. The most widely quoted reason for such belief is the profusion of phylla that appeared in Cambrian times. There is much reduced carbon in Precambrian sediments but very little extractable organic compounds. Swain (1958) is one of few who have reported such substances, and the concentrations he found are quite low. There is marked contrast between the abundance of petroleum in Ordovician and earlier times. Failure to find petroleum in the older rocks has been ascribed to metamorphism. In view of the comparatively great stability of hydrocarbons (fig. 2) this would involve elevated temperatures and sizable depths of burial. It seems strange that the accidents of tectonics should subject all the older sediments to elevated temperatures with resultant destruction of virtually all organic material. A diligent search around the stable shields might uncover old undisturbed sediments containing quantities of extractable organic substances.

At least one alternative explanation for the paucity of old organic chemicals can be suggested: that Precambrian living forms did not have all the biochemical patterns of those today. Speculations on the origin of life [see, for instance, Oparin (1957)] tend to agree that early life was relatively simple. Laboratory experiments have demonstrated synthesis of some amino acids from inorganic materials (Miller, 1955, 1957; Abelson, 1956, 1957). Long straight-chain fatty acids, however, were not noted, and, in fact, even if they formed in a primitive environment, their insoluble salts would be scavenged by sediments and buried. It is unlikely that fatty acids were present on earth in substantial quantities until creatures arose that could synthesize them. To attain present synthetic patterns may have required a series of inventions. The present-day process employs relatively sophisticated chemistry using enzymatically catalyzed condensation of acetate and reduction of the resultant ketones and alcohols. It is possible that present-type large-scale, highly efficient synthesis of fats did not begin until relatively late.

References

Abelson, P. H. 1954. Annual Report of the Director of the Geophysical Laboratory, 1953–1954, *Carnegie Inst. Wash. Year Book 53,* 97–101.

Abelson, P. H. 1955. Annual Report of the Director of the Geophysical Laboratory, 1954–1955, *Carnegie Inst. Wash. Year Book 54,* 107–109.

Abelson, P. H. 1956. Annual Report of the Director of the Geophysical Laboratory, 1955–1956, *Carnegie Inst. Wash. Year Book 55,* 171–174.

Abelson, P. H. 1957. Annual Report of the Director of the Geophysical Laboratory, 1956–1957, *Carnegie Inst. Wash. Year Book 56,* 179–185.

Baldwin, Ernest. 1949. *An Introduction to Comparative Biochemistry,* Cambridge University Press, Cambridge, England, 164 pp.

Barghoorn, E. S. 1948. Sodium chlorite as an aid in paleobotanical and anatomical studies of plant tissues, *Science, 107,* 480–481.

Barghoorn, E. S. 1949*a*. Paleobotanical studies of the fishweir and associated deposits, in *The Boylston Street Fishweir II* (Frederick Johnson, ed.), *Papers of the Robert S. Peabody Foundation for Archaeology, 4,* 49–83.

Barghoorn, E. S. 1949*b*. Degradation of plant remains in organic sediments, *Botan. Museum Leaflets, Harvard Univ., 14* (no. 1), 1–20.

Barghoorn, E. S., and W. Spackman. 1950. Geological and botanical study of the Brandon lignite, and its significance in coal petrology, *Econ. Geol., 45,* 344–357.

Bergmann, W. 1949. Comparative biochemical studies on the lipids of marine invertebrates, with special reference to the sterols, *J. Marine Research* (*Sears Foundation*), *8,* 137–176.

Blanchard, K. C., and J. MacDonald. 1935. Bacterial metabolism, I, The reduction of propionaldehyde and of propionic acid by *Clostridium acetobutylicum, J. Biol. Chem., 110,* 145–150.

Blumer, M. 1950. Porphyrin dyes and porphyrin-metal complexes in Swiss bitumens, *Helv. Chim. Acta, 33,* 1627.

Blumer, M. 1956. Separation of porphyrins by paper chromatography, *Anal. Chem., 28,* 1640.

Conway, D., and W. F. Libby. 1958. The measurement of very slow reaction rates; decarboxylation of alanine, *J. Am. Chem. Soc., 80,* 1077–1084.

Daniels, F., and R. A. Alberty. 1955. *Physical Chemistry,* John Wiley & Sons, New York, 671 pp.

Dunning, H. N., J. W. Moore, and A. T. Myers. 1954. Properties of porphyrins in petroleum, *Ind. Eng. Chem., 46,* 2000–2007.

Erdman, J. G., E. M. Marlett, and W. E. Hanson. 1956. Survival of amino acids in marine sediments, *Science, 124,* 1026.

Florkin, Marcel. 1949. *Biochemical Evolution,* Academic Press, New York, 157 pp.

Fox, S. W. 1957. The chemical problem of spontaneous generation, *J. Chem. Educ., 34,* 472–479.

Gothan, W. 1922. Neue Arten der Braunkohlenuntersuchung, IV, *Braunkohle, 21,* 400–401.

Hancock, K., and H. L. Lochte. 1939. Acidic constituents of a California straight-run gasoline distillate, *J. Am. Chem. Soc., 61,* 2448–2452.

Kiebler, M. W. 1945. The action of solvents on coal, chapter 19 in *Chemistry of Coal Utilization, I,* 677–760 (H. H. Lowry, ed.), John Wiley & Sons, New York.

Kirner, W. R. 1945. The occurrence of nitrogen in coal, chapter 13 in *Chemistry of Coal Utilization, I,* 450–484 (H. H. Lowry, ed.), John Wiley & Sons, New York.

Lochte, H. L. 1952. Petroleum acids and bases, *Ind. Eng. Chem., 44,* 2597–2601.

McNab, J. G., P. V. Smith, Jr., and R. L. Betts. 1952. The evolution of petroleum, *Ind. Eng. Chem., 44,* 2556–2563.

Miller, S. L. 1955. Production of some organic compounds under possible primitive earth conditions, *J. Am. Chem. Soc., 77,* 2351.

Miller, S. L. 1957. The formation of organic compounds on the primitive earth, *Ann. N. Y. Acad. Sci., 69* (art. 2), 260–275.

Milner, H. W. 1953. The chemical composition of algae, chapter 19 in *Algal Culture from Laboratory to Pilot Plant,* ed. by John S. Burlew, Carnegie Institution of Washington Publication 600, 285–302.

Ney, W. O., W. W. Crouch, C. E. Rannefeld, and H. L. Lochte. 1943. Petroleum acids, VI, Naphthenic acids from California petroleum, *J. Am. Chem. Soc., 65,* 770–777.

Oparin, A. I. 1957. *The Origin of Life on the Earth,* translated by Ann Synge, Academic Press, New York, 495 pp.

Quebedeaux, W. A., G. Wash, W. O. Ney, W. W. Crouch, and H. L. Lochte. 1943. Petroleum acids, V, Aliphatic acids from California petroleum, *J. Am. Chem. Soc., 65,* 767–770.

Rossini, F. D., B. J. Mair, and A. J. Streiff. 1953. *Hydrocarbons from Petroleum,* ACS Monograph 121, Reinhold Publishing Corp., New York, 556 pp.

Rubey, W. W. 1951. Geologic history of sea water, *Bull. Geol. Soc. Am., 62,* 1111–1148.

Schönbrunner, J. 1940. Bacterial hydrogenation of oleic acid and sorbic acid and the effect of bile acids, *Biochem. Z., 304,* 26–36.

Schreiner, O., and E. C. Shorey. 1908. The isolation of dihydroxystearic acid from soils, *J. Am. Chem. Soc., 30,* 1599–1607.

Schreiner, O., and E. C. Shorey. 1910. Some acid constituents of soil humus, *J. Am. Chem. Soc., 32,* 1674–1680.

Shabarova, N. T. 1954. The organic matter of marine sediments, *Uspekhi Sovremennoĭ Biol., 37,* 203–208.

Staudinger, H., and I. Jurisch. 1939. Ueber makromolekulare Verbindungen, 212 Mitteilung, Ueber den Polymerisationsgrad der Cellulose in Ligniten, *Papier-Fabr. (Tech.-Wiss. Teil), 37,* 181–184.

Swain, F. M., A. Blumentals, and N. Prokopovich. 1958. Bituminous and other organic substances in Precambrian of Minnesota, *Bull. Am. Assoc. Petrol. Geologists, 42,* 173–189.

Tanaka, J., and T. Kuwata. 1928. Higher fatty acids in petroleum, *J. Faculty Eng. Tokyo Imp. Univ., 17,* 293–303.

Treibs, A. 1934*a*. Organic mineral substances, II, Occurrence of chlorophyll derivatives in an oil shale of the Upper Triassic, *Ann., 509,* 103.

Treibs, A. 1934*b*. Organic minerals, III, Chlorophyll and hemin derivatives in bituminous rocks, petroleums, mineral waxes, and asphalts, Origin of petroleum, *Ann., 510,* 42.

Treibs, A. 1935*a*. Organic mineral substances, IV, Chlorophyll and hemin derivatives in bituminous rocks, petroleums, coals, and phosphorites, *Ann., 517,* 172.

Treibs, A. 1935*b*. Organic mineral substances, V, Porphyrins in coals, *Ann., 520,* 144.

Treibs, A. 1936. Chlorophyll and hemin derivatives in organic mineral substances (a review), *Angew. Chem., 49,* 682–686.

Vallentyne, J. R. 1957*a*. Annual Report of the Director of the Geophysical Laboratory, 1956–1957, *Carnegie Inst. Wash. Year Book 56,* 185–186.

Vallentyne, J. R. 1957*b*. The molecular nature of organic matter in lakes and oceans, with lesser reference to sewage and terrestrial soils, *J. Fisheries Research Board Canada, 14,* 33–82.

Vallentyne, J. R., and R. G. S. Bidwell. 1956. The relation between free sugars and sedimentary chlorophyll in lake muds, *Ecology, 37,* 495–500.

Waksman, S. A. 1936. *Humus: Origin, Chemical Composition, and Importance in Nature,* Williams and Wilkins Co., Baltimore, Md., 494 pp.

Whittaker, J. R., and J. R. Vallentyne. 1957. On the occurrence of free sugars in lake sediment extracts, *Limnol. Oceanogr., 2,* 98–110.

Williams, M., and G. H. Richter. 1935. Acidic constituents of a West Texas pressure distillate, *J. Am. Chem. Soc., 57,* 1686–1688.

Some Chemical Aspects of Petroleum Genesis[1]

WILLIAM E. HANSON[2]
Mellon Institute

Probably the least well understood aspect of petroleum genesis is the chemistry involved in the transformation of the source materials into crude oil. Two extreme views have been current on the subject. Earlier opinion held that petroleum was entirely the result of chemical reactions within the source substances, possibly aided by the catalytic effects of the associated inorganics; a more recent idea is that oil is simply the accumulation of plant- and animal-produced hydrocarbons which have been incorporated in the sediments along with other, non-hydrocarbon debris. Only recently has information become available which permits these diverse points of view to be evaluated. It is the purpose of this paper to examine the nature of certain of the source materials and to consider how hydrocarbons of the type present in petroleum might be formed from them. To provide perspective for the discussion, the now generally accepted boundary conditions for petroleum formation are reviewed and comments are offered on some of the more critical studies on the organic components of recently deposited aquatic sediments.

Limiting Conditions of Petroleum Formation

Practically all present-day thinking on oil origin has been guided by a framework of widely accepted limiting conditions, based on a

[1] This paper is taken, in part, from a more general discussion of petroleum genesis, prepared by the writer as a chapter for *The Chemical Technology of Petroleum,* 3d ed., by W. A. Gruse and D. R. Stevens, McGraw-Hill Book Company, New York (in press), and is presented with permission of the publisher.

[2] Administrative Fellow, Multiple Fellowship of Gulf Research & Development Company.

wealth of field observations by geologists; these, first summarized by Cox (1946), may be stated briefly as follows:

(*a*) Petroleum and other types of bitumen are always associated with sedimentary rocks. Even when crude oil occurs in fractured metamorphic or igneous strata, close association with sedimentaries, from which the oil could have migrated, can be demonstrated.

(*b*) Practically all petroleum appears to have originated in brackish to full marine sediments. This observation is complicated by the fluid and usually volatile nature of the crude, which permits it to move away from the point of origin. In fact, only rarely can a petroleum be identified unequivocally with its particular source bed. Instances have been cited (Felts, 1954; Kent, 1954) of oil of possible nonmarine origin, and it is not unlikely that such may exist. It seems reasonable to assume that, somewhere between the truly marine sediments and those of clearly nonmarine character, a transition from the liquid to the essentially solid type bitumen must occur. Where this zone lies is uncertain, and no generalizations appear to be possible; perhaps it is a matter of how petroleum is defined.

(*c*) High pressure is probably not necessary for the generation of petroleum. Some petroliferous basins, at least, could never have had a stratigraphic thickness of much more than 5000 ft. The corresponding hydrostatic head at the deepest part of such a basin could not have exceeded 2500 psi, although actual pressure of rock overburden might have been twice this value; much higher figures could obtain at grain-to-grain contact points, but laboratory experiments in which high hydraulic or shear pressures have been applied to shales have given either indecisive or negative results (Hawley, 1929*a* and *b*, 1930; Rand, 1933; Uwatoko, 1932). The minimum depth value cited appears more likely to be related to the pressure required to expel oil from a fine-grained sediment.

(*d*) Temperatures above 200° F are probably not required. Under the normal geothermal gradient and at the presumed minimum required depth of burial (5000 ft), temperatures could hardly have exceeded 150° F. The conclusion is that petroleum generation is a low-temperature process; chemical considerations have amply supported this view.

(*e*) Petroleum has apparently been generated in strata laid down as early as Cambrian and certainly Ordovician time. There is no reason to believe that oil could not or did not form in earlier times. Precambrian sediments have all been metamorphosed, however, and any bitumen that did form must have been destroyed; carbon 13 to carbon 12 ratios determined on carbonaceous particles in Precambrian rocks suggest that this carbon has passed through the life cycle and may, therefore, represent the indurated remains of crude oil or some other type of bitumen (Rankama, 1954). One interesting conclusion can be drawn from the great antiquity of some petroleums: the relatively primitive marine forms which were the only living organisms of that day were evidently an adequate source material for crude oils; whatever mechanism of formation is proposed, it is unnecessary to postulate the need for higher-order marine organisms or land plants.

Beginning with the Ordovician or possibly the Cambrian, every geological age has produced oil; some ages were more prolific than others, but none was barren. Until recently it was believed that Pliocene oil was the youngest, and the apparent absence of petroleum in Pleistocene sediments was commonly credited to insufficient time for generation or perhaps to unfavorable climatic conditions imposed by extensive glaciation. Owing to the accumulation of water in the polar ice caps during the Pleistocene, sea levels around the world were reduced by at least 300 ft (Flint, 1947), and, as a result, marine sediments laid down during this epoch are now largely under water. Only with the advent of offshore drilling have these sediments been explored to any extent and, in particular, at depths sufficient to result in the expulsion of fluids from the muds. Recent geological observations in certain Gulf of Mexico operations have indicated that, with respect to petroleum formation, the Pleistocene may not be essentially different from any of the earlier periods (Hanna, 1958).

Accumulation of Organic Material

With the exception of certain relatively minor sterile areas, the sea supports a tremendously complex floral and faunal population. Free-floating (planktonic) forms greatly predominate over the swimming or bottom-frequenting forms. As these organisms die, their remains fall to the bottom to be incorporated into the sediments. If the area is one in which there are active bottom currents, the fines will be winnowed away, leaving a sandy or otherwise coarse-grained bottom, through which oxygen-bearing waters can circulate freely. Organic material deposited in such an environment is destroyed quickly by aerobic bacteria to yield carbon dioxide and water. If the bottom waters are quiet, muddy sediments can accumulate, and the entrapped organic matter can be, at least partly, preserved.

In general, the free oxygen content of the water drops as an organic-rich bottom is approached and becomes practically zero in the uppermost mud layers. Completely stagnant conditions are not at all essential to the accumulation of organic material, however. Organic-rich muds occur in quantity in relatively shallow depressions over many shelf areas of the world, as, for example, in the northern Gulf of Mexico.

Bacterial Workover; Development of a Reducing Environment

The drop in oxygen content and, hence, E_h value that is noted on passing from the bottom water into an organic-rich mud is primarily the result of bacterial action. If the bottom is stagnant and the organic content high, E_h values of zero or less will be observed even in the upper layers; for less rich sediments, low positive values may persist to depths of several feet (Emery and Rittenberg, 1952). With the disappearance of the aerobes in the uppermost portion of the bottom muds, a new and prolific flora takes over (ZoBell, 1946*a;* Stone and ZoBell, 1952; Beerstecher, 1954). These organisms, which can grow under anaerobic as well as aerobic conditions, are represented by such genera as *Pseudomonas, Vibrio, Spirillum, Achromobacter,* and *Flavobacterium.* The populations vary widely with sediment type, proximity to land, depth of water, and other factors. Typical bottom muds may have several hundred million organisms per gram for the first few centimeters of depth. With increasing depth of burial, the numbers fall off rapidly, although bacteria have been reported in cores of ancient sediments and in fluids at depths of several thousand feet (ZoBell, 1944, 1946*b*, 1952; ZoBell and Johnson, 1949). The enormous numbers of bacteria in the upper sediment zones imply some action on the entrapped organic detritus. Presumably a part of it is destroyed; possibly much of it is extensively altered.

An important reaction that takes place in organic-rich muds is the reduction of sulfate ion to sulfide. It is occasioned by the activity of *Desulfovibrio,* a strict anaerobe, which is widely distributed in the sea and which utilizes the oxygen in sulfate ion as a hydrogen acceptor in its energy-producing reactions, to yield hydrogen sulfide. With the generation of sulfide the E_h drops steadily, usually becoming stabilized in the -200 to -500 mv range. Short of later exposure of the sediment to oxygen-bearing waters or to the atmosphere, this reduced condition persists through the processes of compaction and ultimate lithification of the sediment. The maintenance of a low E_h is believed to be of first importance, not only in preventing early oxidative destruction of the organic matter but probably also in promoting the reductive conversion of the organic debris to hydrocarbons.

Hydrocarbons in Recent Sediments

Largely as the result of pioneer work by Trask (1932), the first impression gained with respect to petroleum genesis was that it must occur at depth and probably through some thermal or catalytic mechanism, since liquid hydrocarbons were not found in freshly deposited sediments. "Paraffin" had been reported (Trask and Wu, 1930) in amounts ranging from 1 to 68 parts per thousand of dry sediment, although the actual presence of paraffins in the fraction was never proved; other waxy materials (e.g., high-molecular-weight alcohols) were recognized as possible components. In view of later results, it is not clear why liquid hydrocarbons were missed; possibly bacterial or chemical oxidative destruction occurred during storage or before extraction.

Some years later Whitmore (1943) pointed out that all living organisms contain hydrocarbons as a part of their chemical make-up. Certain of these, such as the paraffins and naphthenes, would be expected to survive in the organic detritus as a result of their chemical stability and to contribute to any petroleum that might ultimately be formed. Quantitative determinations of the hydrocarbon contents of a variety of algae and bacteria by Sirahama (1938), Whitmore and Oakwood (1944–1945), Larsen and Haug (1956), and others have indicated concentrations up to several tenths per cent, dry-weight basis. Depending on the identity of the organism, the extracts contained not only paraffins and naphthenes but other hydrocarbons of varying degrees of unsaturation. The molecular weights covered a wide range.

Considered on a world basis, the volume of hydrocarbons is huge; Whitmore (1943) estimated a total production from marine plant sources alone to be possibly as great as 60 million barrels per year. The estimate is highly approximate and accounts only for the observed heavier hydrocarbons. Nevertheless, the idea that all hydrocarbons in crude might be so formed was attractive, and the consequent hypothesis that crude-oil formation involved merely the accumulation and segregation of this hydrocarbon material was rather widely accepted. This thesis received further impetus with the announcement by Smith (1952, 1954) of the isolation of hydrocarbons from recent sediments in amounts varying from 9 to nearly 12,000 parts per million of dried sample. The hydrocarbon fractions were demonstrated to be of recent origin by carbon 14 dating. By means of chromatographic methods, paraffinic, naphthenic, and aromatic fractions were isolated. Average molecular weights fell in the 250 to 300 range.

An interesting conclusion from Smith's data is that, with respect to hydrocarbon content, no sharp distinction can be drawn between fresh-water and marine sediments; from the results, it might be inferred that fresh-water samples were richer in hydrocarbons, although their proportion of the total organic content was usually smaller than that of the marine sediments. Swain (1956) has recently reported the isolation of hydrocarbon materials from the bottom sediments of five fresh-water lakes in Minnesota. Careful fractionation of the lipoid extracts revealed the presence of liquid and solid hydrocarbons of both saturated and aromatic type. A similar occurrence of hydrocarbons has been reported by Judson and Murray (1956) for two Wisconsin lakes. In both instances, the recent character of the hydrocarbons was established by carbon 14 dating.

Petroleum Not Formed in Recent Sediments

A critical study of the hydrocarbon content and character of a series of marine muds from the northern Gulf of Mexico has been presented by Stevens et al. (1956) and by Evans et al. (1957). Quantities comparable to those reported by earlier workers were isolated, and their recent origin was demonstrated by the radiocarbon method. Mass spectrometric measurements on the normal paraffinic fractions, however, showed clearly a strong predominance for molecules containing an odd number of carbon atoms; the same was true for hydrocarbons isolated from soil. These observations are significant in view of the fact that, in contrast with molecules of the natural fatty acids and alcohols, which are largely of the straight-chain type and, with rare exceptions, contain an even number of carbon atoms, many of the plant and animal hydrocarbon molecules have branched chains and contain an odd number of carbon atoms (Deuel, 1951). Hydrocarbons of comparable molecular-weight range isolated from crude oils and from the Woodford shale (a petroliferous rock of Mississippian age) exhibited no such preference. A sample of plankton, however, showed only slight odd-carbon preference, the odd-to-even ratio being 1.1 as compared with 2.1 for the recent sediment hydrocarbons. Brenneman (1957) has confirmed the high odd-to-even carbon ratio for Gulf Coast sediment extracts of late Pleistocene age but has observed a more nearly equal distribution for hydrocarbons of some younger deposits.

A distinction has also been noted between the types of aromatic hydrocarbons derived from recent and from ancient sediments. Judging from spectral absorption characteristics, Stevens et al. (1956) have concluded that the mixtures obtained from the fresh Gulf muds are substantially less complex than those derived from crude oil or from the Woodford shale. Recent work by Erdman et al. (1958) has shown that benzene and naphthalene and their more volatile alkyl derivatives (up to about C_{16}) are absent in a variety of fresh aquatic sediments ranging from acid fresh water to marine in type.

The conclusion that hydrocarbons make up a normal component of recent sediments is now established beyond any doubt. It is further evident that this is true also for sediments which geologically are not ordinarily considered potential source sediments of petroleum. It appears, however, that crude oil, as we know it, is not formed in recent sediments, at least in the uppermost zones, even for marine shelf deposits. The inference is that, if the sediment is of a type to yield petroleum, the missing components must be generated at some greater depth. This, in turn, argues for the idea that source material other than plant- and animal-generated hydrocarbon is required.

Source Materials

Because of the tremendous variety in the plant and animal forms that contribute organic substance to the sediments, it is possible to describe the source materials only in terms of gross chemical classes: the lipids; the proteins and their component amino acids; the carbohydrates; the pyrrole pigments; the lignins; etc. Since the organisms involved are very largely of the marine to semimarine aquatic type, the organic debris might be expected to be relatively rich in both fatty and proteinaceous material; carbohydrates would probably be of lesser importance, in view of the general absence of rigid organic skeletal structures in marine plankton, as opposed to the grasses and woody plants of the coastal and land areas.

Thermal Transformation of the Lipids

Of special interest with respect to the potential formation of petroleum hydrocarbons are the lipids. This class includes not only the organic acids, alcohols, and esters but also the polyenes, in addition, of course, to the plant- and animal-generated hydrocarbons of paraffinic and naphthenic-aromatic type. The polyenes, in turn, include the the terpenes and the carotenoid pigments. As yet, very little is known about the marine terpenes; the carotenoids have been studied extensively and have been shown to be important constituents of aquatic flora and fauna of all types (Goodwin, 1954). Fox (1937, 1944) and Fox et al. (1941, 1944) have demonstrated their survival in marine sediments for many thousands of years. Under mild thermal conditions, cyclization and carbon-carbon cleavage reactions take place with the production of a variety of aromatic hydrocarbons. Thus, *m*-xylene has been produced in the low-temperature pyrolysis of bixin ($C_{25}H_{30}O_4$) (Van Hasselt, 1911), and of capsanthin ($C_{40}H_{58}O_3$) (Zechmeister and Cholnoky, 1930), while toluene (Kuhn and Winterstein, 1932) and 2,6-dimethylnaphthalene (Jones and Sharpe, 1948; Kuhn and Winterstein, 1933), in addition to *m*-xylene, have been obtained from other carotenoids. Temperatures around 200° C appear to be optimum (Jones and Sharpe, 1948).

In each instance, cyclization occurs involving one or more of the basic units, figure 1, presumably to yield a cyclic diene as intermediate;

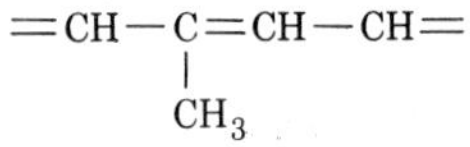

$$=CH-\underset{\underset{CH_3}{|}}{C}=CH-CH=$$

Fig. 1.

by oxidation or hydrogen transfer the aromatic is formed. Under the prevailing reducing conditions in the sediments, it seems likely that a corresponding naphthene could also be easily generated. See figure 2.

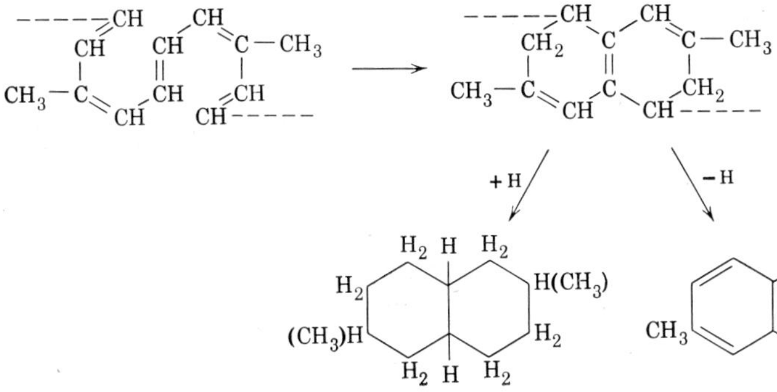

Fig. 2.

Carotene, for example, might react to yield a naphthene or a derivative of decalin (fig. 3).

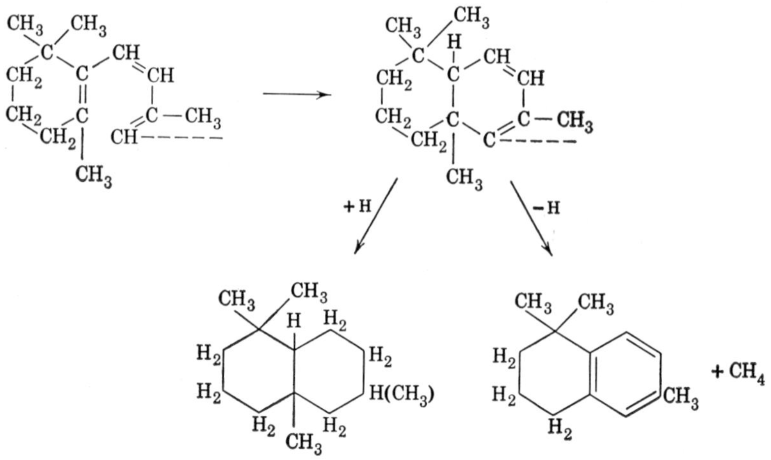

Fig. 3.

As was pointed out by Jones and Sharpe (1948), the experimental conditions imposed in the carotenoid degradation studies have favored intermolecular reactions. If the polyene had been heated in dilute solution, intramolecular condensation might have been expected to occur with the formation of tri- and tetracyclic ring systems. This latter situation would probably more nearly simulate conditions in the source bed and would afford an attractive explanation for the generation of petroleum-type, polycyclic naphthenics and aromatics.

The fatty acids have long been regarded favorably as source materials for petroleum, because of their diversity in chemical structure and the fact that they could be converted to hydrocarbons by the simple elimination of the carboxyl group. As indicated earlier, the natural fatty acids are largely of the straight-chain type and, with rare exceptions, contain an even number of carbon atoms; many are unsaturated, however, the polyethenoid type exhibiting wide variations in the arrangement of the double bonds. Hilditch (1956) has noted the interesting fact that the fats of the simplest and most primitive organisms are usually composed of very complex mixtures of fatty acids, in contrast to the higher plants and animals, for which the component acids are fewer.

Cyclization reactions of the same type as noted above for the polyene pigments have been demonstrated by Farmer and van den Heuvel (1938*a* and *b*) for poly-unsaturated acids of marine organisms. Again, temperatures no higher than 260° C were sufficient to yield ample products for study within a 24-hour period. The observation is important because, owing to the great variety of the acids available, a wide spectrum of aromatic and naphthenic hydrocarbons might be formed. The possibilities are further multiplied if double bond migration takes place or if chain scission occurs, as was demonstrated above for the carotenoid compounds. Reaction possibilities for two of the more common polyethenoic acids may be cited as illustrative (fig. 4).

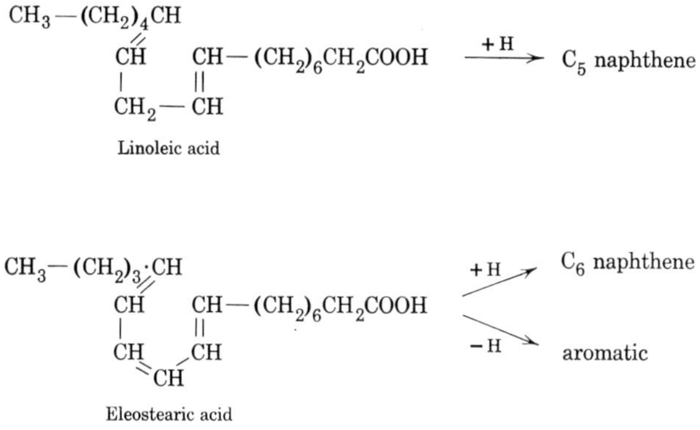

$CH_3—(CH_2)_4CH$
$CH \quad CH—(CH_2)_6CH_2COOH \xrightarrow{+H}$ C_5 naphthene
$CH_2—CH$

Linoleic acid

$CH_3—(CH_2)_3CH$
$CH \quad CH—(CH_2)_6CH_2COOH$ $\xrightarrow{+H}$ C_6 naphthene; $\xrightarrow{-H}$ aromatic
$CH \quad CH$
CH

Eleostearic acid

Fig. 4.

Possible Role of Proteins

Little consideration has been given to protein as a potential source of hydrocarbons, primarily because of the widespread opinion that it was hydrolyzed rapidly to the component amino acids and probably destroyed in the aqueous phase by bacteria. Recent work by Abelson (1954*a* and *b*) on the thermal stability of amino acids has indicated that these substances should survive under the normal low-temperature earth conditions for long periods of time. That such was the case was demonstrated by the detection of proteins or peptides in fossil clam shells from the Pleistocene and of amino acids in older invertebrate and vertebrate fossils, including an Ordovician trilobite. More recently, Erdman et al. (1956) have shown that a variety of amino acids are present in the noncalcareous as well as the calcareous portions of recent marine sediments and in Oligocene shales, estimated to be some 30 million years old; a similar report on the Posidonia shales of northwestern Germany has also been published (von Gaertner and Kroepelin, 1956).

The reaction involved in the low-temperature thermal degradation of amino acids is the loss of carbon dioxide to yield the corresponding amine. Marlett and Erdman (1959) have suggested that the thermal reaction may go one step further, eliminating the amino group as ammonia (reductive deamination) to form the hydrocarbon. They have pointed out that, among the common amino acids, there is a structure corresponding to every paraffinic hydrocarbon up through the pentanes (exclusive of neopentane, which is exceedingly rare in petroleum). Thus, alanine or aspartic acid would yield ethane; α-amino-n-butyric acid and glutamic acid, propane; arginine, n-butane; valine, isobutane; leucine and isoleucine, isopentane; and lysene, n-pentane. Glycine might yield methane, although there are other good sources for this gas. Phenylalanine should produce ethyl benzene. The suggestion is particularly interesting since, to the writer's knowledge, no other equally plausible hypothesis for the formation of these hydrocarbons has been advanced. Preliminary calculations based on the amino acid contents of recent and ancient sediments indicate that ample material is available to account for the light paraffins in even the most volatile crude oils.

Summary and Indicated Research

By way of summarizing the foregoing discussion, the following points may be made: (1) Although hydrocarbons form an important part of the organic fraction of recent sediments, crude oil as we know it has not formed in these sediments even well beyond the zone of major bacterial activity. (2) To account for the missing or deficient components of petroleum, source material other than plant- and animal-generated hydrocarbons must be involved. (3) Of the several classes of organic matter, the fatty material, including the polyene pigments, and protein appear to be most attractive as potential sources of hydrocarbons. (4) There exists a wide variety of chemically reasonable thermal reactions for the production of paraffinic, naphthenic, and aromatic hydrocarbons of the types that are universally present in petroleum but absent or present in clearly insufficient amounts in the total hydrocarbon fraction of recent sediments; certain of these reactions have already been shown to proceed sufficiently rapidly under earth conditions to be significant over long periods of time. (5) It is believed that reactions of this sort should be explored further, the probable nature of the source materials and the physicochemical conditions to which they are subjected, including possible catalytic effects of the inorganic matrix, being kept in mind. Data obtained in such a study should aid materially in a better understanding of the chemistry of petroleum genesis.

References

Abelson, P. H. 1954*a*. Amino acids in fossils, *Science, 119,* 576.

Abelson, P. H. 1954*b*. Studies in paleobiochemistry, *Carnegie Inst. Wash. Year Book 53,* 97–101.

Beerstecher, E., Jr. 1954. *Petroleum Microbiology,* Elsevier Press, New York.

Brenneman, M. C. 1957. Carbon number distribution of normal paraffins from Quaternary sediments, preprint, Division of Petroleum Chemistry, American Chemical Society, 131st Meeting, Miami, April.

Cox, B. B. 1946. Transformation of organic material into petroleum under geological conditions, *Bull. Am. Assoc. Petrol. Geologists, 30,* 645.

Deuel, H. J., Jr. 1951. *The Lipids,* I, p. 400, Interscience Publishers, New York.

Emery, K. O., and S. C. Rittenberg. 1952. Early diagenesis of California basin sediments in relation to origin of oil, *Bull. Am. Assoc. Petrol. Geologists, 36,* 735.

Erdman, J. G., E. M. Marlett, and W. E. Hanson. 1956. Survival of amino acids in marine sediments, *Science, 124,* 1026.

Erdman, J. G., E. M. Marlett, and W. E. Hanson. 1958. The occurrence and distribution of low molecular weight aromatic hydrocarbons in recent and ancient carbonaceous sediments, preprint, Division of Petroleum Chemistry, American Chemical Society, 134th Meeting, Chicago, September.

Evans, E. D., G. S. Kenny, W. G. Meinschein, and E. E. Bray. 1957. Distribution of *n*-paraffins and separation of saturated hydrocarbons from recent marine sediments, *Anal. Chem., 29,* 1858.

Farmer, E. H., and M. H. van den Heuvel. 1938*a*. Separation of the highly unsaturated acids of fish oils by molecular distillation, *J. Soc. Chem. Ind., 57,* 24.

Farmer, E. H., and M. H. van den Heuvel. 1938*b*. Unsaturated acids of natural oils, VII, Docosahexaenoic acid, an abundant highly unsaturated acid of cod-liver oil, *J. Chem. Soc., 1938,* 427.

Felts, W. M. 1954. Occurrence of oil and gas and its relation to possible source beds in continental Tertiary of intermountain region, *Bull. Am. Assoc. Petrol. Geologists, 38,* 1661.

Flint, R. F. 1947. *Glacial Geology and the Pleistocene Epoch,* p. 427, John Wiley & Sons, New York.

Fox, D. L. 1937. Carotenoids and other lipoid-soluble pigments in the sea and and in deep marine mud, *Proc. Natl. Acad. Sci. U. S., 23,* 295.

Fox, D. L. 1944. Biochemical fossils, *Science, 100,* 111.

Fox, D. L., and L. J. Anderson. 1941. Pigments from marine muds, *Proc. Natl. Acad. Sci. U. S., 27,* 333.

Fox, D. L., D. M. Updegraff, and G. D. Novelli. 1944. Carotenoid pigments in the ocean floor, *Arch. Biochem., 5,* 1.

Gaertner, H. R. von, and H. Kroepelin. 1956. Petrographische und chemische

Untersuchungen am Posidonienschiefer Nordwestdeutschlands, *Erdöl u. Kohle, 9,* 680.

Goodwin, T. W. 1954. *Carotenoids,* Chemical Publishing Company, New York.

Hanna, M. A. 1958. Chief Paleontologist, Gulf Oil Corporation, Houston, Texas, personal communication.

Hawley, J. E. 1929*a*. Generation of oil in rocks by shearing pressures, I, The problems: methods of determining the soluble organic contents of oil shales, *Bull. Am. Assoc. Petrol. Geologists, 13,* 303.

Hawley, J. E. 1929*b*. Generation of oil in rocks by shearing pressures, II, Effect of shearing pressures on oil shales and oil-bearing rocks, *Bull. Am. Assoc. Petrol. Geologists, 13,* 329.

Hawley, J. E. 1930. Generation of oil in rocks by shearing pressures, III, Further effects of high shearing pressures on oil shales, *Bull. Am. Assoc. Petrol. Geologists, 14,* 451.

Hilditch, T. P. 1956. *The Chemical Constitution of Natural Fats,* p. 9, John Wiley & Sons, New York.

Jones, R. N., and R. W. Sharpe. 1948. The pyrolysis of carotene, *Can. J. Research, 26B,* 728.

Judson, S., and R. C. Murray. 1956. Modern hydrocarbons in two Wisconsin lakes, *Bull. Am. Assoc. Petrol. Geologists, 40,* 747.

Kent, P. E. 1954. Oil occurrences in Coal Measures of England, *Bull. Am. Assoc. Petrol. Geologists, 38,* 1699.

Kuhn, R., and A. Winterstein. 1932. Thermischer Abbau der Carotin-Farbstoffe (Über konjugierte Doppelbindungen, XXV Mitteil.), *Ber., 65,* 1873.

Kuhn, R., and A. Winterstein. 1933. Über die Konstitution des β-Carotins; 2,6-Dimethylnaphthalin aus der Polyen-Kette, *Ber., 66,* 429.

Larsen, B., and A. Haug. 1956. Carotene isomers in some red algae, *Acta Chem. Scand.,* 10, 470.

Marlett, E. M., and J. G. Erdman. 1959. Carbon-nitrogen distribution and nitrogen type relationships in recent and ancient sediments. Preprint, Division of Petroleum Chemistry, American Chemical Society, 135th Meeting, Boston, April.

Rand, W. P. 1933. Generation of oil in rocks by shearing pressures, IV and V, Further studies of effects of heat on oil shales, *Bull. Am. Assoc. Petrol. Geologists, 17,* 1229.

Rankama, K. 1954. The isotopic constitution of carbon in ancient rocks as an indicator of its biogenic or non-biogenic origin, *Geochim. et Cosmochim. Acta, 5,* 142.

Sirahama, K. 1938. Liquid unsaponifiable matter of the brown algae fat, VII, Some new ingredients of brown algae, *J. Agr. Chem. Soc. Japan, 14,* 743.

Smith, P. V., Jr. 1952. The occurrence of hydrocarbons in Recent sediments from the Gulf of Mexico, *Science, 116,* 437.

Smith, P. V., Jr. 1954. Studies on origin of petroleum: occurrence of hydrocarbons in recent sediments, *Bull. Am. Assoc. Petrol. Geologists, 38,* 377.

Stevens, N. P., E. E. Bray, and E. D. Evans. 1956. Hydrocarbons in sediments of the Gulf of Mexico, *Bull. Am. Assoc. Petrol. Geologists, 40,* 975.

Stone, R. S., and C. E. ZoBell. 1952. Bacterial aspects of the origin of petroleum, *Ind. Eng. Chem., 44,* 2564.

Swain, F. M. 1956. Stratigraphy of lake deposits in central and northern Minnesota, *Bull. Am. Assoc. Petrol. Geologists, 40,* 600.

Trask, P. D. 1932. *Origin and Environment of Source Sediments of Petroleum,* Gulf Publishing Company, Houston, Texas.

Trask, P. D., and C. C. Wu. 1930. Does petroleum form in sediments at time of deposition? *Bull. Am. Assoc. Petrol. Geologists, 14,* 1451.

Uwatoko, K. 1932. Genesis of oil by high radial axial pressure, *Bull. Am. Assoc. Petrol. Geologists, 16,* 1029.

Van Hasselt, J. F. B. 1911. Études sur la constitution de la bixine, *Rec. trav. chim., 30,* 1.

Whitmore, F. C. 1943. *Fundamental Research on Occurrence and Recovery of Petroleum,* p. 124, American Petroleum Institute, New York.

Whitmore, F. C., and T. S. Oakwood. 1944–1945. *Fundamental Research on Occurrence and Recovery of Petroleum,* p. 99, American Petroleum Institute, New York.

Zechmeister, L., and L. von Cholnoky. 1930. Untersuchungen über den Paprika-Farbstoff, IV, Einige Umwandlungen des Capsanthins, *Ann., 478,* 95.

ZoBell, C. E. 1944. Fourth Quarterly Report, Research Project 43A, American Petroleum Institute, June 30.

ZoBell, C. E. 1946*a*. *Marine Microbiology,* Chronica Botanica Company, Waltham, Mass.

ZoBell, C. E. 1946*b*. Functions of bacteria in the formation and accumulation of petroleum, *Oil Weekly, 120,* 30 (February 18).

ZoBell, C. E. 1952. Bacterial life at the bottom of the Philippine Trench, *Science, 115,* 507.

ZoBell, C. E., and F. H. Johnson. 1949. The influence of hydrostatic pressure on the growth and viability of terrestrial and marine bacteria, *J. Bacteriol., 57,* 179.

Mineral Assemblages of the Green River Formation[1]

CHARLES MILTON

U. S. Geological Survey

and

HANS P. EUGSTER

Geophysical Laboratory
Carnegie Institution of Washington
and The Johns Hopkins University

The Green River formation in Wyoming, Colorado, and Utah (fig. 1) has been of interest, both scientific and economic, for a long time. The fundamental studies of Bradley (1929*a*, 1929*b*, 1931, 1936, 1948) revealed the extraordinary nature of these beds. In the two decades since, beginning with the discovery of shortite (Fahey, 1939), many new mineral species have been found. Others, which until then were known only from igneous or metamorphic terranes, have been observed as authigenic sedimentary minerals. The Green River formation produces a large amount of soda, and it also constitutes the world's largest known reserve of hydrocarbons.

The uncommon mineralogy of many beds of the Green River (table 1), particularly the saline ones, is a direct consequence of special conditions prevailing during sedimentation and diagenesis, and the unusual composition of the waters in which precipitation and sedimentation took place. The mineral assemblages of the saline beds bear no resemblance to the usual salt deposits. Their relationships, as well as those of minerals formed by interaction of the brines with calcareous and other muds, may be readily understood from phase-rule considerations and from available experimental data. Systematic differences between isolated basins can be related to environmental differences of physical, chemical, or biological nature.

[1] Publication authorized by Director, U. S. Geological Survey.

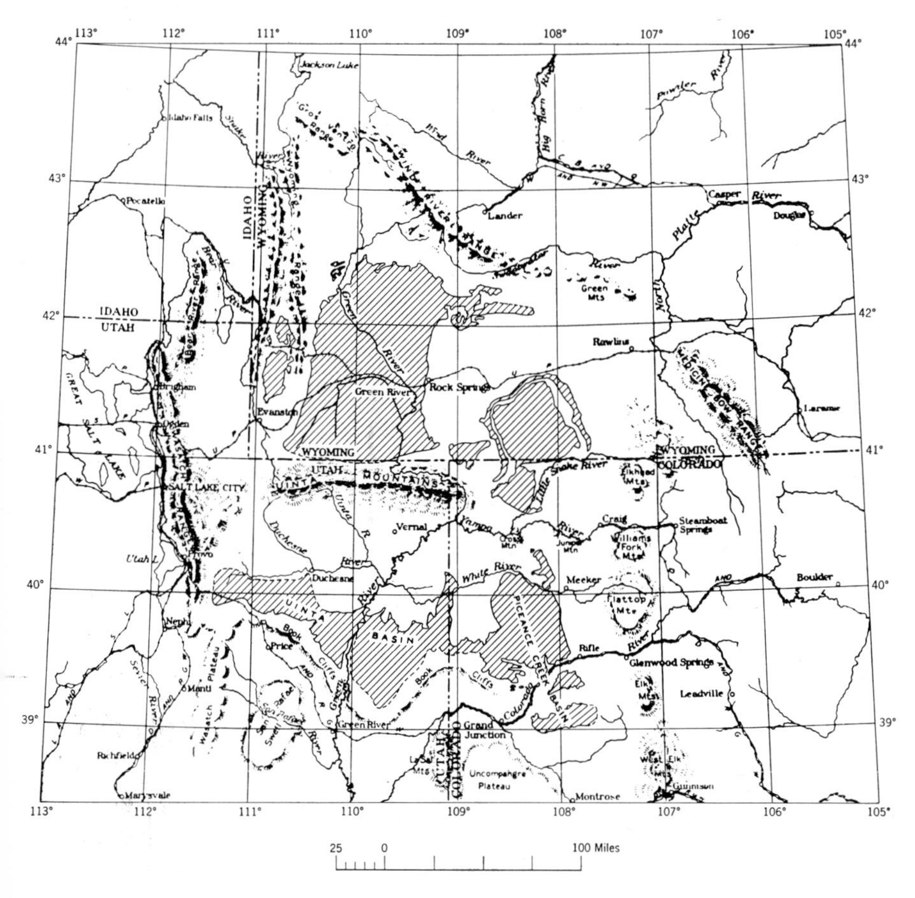

Fig. 1. Map showing outcrop of Green River formation in Colorado, Wyoming, and Utah (shaded areas). The formation also underlies much of the region between the Uinta Mountains and the major outcrops to the south. (From Bradley, 1931.)

This paper first reviews the general geological conditions during Green River time, and then discusses and interprets the various minerals and mineral assemblages found in the Green River formation.

Origin and Nature of the Green River Formation

Before the Tertiary, an Upper Cretaceous sea spread over much of what is now the Rocky Mountain area; but since the end of the Mesozoic the Colorado Plateau, which includes the Green River region, has been emergent. Streams wandering across the terrane during the early Tertiary (Wasatch) deposited fluviatile beds, such as sandstone, conglomerate, mudstone, and occasionally limestone. Locally the streams were impounded in lakes, depositing more extensive layers of limestone, siltstone, carbonaceous shale, and coal beds. After this period the region was generally submerged during a dominantly lacustrine early and middle Eocene epoch known as Green River time. Vast structural depressions—in Utah the Uinta basin, in Colorado the Piceance Creek basin, and in Wyoming the Green River basin—received many thousand feet of sediments, over a period lasting hundreds of thousands, perhaps millions, of years, an extraordinary duration for a feature so ephemeral as a lake. From the marine aspect of the fish fauna whose remains are found in these lake deposits, Bradley (1936) infers that for a long time a perennial river ran into the sea from Lake Uinta south of the recently formed Uinta Mountains. During that time, the lake waters remained relatively dilute and free from excessive saline accumulations. During its youth and maturity, tremendous quantities of fine-grained weathered rock detritus found their way into a steadily sinking shallow basin, whose waters supported a rich and varied flora and fauna. The Green River sediments in Utah and Colorado are characteristically varved, each varve consisting of an organic rich lamina and a lamina poorer in organic matter. Counts on these varves establish the long duration of the Green River sedimentation (Bradley, 1929*b*).

Jones (1957) discusses the gentle but progressive subsidence of the lake basin during these hundreds of thousands of years: ". . . the rate of subsidence of the Uinta basin kept pace with the sedimentation and at times exceeded it; otherwise it would have been impossible to accumulate more than 7000 feet of lacustrine sediments. . . ." Bradley (oral communication) now believes that much of this large lake had a depth of several hundred feet, and, in the parts where the oil shale accumulated, it may have been over 1000 feet deep.

Hunt, Stewart, and Dickey (1954) clarify the use of the terms Wasatch, Green River, and Uinta. They point out that since the early Tertiary, "the sediments of the Uinta basin were characteristically fluviatile and deltaic around its edges, . . . grading sharply over into siliceous dolomites, often highly bituminous, apparently deposited . . . from the salty water in the center of the lake." They point out that large fluctuations occurred ". . . in the area covered by the lake so that the lacustrine and fluviatile deposits interfinger in a very complex manner. . . ." From oldest to youngest, are the Wasatch, the Green River, and the Uinta formations. These names have been used by some largely as facies terms to differentiate sediments which were believed to be of different ages but actually were deposited simultaneously. The Wasatch is predominantly fluviatile and continental, consisting of red beds and heavy sands. Much of what has been called Wasatch in the cliffs along the south side of the basin was deposited at the same time as what has been called Green River in the center of the basin. The Green River includes those beds of lacustrine lithologic type of which the most distinctive are the oil shales. The Uinta formation consists of red and green shales with channel sands. It is particularly well developed in the northeastern part of the basin and grades into lacustrine beds which have been called Green River toward the center of the basin. The three terms, therefore, denote properly and primarily time-stratigraphic units; but they can also be, and have been, used as facies terms covering a single such unit, e.g. "Green River lithology," applicable to characteristic rock types of either Wasatch, Green River, or Uinta age, as in this paper.

Until late maturity, the sedimentary history of the lake could not be considered especially remarkable. The waters entering the Green River basins were of normal river type. Materials held in suspension were deposited near the edges of the lake. Potassium may have become fixed in the clay minerals. Thus, by a process of elimination, dilute solutions containing essentially calcium, magnesium, and sodium bicarbonates reached the more central part of the basin; chlorides, sulfates, silica, iron, and alumina were of minor importance.

The formation of calcite or dolomite with evaporation left the lake waters enriched in sodium. Anaerobic reduction, bacterial or otherwise, of sulfate and iron caused pyrite to form. Hunt, Stewart, and Dickey (1954) describe the chemical stratification of the later stages of the lake, when saline layers charged with toxic hydrogen sulfide formed on the bottom, and, above, relatively clear and fresh layers supported a flora and fauna, whose remains became preserved in the underlying muds.

With increasing desiccation, as described so vividly by Bradley (1936), the lake level sank below that of its outlet to the sea. Wide mud flats were intermittently exposed, with crystallization of saline compounds on the surface, and then flooded and buried in accretions of saline muds. The dissolved salts became concentrated into smaller and smaller basins, from which sodium, sodium-calcium, barium, and complex carbonates were deposited along with calcite, dolomite, and pyrite. The lake bottom muds, saturated with alkaline brines, underwent chemical attack whereby were formed new or unusual sodium boron silicates such as reedmergnerite, leucosphenite, garrelsite, and searlesite, and sodium-bearing silicates such as acmite, riebeckite, loughlinite, labuntsovite, and especially analcite.

The desiccation of the lake was not a catastrophic occurrence, but rather an alternation of ever-shortening wet periods and lengthening dry ones. Thus a period of saline deposition would be succeeded by a period in which small amounts of sodium carbonates or none at all were deposited, so that the saline beds are intercalated between varying thicknesses of almost or wholly nonsaline beds.

Whatever reactions occurred in the concentrated brines of the lake, and in the bottom muds beneath the brine, there were periods of mineral formation in the sediments long after the final drying of the lake. Vertical or steeply dipping fissures in the Green River formation vary from many feet across and miles in length (containing the extraordinary deposits of the hydrocarbon gilsonite) to microscopic cracks on which various minerals (especially calcite and quartz, but also barite, garrelsite, and dawsonite) have deposited, usually in beautifully developed crystals. Calcite and quartz are often associated with solid hydrocarbons. Other silicates, disseminated in the dolomitic mudstones, leucosphenite and reedmergnerite notably, characteristically exhibit zoned inclusions of organic matter and dolomite, arranged in crystallographic directions.

It is noteworthy that for the entire period of its existence the basin itself shows no igneous activity. There are, however, many beds, inches or feet in thickness, which formed from settling of volcanic ash. As a rule these volcanic sediments are fine grained, indicative of distant origin. Although the extent and number of these ash beds is greater than was formerly recognized (Dane, 1955), they are quantitatively a distinctly minor feature of Green River stratigraphy.

Metamorphism cannot readily be invoked to explain features of the Green River mineralogy. Hunt, Stewart, and Dickey (1954), in discussing the nature of the varied hydrocarbons of the Uinta basin, discount the effect of any metamorphism, catalytic cracking, or depth of burial, and affirm that the diversity of the hydrocarbons can be correlated with lithologic changes and therefore depositional environment.

It is not a simple matter to estimate the mineral composition of the Green River rocks as a whole, or even regionally. By far the greater part of the formation consists of dolomitic marlstone or limestone or fine-grained clastic material. Although the term "shale" has been applied to these beds, it is a misnomer. The rocks are by no means clastic shales, but essentially calcareous chemical precipitates. Many of the oil shales may best be classified as varved, kerogeneous dolomites (Picard, 1957; Abbott, 1957).

Our knowledge of Green River mineralogy is very scanty; almost all of it is based on intensive study of a few minute areas (e.g., the trona mine in Wyoming, several oil wells in Utah) and the work of Bradley followed by that of Dane, Picard, Hunt, Stewart, and Dickey, and a few others (see references). Authigenic minerals of primary abundance are dolomite, calcite, quartz, trona, shortite, pyrite, and an undetermined proportion of clay minerals.[2] These, with varying admixture of altered or unaltered detrital minerals—clays, quartz, feldspars, and ferromagnesian silicates such as hornblende and biotite—make up the bulk of the Green River formation. These lacustrine beds are remarkable in their widespread content of two minerals rare or unknown in other lake deposits, namely analcite and shortite. Searlesite and barytocalcite may be equally widespread, though much less abundantly. Locally important are trona and nahcolite. Found rarely and sparsely, but over wide areas (Utah and Wyoming), are leucosphenite, burbankite, acmite, riebeckite-crocidolite, fluorapatite, and barite. Found only in single localities as yet, and sparsely, are wurtzite, pyrrhotite, siderite, magnesite, witherite, eitelite, dawsonite, pirssonite, gaylussite, bradleyite, northupite, albite, loughlinite, labuntsovite, sepiolite, reedmergnerite, and garrelsite. As further study continues, many of these minerals will doubtless be discovered in wider range and perhaps in significantly greater abundance. Table 1 lists all authigenic minerals found to date in the Green River formation.[3]

[2] Recent studies by Regis and Sand (1957) indicate that, at the trona mine in Wyoming, montmorillonite and illite are the fourth and fifth most abundant constituents in the sediments—the order being quartz, calcite, dolomite, montmorillonite, and illite. The same does not appear to be true in Utah, however. Hunt, Stewart, and Dickey (1954) state that of a large number of samples from the Uinta basin, "more than three fourths of the samples do not carry any illite, montmorillonite, or kaolinite."

[3] Table 1 also has some interesting omissions. In view of the formation of leucosphenite and labuntsovite, whose titanium presumably derives from detrital ilmenite, sphene, or rutile, it is surprising that the common authigenic anatase and brookite have not been found in the Green River. Again with a relative abundance of barium mineralization—seven species—strontium has been found only in the rare and extremely scanty burbankite. No authigenic tourmaline has been found, though much rarer boron minerals are widespread.

TABLE 1. Authigenic Minerals in the Green River Formation

Species capitalized are unique to the Green River, and those in italics are known elsewhere only in igneous or metamorphic rocks.

Carbonates

Locality	Mineral
(UC)	Nahcolite $NaHCO_3$ (*c*)
(W)	Trona $Na_2CO_3 \cdot NaHCO_3 \cdot 2H_2O$ (*g*)
(UW)	SHORTITE $Na_2Ca_2(CO_3)_3$ (*g*)
(U)	EITELITE $Na_2Mg(CO_3)_2$ (*e*)
(C)	Dawsonite $Na_3Al(CO_3)_3 \cdot 2Al(OH)_3$ (*b*)
(UW)	Burbankite $Na_2(Ca,Sr,Ba,Ce)_4(CO_3)_5$ (*n*)
(W)	Thermonatrite $Na_2CO_3 \cdot H_2O$ (*f*)
(W)	Pirssonite $Na_2Ca(CO_3)_2 \cdot 2H_2O$ (*d*)
(W)	Gaylussite $Na_2Ca(CO_3)_2 \cdot 5H_2O$ (*d*)
(ub.)	Calcite $CaCO_3$
(ub.)	Dolomite $CaMg(CO_3)_2$
(UW)	Siderite $FeCO_3$ (*b*)
(U)	Magnesite $MgCO_3$ (*b*)(*h*)
(W)	Witherite $BaCO_3$ (*b*)
(?)	"Alstonite-bromlite" $CaBa(CO_3)_2$ (*d*)
(UW)	Barytocalcite $CaBa(CO_3)_2$ (*b*)
(W)	(New unnamed) $BaMg(CO_3)_2$ (*b*)

Carbonate-phosphates

Locality	Mineral
(W)	BRADLEYITE $Na_3PO_4 \cdot MgCO_3$ (*d*)

Carbonate-chlorides

Locality	Mineral
(W)	Northupite $Na_2CO_3 \cdot MgCO_3 \cdot NaCl$ (*d*)

Silicates

Locality	Mineral
(ub.)	Analcite $NaAlSi_2O_6 \cdot H_2O$ (*h*)
(C)	Albite $NaAlSi_3O_8$ (*q*)
(W)	*Labuntsovite* $(K,Ba,Na,Ca,Mn)(Ti,Nb)(Si,Al)_2(O,OH)_7H_2O$ (*o*)
(UW)	Searlesite $NaBSi_2O_6 \cdot H_2O$ (*p*)
(U)	REEDMERGNERITE $NaBSi_3O_8$ (*e*)
(U)	GARRELSITE $(Ba,Ca,Mg)B_3SiO_6(OH)_3$ (*a*)
(U)	*Acmite* $NaFe^{+++}Si_2O_6$ (*b*)
(U)	*Riebeckite-magnesioriebeckite* $Na_2(Mg,Fe^{++})_3(Fe^{+++},Al)_2Si_8O_{22}(OH)_2$ (*b*)
(U)	Sepiolite $Mg_2Si_3O_6(OH)_4$ (*h*)
(W)	LOUGHLINITE $(Na_2,Mg)_2Si_3O_6(OH)_4$ (*i*)
(U)	*Elpidite* $Na_2ZrSi_6O_{15} \cdot 3H_2O$ (*b*)
(UW)	*Leucosphenite* $CaBaNa_3BTi_3Si_9O_{29}$ (*k*)
(ub.)	Clay minerals (*m*)

Sulfides

Locality	Mineral
(ub.)	Pyrite FeS_2
(U)	Marcasite FeS_2 (*b*)
(UW)	Pyrrhotite $Fe_{1-x}S$
(UW)	Wurtzite ZnS (*a*)

Oxides

Locality	Mineral
(ub.)	Quartz SiO_2

Phosphates

Locality	Mineral
(UW)	Fluorapatite $Ca_{10}(PO_4)_6F_2$ (*b*)
(ub.)	Collophane $Ca_{10}(PO_4)_6CO_3 \cdot H_2O$ (*h*)

Fluoride

Locality	Mineral
(U)	(New unnamed) Sodium magnesium fluoride (*b*)

Sulfates

Locality	Mineral
(?)	Anhydrite $CaSO_4$ (*b*)
(?)	Bassanite $CaSO_4 \cdot \frac{1}{2}H_2O$ (*b*)
(?)	Gypsum $CaSO_4 \cdot 2H_2O$ (*b*)
(UC)	Barite $BaSO_4$

Hydrocarbons

(ub.) Gilsonite, uintahite, utahite, tabbyite, ozokerite, ingramite, albertite, coal. (*l*)

(U) indicates that mineral has been found in Utah. (W) stands for Wyoming, (C) for Colorado, and (ub.) for ubiquitous.

"(?)" preceding mineral name indicates uncertainty as to its existence in the Green River. "Alstonite-bromlite" may be barytocalcite. Anhydrite, bassanite, and gypsum may have formed in the wet drill cuttings during storage.

Reference to literature

(*a*) Milton, Axelrod, and Grimaldi, 1955.
(*b*) Milton, unpublished data, 1958.
(*c*) Ertl, 1947.
(*d*) Fahey, 1941.
(*e*) Milton, Axelrod, and Grimaldi, 1954.
(*f*) Fahey et al., unpublished data, 1958.
(*g*) Fahey, 1939.
(*h*) Bradley, 1929*a* and *b*, 1931.
(*i*) Fahey, 1948.
(*k*) Milton, Axelrod, and Sherwood, 1954.
(*l*) Crawford, 1957; Davis, 1957; Henderson, 1957; Merrow, 1957; Hunt, Stewart, and Dickey, 1954.
(*m*) Regis and Sand, 1957.
(*n*) Pecora and Kerr, 1953.
(*o*) Milton, Mrose, Fahey, and Chao, 1958.
(*p*) Fahey, 1950.
(*q*) Moore, 1950.

Minerals and Mineral Assemblages of the Green River Formation

Carbonates

The most common and abundant carbonates in the Green River formation are dolomite, calcite, nahcolite, trona, and shortite. Of more local importance but perhaps not less significant are eitelite, dawsonite, burbankite, thermonatrite, pirssonite, gaylussite, magnesite, siderite, witherite, and barytocalcite. The sodic carbonates are most characteristic of the Green River and will be treated in greater detail.

Trona and nahcolite. The occurrences and associations of nahcolite, trona, and shortite represent an important key to the understanding of the saline beds. In Utah nahcolite is widespread, occurring predominantly in nodules inches to several feet in diameter (Bradley, 1931, plate 5*b*) in a dolomitic matrix, whereas trona is virtually absent. In Wyoming trona forms a massive continuous bed some 10 or more feet thick, free of nahcolite. Shortite is widespread in Utah and also abundant over vast areas in Wyoming. An analysis of existing data on sodium carbonate systems helps to clarify these relationships.

Some of the important phases in the system $NaHCO_3$–Na_2CO_3–$CaCO_3$–H_2O are shown in figure 2. All known minerals lie on two sides of the tetrahedron (left and front) with nahcolite, trona, soda (=natron), shortite, and calcite being most abundant in the Green River. Freeth (1923) [4] determined the composition of the solutions in equilibrium with solids in the system $NaHCO_3$–Na_2CO_3–H_2O between 0° C and 60° C at 1 atm total pressure. Column A in table 2 gives his values for the univariant and invariant equilibria. Since all equilibria can be considered at a constant total pressure (1 atm), not more than three solids can coexist with a saturated solution. The locations of these equilibria are a function of temperature and the carbonate/bicarbonate ratio in the solution, or of temperature and the hydrogen-ion activity (a_{H^+}) of the solution, or of temperature and the activity of CO_2 in solution (a_{CO_2}), or of temperature and the partial pressure of $CO_2(P_{CO_2})$ of the gas phase equilibrated with the solution. These dependencies are evident from the following equations.

$$(1) \qquad \underset{\text{nahcolite}}{2NaHCO_3} + 9H_2O \rightleftharpoons \underset{\text{soda}}{Na_2CO_3 \cdot 10H_2O} + CO_2$$

$$(2) \qquad \underset{\text{nahcolite}}{3NaHCO_3} + H_2O \rightleftharpoons \underset{\text{trona}}{Na_2CO_3 \cdot NaHCO_3 \cdot 2H_2O} + CO_2$$

[4] See also *International Critical Tables* (1928), *4*, 371 and 393.

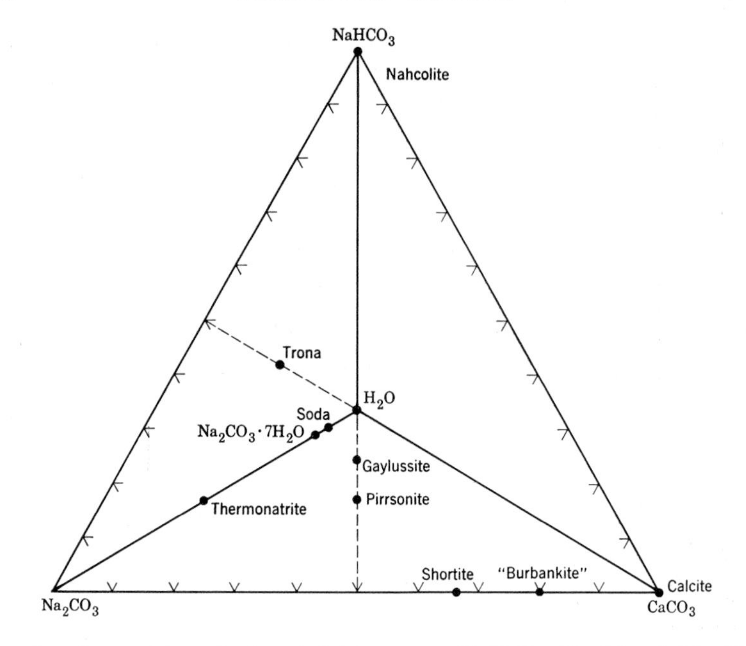

Fig. 2. Composition of minerals in the system $NaHCO_3$–Na_2CO_3–$CaCO_3$–H_2O.

$$(3)\quad \underset{\text{trona}}{2[Na_2CO_3\cdot NaHCO_3\cdot 2H_2O]} + 25H_2O \rightleftharpoons \underset{\text{soda}}{3[Na_2CO_3\cdot 10H_2O]} + CO_2$$

Freeth's determinations are given in terms of the total carbonate and bicarbonate contents of 100 grams of the saturated solution. His values can be recalculated to the hydrogen-ion activity of the solution,[5] using the equilibrium constants K_1 determined by Harned and Scholes (1941), and extrapolated to higher salt concentrations.

$$(4)\qquad K_1 = \frac{m_{\mathrm{H}}\cdot m_{\mathrm{CO_3}}\cdot \gamma_{\mathrm{H}}\cdot \gamma_{\mathrm{CO_3}}}{m_{\mathrm{HCO_3}}\cdot \gamma_{\mathrm{HCO_3}}}$$

The densities of concentrated carbonate solutions given by Roberts and Mangold (1939) were used. Activity coefficients for both (HCO_3^-) and

[5] In solutions of this concentration (1.5 to 5 normal in Na^+) the calculated hydrogen-ion activities cannot be safely expressed in terms of pH as determined by standard procedures (see Bates, 1954). Bedekar (1955) has measured pH of concentrated sodium carbonate–sodium bicarbonate solutions at 25° C. His values are considerably lower than pH values corresponding to the calculated hydrogen-ion activities.

TABLE 2. Carbonate Content, Bicarbonate Content, Hydrogen-Ion Activities, Carbon Dioxide Content, and Partial Pressure of Carbon Dioxide of Saturated Solutions in the System Na_2CO_3–$NaHCO_3$–H_2O

Temperature, °C	Phases	A: g Na_2CO_3 per 100 g Solution	A: g $NaHCO_3$ per 100 g Solution	B a_{H^+} moles/l	C m_{CO_2}, moles/l	D P_{CO_2}, atm
0	Nahcolite + soda + solution	5.6	4.6	$10^{-10.78}$	$10^{-4.89}$	$10^{-3.66}$
15	Nahcolite + soda + solution	13.3	4.3	$10^{-11.12}$	$10^{-5.35}$	$10^{-3.81}$
20	Nahcolite + soda + solution	17.1	4.0	$10^{-11.27}$	$10^{-5.65}$	$10^{-4.05}$
25	Nahcolite + trona + solution	18.0	4.0	$10^{-11.25}$	$10^{-5.54}$	$10^{-3.80}$
25	Trona + soda + solution	22.6	1.5	$10^{-11.81}$	$10^{-6.52}$	$10^{-4.77}$
30	Nahcolite + trona + solution	17.6	4.3	$10^{-11.17}$	$10^{-5.44}$	$10^{-3.73}$
30	Trona + soda + solution	27.1	1.3	$10^{-11.98}$	$10^{-6.70}$	$10^{-4.94}$
35	Nahcolite + trona + solution	17.3	4.7	$10^{-11.08}$	$10^{-5.34}$	$10^{-3.54}$
35	Trona + $Na_2CO_3 \cdot 7H_2O$ + solution	32.5	0.6	$10^{-12.46}$	$10^{-7.50}$	$10^{-5.62}$
45	Nahcolite + trona + solution	16.9	5.9	$10^{-10.88}$	$10^{-5.06}$	$10^{-3.17}$
45	Trona + thermonatrite + solution	31.7	0.9	$10^{-12.19}$	$10^{-7.10}$	$10^{-4.94}$
60	Nahcolite + trona + solution	16.9	7.4	$10^{-10.80}$	$10^{-4.87}$	$10^{-2.87}$
60	Trona + thermonatrite + solution	30.7	1.3	$10^{-11.93}$	$10^{-6.67}$	$10^{-4.52}$

(CO_3^{--}) should be included in the calculations. Taylor (1955) has reported activity coefficients for (CO_3^{--}) in very concentrated solutions, but there are no reliable data for the activity coefficients of (HCO_3^-) in the same environment. Therefore concentrations were used throughout, and values reported in columns B, C, and D, table 2, must be regarded as approximations. The hydrogen-ion activity depends on the molar content of CO_2 (m_{CO_2}). m_{CO_2} can be calculated using the equilibrium constant K_2 given by Harned and Bonner (1945)

$$(5) \qquad K_2 = \frac{m_H \cdot m_{HCO_3} \cdot \gamma_H \cdot \gamma_{HCO_3}}{m_{CO_2} \cdot \gamma_{CO_2} \cdot a_{H_2O}}$$

and extrapolated analytically to higher ionic strengths (see equations 19 to 22 of Harned and Bonner; see also Harned and Owen, 1958). The values thus obtained are given in column C, table 2. Harned and Davis (1943) have determined Henry's law constants of carbon dioxide in salt solutions of various strengths.

$$(6) \qquad S = m_{CO_2}/P_{CO_2}$$

From this relationship the partial pressure of CO_2 (P_{CO_2}) in the saturated solutions can be calculated (see column D, table 2). Figure 3 is a P_{CO_2}–T diagram at 1 atm total pressure of the system Na_2CO_3–$NaHCO_3$–H_2O based on the calculated values of column D, table 2. It shows three (isobaric) invariant points, with the following equilibrium assemblages:

(1) Soda + nahcolite + trona + solution
(2) Soda + $Na_2CO_3 \cdot 7H_2O$ + trona + solution
(3) $Na_2CO_3 \cdot 7H_2O$ + thermonatrite + trona + solution

and seven univariant equilibria:

(1) Soda + nahcolite + solution
(2) Nahcolite + trona + solution
(3) Soda + trona + solution
(4) Soda + $Na_2CO_3 \cdot 7H_2O$ + solution
(5) $Na_2CO_3 \cdot 7H_2O$ + trona + solution
(6) $Na_2CO_3 \cdot 7H_2O$ + thermonatrite + solution
(7) Thermonatrite + trona + solution

The most recent determinations of the three invariant temperatures are as follows:

(1) Soda + nahcolite + trona + solution: 19.7° C (Freeth, 1923)
(2) Soda + $Na_2CO_3 \cdot 7H_2O$ + trona + solution: 32° C (Kobe and Sheehy, 1948)
(3) $Na_2CO_3 \cdot 7H_2O$ + thermonatrite + trona + solution: 35.37° C (Kobe and Sheehy, 1948)

Nahcolite is stable over the whole temperature range considered at high CO_2 pressures. Soda occupies the low temperature–low P_{CO_2} region, and will precipitate preferentially in cooler environments [6] since

[6] In some lakes soda is known to precipitate only during the colder seasons of the year.

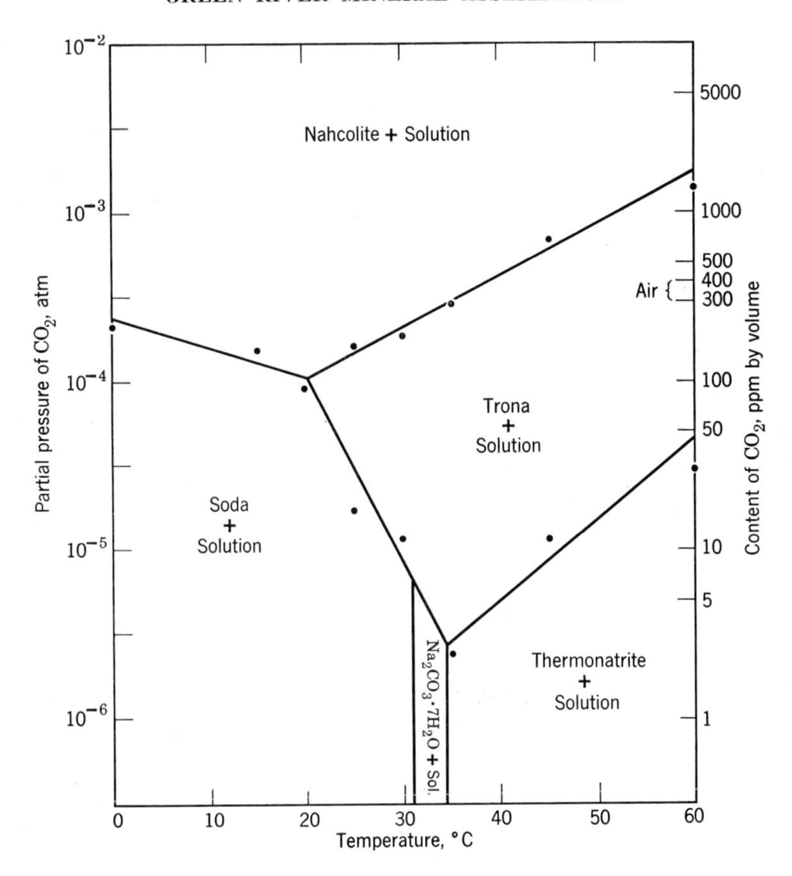

Fig. 3. P_{CO_2}–T diagram of the system $NaHCO_3$–Na_2CO_3–H_2O. The CO_2 content of present-day air has been indicated on the right. Locations of phase boundaries were calculated from the data of Freeth (1923). After *Carnegie Institution of Washington Year Book 57*.

the soda–trona boundary drops sharply from the invariant temperature to very low CO_2 pressures. The fact that the field of stability of $Na_2CO_3 \cdot 7H_2O$ is very restricted explains why this phase has never been found in nature. Thermonatrite is characteristic either of very low CO_2 pressures or (geologically more significant) higher temperatures (deeper burial). Trona occupies a field intermediate between nahcolite and thermonatrite. It cannot form as a stable phase below 20° C.

Crucial to interpretation of the mineral assemblages of the saline beds of the Green River formation is the location of the nahcolite–trona boundary with respect to the CO_2 pressure of the atmosphere. Keeling (1958) measured the CO_2 content of the atmosphere at the earth's surface for different environments; he found values ranging from 300 to 400 ppm, with the air over desert and beach close to 300 ppm both night and day. The location of the nahcolite–trona boundary in figure 3 indicates that if the CO_2 pressure in the air during the formation of the Green River beds was about the same as it is today, and if the saturated solution was equilibrated with the air, nahcolite and trona would precipitate simultaneously at about 35° C. Below this temperature nahcolite would form, and above, trona.[7]

A geologically significant consequence of figure 3 is the fact that the formation of trona in Wyoming need not be explained by special processes impoverishing the lake water in CO_2. Trona may have precipitated simply by evaporation of the brines in warm and shallow pools in equilibrium with air. In Utah nahcolite formed rather than trona because the brines were cooler or because the CO_2 pressure was higher or both.

Further insight can be gained from considering the concentrations necessary to precipitate either trona or nahcolite. In figure 4 Freeth's data are reproduced in terms of temperature and the total concentration of sodium ions in the saturated solutions (solid lines). At the temperature at which nahcolite and trona are in equilibrium at the P_{CO_2} of average air (≈35° C), trona will precipitate from solutions 4.2 normal in Na^+. At lower CO_2 pressures and the same temperature (within the field of stability of trona) correspondingly higher concentrations are necessary. Thermonatrite does not appear until a normality of 6.8 is reached. Figure 4 also contains curves for the limiting systems $NaHCO_3$–H_2O and Na_2CO_3–H_2O, taken from the *International Critical Tables* (1927) (dashed curves). At 35° C nahcolite itself crystallizes from much more dilute solutions if the CO_2 pressures are high. With decreasing P_{CO_2} the evaporation necessary for precipitation increases, until again at 300 to 400 ppm CO_2 a normality of 4.2 is required.

With these deductions in mind we can arrive at a reasonable explanation of the differences between the Wyoming and Utah basins. Mineral associations as well as mode of occurrences can best be explained by assuming that the Wyoming basin in which the trona bed formed was very shallow, while the Utah basin, in which nahcolite crystallized, never became so shallow. The Wyoming brines would have been warm, equi-

[7] Preliminary experiments using average air indicate that this calculated temperature is correct within a few degrees. A direct determination of the phase boundaries in figure 3 is planned.

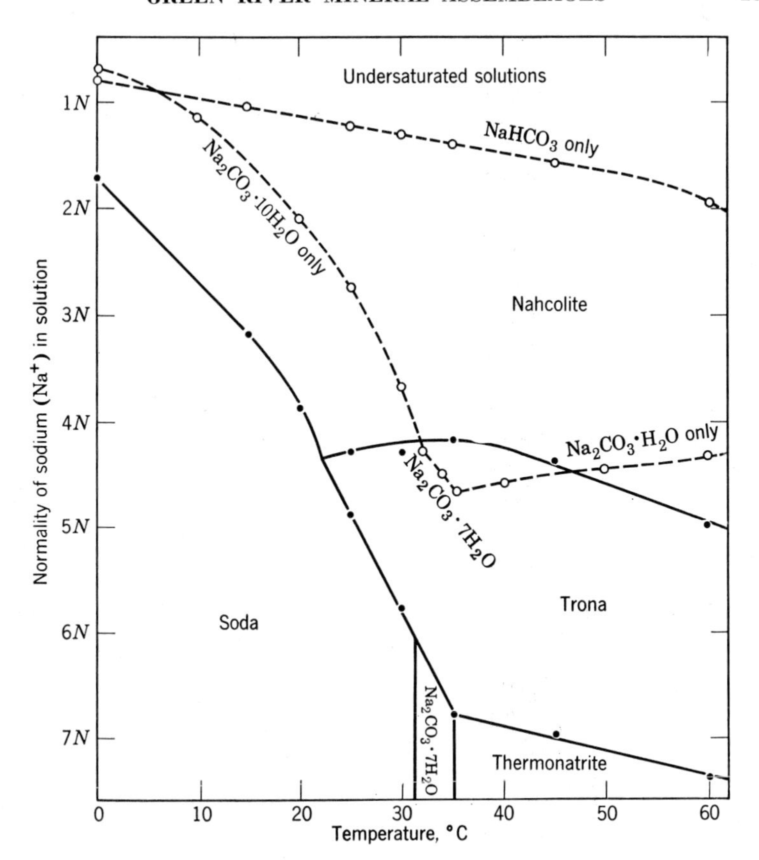

Fig. 4. Concentration of sodium ion in solution as a function of temperature. Solid lines are for the system $NaHCO_3$–Na_2CO_3–H_2O as determined by Freeth (1923). Broken lines are for the systems $NaHCO_3$–H_2O and Na_2CO_3–H_2O, respectively (*International Critical Tables*). After *Carnegie Institution of Washington Year Book 57*.

librated with air, and at least 4.2 normal in sodium. They were saturated simultaneously over a great lateral extent, since trona forms a continuous bed, covering thousands of square miles.[8] Brines in the Utah basin probably were flooded by fresh waters before trona could form. They would have been preserved in the cooler bottom layers (densities

[8] The actual crystallization of trona from the brines may have taken place under the cover of an epilimnion of fresher water. In modern brine lakes of this kind temperatures up to 56° C have been measured (Bradley, oral communication).

of such brines are as high as 1.2) of the deep permanent stagnant hypolimnion of Lake Uinta. These bottom layers also must have had a higher P_{CO_2}, partly because of greater depth and partly because biogenic CO_2 was not exchanged rapidly with the air. Continuous precipitation of dolomite muds may have isolated the brines into pockets, from which, on dehydration, nahcolite crystallized. This would well explain why nahcolite does not form thick persistent beds, but rather concretions and pockets (for a good illustration see Bradley, 1931, plate 5*b*).

The presence of nahcolite in Utah and of trona in Wyoming could be related simply to temperature differences; but this explanation does not fit all observations equally well. It must also be remembered that crystallization took place either wholly within the trona field or wholly within the nahcolite field.

Considerations of the kind presented here may eventually, in conjunction with independent temperature determinations, lead to estimations of the CO_2 contents of ancient atmospheres. Indications are that Eocene air differed little from present-day air in CO_2 content.

Shortite and eitelite. Shortite is very abundant in both Utah and Wyoming, whereas eitelite has been found only in one Utah locality. Although no data on the stability of these two minerals are available, certain possible mineral assemblages and sets of conditions can be predicted. Figure 5, a plot of the system Na_2CO_3–$CaCO_3$–$MgCO_3$–H_2O, shows the compositions of the most important minerals, including shortite and eitelite.

Shortite is related to nahcolite and calcite by

$$(7) \quad \underset{\text{nahcolite}}{2NaHCO_3} + \underset{\text{calcite}}{2CaCO_3} \rightleftharpoons \underset{\text{shortite}}{Na_2CO_3 \cdot 2CaCO_3} + CO_2 + H_2O$$

At a constant water pressure the P_{CO_2}–T curve for this reaction must for thermodynamic reasons lie to the left of that for reaction 2, since at a given CO_2 pressure nahcolite itself is stable to a higher temperature than nahcolite + calcite. The amount of displacement and the slope of the curve, of course, are not known since shortite has not been synthesized, but a suggested location has been drawn in figure 6. The curve terminates at the nahcolite–soda boundary. Shortite can coexist with soda for appropriate bulk compositions at all CO_2 pressures of the soda field, since the reaction

$$(8) \quad \underset{\text{soda}}{Na_2CO_3 \cdot 10H_2O} + \underset{\text{calcite}}{2CaCO_3} \rightleftharpoons \underset{\text{shortite}}{Na_2CO_3 \cdot 2CaCO_3} + 10H_2O$$

does not involve a release of CO_2 from the solids. Fields in figure 6 have been labeled for a sodium-rich environment. The three assemblages nahcolite + calcite, nahcolite + shortite, and trona + shortite are common in the Green River formation, with trona + shortite restricted, as far as known, to Wyoming. The necessary relationships between nahcolite + calcite and nahcolite + shortite assemblages in Utah are noteworthy. The coexistence of nahcolite with calcite under equilibrium conditions is possible only at higher CO_2 pressures and/or lower temperatures than those of a nahcolite–shortite assemblage. A possible lower temperature limit for the formation of shortite will be discussed on page 137.

The relationships between eitelite, nahcolite, and magnesite are analogous to those between shortite, nahcolite, and calcite.

$$\underset{\text{nahcolite}}{2NaHCO_3} + \underset{\text{magnesite}}{MgCO_3} \rightleftharpoons \underset{\text{eitelite}}{Na_2CO_3 \cdot MgCO_3} + CO_2 + H_2O \tag{9}$$

Nahcolite can also interact with dolomite to form shortite and eitelite simultaneously.

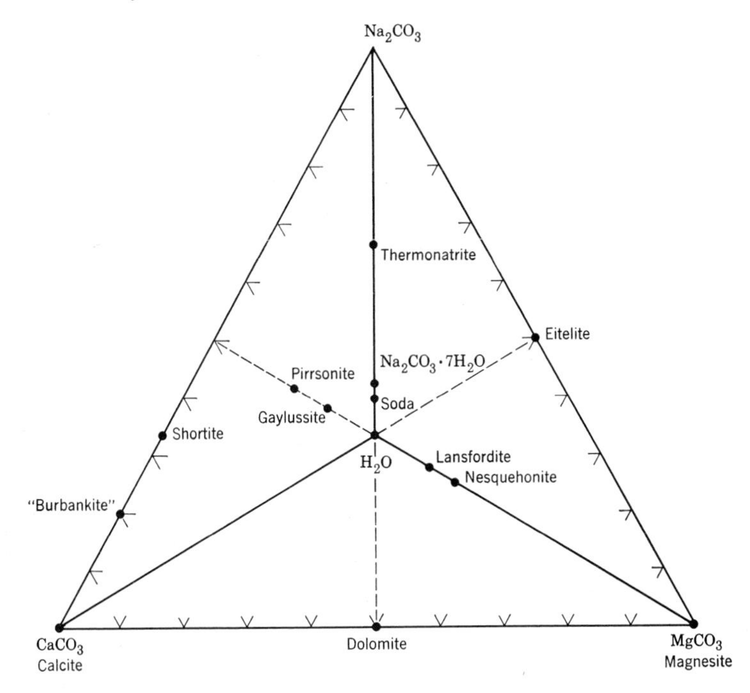

Fig. 5. Composition of minerals in the system Na_2CO_3–$CaCO_3$–$MgCO_3$–H_2O. The existence of the compound $Na_2CO_3 \cdot CaCO_3$ has been demonstrated by Niggli (1916) and by Eitel and Skaliks (1929). It has not yet been found in nature and is not considered in this paper.

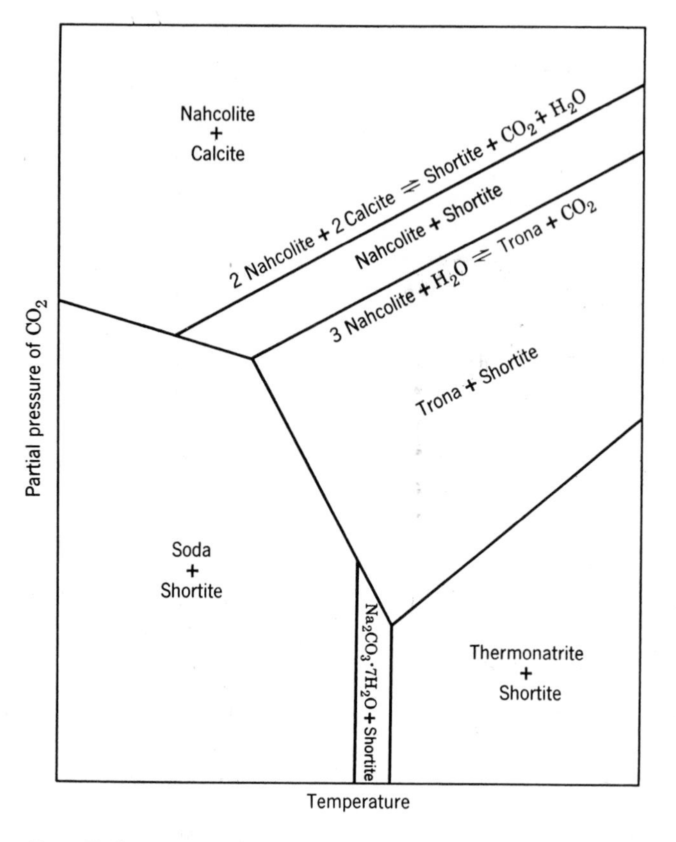

Fig. 6. P_{CO_2}–T diagram of a portion of the system $NaHCO_3$–Na_2CO_3–$CaCO_3$–H_2O. Fields labeled as seen from the Na_2CO_3 corner.

$$(10)\quad \underset{\text{nahcolite}}{6NaHCO_3} + \underset{\text{dolomite}}{2[CaCO_3 \cdot MgCO_3]} \rightleftharpoons \underset{\text{eitelite}}{2[Na_2CO_3 \cdot MgCO_3]} + \underset{\text{shortite}}{Na_2CO_3 \cdot 2CaCO_3} + 3CO_2 + 3H_2O$$

The P_{CO_2}–T curves for reactions 9 and 10 must both lie to the left of that for reaction 2, at a constant water pressure, but their relative sequence is not known. The most likely sequence has been drawn in figure 7. It could be tested either experimentally or by careful observation of the mineral assemblages. For instance, if this sequence is correct, the succession of assemblages with rising temperature of a rock or mud consisting of nahcolite + calcite + dolomite must be: nahcolite + calcite

+ dolomite → nahcolite + calcite + shortite + eitelite → nahcolite + shortite + eitelite → trona + shortite + eitelite.

Since dolomite is as common in the Green River formation as calcite is, eitelite could be expected to occur frequently together with shortite. Eitelite has been encountered in only one drill core. It may either have been frequently overlooked or be stable in a very much narrower range of conditions than shortite.

The conditions necessary for the precipitation of nahcolite and trona differ considerably from those for the more common carbonates calcite and dolomite, which make up the bulk of the Green River formation. Shortite and eitelite may have formed not by direct crystallization from saturated solutions but by the interaction of sodium-rich solutions perco-

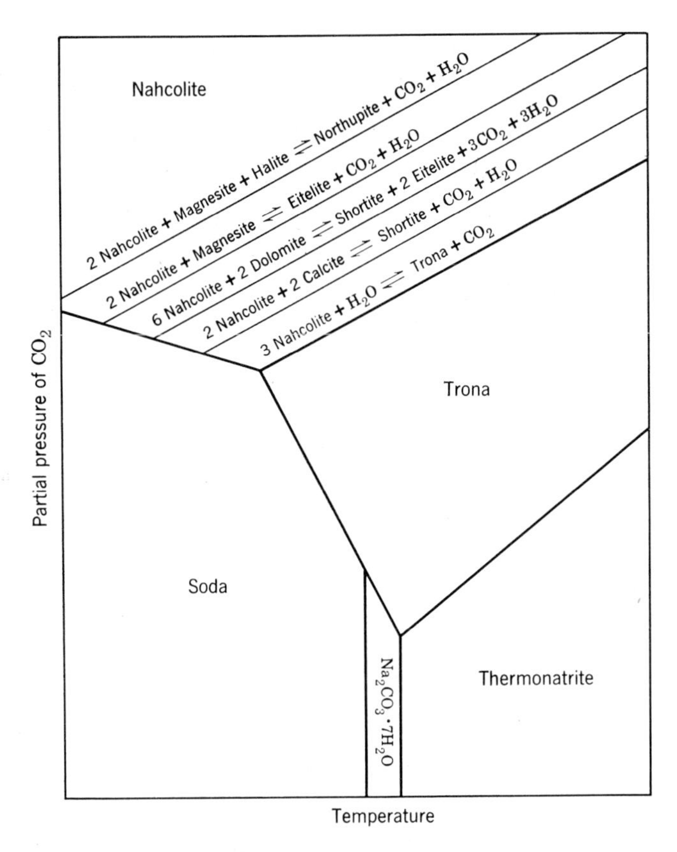

Fig. 7. Probable sequence of P_{CO_2}-T curves involving minerals of the saline beds.

lating through calcite-dolomite muds formed during a period of higher water levels. Shortite and eitelite may also form during any period of diagenesis at the interfaces between saline and calcite-dolomite beds, provided either that P_{CO_2} is low or that the temperature is raised appropriately.

Dawsonite, burbankite, thermonatrite, pirssonite, gaylussite. Sodic solutions are certainly responsible for the occurrence of dawsonite, which was found in vugs and in fissures of the oil shale in Colorado. The rarity of this mineral may be due to the special compositional requirements.

Burbankite is associated with nahcolite in Utah and with trona in Wyoming, occurring in pinkish fibrous spheroidal aggregates of microscopic size. It is not yet known whether its strontium and rare-earth contents are essential or whether the phase $Na_2CO_3 \cdot 4CaCO_3$ exists.

Thermonatrite has only been found in one instance (Wyoming). At room temperatures it is in equilibrium with solutions of low activities of CO_2. If authigenic, and not produced on processing the core studied, it would probably indicate local higher temperatures.

Pirssonite and gaylussite have been identified positively in the Green River formation of Wyoming by Fahey (oral communication). Data on the relationships between these minerals and shortite are scarce. Pirssonite and gaylussite form from nahcolite and calcite by

$$(11)\quad \underset{\text{nahcolite}}{2NaHCO_3} + \underset{\text{calcite}}{CaCO_3} + H_2O \rightleftharpoons \underset{\text{pirssonite}}{Na_2CO_3 \cdot CaCO_3 \cdot 2H_2O} + CO_2$$

$$(12)\quad \underset{\text{nahcolite}}{2NaHCO_3} + \underset{\text{calcite}}{CaCO_3} + 4H_2O \rightleftharpoons \underset{\text{gaylussite}}{Na_2CO_3 \cdot CaCO_3 \cdot 5H_2O} + CO_2$$

The P_{CO_2}–T curves at constant P_{H_2O} for both (11) and (12) coincide with that of reaction 7, since pirssonite and gaylussite are related to shortite by

$$(13)\quad \underset{\text{shortite}}{Na_2CO_3 \cdot 2CaCO_3} + 2H_2O \rightleftharpoons \underset{\text{pirssonite}}{Na_2CO_3 \cdot CaCO_3 \cdot 2H_2O} + \underset{\text{calcite}}{CaCO_3}$$

$$(14)\quad \underset{\text{shortite}}{Na_2CO_3 \cdot 2CaCO_3} + 5H_2O \rightleftharpoons \underset{\text{gaylussite}}{Na_2CO_3 \cdot CaCO_3 \cdot 5H_2O} + \underset{\text{calcite}}{CaCO_3}$$

The occurrence of shortite rather than pirssonite or gaylussite in most instances must be related to differences in the P_{H_2O}–T conditions. At constant water pressure the sequence of assemblages from low temperature to higher temperatures are gaylussite + calcite → pirssonite + calcite → shortite. At constant temperature from low P_{H_2O} to higher P_{H_2O} it would be shortite → pirssonite + calcite → gaylussite + calcite. Bury and Redd (1933) found pirssonite + gaylussite + calcite + solution to coexist at 40° C and 1 atm pressure. Shortite was not encountered. If the assemblage quoted was an equilibrium assemblage, shortite cannot form in stable equilibrium below 40° C at $P_{H_2O} = 1$ atm. Since attainment of equilibrium was not demonstrated in the experiments, this lower limit for the stable formation of shortite must be interpreted with caution.

Other carbonates. The most common carbonates in the Green River formation are calcite and dolomite, occurring in beds hundreds of feet thick.

Magnesite crystals several millimeters across have been noted in dolomite outcrops in Utah.

Siderite has been observed as a major constituent in a pyritic rock with marcasite and pyrrhotite, and gilsonite. It is also widespread in microscopic grains in the oil shale.

Witherite is present in a variety of habits with trona, associated with barytocalcite, dolomite, and a (new) barium magnesium carbonate in Wyoming.

Barytocalcite occurs as mentioned under witherite, and is also widespread in the saline sections of the Green River in Utah.

Chlorides and absence thereof

A characteristic feature of the evaporites of the Green River is the absence of chlorides such as halite and sylvite. Vast salt beds exist in other nonmarine basins, like that of the Pleistocene Lake Bonneville. Northupite, a chloride-carbonate, is the only chlorine-bearing mineral known in the Green River formation. Fahey (oral communication) observed it over a considerable range in a well drilled near the trona mine, but not within the trona mine itself. The relationships between nahcolite, magnesite, halite, and northupite are given by (15).

$$(15)\quad \underset{\text{nahcolite}}{2NaHCO_3} + \underset{\text{magnesite}}{MgCO_3} + \underset{\text{halite}}{NaCl} \rightleftharpoons \underset{\text{northupite}}{Na_2CO_3 \cdot MgCO_3 \cdot NaCl} + CO_2 + H_2O$$

The P_{CO_2}–T curve for this reaction is given schematically in figure 7. It must lie to the left of the nahcolite–magnesite–eitelite curve. Northupite could well coexist both with nahcolite and with trona if the bulk compositions were appropriate.

The assemblage northupite + nahcolite + halite + solution was found by Wilson and Ch'iu (1934) in the system sodium bicarbonate–sodium chloride–magnesium carbonate–water at 50° C and $P_{CO_2} = 0.25$ atm. This provides a tentative location for the P_{CO_2}–T curve of reaction 15.

The absence of halite permits an estimate of the maximum possible chlorine contents of the waters of the Green River basins, even during the most intense evaporation. Data by Freeth (1923) on the system Na_2O–CO_2–NaCl–H_2O indicate that this maximum content in the range of 20° to 60° C is 10 weight per cent Cl^-.

The absence of halite in the Green River formation and its abundance in Pleistocene and Recent lakes also of nonmarine origin may be explained in terms of the tectonic history of the respective lakes. Block faulting which produced the basins themselves exposed ancient Pennsylvanian salt beds (e.g., those known by drilling in the Paradox Basin of central Utah), whose leaching and subsequent concentration produced the salt lakes. "Collapse structures" indicating the former existence of Pennsylvanian salt beds plunge northward under the Book Cliffs now the southern border of the Uinta Basin (Ritzma, 1957). According to Herman and Sharps (1956), "the Paradox Salt Embayment probably did not cover an area larger than that preserving the evaporitic sequence today," and Stokes (1956) observes that "the present Paradox basin is surrounded by higher ground and has essentially the same configuration it had in late Paleozoic time." The Green River lake drainage system therefore never tapped these marine salt beds.

Analcite

The interactions between sodic solutions and common carbonate muds gave rise to unusual Na–Ca–Mg carbonates. The interactions of the same solutions with siliceous materials are responsible for a not less spectacular mineralogy. Silica as well as some other constituents required for the formation of these minerals must have been supplied by the river waters, by detrital quartz and feldspars, or by the abundant tuff beds that are so characteristic for the Green River formation. Some of these authigenic silicates are minerals unique to the Green River; some are common minerals, but elsewhere found only in entirely different environments; others are characteristic of authigenic associations the world over. Data on the stability of these minerals are very scarce, several not having been synthesized. Interpretations must be qualitative.

Probably the most abundant common silicate in the Green River formation is analcite. It is widespread and often forms beds several inches thick together with calcite, chalcedony, and detrital material. Analcitization of tuff beds is a recurrent and striking feature of the Green River lithology (Bradley, 1929*a*). Individual crystals are usually of microscopic size, and many exhibit the characteristic icositetrahedron.

The presence of analcite itself is not surprising, since it can easily have formed at the interface between saline and tuffaceous beds or more commonly during diagenesis by contact of sodic solutions with siliceous materials containing the necessary amounts of alumina. More remarkable is the almost constant association of analcite with free silica (chalcedony) and the virtual absence of albite in the Green River.[9] The relationships are given by the following reaction:

$$\underset{\text{analcite}}{NaAlSi_2O_6 \cdot H_2O} + SiO_2 \rightleftharpoons \underset{\text{albite}}{NaAlSi_3O_8} + H_2O \tag{16}$$

The location of the P_{H_2O}–T curve is not known in the low-temperature region. MacKenzie (1957, p. 512) quotes a value given by W. S. Fyfe, stating "that the univariant equilibrium curve for this reaction lies at about 300° C at $P_{H_2O} = 1000$ bars." Insufficient thermochemical data are available to calculate the temperature for $P_{H_2O} = 1$ atm, but it probably lies above 30° C. Analcite may have persisted metastably, although authigenic albite is commonly observed in dolomites and limestones of as young as Eocene age (Baskin, 1956). Furthermore, authigenic albite is known in the Green River formation. It formed in these few cases rather than analcite possibly because temperatures were slightly higher.

Interesting structural features studied by H. D. Curry (Shell Oil Co., Salt Lake City, Utah, oral communication, 1957) relate to the volume change involved in the hydration of the volcanic glasses and the crystallization of analcite. Confining beds are forced apart and cut by "sedimentary dikes" consisting largely of authigenic carbonate and analcite.

Boron silicates

Four boron-bearing silicates are known in the Green River formation: leucosphenite, reedmergnerite, garrelsite, and searlesite. Tourmaline is unknown.

Leucosphenite is known from a pegmatite at Narssarsuk in southwestern Greenland; in the Green River it occurs in Wyoming and Utah, of quite different aspect in each, and altogether different in aspect from the Greenland mineral. Reedmergnerite and garrelsite are known so far from the Utah Green River only, in restricted areas.

[9] Albite has been noted very sparingly as an authigenic mineral in oil shale in Colorado (Moore, 1950; Milton, 1957).

Searlesite occurs in Wyoming and Utah, and has been described from a few other localities, notably Searles Lake in California. It is the most widespread and abundant of the boron minerals in the Green River.

Leucosphenite from Utah (plate 3*a*), analyzed by A. M. Sherwood (U. S. Geological Survey), contains 17.38 per cent TiO_2 with 0.0*X* per cent Zr (spectrographic analysis by J. D. Fletcher, U. S. Geological Survey). The Greenland leucosphenite analyzed by Mauzelius (Flink, 1901) contains 13.20 per cent TiO_2, with 0.*X* per cent Zr (Fletcher). Sherwood also found 3.01 per cent B_2O_3 in Utah leucosphenite, and Fletcher reported *X* per cent in the Greenland mineral; B_2O_3 was not

Plate 1. Reedmergnerite $NaBSi_3O_8$ in brown dolomitic "shale." From Joseph Smith #1 well, Duchesne County, Utah. Thin section $\times 30$.

reported at all by Mauzelius. Evidently, then, leucosphenite is a boron, not a zirconium, mineral, as originally reported (Flink, 1901).

Reedmergnerite appears to be the only known feldspar in which boron takes the place of aluminum. Although anhydrous, it was not encountered at high temperatures in the ternary system Na_2O–B_2O_3–SiO_2 (Morey, 1951). Its habit as a rock-forming mineral is illustrated in plate 1.

Garrelsite has been found in Utah, significantly as a fissure-filling mineral in vertical cracks, as well as in isolated though well developed crystals disseminated in the dolomitic oil shale. These latter crystals usually, though not invariably, include large amounts of matrix material, indicating growth from a solution impregnating a porous rock.

Genetically most interesting are the relationships between reedmergnerite, the boron analogue of albite, and searlesite, the boron analogue of analcite:

$$\underset{\text{searlesite}}{NaBSi_2O_6 \cdot H_2O} + SiO_2 \rightleftharpoons \underset{\text{reedmergnerite}}{NaBSi_3O_8} + H_2O \tag{17}$$

The 1 atm point of the P_{H_2O}–T curve for this reaction probably lies at a lower temperature than that of reaction 16, since reedmergnerite is observed more frequently than albite. Nevertheless, both searlesite and analcite are much more abundant. The appearance of reedmergnerite rather than searlesite must be caused by higher temperatures (burial). Figure 8 shows the suggested sequence of P_{H_2O}–T curves. The slopes of the curves must be steep, since reactions proceed in the region of liquid water.

Apparently the boron content in the waters of the Green River basins was never high enough to precipitate borates. Locally formed boron-rich solutions immediately interacted with silica to form borosilicates.

Iron and magnesium silicates

Acmite, riebeckite, sepiolite, and loughlinite belong to this group. The presence of authigenic acmite and an intermediate member of the magnesioriebeckite–riebeckite series in the Green River formation has been a surprise (plate 2*a* and *b*). They unquestionably have formed at or near room temperature, and they are often intimately associated with "salines" such as shortite—for example, well crystallized acmite occurs enclosed in shortite. The oxygen pressures in the Green River formation are generally considered to have been low, as evidenced by the presence of hydrocarbons. Yet both acmite and the magnesioriebeckite–riebeckite contain essentially ferric iron only. Recent labora-

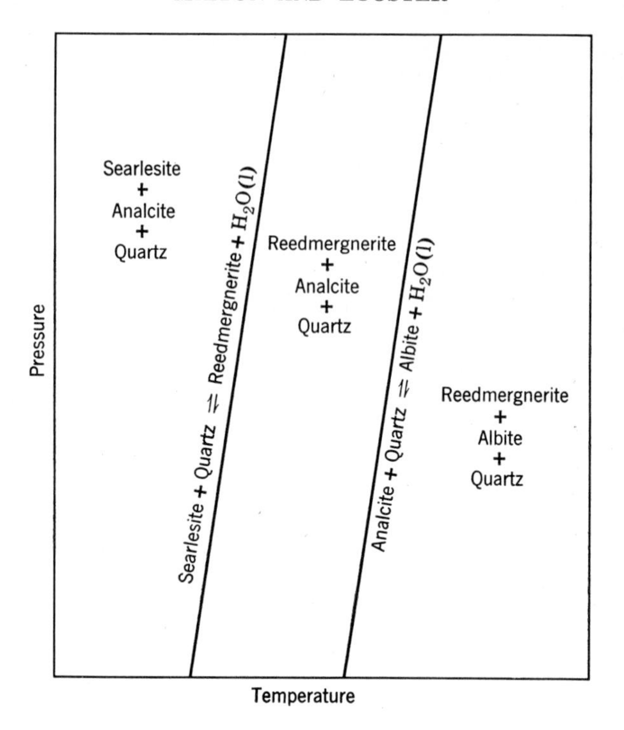

Fig. 8. Probable sequence of P_{H_2O}-T curves involving searlesite, reedmergnerite, analcite, albite, and quartz.

tory investigations of the magnesioriebeckites by Ernst (1957) have demonstrated conclusively that this mineral can exist at very low oxygen pressures.

The presence of sepiolite and loughlinite gives rise to some interesting speculations. The relations between sepiolite, magnesite, and quartz are given by

$$(18)\quad \underset{\text{magnesite}}{2MgCO_3} + 3SiO_2 + 2H_2O \rightleftharpoons \underset{\text{sepiolite}}{2[MgO \cdot 3SiO_2 \cdot 2H_2O]} + 2CO_2$$

Figure 9 shows that for constant P_{H_2O} sepiolite is the high-temperature–low-P_{CO_2} phase, and that for constant P_{CO_2} it is the low-temperature–high-P_{H_2O} phase. Magnesite + chalcedony is known from the Green River formation, and it is possible that the sepiolite encountered by Bradley (1929*a*, 1931) and others formed at a temperature above 25° C.

Loughlinite was found and described by Fahey (1948) from veins in

Plate 2*a*. Thin section, tuff bed, Avintaquin Canyon, Duchesne County, Utah. Shows (ordinary light ×225) detrital brown hornblende, with secondary blue regenerated amphibole (black areas at end of hornblende crystals).

Plate 2*b*. Single grains of detrital brown hornblende, with light blue secondary riebeckite (ordinary light ×350). Utah.

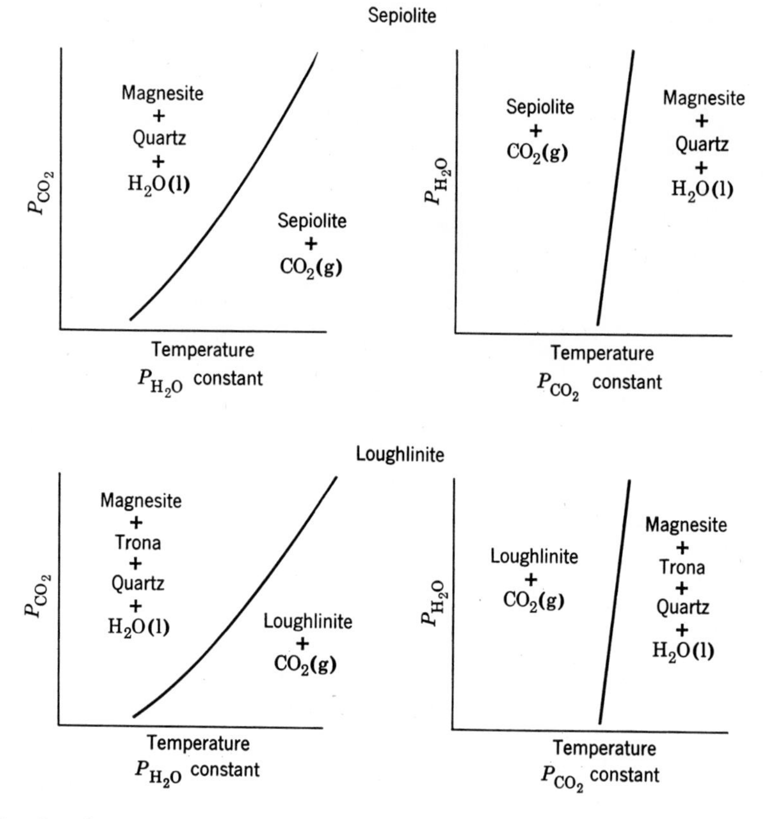

Fig. 9. General shapes of P_{CO_2}–T and P_{H_2O}–T curves for sepiolite and loughlinite.

the oil shale near the trona mine in Wyoming, occurring together with trona. It forms from trona, magnesite, and SiO_2 by the reaction

$$(19)\quad \underset{\text{magnesite}}{9MgCO_3} + 18SiO_2 + \underset{\text{trona}}{2[NaHCO_3 \cdot Na_2CO_3 \cdot 2H_2O]} + 7H_2O \rightleftharpoons \underset{\text{loughlinite idealized}}{3[Na_2O \cdot 3MgO \cdot 6SiO_2 \cdot 4H_2O]} + 13CO_2$$

Schematic P_{CO_2}–T and P_{H_2O}–T curves are also given in figure 9. Regis and Sand (1957) mention the formation of loughlinite at the expense of dolomite + quartz.

Titanium and zirconium silicates

Several rare zirconium and titanium silicates have been found in the Green River: elpidite, labuntsovite, and leucosphenite.

Elpidite occurs in Utah in microscopic prismatic crystals, associated with barytocalcite and a (new) sodium magnesium fluoride, in the drusy lining of cavities filled with nahcolite. It is known elsewhere from Narssarsuk, southern Greenland, where it is associated with leucosphenite; from the Bearpaw Mountains, Montana, where it has been found in a nepheline syenite pegmatite; and possibly from Rockall Island in the northeast Atlantic Ocean, associated with alkalic granite. Its formation requires unusual simultaneous concentrations of sodium and zirconium.

Labuntsovite is a hydrous barium potassium sodium magnesium titanosilicate, with 25.6 per cent TiO_2 and 0.25 per cent Nb_2O_5 (Fahey, oral communication, 1958). The same mineral with but a slight variation in composition, e.g. 29.49 per cent TiO_2 and 1.45 per cent Nb_2O_5, has been described by Semenov and Burova (1955) from the Khibinsk pegmatites in an alkalic massive at Lovozero, Kola peninsula. In the Green River formation it is found in the trona mine in Wyoming; it occurs in two ways, as well developed prismatic crystals up to a millimeter or two in length, first in black, very rich oil shale, underlying the main trona bed, and second in the massive trona itself. The significance, if any, of the labuntsovite–trona association is not yet clear.

Leucosphenite was discussed with the boron silicates.

Sulfides

Pyrite is very abundant in Green River beds. Its crystal form is varied and unusual, much of it (in Utah) being in platy crystals of bizarre shapes, and in Wyoming, in extraordinary trillings(?) (plate 3*b*). The other sulfides, pyrrhotite, marcasite, and wurtzite, are rather rare. Pyrrhotite has been observed in a sideritic rock with pyrite and marcasite associated with gilsonite, in oil shale with pyrite, and in the trona mine with pyrite. However, Bradley (oral communication) reports that pyrrhotite is characteristic of the group of oil shale beds at the top of the Tipton shale member of the Green River in Wyoming. It is very abundant there and over hundreds or thousands of square miles. Marcasite has been found only once.

Wurtzite has been found in sharply euhedral, hemimorphic crystals in dolomitic beds in Utah.

Plate 3*a*. Leucosphenite crystal with shortite vein in oil shale. Utah. Thin section ×20 in ordinary light.

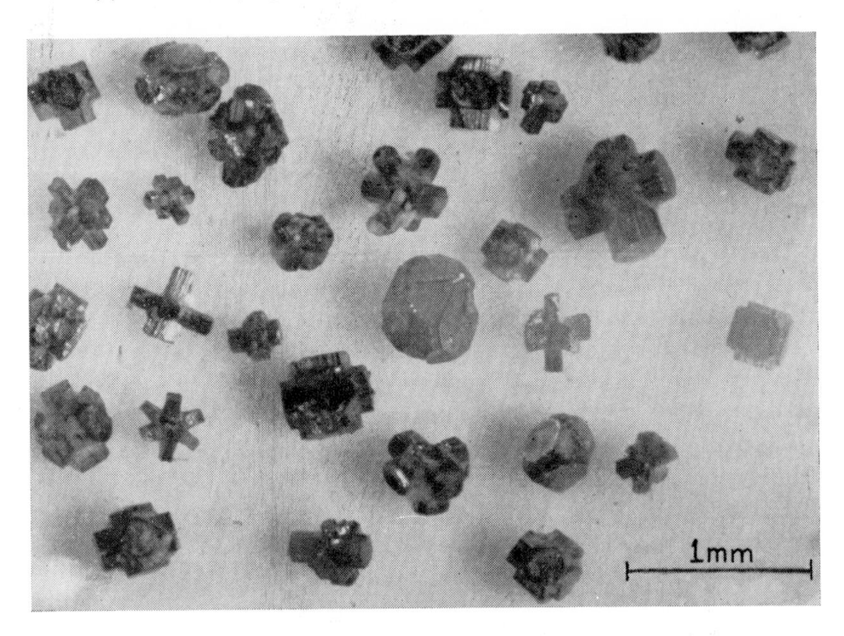

Plate 3*b*. Pyrite crystals from trona mine. Wyoming ×25.

Phosphates, sulfates, and fluorides

Bradleyite, apatite, and collophane are phosphates present in the Green River formation. Bradleyite occurs in the trona mine and elsewhere in Wyoming. Recently it has been synthesized at temperatures as low as 50° C (Berdesinski, 1958).

Microscopic, clear, colorless prismatic crystals of fluorapatite have been found in well cuttings in Utah and in the "insolubles" from the massive trona bed being mined in Wyoming; they are almost certainly authigenic, not detrital. A second fluorine mineral, probably new, is under study; it appears to be a sodium magnesium fluoride. The occurrence is interesting; it has been found only at the contact of massive nahcolite with the enclosing oil shale, in Utah. At this contact, the "shale" is lined with well crystallized barytocalcite; also present very sparingly are microscopic elongated prisms of elpidite. The fluoride mineral occurs usually as aggregates of turbid rounded grains, but recently has been noted in clear, colorless octahedral crystals. Fossil fish remains (mineralogically collophane) are locally abundant in the Green River formation.

Barite occurs rarely in rounded grains, presumably authigenic in Utah, and certainly authigenic as fissure fillings in Colorado.

Gypsum is known only where outcropping pyrite weathers; bassanite has been reported, but it may have been artificially formed in preparing the well cuttings for study. The same may be true of the few traces of anhydrite reported. Bedded anhydrite, characteristic of marine deposition, is unknown in the Green River.

Acknowledgments

All studies on the Green River geology begin with the fundamental work of Bradley (1929*a*, 1929*b*, 1931, 1936, 1948). In the years since, many others whose work is cited in the text have contributed. The friendly interest and cooperation of many oil-company geologists and the helpful discussion and criticism of our colleagues of the U. S. Geological Survey and the Geophysical Laboratory are gratefully acknowledged.

References

Abbott, W. 1957. Tertiary of the Uinta basin, *Intermountain Assoc. Petrol. Geologists, Guidebook to the Unita Basin,* 8th Annual Field Conference, 102–109.

Baskin, Y. 1956. Study of authigenic feldspars, *J. Geol., 64,* 132–155.

Bates, R. G. 1954. *Electrometric pH Determinations,* John Wiley & Sons, New York.

Bedekar, S. G. 1955. Properties of sodium carbonate–sodium bicarbonate solutions, *J. Appl. Chem., 5,* 72.

Berdesinski, W. 1958. Synthetische Darstellung von Bradleyit, *Kali und Steinsalz, 2,* 225–229.

Bradley, W. H. 1929*a*. The occurrence and origin of analcite and meerschaum beds in the Green River formation of Utah, Colorado, and Wyoming, *U. S. Geol. Survey Profess. Paper 158-A,* 1–8.

Bradley, W. H. 1929*b*. The varves and climate of the Green River epoch, *U. S. Geol. Survey Profess. Paper 158-E,* 87–110.

Bradley, W. H. 1931. Origin and microfossils of the oil shale of the Green River formation of Colorado and Utah, *U. S. Geol. Survey Profess. Paper 168,* 1–58.

Bradley, W. H. 1936. The biography of an ancient American lake, *Scientific Monthly, 42,* 421–430.

Bradley, W. H. 1948. Limnology and the Eocene lakes of the Rocky Mountain Region, *Bull. Geol. Soc. Am., 57,* 635–648.

Bury, C. R., and R. Redd. 1933. The system sodium carbonate–calcium carbonate–water, *J. Chem. Soc.* (London), 1160.

Crawford, A. L. 1957. Gilsonite, its discovery and early history in the industry, *Intermountain Assoc. Petrol. Geologists, Guidebook to the Uinta Basin,* 8th Annual Field Conference, 149–151.

Dane, C. H. 1955. Stratigraphic and facies relationships of upper part of Green River formation in Duchesne, Uintah, and Wasatch Counties, Utah, *U. S. Geol. Survey Oil and Gas Investigations Preliminary Chart 52.*

Davis, L. J. 1957. The geology of gilsonite, *Intermountain Assoc. Petrol. Geologists, Guidebook to the Uinta Basin,* 8th Annual Field Conference, 152–156.

Eitel, W., and W. Skaliks. 1929. Über einige Doppelcarbonate der Alkalien und Erdalkalien, *Z. anorg. allgem. Chem., 183,* 263.

Ernst, W. G. 1957. Annual Report of the Director of the Geophysical Laboratory, 1956–1957, *Carnegie Inst. Wash. Year Book 56,* 228.

Ertl, T. 1947. Sodium bicarbonate (nahcolite) from Colorado oil shale, *Am. Mineralogist, 32,* 117–120.

Fahey, J. J. 1939. Shortite, a new carbonate of sodium and calcium, *Am. Mineralogist, 24,* 514–518.

Fahey, J. J. 1941. Bradleyite, a new mineral, sodium phosphate–magnesium carbonate, with x-ray analysis by George Tunell, *Am. Mineralogist, 26,* 646–650.

Fahey, J. J. 1948. Loughlinite, a new hydrous magnesium silicate (with x-ray analysis by Joseph M. Axelrod), *Am. Mineralogist, 33,* 195; (Abstract), *Bull. Geol. Soc. Am.,* 1947, *58,* 1178–1179.

Fahey, J. J. 1950. Searlesite from the Green River formation of Wyoming (with x-ray notes by Joseph M. Axelrod), *Am. Mineralogist, 35,* 1014–1020.

Flink, G. 1901. *Medd. Grønland, 24,* 137.

Freeth, F. A. 1923. The system Na_2O–CO_2–NaCl–H_2O, considered as two four-component systems, *Phil. Trans. Roy. Soc. London, A223,* 35–87.

Harned, H. S., and F. T. Bonner. 1945. The first ionization of carbonic acid in aqueous solutions of sodium chloride, *J. Am. Chem. Soc., 67,* 1026.

Harned, H. S., and R. Davis. 1943. The ionization constant of carbonic acid in water and the solubility of carbon dioxide in water and aqueous salt solutions from 0 to 50°, *J. Am. Chem. Soc., 65,* 2030.

Harned, H. S., and B. B. Owen. 1958. *The Physical Chemistry of Electrolytic Solutions,* American Chemical Society Monograph 137, Reinhold Publishing Corporation, New York.

Harned, H. S., and S. R. Scholes. 1941. The ionization constant of HCO_3^- from 0 to 50°, *J. Am. Chem. Soc., 63,* 1706.

Henderson, J. H., Jr. 1957. The gilsonite refining project of the American Gilsonite Co., *Intermountain Assoc. Petrol. Geologists, Guidebook to the Uinta Basin,* 8th Annual Field Conference, 157–160.

Herman, G., and S. C. Sharps. 1956. Pennsylvanian and Permian stratigraphy of the Paradox Salt Embayment, *Intermountain Assoc. Petrol. Geologists, Geology and Economic Deposits of East Central Utah,* 7th Annual Field Conference, 77–84.

Hunt, J. M., F. Stewart, and P. A. Dickey. 1954. Origin of hydrocarbons of Uinta Basin, Utah, *Bull. Am. Assoc. Petrol. Geologists, 38,* 1671–1698.

Jones, D. J. 1957. Geosynclinal nature of the Uinta Basin, *Intermountain Assoc. Petrol. Geologists, Guidebook to the Uinta Basin,* 8th Annual Field Conference, 30–34.

Keeling, C. D. 1958. The concentration and isotopic abundances of atmospheric carbon dioxide in rural areas, *Geochim. et Cosmochim. Acta, 13,* 322.

Kobe, K. A., and T. M. Sheehy. 1948. Thermochemistry of sodium carbonate and its solutions, *Ind. Eng. Chem., 40,* 99.

MacKenzie, W. S. 1957. The crystalline modifications of $NaAlSi_3O_8$, *Am. J. Sci., 255,* 481.

Merrow, J. 1957. Ozokerite at Soldier Summit, Utah, *Intermountain Assoc. Petrol. Geologists, Guidebook to the Uinta Basin,* 8th Annual Field Conference, 161–163.

Milton, C. 1957. Authigenic minerals of the Green River formation of the Uinta Basin, Utah, *Intermountain Assoc. Petrol. Geologists, Guidebook to the Uinta Basin,* 8th Annual Field Conference, 136–143.

Milton, C., J. M. Axelrod, and F. S. Grimaldi. 1954. New minerals reedmergnerite ($Na_2O \cdot B_2O_3 \cdot 6SiO_2$) and eitelite ($Na_2O \cdot MgO \cdot 2CO_2$) associated with leucosphenite, shortite, searlesite, and crocidolite in the Green River formation, Utah (Abstract), *Bull. Geol. Soc. Am., 65,* 1286–1287.

Milton, C., J. M. Axelrod, and F. S. Grimaldi. 1955. New mineral garrelsite $(Ba,Ca,Mg)_4H_4Si_{26}BO_{20}$ from the Green River formation, Utah (Abstract), *Bull. Geol. Soc. Am., 66,* 1597.

Milton, C., J. M. Axelrod, and A. M. Sherwood. 1954. New occurrence of leucosphenite in oil shale from Utah (Abstract), *Am. Mineralogist, 39,* 337.

Milton, C., M. Mrose, J. J. Fahey, and E. C. T. Chao. 1958. Labuntsovite from the Trona Mine, Sweetwater County, Wyoming (Abstract) *Bull. Geol. Soc. Am., 69,* 1614–1615.

Moore, F. E. 1950. Authigenic albite in the Green River oil shales, *J. Sediment. Petrol., 20,* 227–230.

Morey, G. W. 1951. The ternary system $Na_2O–B_2O_3–SiO_2$, *J. Soc. Glass Technol., 35,* 270–283.

Niggli, P. 1916. Gleichgewichte zwischen TiO_2 und CO_2, sowie SiO_2 und CO_2 in Alkali-, Kalk-Alkali und Alkali-Aluminatschmelzen, *Z. anorg. allgem. Chem.*, *98*, 241.

Pecora, W. T., and J. H. Kerr. 1953. Burbankite and calkinsite, two new carbonate minerals from Montana, *Am. Mineralogist*, *38*, 1169–1183.

Picard, M. 1957. Green River and Lower Uinta formations—subsurface stratigraphic changes in central and eastern Uinta Basin, Utah, *Intermountain Assoc. Petrol. Geologists, Guidebook to the Uinta Basin*, 8th Annual Field Conference, 116–130.

Regis, A. J., and L. B. Sand. 1957. Mineral associations in the Green River formation, Westvaco, Wyoming (Abstract), *Bull. Geol. Soc. Am.*, *68*, 1784.

Ritzma, H. R. 1957. Tectonic map of Uinta Basin, *Intermountain Assoc. Petrol. Geologists, Guidebook to the Uinta Basin*, 8th Annual Field Conference, 24.

Roberts, L. D., and G. B. Mangold. 1939. Properties of concentrated solutions of sodium carbonates, *Ind. Eng. Chem.*, *31*, 1293.

Semenov, E. I., and T. A. Burova. 1955. On the new mineral labuntsovite and on the so-called titanoelpidite, *Doklady Akad. Nauk S. S. S. R.*, *101*, 1113–1116.

Stokes, W. L. 1956. Nature and origin of Paradox basin salt structures, *Intermountain Assoc. Petrol. Geologists, Geology and Economic Deposits of East Central Utah*, 7th Annual Field Conference, 42–47.

Taylor, C. E. 1955. Thermodynamics of sodium carbonate in solution, *J. Phys. Chem.*, *59*, 653.

Wilson, E. O., and Y. Ch'iu. 1934. Brine purification, *Ind. Eng. Chem.*, *26*, 1099.

Tritium in Hydrology and Meteorology

W. F. LIBBY [1]
Geophysical Laboratory
Carnegie Institution of Washington

It has been clear from the beginning of the researches on the tritium produced by cosmic radiation (Grosse et al., 1951; Libby, 1946; Faltings and Harteck, 1950) that the labeled water resulting from the production of tritium in the higher levels of the atmosphere would be of real usefulness (Libby, 1953), and the initial results justified these expectations (Kaufman and Libby, 1954; von Buttlar and Libby, 1955; Begemann and Libby, 1957). In the spring of 1954 man-made tritium produced by the thermonuclear weapons tested in the Pacific created a new and abundant source larger than the cosmic rays themselves, which because of its placement in time was in some ways more useful for measurements of rates of natural water processes. More recently, the use of reactor-produced tritium in planned experimentation is showing rich promise as a valuable tool for research.

This paper will review some of the findings stemming from nuclear tests, including atmosphere-storage time for water; Castle bomb tritium deposition in the northern hemisphere; ground-water inventory, storage times, and water balance for the northern Mississippi Valley; surface ocean mixing rates; and regional hydrological applications. It will conclude with a brief description of possible uses of synthetic tritium in studies of local hydrology.

[1] On leave of absence from University of Chicago to serve as member of U. S. Atomic Energy Commission.

Atmospheric Storage Time for Castle Tritium

More than 50 samples of rain and snow, covering the period from March 1, 1954, to May 1956, have been collected in various places in the northern hemisphere and analyzed for their tritium content. Figures 1, 2, and 3 present some of the data obtained on these samples.

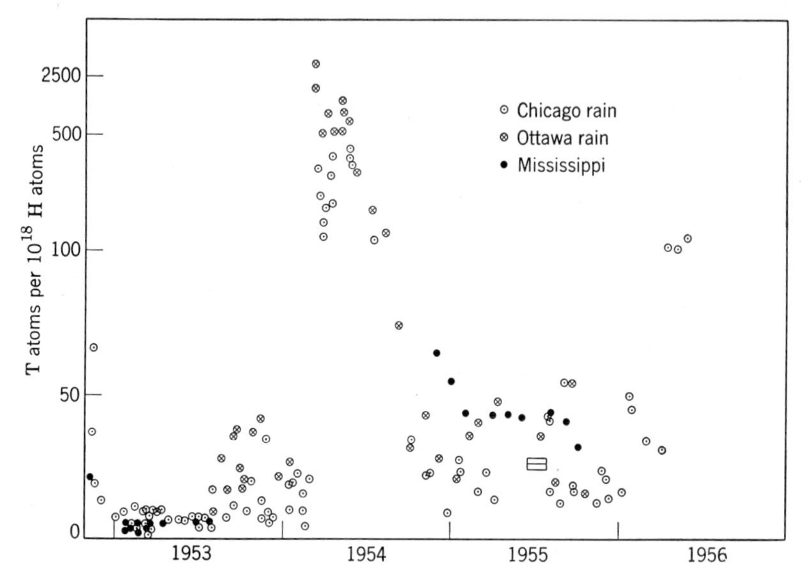

Fig. 1. Chicago and Ottawa rains and Mississippi River tritium contents (from Begemann and Libby (1957), by permission).

During the production period of the "excess" tritium in the spring of 1954 the results scatter widely. From June 1954 on, however, the tritium content decreases steadily, remains at a constant level for about one year, and starts to rise again at the beginning of 1956.

It is clear from figure 3 that an air-borne residence time [2] of about 40 days for the Castle tritium is indicated, in good agreement with the 50-day figure of Brown and Grummitt (1956). This is in sharp contrast not only with the 3-day figure for tropospheric moisture (von Buttlar and Libby, 1955), but also with the approximate 10-year figure for stratospheric fission products (Libby, 1956), particularly strontium 90 and cesium 137. It is close to the 32-day residence time for tropospheric fission products produced by weapons fired in Nevada

[2] In this paper we use the term "residence time" to mean the time spent on the average when the fallout probability is the same for all particles, i.e., an exponential decay.

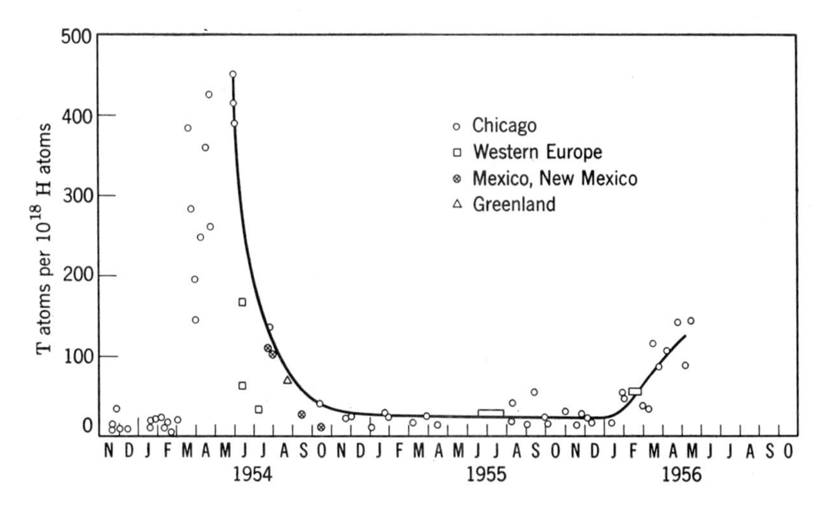

Fig. 2. Tritium content of rain and snow collected in the northern hemisphere (from Begemann and Libby (1957), by permission).

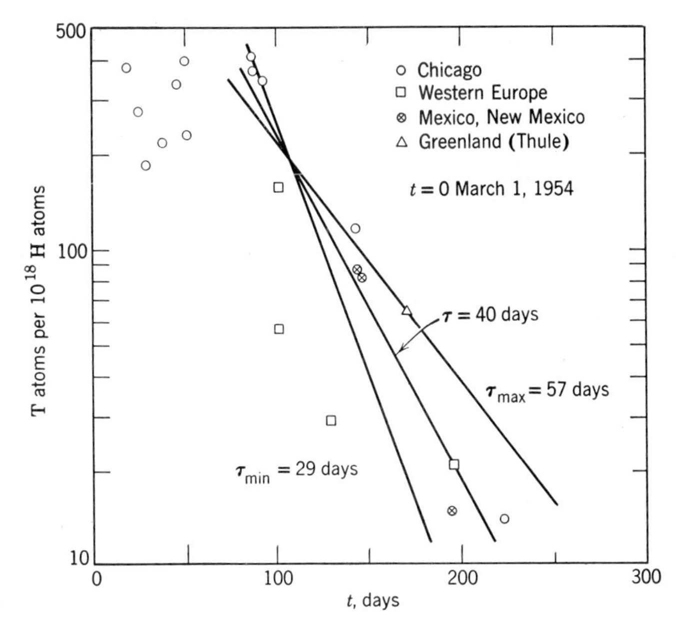

Fig. 3. Excess tritium in rains and snows in the northern hemisphere (from Begemann and Libby (1957), by permission).

(Stewart, Crooks, and Fisher, 1956), although there is no apparent connection. Since the bomb clouds rose into the stratosphere the rate corresponds most likely to the time of descent into the troposphere where the much more rapid ordinary weather processes control with the shorter water residence time of perhaps 3 days. The water in the fireball condensed separately and in relatively large drops or crystals, because the Castle weapons vaporized enormous quantities of water and carried them into the stratosphere well labeled with the bomb tritium which burned to water (measurements of atmospheric hydrogen collected at the earth's surface by the Linde Air Products Company both before and after Castle showed no increase over the previous cosmic-ray level). The particles of ice or supercooled water formed, therefore, were much larger than those containing the radiostrontium and radiocesium, and large enough to settle at this relatively rapid rate through the tropopause into the troposphere where they

TABLE 1. Tritium Content of Samples from Southern Hemisphere

Sample No.	Location and Sample	Date of Collection	$T/H \times 10^{18}$
179	Valparaiso, Chile, rain water (von Buttlar and Libby, 1955)	4/4/54	4.3 ± 0.2
199	Livingstone, S. Africa, Zambesi River	5/–/54	6.5 ± 0.2
260	Cape Province, S. Africa, Berg River	1/–/55	2.8 ± 0.2
286	Admiral Byrd Bay, snow; 69° 34′ S; 00° 41′ W; top, 1st ft	2/19/55	24 ± 4
287	Admiral Byrd Bay, snow; 69° 34′ S; 00° 41′ W; top, 2d ft	2/19/55	12.5 ± 0.8
288	Admiral Byrd Bay, snow; 69° 34′ S; 00° 41′ W; top, 3d ft	2/19/55	13.5 ± 0.7
284	Admiral Byrd Bay, snow; 69° 34′ S; 00° 41′ W; bottom, 5th ft	2/19/55	9.6 ± 1
285	Admiral Byrd Bay, snow; 69° 34′ S; 00° 41′ W; bottom, 6th ft	2/19/55	5.2 ± 0.5
321	Antarctic snow; Atka Bay, 60° 34′ S; 08° 06′ W; 6 miles south of the edge of the Bay; top 8 in.	2/20/55	19.2 ± 0.8
306	Antarctic snow; ½ mile east of Emergency Quonset at Little America III; top 8 in.	1/17/55	7.5 ± 0.6
310	Antarctic snow; ½ mile east of Emergency Quonset at Little America III; top 8 in.	1/15/55	14.1 ± 1
323	Antarctic snow; snow pit near Emergency Quonset at Little America III; 1–2 ft depth	1/15/55	28.0 ± 1.5
324	Antarctic snow; snow pit near Emergency Quonset at Little America III; 2–3 ft depth	1/15/55	13.0 ± 0.5

melted and were precipitated as rain in about two or three days.

Table 1 shows the tritium content of samples collected in the southern hemisphere after the Castle test series. None of these samples had a higher tritium content than similar ones collected in the northern hemisphere before Castle, although the number of samples is small. This is in sharp contrast to similar data for the northern hemisphere shown in figures 1 and 2. In particular, the samples representing the top layer of snow from the Antarctic did not show any increase in their tritium content over those from the 1- to 3-foot layer, the snow of which definitely fell before 1954. Thus, until about a year after Castle there was no indication of any appreciable mixing of Castle-produced tritium across the equator. This, of course, is in agreement with the short time (40 days) the Castle tritium spent in the atmosphere.

Castle Tritium Deposition in the Northern Hemisphere

In order to be able to make an estimate on the amount of "excess" tritium deposited per square centimeter in the northern hemisphere, samples which were expected to be representative have been collected and measured. The results are given in tables 2 and 3 and figure 4. These values may be compared with those obtained from pre-Castle ocean water samples shown in table 4. The results of the calculations for the total Castle tritium deposited in the northern hemisphere are given in table 5.

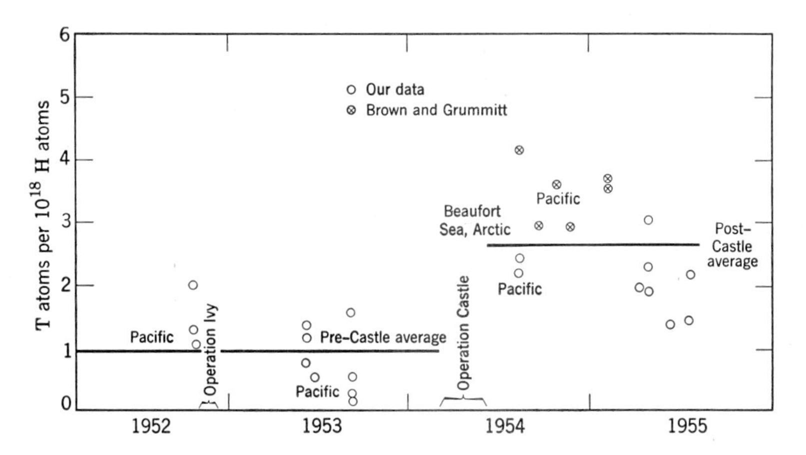

Fig. 4. Surface ocean water tritium (Atlantic, unless labeled) (from Begemann and Libby (1957), by permission).

TABLE 2. Continental Water Samples (Northern Hemisphere)

Sample No.	Description of Sample	Date of Collection	T/H × 10^{18}
	Crater Lake, Oregon		
251	surface	10/3/54	6.9 ± 0.3
252	1900 ft (bottom)	10/3/54	3.5 ± 0.5
340	Position 1, surface	8/20/55	4.2 ± 0.3
341	1100 ft		6.0 ± 1
342	2000 ft (bottom)		7.6 ± 0.3
343	Position 2, surface		4.7 ± 0.2
344	1200 ft		3.4 ± 0.3
345	1400 ft (bottom)		8.5 ± 1
346	Position 3, surface		5.2 ± 0.5
347	550 ft		6.0 ± 1
348	1300 ft		9.5 ± 0.5
248	Lake Michigan, surface, 2 miles off shore, 79th	2/8/55	10 ± 1
256	St., Chicago	3/10/55	7.3 ± 0.3
304		6/13/55	7.6 ± 0.4
223	Zurichsee, Switzerland, surface	9/20/54	29.5 ± 1.5
264	Lake Tahoe, California, surface	2/15/55	10 ± 0.8

It is clear from figure 4 that the Castle tritium fallout raised the level in the surface ocean water by about 2 tritium atoms per 10^{18} hydrogen atoms on the average, and this figure is used in table 5 together with a 75-meter average depth of the thermocline in the ocean. The rise in assay of Lake Michigan (table 2) was 5.6 tritium atoms per 10^{18} hydrogen atoms from 1.7 to 7.3; this figure, when corrected for the contribution of the water drainage area, which is about equal to the direct rainfall into the lake, is about 50 per cent larger than that of the average ocean. Since Lake Michigan has an average depth of 95 meters (Kaufman and Libby, 1954) the effective average depths of mixing in the oceans would appear to be about 150 meters, somewhat more than, but near, the average depth of the thermocline, and possibly indicating some mixing below the thermocline. The data in figure 4, however, do not conclusively indicate a decrease in surface concentration with time, though the scatter is such that a decrease may be suggested by the data. The mixing down to the thermocline apparently is rapid but is much slower beyond the thermocline.

The drainage of rain water into Lake Michigan was assumed to take place before appreciable mixing with the ground-water reservoir occurred. This assumption was made since the distances are small

TABLE 3. Ocean Water Samples (Northern Hemisphere)

Sample No.	Location	Depth	Date of Collection	T/H × 10^{18}
	Atlantic (Sargasso Sea)			
219	36° 04′ N; 65° 00′ W	100 m	9/24/54	2.8 ± 0.1
220		200 m		1.33 ± 0.1
221		600 m		0.48 ± 0.05
	Atlantic			
282	43° 17.5′ N; 45° 26′ W	Surface	4/6/55	1.6 ± 0.2
280		42 m		2.2 ± 0.15
281		81 m		2.1 ± 0.1
	Atlantic			
290	49° 01′ N; 49° 18′ W	Surface	4/27/55	3.1 ± 0.2
291		62 m		3.25 ± 0.15
	Atlantic			
293	48° 49′ N; 48° 07′ W	Surface	4/28/55	1.6 ± 0.2
294		60 m		2.0 ± 0.1
295		120 m		1.1 ± 0.2
296		180 m		3.0 ± 0.2
	Atlantic			
297	48° 28′ N; 48° 20′ W	Surface	4/28/55	2.3 ± 0.15
	Atlantic			
360	55° 01.5′ N; 53° 09′ W	Surface	7/15/55	2.2 ± 0.2
361		56 m		0.40 ± 0.15
362		111 m		2.2 ± 0.2
363		170 m		0.60 ± 0.2
	Atlantic			
371	56° 28.5′ N; 50° 30′ W	Surface	7/17/55	1.3 ± 0.25
372		51 m		1.7 ± 0.2
373		85 m		2.4 ± 0.2
374		124 m		1.3 ± 0.15
	Atlantic			
375	52° 03′ N; 49° 38′ W	Surface	6/3/55	0.80 ± 0.05
376		58 m		1.2 ± 0.1
377		115 m		1.4 ± 0.2
378		171 m		1.2 ± 0.1
	Pacific			
257	37° 38′ N; 123° 09′ W	Surface	8/6/54	2.2 ± 0.1

and the flow times correspondingly short. Since the information on drainage into Lake Tahoe and the Zurichsee was incomplete, it was necessary to estimate this contribution and accept the consequent uncertainty in the figures for the Castle tritium deposition in these lakes.

All these data indicate that—with the exception of Crater Lake, where an abnormal behavior might be expected because of its small

TABLE 4. Tritium Content of Pre-Castle Ocean Water Samples (Surface)

Sample No.	Location	Date of Collection	T/H × 10^{18}
	Atlantic		
314	44° 00′ N; 41° 00′ W	10/31/52	2.2 ± 0.25
314		Same sample as a check	1.8 ± 0.25
	Atlantic		
319	56° 34′ N; 51° 01′ W	10/22/52	1.3 ± 0.1
	Pacific		
320	27° 41′ N; 145° 35′ W	10/28/52	1.05 ± 0.1
320		Same sample as a check	1.0 ± 0.1
	Pacific		
315	33° 04′ N; 165° 17′ E	11/26/52	1.5 ± 0.2
	Pacific		
316	50° 09′ N; 144° 31′ W	12/19/52	16.3 ± 1
	Pacific		
318	09° 00′ N; 167° 03′ E	11/18/52	10 ± 1

Two of the samples have been measured twice as a check and to eliminate the possibility of having the samples contaminated during the processing. All results are corrected for radioactive decay.

TABLE 5. Castle Tritium Deposition in the Northern Hemisphere

Location	Area of Water Body, sq mi	Drainage Area, sq mi	Average Depth, m	Increase in T per 10^{18} Atoms of H	T Atoms Deposited / cm²
Lake Michigan	22,336	43,148 $\left(\frac{14.5}{31.3}\text{ fractional runoff}\right)$	93	5.6	187 ± 20 × 10^7
Zurichsee, Switzerland	34.2	770 (Assumed same fractional runoff as Lake Michigan)	45	26	67 × 10^7
Lake Tahoe, Calif.	193	1,500 (Assumed same fractional runoff as Lake Michigan)	191	7	190 × 10^7
Crater Lake, Ore.	19.3	Approx. 6	490	6	1800 × 10^7
North Atlantic and North Pacific	...	...	75 *	2	100 × 10^7

* Average depth of the thermocline.

size—there is fair agreement that as a result of Operation Castle about 200×10^7 tritium atoms were deposited on each square centimeter of the northern hemisphere (10^7 tritium atoms give 1 disintegration per minute; Jones, 1955). Of course the uncertainty in this number is large because of the limited number of data available.

Ground-Water Inventory, Storage Times, and Water Balance for the Northern Mississippi Valley

As a consequence of this deposition of "excess" tritium a remarkable increase in the tritium content of rivers and streams was noticeable. In table 6 the results are presented.

For the samples collected in the United States later than January 1955 there is no remarkable dependence of the tritium content on the

TABLE 6. Post-Castle Tritium Content of Rivers

Sample No.	Location	Date of Collection	$T/H \times 10^{18}$
231	Blue Nile, Khartoum, Sudan	5/18/54	11.9 ± 0.5
230	White Nile, Khartoum, Sudan	5/18/54	21.1 ± 0.5
222	Ticino, Switzerland	9/24/54	40.5 ± 2
250	Aare, Bern, Switzerland	12/30/54	16.0 ± 0.8
275		2/18/55	15.5 ± 0.8
300		4/15/55	13.5 ± 1.5
236	Mississippi	12/3/54	65 ± 3
246	Rock Island, Ill.	1/3/55	55 ± 3
247		2/3/55	44 ± 2
254		3/1/55	40 ± 2
261		4/1/55	43 ± 3
289		5/4/55	43.5 ± 1
303		6/2/55	41.5 ± 1
333		8/1/55	44 ± 5
338		9/3/55	41 ± 2
351		10/1/55	32 ± 1.5
190	Steamboat Creek, Nev.	7/20/54	280 ± 10
265		2/16/55	37.5 ± 2
270	Different sampling site	2/16/55	42 ± 3
267	Galena Creek, Nev.	2/16/55	28 ± 1.0
189	Firehole River, Yellowstone Park, Wyo.	7/15/54	205 ± 8
353		9/17/55	36.2 ± 2
197	Gibbon River, Yellowstone Park, Wyo.	7/14/54	170 ± 10
352		9/17/55	28 ± 3

size of the rivers the samples come from. Therefore, for the following we shall take the Mississippi samples as representative for average continental water. The approximately 200×10^7 tritium atoms deposited per square centimeter of the northern hemisphere raised the tritium content by about 39×10^{-18} T/H from 4.7 (Kaufman and Libby, 1954; von Buttlar and Libby, 1955; Begemann and Libby, 1957) to 44 (in units of 10^{-18} T/H). Therefore, on the average about 7.7 meters of water or the equivalent amount of exchangeable hydrogen, part of which may have been bound to clay as hydroxyl groups, were mixed with the rain which carried down the Castle tritium in making up the river water, this amount being the average inventory for the northern Mississippi Valley drainage area. This would be true, as pointed out to us by Professor W. J. Kaufman, of the University of California, even if the mixing were incomplete, provided that the rate of removal of water to the river did not vary appreciably with the amount of water above the contributing layer. This constancy of the rate of contribution of water to the river with head of water above, or the completeness of mixing in the first few months, is supported by the constancy of the tritium concentration of the river water during the period of about a year following the Castle deluge. If the mixing had been only superficial, re-evaporation would have caused the rains to be richer in tritium than the river waters. Since the opposite was true, as shown in figures 1, 2, and 3 and table 6, appreciable mixing must have occurred in a matter of a few months, and therefore it is likely that further mixing would have occurred during the next year had the mixing been incomplete.

At the same time that the tritium content of Mississippi water was at a nearly constant level of 44×10^{-18} T/H the rains and snows in the Chicago area showed a rather constant tritium content of 21×10^{-18} T/H (see figs. 1 and 2). This leads us to the conclusion that one-third of the average rainfall is re-evaporated water and two-thirds ocean water, since under the conditions obtaining during 1955 the tritium content of oceanic water vapor would have been about 2.5×10^{-18} T/H. (In this calculation correction is made for cosmic-ray tritium, so just the bomb tritium is used. Thus 5 and 7 units are subtracted from the river and rain water tritium contents, respectively.) As the average rate of annual precipitation is 0.77 meter, this means that per year about 0.52 meter of ocean water and about 0.25 meter of re-evaporated water rain out over the upper Mississippi Valley as shown in figure 5. This conclusion, of course, is to be taken in the sense that Mississippi River water is defined to be typical of the water

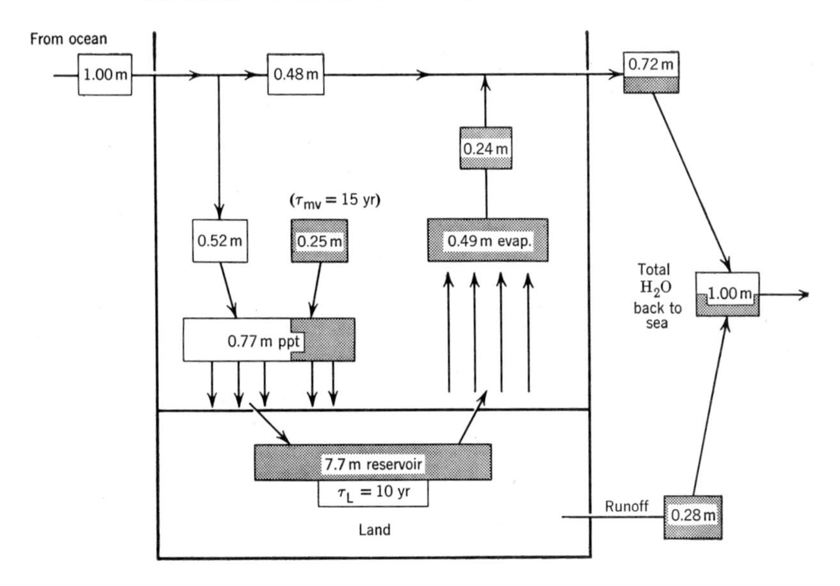

Fig. 5. Mississippi Valley water balance (from Begemann and Libby (1957), by permission).

available for evaporation, a postulate that seems to be reasonable because incomplete mixing is hardly compatible with the constancy of the compositions of the rain and river waters.

The total of 0.77 meter annual precipitation must be balanced by re-evaporation and runoff water. In order to determine the net water balance for the upper Mississippi Valley, we note that the annual runoff in rivers and streams, which is about 0.28 meter, leaves 0.49 meter per year as the average evaporation rate of ground water. In order that this be only one-third of the air moisture, the winds must carry in about 1.0 meter per year from the oceans, of which 0.52 meter precipitates as rain in the valley. The remaining 0.48 meter together with 0.24 meter of evaporated ground water is carried by the winds back from the continent to the oceans. Thus the wind transport of ground-water moisture from the land in the northern Mississippi Valley back to the oceans is somewhat less than that carried by the Mississippi River, 0.24 meter per year versus 0.28 meter per year. These conclusions are displayed in figure 5.

It is interesting to compare these results for the northern Mississippi Valley with those for the whole North American continent as obtained by Benton, Estoque, and Dominitz (1953), who measured the net inflow and outflow of water across the boundaries of the North American continent during 1949. They obtained 0.91 meter per year inflow, 0.76 meter per year outflow in winds, and 0.15 meter per year runoff. Of course, our data differ in giving a figure for the interchange between the air moisture and ground waters, but the two sets show considerable agreement where they are comparable; for example, 1.0 meter per year inflow and 0.72 meter per year outflow, with the Mississippi River playing an abnormally important role in the return mechanism.

Concluding, we can say: There appear to be the equivalent of about 8 meters of ground water which mix within a few months with rainfall in the Mississippi Valley, about 0.52 meter of ocean water falls as rain per year, about 0.49 meter per year re-evaporates, about 0.28 meter per year drains off to the ocean from the rivers, and about 0.24 meter of ground water per year returns to the oceans via the atmosphere. Thus, the average residence time of water in the upper Mississippi Valley is about 15 years. This means that about 6.7 per cent of the Castle tritium is carried to the ocean and deposited each year—about 3.6 per cent being carried as river water and about 3.1 per cent as water vapor in the form of clouds and moisture in the air masses which are seaward bound where the water will be rained out as ocean precipitation. (In addition, of course, owing to the radioactive decay 5.6 per cent of the tritium disintegrates into He^3 each year, so the average expected life of the Castle tritium on the continental land masses will be about 8.2 years, with a half-life of 5.7 years.) Other areas will differ somewhat, though possibly not greatly in the amount of ground-water storage, atmospheric transport of water vapor, and runoff in rivers. It seems not unlikely that the 6-year half-life figure for the persistence of the Castle tritium in the northern Mississippi Valley may obtain rather widely. It will be most interesting to observe whether this is so.

Surface Ocean Mixing Rates and Cosmic-Ray Tritium Production Rate, $\overline{Q}$

The tritium contents of the surface ocean samples measured earlier were interpreted (von Buttlar and Libby, 1955) as indicating that the oceans do not mix below the thermocline in the average lifetime of tritium, 18 years. Further measurements are presented in tables 3 and 4 and figure 4. Unfortunately our data on samples collected after Castle do not yet cover a long enough time so that an appreciable decrease in the tritium content of the surface samples would enable us to calculate more accurately the average residence time of ocean water in the layers above the thermocline. They do indicate, however, that this time might be as short as 5 years.

These data, and the long ground-water residence time of about 15 years, which is not negligible with respect to the average life of tritium as was assumed earlier (Kaufman and Libby, 1954; von Buttlar and Libby, 1955), as well as the difference in the amount of tritium entering and leaving the continent as vapor which is more important than was realized formerly (von Buttlar and Libby, 1955; Craig, H., private communication, August 1956) and the probability of a stratospheric storage time of about 10 years (Libby, 1956), make it necessary for us to recalculate the mean production rate for the cosmic-ray tritium (Kaufman and Libby, 1954; von Buttlar and Libby, 1955). In this connection it is interesting to note that the mean assays of tritium in the Mississippi Valley agree with those for wines which definitely were bottled before the firing of any thermonuclear weapons, when the tritium assays of the wines are corrected for radioactive decay (Kaufman and Libby, 1954; von Buttlar and Libby, 1955). Furthermore, the assay of Lake Michigan, which was due to tritium deposited over the preceding 18 years, agrees well with the mean tritium content of rains during the year 1953, considering the known hydrologic conditions of the lake. It follows, therefore, that the tritium from Operation Ivy conducted in November 1952 was small in its contamination of the continental water masses as compared with that of Operation Castle, since otherwise these agreements probably could not have been obtained.

The value of $\bar{Q}$, the mean natural tritium production rate, neglecting for the moment the effect of stratospheric storage, is to be calculated by using the earlier data (Kaufman and Libby, 1954; von Buttlar and Libby, 1955) but taking account of the ground-water storage time and the wind transport of continental ground water to sea. If Q is the average production rate in the northern Mississippi Valley (T atoms/cm^2/sec), we calculate it to be

$$Q = \left[(7.7 \times 5 \times 10^{-18}) \times \left(\frac{0.693}{12.26} + 0.72 \times 6 \times 10^{-18} \right) - (0.28 \times 5 \times 10^{-18}) - (1.00 \times 2.5 \times 10^{-18}) \right] \times \frac{100}{18} \times \frac{2 \times 6.02 \times 10^{23}}{3.15 \times 10^{7}}$$

where the first term within the brackets is the radioactive decay in the ground-water reservoir, the second is the wind-borne outflow where the observed value of 8 for New York rain (samples 148 and 149, Eidinoff, 1947) has been corrected to 6 for the expected fractionation of tritium in the condensation process (Craig, Boato, and White, 1956), the third the runoff in the Mississippi, and the last is the tritium brought in from the oceans bearing the tritium concentration found on the California coast. The result, 1.16 T atoms/cm^2/sec, is not to be multiplied by the factor 0.6 (Kaufman and Libby, 1954; von Buttlar and Libby, 1955) used formerly to correct for the variation of the cosmic-ray intensity with latitude, since the main part, the direct solar accretion as suggested in the next paragraph, probably should be uniform in intensity over the earth. This was pointed out to us by H. Craig. Finally, in addition, stratospheric storage for a period of perhaps 10 years on the average (Libby, 1956) leads to further correction to a total Q value of 2.0, which should probably be close to the world-wide average $\overline{Q}$.

We note that direct measurements of tritium production cross sections in the laboratory (Fireman, 1955; Fireman and Rowland, 1955; Currie, Libby, and Wolfgang, 1956) have given lower results more nearly in agreement with the earlier $\overline{Q}$ value. This discrepancy may be due, as suggested by J. R. Arnold (private communication, October 1956) and B. Feld (in Craig, Boato, and White, 1956), independently, to an appreciable accretion of tritium directly from the sun not included in the earlier calculation. Therefore, it appears that we have determined Q the tritium production rate for natural tritium of either primary or secondary origin to be about 1 T atom/cm^2/sec at the earth's surface and 2 T atoms/cm^2/sec total with little variation with latitude to be expected (even if the entire production were by cosmic rays the long stratospheric storage time and the completeness of stratospheric mixing indicated by the fission product data would be expected to reduce the variation with latitude to a minimum). The uncertainty in this value of Q is probably about 50 per cent. It is becoming clear that the opportunities for further measurements of $\overline{Q}$ are rapidly disappearing as man-made tritium becomes more abundant than the cosmic-ray product.

H. Craig (private communication, August 1956), before learning of the results of this research, had deduced from C^{14} mixing rates for the sea that $\overline{Q}$ at the surface of the earth might well be as high as 1.2 ± 0.5, and that, considering the stratosphere holdup, $\overline{Q} = 1.7$ total. A $\overline{Q}$ value at the surface of 1 and a thermocline depth of 86 meters corresponds to an expected tritium content of surface ocean water of 1 T atom/10^{18} H atoms, if the mixing time for waters above the thermocline with the deeper water is taken as very much longer than 18 years. This is an acceptable figure in view of the data in figure 4, several of which were taken before Operation Ivy; the shorter storage times of perhaps 5 years deduced by Craig (private communication, August 1956) would reduce the expected surface tritium concentration but would not place it below the range of mixing times consistent with the experimental errors in Q and the tritium content of surface ocean water.

The consequences of the change in both $\overline{Q}$ total and $\overline{Q}$ at the surface are important to both the steady-state natural tritium inventory and the He^3 rate of escape from the earth. The world-wide steady inventory of natural tritium rises from 1.8 kg (Kaufman and Libby, 1954; von Buttlar and Libby, 1955) to 30 kg, of which about one-half is above the tropopause mainly as water of about 10^{-13} T/H ratio, and the average escape time (von Buttlar and Libby, 1955) for He^3 from the earth's atmosphere is reduced to about 2.5 million years.

Hydrological Applications

In cooperation with Dr. E. C. Reed, of the University of Nebraska, two sets of samples from selected wells in the state of Nebraska have been analyzed for their tritium content. The results are listed in table 7.

When the first set of samples was collected we had hoped that there might not yet be any contribution from Castle-produced tritium in these waters. Most probably there was none in the Howard or York

TABLE 7. Nebrasks Wells

Location of Sampling Site	Date of Collection	$T/H \times 10^{18}$
Howard County		
Drilled well, depth 80′	10/28/54	0.44 ± 0.1
Merrick County		
Drilled well, depth 44′	10/28/54	2.5 ± 0.2
York County		
Drilled well, depth 155′	10/28/54	0.18 ± 0.03
Same well	4/28/55	3.0 ± 0.2
Seward County		
Drilled well, depth 130′	4/28/55	2.2 ± 0.2
Seward County		
Drilled well, depth 100′	4/28/55	1.4 ± 0.4
Clay County		
Drilled well, depth 100′	4/19/55	1.2 ± 0.1

County samples, but for the one from Merrick County the possibility cannot be excluded.

The main point of interest in these samples was not only their "average age" as defined before but also the difference in the tritium content of the different samples, in order to determine the rate of ground-water movement or the rate of replacement of connate water by meteoric water. The sampling sites were chosen to provide as much information as possible. The area where the Howard County sample was taken is known to be an excellent infiltration area for ground water. According to geological and hydrological evidence—the ground-water movement is fairly well known—this sample should have had the highest tritium content, the one from York County the lowest. A high reading was expected for the Merrick County sample because of the relatively shallow water table in this area.

Our measurements on the first set of samples confirm this general picture, the only exception being the unexpectedly low tritium content for the Howard County sample.

The results on the second set of samples, especially the one on the duplicate sample from York County, can be interpreted in two ways. These samples were collected in the spring, after a period of recharge of the ground-water reservoir, and most probably came from a lesser depth than those collected in October, after a period of extensive use of the ground water. The fact that the water in a thick layer of aquifer does not necessarily have to have the same age throughout, but may very well vary from youngest on the top to oldest at the bottom, would explain our results without assuming any contribution from recent rains. The other possibility would be that again we do not have a simple replacing of connate water of a uniform age by meteoric water but rather a mixing of recent rain water with old ground water. The mixing would have to take place fairly close to the sampling sites. The results cannot be explained by assuming that this recent rain water comes from the Howard County infiltration area; the time would be much too short. About 1 per cent recent rain water mixed with the ground water would be sufficient to explain the increase in the tritium content we found. It does not seem impossible that such a small amount of rain water mixed with the ground water locally.

Again, further measurements must be made before the final answer can be given.

Local Hydrology with Synthetic Tritium

Synthetic tritium can be used for limited areas in hydrology, and it seems likely that the applications will be of practical value because the freedom from the need for isotopic enrichment and the possibility of detailed control of the placement of the tracer water both are of such importance.

The concentrations and amounts of tritium necessary are 10^{-15} T atom per H atom for direct counting without enrichment as a lower limit. This means that, for a ground-water inventory of about 8 meters, 45 curies of tritium, or about $100 worth at present prices, will be needed per square mile. This certainly is reasonable and practical at the dilutions that will obtain. These quantities, of course, are far below health hazard levels and are allowable for general use.

Various applications of this technique suggest themselves:

1. *Flow pattern underground in a watershed.* Mixing rate for reservoir.
   (*a*) Inject 10 mc every 100 yards on square grid 1 meter below water line (31 c/mi^2).
   (*b*) Sample wells in area and count vs. time.
   (*c*) Dig sample wells on centers of every square and measure (T) vs. time.

2. *Local runoff and re-evaporation rates.* Sprinkle 1 acre with T-labeled water at various equivalent rain rates, and then measure the amount in the ground and foliage vs. time thereafter to infinite time. This gives the amount of runoff plus re-evaporation. In doing this, tests of the effects of various surface conditions to reveal beneficial effects of grass, trees, plowing, etc., should be made. For this application one should use about 10^{-13} T/H or 6.7×10^{12} T atoms/liter or 0.031 mc/liter, and perhaps 1 in. of rain or 0.073 mc/ft^2 or 3.1 c/acre.

3. *Ground-water inventory.* Inject at rate of about 30 c/mi^2 in many points at level of 1 meter below the surface so that evaporation would be negligible, and measure the composition of the ground water by taking samples at depths down to 100 ft vs. time.

We can expect that the tritium will prove to be of great benefit in practical hydrology. Our examples are merely initial efforts, and there is every reason to suppose that practical applications of tritiated water to hydrology, meteorology, and geophysics can now be made.

References

Begemann, F., and W. F. Libby. 1957. Continental water balance, ground water inventory and storage time, surface ocean mixing rates, and world-wide water circulation patterns from cosmic-ray and bomb tritium, *Geochim. et Cosmochim. Acta, 12,* 277–296.

Benton, G. S., M. A. Estoque, and J. Dominitz. 1953. The Johns Hopkins University, Department of Civil Engineering, Scientific Report 1, Contract AF19(122)-365 of Geophysics Research Division, Air Force, Cambridge Research Center.

Brown, R. M., and W. E. Grummitt. 1956. The determination of tritium in natural waters, *Can. J. Chem., 34,* 220–226.

Buttlar, H. von, and W. F. Libby. 1955. Natural distribution of cosmic-ray produced tritium, II, *J. Inorg. & Nuclear Chem., 1,* 75–91.

Craig, H., G. Boato, and D. E. White. 1956. Nuclear processes in geologic settings, Second Conference, September 8–10, 1955, Publication 400, Natl. Acad. Sci., Nuclear Science Series Report 19.

Currie, L. A., W. F. Libby, and R. L. Wolfgang. 1956. Tritium production by high-energy protons, *Phys. Rev., 101,* 1557–1563.

Eidinoff, M. L. 1947. The cathodic protium-tritium separation factor, I, Apparatus; Platinum cathode-alkaline solution, *J. Am. Chem. Soc., 69,* 977, 2507–2509.

Faltings, V., and P. Harteck. 1950. Tritium content of the atmosphere, *Z. Naturforsch., 5A,* 438–439.

Fireman, E. L. 1955. Tritium production by 2.2-bev protons on iron and its relation to cosmic radiation, *Phys. Rev., 97,* 1303–1304.

Fireman, E. L., and F. S. Rowland. 1955. Tritium and neutron production by 2.2-bev protons on nitrogen and oxygen, *Phys. Rev., 97,* 780–782.

Grosse, A. V., W. M. Johnston, R. L. Wolfgang, and W. F. Libby. 1951. Tritium in nature, *Science, 113,* 1–2.

Jones, W. M. 1955. Half-life of tritium, *Phys. Rev., 100,* 124–125. (This reference gives the half-life of tritium to be 12.26 years.)

Kaufman, S., and W. F. Libby. 1954. The natural distribution of tritium, *Phys. Rev., 93,* 1337–1344.

Libby, W. F. 1946. Atmospheric helium three and radiocarbon from cosmic radiation, *Phys. Rev., 69,* 671–673.

Libby, W. F. 1953. The potential usefulness of natural tritium, *Proc. Natl. Acad. Sci. U. S., 39,* 245–247.

Libby, W. F. 1956. Radioactive strontium fallout, *Proc. Natl. Acad. Sci. U. S., 42,* 365–390.

Stewart, N. G., R. N. Crooks, and E. M. R. Fisher. 1956. The radiological dose to persons in the U. K. due to debris from nuclear test explosions, U. S. Atomic Energy Commission, A.E.R.E. HP/R 1701.

Measurement and Use of Natural Radiocarbon

HESSEL DE VRIES

University of Groningen

The "radiocarbon method" developed by W. F. Libby (1952) quickly became established as a valuable dating technique. It would be difficult to overemphasize the importance of this new dating tool to rate and chronology studies in the fields of geology, climatology, palynology, archeology, and oceanography. No modern research in these fields can be considered complete unless time markers of radiocarbon dates are included. More than 3000 published dates have been used in many reports in the various disciplines—reports so numerous that from time to time summaries of the significant dates in each field are published. In Pleistocene geology, the articles by Flint and Deevey (1951), Flint and Rubin (1955), and Flint (1956) are examples of this type of review article, on North American material primarily. In climatology, the report of the California Conference on Climatology at Scripps Institution in 1956 includes many papers utilizing C^{14} dates. Pollen analysis has advanced considerably because of this powerful tool given by Libby. American pollen studies with C^{14} dating have been summarized by Deevey and Flint (1957), and the European studies by Gross (1955). Archeological samples are treated by Braidwood (1958), Johnson (1951), and many others. Oceanography studies based on C^{14} dating are exemplified by the deep-sea core temperature work done by Emiliani (1955) and Broecker et al. (1957, unpublished).

The striking feature about all these chronology studies is that the climatic curves derived from the C^{14} dates agree with one another in their essential fluctuations. To have the different sciences yield corroborating pictures on the climates of the past is encouraging. In general, the over-all patterns of cold and warm fluctuations correlate in time between the North American and European continents, as well as between the northern and southern hemispheres. Only some of the details remain to be clarified.

With the advance in the technique of radiocarbon dating, the range of the method was increased and problems of dating older samples were investigated. Libby's carbon-black method had sufficient range to establish that the last advance or substage of the Wisconsin stage of glaciation occurred approximately 10,000 to 11,000 years ago. He dated the forest bed at Two Creeks, Wisconsin, at 11,300 years of age, a date confirmed by many laboratories since. The Two Creeks horizon is a warm interval separating the Valders substage from the older Mankato substage. Later dating showed that this interstadial correlated in Europe with the Allerød, and that the stadials before and after were the Older Dryas and Younger Dryas, respectively.

With the advent of gas counting, the range was extended so that a significant portion of the Last Glaciation could be investigated. In addition to establishing a chronology of events of older stadials, the details of the younger stages were elaborated.

In North America, the work of the Geological Survey in Washington established a major glacial advance beginning at 25,000 years ago and culminating at 18,000 (Flint and Rubin, 1955). These intermediate dates placed an interstadial (the weathering of the Farmdale) at 25,000 years; the Tazewell stadial with climax at 18,000; an interstadial and then the Cary stadial with climax at 14,500; followed by an interstadial and then the Mankato stadial with climax at approximately 12,500. A series of samples were dated at "older than," and their significance awaited improvements in the method.

Work at the laboratory in Groningen has extended the available time range and improved the accuracy of the procedures. The range of the method is now about 70,000 years; this makes it possible to date another interstadial between about 50,000 and 70,000 years; there is some evidence that the end of the Last Interglacial is just within the range. This chapter will discuss some of the more recent improvements in methods, review highlights of some older chronology in North America and Europe (early Wisconsin, and early Würm, respectively), and discuss some new measurements of the variation of radiocarbon with time and location on earth.

Production of Radiocarbon

Radiocarbon (C^{14}) is formed when nitrogen of the atmosphere is bombarded with neutrons, according to the equation

$$N^{14} + {}_0^1n \rightarrow C^{14} + {}_1^1H$$

The neutrons are produced by cosmic radiation in the higher atmosphere, the radiocarbon also being formed there. The radiocarbon soon combines with oxygen to make CO_2 and as such comes down to the surface of the earth by convection. Equilibrium is established between production and decay of C^{14}, and if no special disturbances occur the concentration of radiocarbon remains constant in time. Some "special disturbances" will be discussed in a later section. For the time being, the fundamental assumption in radiocarbon dating is the constancy of concentration of radiocarbon in the atmosphere.

An important aspect of radiocarbon is that it is incorporated in organic material by the process of photosynthesis. Thus it primarily appears in plants but it also is taken in by animals that live on plants. If the organic matter is preserved after death, the radiocarbon decays in the normal exponential way with a half-life of 5570 years. The carbon no longer exchanges with the atmosphere. The age can be calculated from the amount of C^{14} in the sample present. If, for example, one-half of the original amount is left, the age is 5570 years.

The Technique of the Measurement—Chemical Aspects

Different experimental procedures have been developed in the course of time, but the first step is always the same: the sample is converted into CO_2. Organic material is combusted; carbonates are treated with acid. This first step is necessary to obtain material of known carbon content without a variable amount of inactive, or perhaps even radioactive, material that would affect the measurement. The next step in Libby's original technique converted the CO_2 into elementary carbon which was put *into* the counter. This was necessary since the penetrating power of the β radiation of C^{14} is small (ca. 2.3 mg/cm^2) and since the natural activity of C^{14} is small even without an absorbing window. This technique has now in general been abandoned, partly because of the recent increase in radioactive fallout produced by atomic-bomb experiments. It is practically impossible to get the carbon on the inner wall of the counter without exposing it to the open air. In this step radioactive fallout may get on the carbon—and it often does—leading to a calculated age younger than the true age.

A different series of techniques was developed in Groningen. Instead of converting the CO_2 into elementary carbon, the gas itself was put into the counter as the counting gas at a pressure of 3 atmospheres. Since this can be done without disassembling the counter, merely by pumping out one sample and permitting the next sample to go in, contamination by radioactive fallout is nearly impossible and apparently has never occurred. Though the idea is simple enough, the first trials were not very successful: the counter with CO_2 had no "plateau"; i.e., with increasing voltage on the counter, no region was obtained where the counting rate became independent of the voltage applied. Fortunately, it turned out that this bad behavior was not due to the CO_2 itself, but to small traces of electronegative gases such as oxides of nitrogen, oxygen, and halogens. Amounts of one part in a million are sometimes sufficient to disturb the normal action of the counter. For an explanation of the origin of this sensitivity, and a description of the purification finally developed, the original publications may be consulted (de Vries and Barendsen, 1953; de Vries, 1955 and 1957*a*).

The simplicity of the procedure may be judged from the fact that combustion, purification, and filling of the counter at present require less than 3 hours. Actual counting generally takes 24 or 48 hours (see below). Besides CO_2 two other gases have come into use: acetylene and methane. Preparation of these compounds, both starting from CO_2, requires more work than the purification of the CO_2. As far as the precision of the results is concerned, there is no special advantage for any of these gases; the danger of explosions with acetylene, however, may be mentioned.

In addition to gas-counting techniques, scintillation counters have been developed. Since they have not yet come into use for dating purposes, they will not be described in detail (Arnold, 1954).

The measurement of the activity. Independent of the chemical form in which the sample is measured, some special problems arise in connection with the counting. The technical difficulties are related to the very low natural activity of carbon. This is true for recent carbon; for old samples the activity is even smaller. In order to get good statistics (see below) it is essential to get much carbon into the counter, which implies that the counter must be large. Typical values of the effective length are from 20 to 60 cm, the diameter varying from about 5 to 7 cm. A counter of these dimensions may give between about 5 and 50 counts per minute for recent carbon. Unfortunately, it not only counts the β particles of carbon but also gives discharges due to other sources, the so-called background. More precisely, background is defined as the counting rate when the counter is filled with a very old (inactive) sample, which is generally produced from anthracite. To illustrate the methods generally used for reduction of background a counter with an effective length of 16 cm, a diameter of 5 cm, and a (net) counting rate for recent carbon of 5.6 cpm (counts per minute) will be considered. The background when the counter is operated unshielded in a normal, uncontaminated room is about 200 cpm. This is much more than the net recent carbon count and must be reduced drastically. The first improvement consisted of putting the counter in an iron shield with a thickness between 10 and 30 cm or sometimes even greater. The shield absorbs γ radiation from the surroundings and from the walls, and also cosmic radiation, reducing the background to about 64 cpm. The major part of this remaining counting rate is due to mesons from cosmic radiation, which cannot be absorbed even by several meters of iron. Though the mesons cannot be prevented from reaching the counter, the counts produced can be eliminated by an anticoincidence ring, i.e. a set of normal Geiger counters surrounding the "carbon counter." If a meson crosses the carbon counter, it has to cross also one or two of the counters of the ring. Thus, two *coinciding* discharges are produced in the ring and in the carbon counter. A simple electronic circuit guarantees that only such pulses in the carbon counter are recorded as are not accompanied by a discharge in the ring (anticoincidence circuit). In this way pulses due to mesons are discarded. Obviously, this system works only for radiation that is detected with high efficiency in the ring of anticoincidence counters. The probability for detection of γ radiation and neutrons is so small that the anticoincidence system does not suppress their effect.

The typical counter considered above gave a background of 4.0 cpm with the anticoincidence system switched on, which may be considered a reasonable residual background for this size of counter. Comparing this figure with a net count of 5.6 cpm for recent carbon in this counter, it is obvious that the background is low enough for measurement of fairly recent samples. For old (less active) samples it is of importance to reduce the background further, and the question arises where this residual background comes from. From later experience it became clear that the greater part of the background was due to radioactive contamination of the material the counter was made of (commercial copper). A new counter made of quartz had a background of only 1.8 cpm in the same shield, although its length was 37 cm instead of 16 cm. A counter made of special electrolytic copper, length 53 cm, diameter 7 cm, showed a background of 5 cpm. The recent carbon counts were 14.5 and 38 cpm, respectively. With these counters older samples can be dated, or more recent samples can be dated with greater precision.

Soon after these larger counters were put in operation, it appeared that the background was not completely constant; it fluctuated with barometric pressure. A similar effect was reported by Fergusson (1955). It seemed obvious that these variations could only be due to cosmic radiation, a high pressure giving more absorption in the atmosphere and a lower background. The effect was shown to be due to neutrons, "locally" produced by the corpuscular component of the cosmic radiation in the iron shield of the counter. This nuclear component (fast protons and neutrons) causes spallation of nuclei of the iron shield. The neutrons set free can pass the anticoincidence ring without being detected and may give a count in the carbon counter. By incorporating a "neutron trap" in the shield, consisting of paraffin mixed with boric acid, the number of neutrons could be reduced appreciably (de Vries, 1956*a* and 1957*b*). For the large counter the background was reduced from 5 cpm to 2.40 cpm, whereas the variations with barometric pressure were reduced from 0.37 cpm/cm mercury change in barometric pressure to 0.05 cpm. Though corrections must still be applied they are less serious than before. An effect of 0.37 cpm is produced by a sample 36,000 years old in this counter, which means that, originally, ages of this order could hardly be measured, especially since the intensity of this nuclear component of the cosmic radiation is controlled not only by barometric pressure but also by the magnetic field of the earth, whereas an enormous increase of this component is sometimes observed during a solar flare (for its effect on radiocarbon dating see de Vries, 1956*b*).

This introduction is completed with a discussion of the precision of radiocarbon measurements. Disregarding some failures of electronics, etc., the error is always the statistical one. For any measurement the relative error is inversely proportional to the square root of the number of disintegrations counted. For a counting rate of 7 cpm and a counting time of 24 hours, about 10,000 events are counted, giving a standard deviation of 1 per cent. It should be emphasized, however, that there is still a 30 per cent chance that the measurement is more than 1 per cent off. Furthermore, the age is calculated from a recent carbon count, a background count, and the run of the unknown sample; the error normally quoted includes these three sources of statistical errors. Since background and recent calibration sample are generally measured several times at regular intervals, they hardly contribute to the final error. Errors in calibration samples affect all dates of one laboratory in a similar way; they could be left out for comparisons of a series of dates from one laboratory. In order to convert the error in the activity into the error of the age, the fact that a 1 per cent change in activity corresponds to 80 years' error in age, independent of the age of the sample, is utilized. Of course, it is more difficult to measure old samples with the same precision, since it takes more time to "collect" the same number of counts. Moreover, for very old samples the net carbon count becomes small relative to the background.

It can easily be shown that for a given sample of low specific activity the time required to attain a particular precision is inversely proportional to $f = S^2/B$, S being the net counting rate for recent carbon and B the background. The factor f is called the figure of merit, though it does not include all relevant factors. Though f determines the total counting time, it is generally preferable to attain a given value of f by a small value of B and accordingly a smaller value of S, since small S means that a smaller amount of sample is required. This is especially important for isotopic enrichment (see below). Typical amounts of carbon required for routine measurements range from 1 to 5 grams, though less material can be counted, at the expense of precision.

With the large counter mentioned above, samples about 50,000 years old can be dated in a reasonable time (48 hours of counting). Dating means here that the activity is significantly above background. Recently the range was considerably increased by applying isotopic enrichment (see Haring et al., 1958). By thermal diffusion the C^{14} from a very large sample (200 liters or more) is concentrated to a smaller volume of about 8 liters, which just fills our large counter at its normal pressure of 3 atmospheres. If the concentration of C^{14} is doubled, the concentration in the original sample may be half of the normal limit; this means that its age may be 5570 years older. In the Laboratory for Mass Spectrometry in Amsterdam enrichments by about a factor of 16 can be obtained in about 8 weeks. This means an extension of the range for radiocarbon dating to about 71,000 years.

Effect of Infiltration of Recent Carbon

Actual measurements of old samples have shown that more errors arise from impurities in the samples (recent infiltration) than from the actual measurement of the activity. The effect of recent infiltration is illustrated by the following calculation. If a sample that is actually "infinitely old"—say more than 1,000,000 years—acquires 1 per cent of recent carbon, its activity will correspond to an age of about 36,000 years. One-half per cent of recent carbon will give it an age of 41,500, etc. Even if, at present, infiltration of recent carbon is improbable, it may have occurred sometime in the past. Though the tolerance becomes larger if infiltration occurred long ago, serious problems still persist.

That errors like those mentioned above actually occur may be illustrated by the following examples. The first old samples we dated came from a Last Interglacial deposit in the Netherlands (de Voorst, see Van der Vlerk and Florschütz, 1953). According to present views they should be at least about 80,000 years old; the age actually found ranged from 40,000 to more than 53,000 from top to bottom of the profile. Attempts to identify and to remove the infiltrated material from these samples have not been successful. A second example is a peat sample from Farmsum (province of Groningen, Netherlands). The age obtained with an acid washing of the sample only was 33,300 $\pm$ 400 years. After the extraction of some humus in a "mild" way, the age of the remaining material was 37,900 $\pm$ 1000 years. The humus was 30,000 $\pm$ 500 years old. For the lower part of the peat layer, the corresponding dates for acid washing only and complete pretreatment were 36,000 and 43,700 years, respectively. Since the total amount of infiltrated recent humus was fairly large, it is not certain that all was completely removed. A more rigorous extraction of humus would have dissolved nearly the whole peat sample. The success of the treatment is probably due to the fact that the infiltrated material (humus) is more mobile than the humus of the peat itself, and the extraction acts with some preference on the infiltrated humus. The infiltrated humus in this sample came from a younger peat layer (7000 years old) which was deposited on top of the old layer separated by about 1 meter of sand.

Another type of recent contamination was shown by a series of samples from Loopstedt (near the town of Schleswig, Germany). The upper peat layers gave ages ranging from 35,000 to 40,000 years (from top to bottom). Since other dates suggested that it could not have been warm enough at that time to produce the flora indicated by the pollen diagram, and since humus extracted gave the same age, we went to the site and found rootlets going down into the peat. New material was collected, and rootlets were removed as completely as possible. The new date was $45{,}000 \pm 2000$. The amount of roots removed was sufficient to account for the discrepancy.

The examples cited indicate the importance of a careful choice of samples, combined with an appropriate pretreatment of the sample in the laboratory. Details of the effects of various treatments on various materials (wood, charcoal, etc.) which were briefly summarized at the C^{14} conference in Copenhagen in 1954 will be published soon. Wood and charcoal are most attractive as sample material since they withstand several chemical treatments that extract infiltrated organic substances. From charcoal, even rootlets can be extracted chemically.

Some Application of Radiocarbon Dating to Pleistocene Chronology

The climatic curve obtained by combining our reliable data is given in figure 1 (see de Vries, 1958*a*). The reliability is estimated from the occurrence in the field, the kind of material, and the amount of recent material extracted (if any). The hump (oscillation) at 11,000 years (Allerød, Two Creeks) is apparently well marked all over the northern hemisphere. Generally, at least in northwestern Europe, it is easily recognized. The next reliable landmark is the last Interglacial, marked by a warm flora, high sea level (and marine deposits), and an intense weathering of the loess (in the loess regions). The period *between* Allerød and Last Interglacial, however, has given considerable difficulties with correlation and chronology. At present, radiocarbon seems to be the only tool to solve this problem.

The period between about 12,000 and 24,000 B.P. (Before Present) has not provided organic samples up to now in northwestern Europe. The first interstadial (going from top to bottom) is found at about 27,000 years ago. Main evidence was derived from samples from the Austrian loess region. The climatic fluctuations are recorded here as follows: During a cold period (stadial) rock debris is produced by frost action and glacier activity. During the second half of the stadial, glaciers retreat. The rock debris formed by earlier glacial action is transported by wind and deposited as loess. In the next interstadial, weathering occurs and vegetation produces a fossil soil (starting from

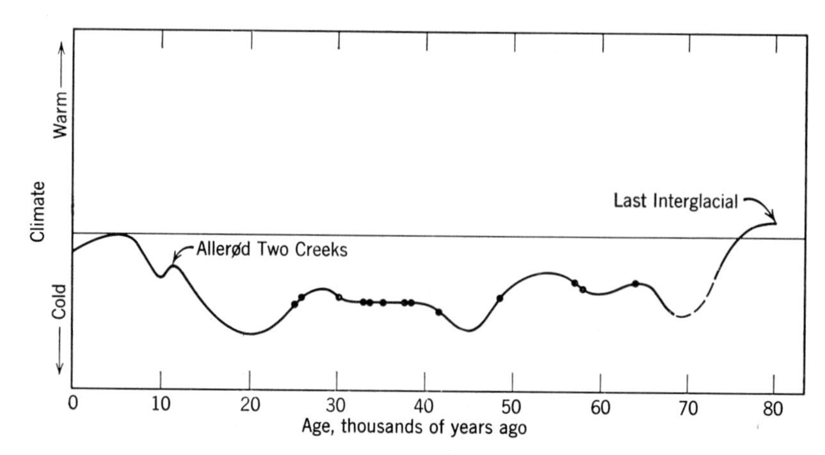

Fig. 1. Climatic curve derived from various sources (see text). Part of the dates represented by points. Minor oscillations have been left out. The part of the curve between 50,000 and 80,000 has been brought up to date after a private discussion with Dr. Zagwijn (Haarlem) and Dr. Andersen (Copenhagen). (From de Vries, 1958*a*.)

the surface). During the next stadial a new loess is produced on top of the previous one (if it has not yet been eroded off). The interstadial at about 27,000 years B.P. corresponds to the so-called fossil soil of *Paudorf*. The point at 25,000 years was obtained from charcoal on top of this soil. The point at 25,600 years was obtained from charcoal collected in the soil at the well known site of Unterwisternitz. Charcoal collected at Willendorf from underneath the same soil horizon gave an age about 30,000 B.P. This brackets the interstadial somewhere between 25,000 and 30,000 years B.P. The period between about 30,000 and 48,000 was fairly cold, though perhaps not always as cold as it was around 18,000 years ago since some organic samples have been collected in northwestern Europe. The samples at 32,000, 33,000, 35,000, and 38,000 were collected in the Netherlands, the samples at 38,000 and 42,000 in England (see de Vries, 1958*a*). At all six of these sites the flora or the fauna indicated a cold climate.

The next interstadial occurred probably between about 49,000 and 70,000 years ago. Four sites have been studied: Loopstedt (mentioned already); Brørup (Denmark) (Andersen, 1957); Amersfoort (Netherlands) (unpublished); and Chelford (England). Loopstedt and Brørup could be correlated by the pollen diagram. Charcoal collected in the upper layer at Loopstedt and peat from the upper layer at Brørup both gave about 49,000 ± 3000 years. Wood from Chelford, which *probably* represents the same interstadial, gave 59,000 ± 1000 after enrichment. If the correlation is correct, it implies that the interstadial began before 59,000 B.P. In the near future peat layers from Brørup will be dated by the enrichment procedure. The climatic sequence shown in figure 1 is mainly based on pollen diagrams from the sites mentioned already and from Amersfoort (province of Utrecht, Netherlands). Amersfoort had provided the type locality of the Eem (= Last Interglacial). The point at 64,000 B.P. has been obtained on a wood sample from Amersfoort after enrichment. Since contamination by recent material can never be excluded completely, it is possible that the actual age of the Amersfoort sample is somewhat older, so that the time for the cold period (stadial) that probably occurred *between* the Amersfoort and Chelford samples could be somewhat longer.

Further supporting evidence of the chronology given by figure 1, which also demonstrates the importance of radiocarbon for "long distance" correlations, is obtained from two new samples recently measured. The samples came from a pluvial lake (Searles lake) in California. Pluvial periods are represented by deposition of mud; during interpluvials the lake dried out, with resultant deposition of a heavy layer of salt. It is generally assumed that pluvials correspond to stadials at higher latitude. Consequently, the second mud layer should correspond to the cold period between 30,000 and 48,000 years B.P. It was very satisfying to find that the top of this mud layer dated 32,000 years old and a sample not completely at the bottom of it gave 45,000. The attractive feature of this type of sample is that a continuous series may be obtained; in general, most profiles are not complete because of erosion. Only deep valleys or subsiding areas can normally give a continuous record of the past. Details of the investigations at Searles lake are being prepared by Flint and his collaborators.

In conclusion, the climatic curve arrived at in figure 1 may be compared with data on glacial advance and retreat in North America. The evidence obtained up to now (Flint and Rubin, 1955; Flint, 1956; Ruhe et al., 1957) presents the same general picture as was arrived at in Europe. The Two Creeks interstadial is correlated with the Allerød in Europe. The colder period following the Allerød (Younger Dryas) correlates with the Valders advance.

Summarizing the information for the period before the Two Creeks, the American sequence was as follows: Advance of the ice at around

25,000, which correlates nicely with the dates for the Paudorf soil. In succession, the substages are Tazewell (maximum of Tazewell around 18,000), Cary, Mankato. This leaves two interstadials before the Two Creeks, the Tazewell-Cary and the Cary-Mankato. The Cary-Mankato interstadial seems to be somewhat older than the Bølling, which began at about 13,200 (de Vries et al., 1958*a* and *b*). For the Tazewell-Cary interstadial at 14,000 B.P., likewise, no evident counterpart has been found in Europe. Critical consideration of all evidence and a discussion with Dr. H. E. Wright (University of Minnesota) led to the conclusion that the American data were more difficult to interpret than the European. In Europe, the climatic sequence was generally derived from analyses of continuous peat deposits, whereas in America the record consisted of isolated samples from moraines.

Many more samples need to be determined, particularly in the older range, to remove minor discrepancies.

Variation in Concentration of Radiocarbon with Time and Location on Earth

It was emphasized above that radiocarbon dating is based on the assumption that the activity of the atmosphere has been constant in the period covered by the method and that the activity is independent of the location on earth. The first assay by Libby confirmed these assumptions. Suess (1955), however, with a more precise technique found that the activity of the atmosphere had decreased by at least 1 per cent in the last century; the decrease was explained as due to dilution of the atmosphere with inactive carbon produced by combustion of fossil fuel. In the last few years the activity has been increasing as a result of atomic-bomb tests (Rafter and Fergusson, 1957; de Vries, 1958*b*).

It was assumed, however, that, neglecting these human interferences, the activity of radiocarbon had been constant in time. In a recent study, de Vries (1958*c*) has shown that even this is not exactly true. The concentration of radiocarbon in the past can be calculated from measurements of the present activity of a series of samples of known age. Tree rings are very suitable for the purpose. The results are shown in figure 2 All activities have been corrected for fractionation by measurement of the C^{12}/C^{13} ratios. If a plant has a preference for the heavier isotope, this preference is shown by the C^{13}/C^{12} ratio. The fractionation for C^{14} is twice the fractionation for C^{13}.

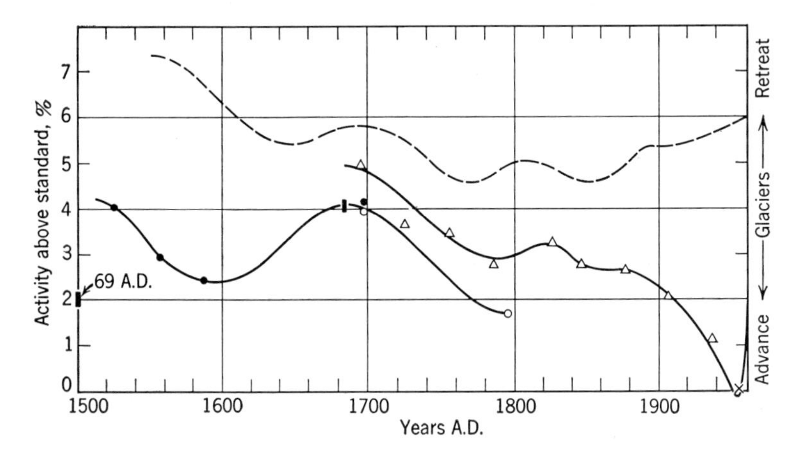

Fig. 2. Initial activities of samples of known age (i.e., corrected for decay). △ Tree *A* from Colorado. ○ Tree *B* from the Bavarian Forest. ● Tree *C* from Spessart Forest. ▮ Charred wheat from A.D. 1684 and 69. × Recent calibration sample. Statistical error 0.2 per cent. Dotted curve: Extension of continental glaciers (schematic). All curves drawn free hand. (From de Vries, 1958*c*, by permission.)

The measurements demonstrate that the concentration of radiocarbon in the atmosphere has fluctuated considerably. The decrease during the last 100 years is probably due to the dilution effect; it amounts to 1.5 per cent between 1845 and 1935. This agrees well with previous results (Suess, 1955; Münnich, 1957). The combustion of fossil fuel before 1850 was much smaller, and it cannot explain the variations found.

In order to understand what processes could have produced these fluctuations it is necessary to consider first the radiocarbon balance and exchange between the various reservoirs. For the present purpose the model developed by Craig (1957) is most suitable (fig. 3).

This model considers the following reservoirs of carbon: atmosphere (A), biosphere (B) including humus (H), upper layer of the ocean (mixed layer) (M), and finally the largest reservoir, the deep sea (D). For physicists and others familiar with electronic circuits the model may become easier to handle if it is converted into an electric analogue (fig. 4). In order to avoid confusion it should be emphasized that the conclusions to be drawn from this analogue are identical with what can be done with the original model. The production of C^{14} in the atmosphere is represented by a current i produced by a

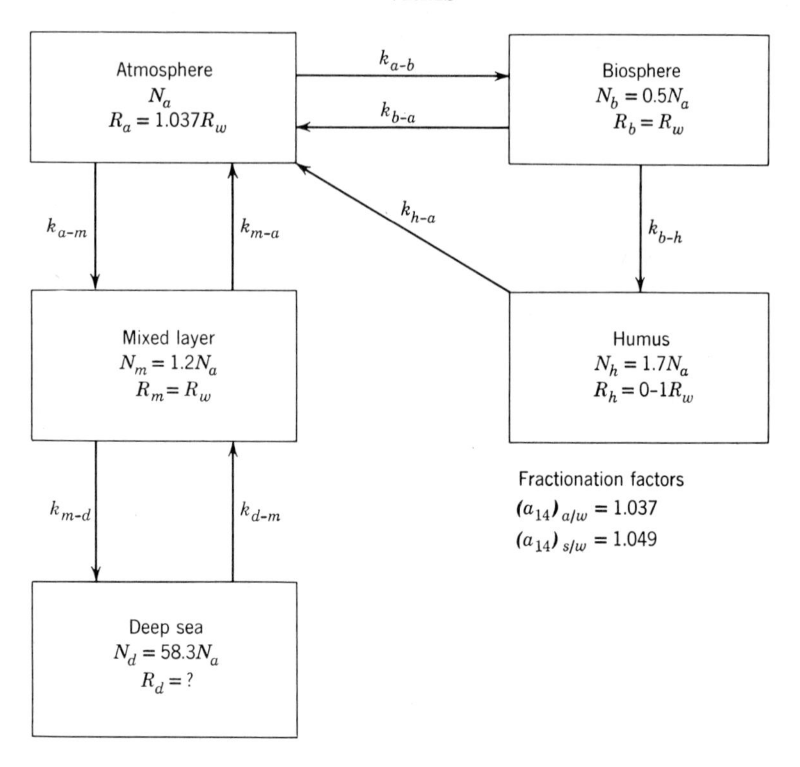

Fig. 3. Carbon reservoirs in the exchangeable system. N = amount of carbon in reservoir. N_a = atmospheric carbon = 0.126 gram C/cm^2. R = specific activity in reservoir. R_w = C^{14}/C^{12} ratio in standard wood = 1.14×10^{-12}. k = exchange rate. (From Craig, 1957, by permission.)

source with a high internal impedance; consequently i is not affected by the circuit. The capacity of each condenser is proportional to the size of the reservoir as estimated by Craig. Even in an isolated reservoir the amount of C^{14} decreases because of decay with a half-life of 5570 years, or a mean life of 8000 years. Thus, the condensers should have a leak giving them a time constant of 8000; radioactive decay and electric leak follow the same exponential law. For demonstrations it is reasonable to take another time scale, for example 0.1 second instead of a year. The resistances in figure 4 were chosen so that a year in the actual situation is 1 second in the model. The values of the resistors between reservoirs were chosen to make the residence time in each reservoir equal to the times arrived at by Craig. The residence time in the atmosphere (before a C^{14} atom is absorbed in the ocean) is about 6 years. This means that the product $C_A R_{AM}$ is 6. Since C_A was arbitrarily chosen as 1 microfarad, it follows that R_{AM} is 6 megohms. The concentrations of C^{14} in each reservoir are represented by the voltage at the corresponding element in the circuit.

In the steady state the condensers can be left out (but not their "leaks"). If the biosphere is neglected also, the circuit reduces to the circuit of figure 5, which shows that the greater part of C^{14} flows from atmosphere into the deep sea, where it decays, since R_D is the smallest resistor to "earth." Radiocarbon stays a considerable time in D, and this explains why the specific activity of carbon in the deep sea is lower than in the atmosphere. In the model it corresponds to a voltage drop from A to D. One per cent in activity corresponds to an apparent age of 80 years. The ages in mixed layer and deep sea which follow from the potentials in figure 5 agree with the experimental determinations, as far as they are available, for the resistances were chosen to fit these data. Actually the concentration of radiocarbon is not constant; consequently, the condensers cannot be left out. Nevertheless, the circuit of figure 5 can be simplified as follows. First of all, the resistors R_A and R_M can be left out without affecting the system because they are very large and do not draw an appreciable

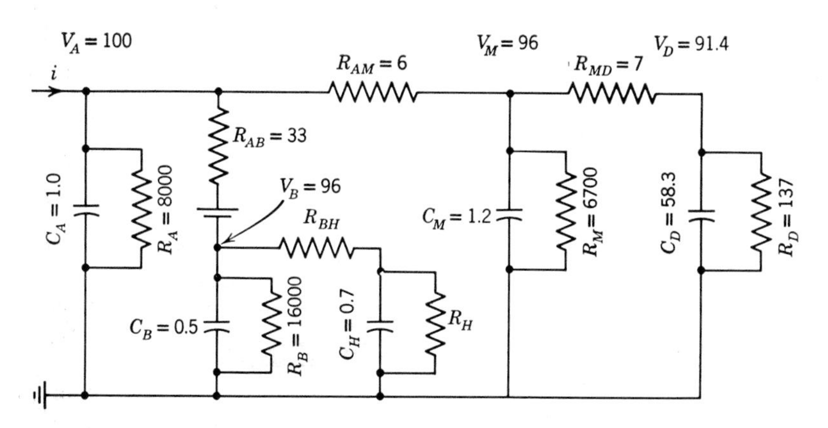

Fig. 4. Electric analogue, representing the distribution and transport of radiocarbon in nature. C = condensers, simulating reservoirs. R with one subscript, leaks simulating the decay of radiocarbon; with two subscripts, resistances representing the exchange between reservoirs. A = atmosphere. M = mixed layer of the ocean. D = deep sea. B = biosphere. H = humus. (From de Vries, 1958*c*, by permission.)

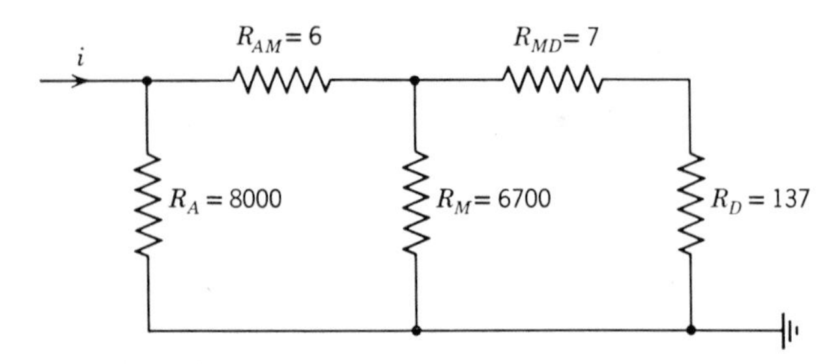

Fig. 5. Simplified model for transport of the radiocarbon under steady-state conditions. (From de Vries, 1958*c*, by permission.)

current. Then the whole biosphere can be neglected, for the present discussion, since $R_{AB} = 33$ is much larger than R_{AM}. For a more detailed discussion this omission is not justified. Thus, the circuit of figure 6 is finally obtained.

Consideration of figure 4 suggests two potential sources of variation in C^{14} content of the atmosphere: variation of the production of C^{14} (input current i), and variation of elements of the circuit, especially the exchange rates R_{AM} and R_{MD}. These possibilities will be considered more quantitatively after the general line of thought has been explained. As long as variations over a period of about 100 years are considered (fig. 4) the condensers C_A and C_M can easily follow them, since the time constants of these condensers are of the order of 10 years; thus C_A and C_M can be omitted. The time constant of C_D is so much larger (8000 years) that it maintains its potential of 91.4 volts. The existence of C_D and R_D may be neglected provided that V_D is kept at 91.4 volts. Figure 4 indicates that, in order to get an increase of radiocarbon in the atmosphere from a concentration 100 to 102, the potential drop from atmosphere to deep sea has to increase from 8.6 to 10.6. Therefore the current has to increase by about 25 per cent, or one of the resistors has to increase by 50 per cent.

Variations in exchange rates between reservoirs. Considering the processes involved, variations in the rate of exchange between atmosphere and mixed layer (R_{AM}) even of a small amplitude are very unlikely; variations in exchange rate between mixed layer and deep sea are far more probable. The mechanism of this exchange is still a problem by itself. Worthington (1954) gave some evidence that at least North Atlantic deep water may be formed sporadically rather than being replenished by a continuous mixing process. The idea is that in periods of low average annual temperature the surface water becomes cold enough to be replaced by deep water. It is also possible, of course, that temperature only accelerates or decelerates a more permanent circulation at higher latitudes. Dr. Broecker at the Andover C^{14} conference in 1956 suggested that this phenomenon could perhaps affect the concentration of C^{14} in the atmosphere, but at that time no further data were available to test the idea. It was shown above that the exchange must be approximately doubled in order to obtain the variations actually observed. If the increase occurs in part of the ocean only, the effect has to be still larger. Qualitatively, the effect of oceanic mixing can be understood without the model of figure 4: increased mixing brings older (less active) water to the surface, where exchange with the atmosphere can occur.

An attractive feature of the present hypothesis is that it can be checked by comparing the time course of the activity in the atmosphere with records of temperature. Unfortunately, reliable records are available only since about 1750. H. P. Berlage (Utrecht) suggested use of data on the extension of glaciers, which are available for a longer period though they may depend on factors other than the temperature. The curve given in figure 2 was kindly provided by Professor Berlage; the underlying data were derived from various sources, but mainly from the *Compendium of Meteorology*, 1951. The agreement with the activity curve is very good, and the significance of the agreement is even greater if the fact that the samples from the Spessart oak were not chosen at random (as the other samples were), but at intervals suggested by the climatic (glacier) curve, is taken into account. The retreat of glaciers in the last century is not accom-

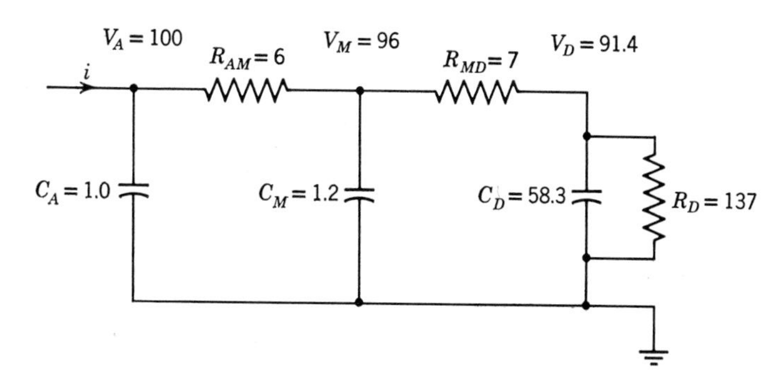

Fig. 6. Simplified model for transport of radiocarbon under nonstationary conditions.

panied by an increase of concentration of radiocarbon in the atmosphere. That the increase is masked by the dilution effect implies that the dilution effect has probably been larger than the curve in figure 2 suggests. If so, it is of importance for various computations about exchange rates.

According to figure 2, the recent standard used at Groningen is about 3 per cent below the average activity of the German trees. Thus all Groningen radiocarbon dates published up to now are about 240 years too low.

Further studies of the time course of the variations in C^{14} content of the atmosphere would certainly be of interest. If a longer series of samples of known age were available it might be possible to obtain some information about minor climatic variations in the past, perhaps even from tree rings of old trees, say from the Allerød, where the absolute age is not known. Finally, the exact time course could give information about the circulation in the ocean in cold periods. Other factors, however, might affect the concentration of C^{14} in the atmosphere. Such a disturbing factor is also suggested by the difference in activity of trees A and B in figure 2.

Other disturbing factors. Though tree B shows the same decrease of activity from 1695 to 1785, it has a lower activity than A. Measurement of the C^{13}/C^{12} ratio has shown that the difference is not due to fractionation; up to now we have not succeeded in finding a satisfactory explanation. Since the charred wheat sample from 1684 is also low in C^{14}, the difference in activity could be a local effect, the C^{14} concentration in western Europe being lower than that in Colorado. We have considered the possibility that the radiocarbon piles up in the continental air masses (in Colorado) which are "disconnected" from the ocean. The rate of increase of the concentration predicted by the model of figure 4, however, is much too small. The current i is equal to $V_A/150$, if V_A is the voltage (concentration) in the atmosphere. If no current flows into the ocean, i gives a rate of increase $i/C_A = V_A/150$. Thus, it takes 150 years before the concentration is doubled. In one month, which is a fairly long residence time for air above a continent, the increase would be only 0.06 per cent. The other currents are even smaller than the current flowing into the ocean.

Up to now it has been assumed that vertical mixing in the atmosphere is fast enough to permit the atmosphere to be considered a homogeneous reservoir. If it were subdivided into thinner layers which mix in times of the order of one month the concentration could go up and down to a larger extent. The capacity C of each individual layer would be smaller than C_A; according to the reasoning above the rates of change would be proportionally larger. It is obvious, however, that this idea is not supported by what is known about the mixing in the atmosphere.

Variations in the production of radiocarbon. It was shown above that the variation in the concentration of radiocarbon actually found could be produced by variations in the production rate if they amounted to about 25 per cent. In our original publication (de Vries, 1958*c*), variations of this magnitude were considered fairly improbable, and moreover they would leave us with a hypothesis *ad hoc*. Nevertheless, variations in production rate may be at least partly, if not completely, the source of the variations in C^{14}. Recently, Simpson (private communications) (Chicago) and Winckler and Ney (Minneapolis) have found that the total amount of neutrons produced in the higher atmosphere (integrated over the whole earth) decreased by a factor of 2 in the last four years. Therefore the (natural) production of C^{14} also decreased by this factor. The decrease is due to solar activity; the sun expels large amounts of charged material which affects magnetic fields, which, in turn, screen part of the cosmic radiation from the earth. The variations in C^{14} should be compared now with variations in solar activity. Fairly good records of sunspots are available over a considerable period (Schove, 1955). The maxima and minima in C^{14} activity between 1500 and 1800 agree just as well with the minima and maxima in solar activity as with the glacier curve in figure 2. At present it is impossible to decide whether the vertical mixing in the ocean also contributes to the variations in C^{14} or not. An 11-year period in the C^{14} activity might be detectable.

Implications for radiocarbon dating. Obviously the fluctuations found now affect the use of radiocarbon for dating purposes. Leaving aside the local effects, the variations of the initial activity with time give rise to errors of 100 years or more (80 years for a variation of 1 per cent). For the period now covered by tree-ring checks the variation of the initial activity can be taken into account, but that does not solve the problem completely, since it may happen that three or even five or more samples of *different* age could have at present the same activity. Radiocarbon measurements thus would not give one well defined age. This assertion is easily understood in the following way. Starting from the present activity of the unknown sample, its activity in the past can be represented by a curve rising exponentially (1 per cent per 80 years, doubling the height in one half-life). The point of intersection with the horizontal line that represents the (constant) initial activity gives the age of the sample. If, however, the initial activity is not constant but represented by a "wavy" line when plotted against time, the exponential curve may cut it in one, three, or five points (etc.), each giving an age compatible with the result of the radiocarbon measurement. Apparently, however, the fluctuations of the initial activity do not exceed about 1 per cent (relative to the average value), implying that the errors introduced in this way will not be larger than about 80 years.

References

Andersen, S. Th. 1957. New investigations of interglacial deposits in Jutland, *Eiszeitalter u. Geg., 8,* 181.

Arnold, J. R. 1954. Scintillation counting of natural radiocarbon, *Science, 119,* 155–158.

Braidwood, R. J. 1958. Near Eastern prehistory, *Science, 127,* 1419–1430.

Craig, H. 1957. The natural distribution of radiocarbon and the exchange time of carbon dioxide between atmosphere and sea, *Tellus, 9,* 1–17.

Deevey, E. S., and R. F. Flint. 1957. Postglacial hypsithermal interval, *Science, 125,* 182–184.

de Vries, Hl. 1955. Purification of CO_2 for use in a proportional counter for ^{14}C age measurements, *Appl. Sci. Research, B5,* 387–400.

de Vries, Hl. 1956*a*. The contribution of neutrons to the background of counters used for ^{14}C age measurements, *Nuclear Phys., 1,* 477.

de Vries, Hl. 1956*b*. Cosmic radiation during the solar flare of February 23rd and its effect on ^{14}C measurements, *Physica, 22,* 357.

de Vries, Hl. 1957*a*. The removal of radon from CO_2 for use in C^{14} age measurements, *Appl. Sci. Research, B6,* 461–470.

de Vries, Hl. 1957*b*. Further analysis of the neutron component of the background of counters used for ^{14}C age measurements, *Nuclear Phys., 3,* 65.

de Vries, Hl. 1958*a*. Radiocarbon dates for Würm interstadial samples, *Eiszeitalter u. Geg., 9,* 10–17.

de Vries, Hl. 1958*b*. Atomic bomb effect, *Science, 128,* 250–251.

de Vries, Hl. 1958*c*. Variation in concentration of radiocarbon with time and location on earth, *Proc. Koninkl. Ned. Akad. Wetenschap., B61.*

de Vries, Hl., and G. W. Barendsen. 1953. A new technique for radiocarbon dating by a proportional counter filled with carbon dioxide, *Physica, 19,* 987–1003.

de Vries, Hl., G. W. Barendsen, and H. T. Waterbolk. 1958*a*. Groningen radiocarbon dates, II, *Science, 127,* 129–137.

de Vries, Hl., and H. T. Waterbolk. 1958*b*. Groningen radiocarbon dates, III, *Science, 128,* 1550–1556.

Emiliani, C. 1955. Pleistocene temperatures, *J. Geol., 63,* 538–578.

Fergusson, G. J. 1955. Radiocarbon dating system, *Nucleonics, 13,* 18–23.

Flint, R. F. 1956. New radiocarbon dates and late-Pleistocene stratigraphy, *Am J. Sci., 254,* 265–287.

Flint, R. F., and E. S. Deevey. 1951. Radiocarbon dating of late-Pleistocene events, *Am. J. Sci., 249,* 257–300.

Flint, R. F., and M. Rubin. 1955. Radiocarbon dates of pre-Mankato events in eastern and central North America, *Science, 121,* 649–658.

Gross, H., 1955. Weitere Beiträge zur Kenntnis des Spätglazials, *Eiszeitalter u. Geg., 6,* 110–115.

Haring, A., A. E. de Vries, and Hl. de Vries. 1958. Radiocarbon dating up to 70,000 by isotopic enrichment, *Science, 128,* 472–473.

Johnson, F. 1951. Radiocarbon dating, *Am. Antiquity, 17* (no. 1, pt. 2).

Libby, W. F. 1952. *Radiocarbon Dating,* University of Chicago Press, Chicago; 2d ed., 1955.

Münnich, K. O. 1957. Heidelberg natural radiocarbon measurements, I, *Science, 126,* 194–199.

Rafter, T. A., and G. J. Fergusson. 1957. "Atom bomb effect"—recent increase of carbon-14 content of the atmosphere and biosphere, *Science, 126,* 557–558.

Ruhe, R. V., M. Rubin, and W. H. Scholtes. 1957. Late Pleistocene radiocarbon chronology in Iowa, *Am. J. Sci., 255,* 671–689.

Schove, J. D. 1955. The sunspot cycle, 649 B.C. to A.D. 2000, *J. Geophys. Research, 60,* 127–146.

Suess, H. E. 1955. Radiocarbon concentration in modern wood, *Science, 122,* 415–417.

Van der Vlerk, I. M., and F. Florschütz. 1953. The paleontological base of the subdivision of the Pleistocene in the Netherlands, *Verhandel. Koninkl. Ned. Akad. Wetenschap. Afdel. Natuurk.,* sect. *I, 20,* 18.

Worthington, L. V. 1954. A preliminary note on the time scale in North Atlantic circulation, *Deep Sea Research, 1,* 244–251.

Geochronology

G. R. TILTON
and
G. L. DAVIS
Geophysical Laboratory
Carnegie Institution of Washington

Twenty years have elapsed since the mass spectrometer began to be used in age determination. The past ten years have seen an advance from procedures requiring samples containing weighable amounts of uranium, thorium, and lead to isotope dilution methods effective in the parts-per-million range. This increased sensitivity has made possible the use of the rubidium-strontium and potassium-argon methods for mica and the extension of the earlier methods to such minerals as zircon. The larger number of minerals for which ages can be measured has made it possible to compare the results of the different methods applied to a single rock. When they agree, as frequently happens, there can be little doubt that the actual time of crystallization of the rock has been measured.

The solutions to many geological problems have awaited the development of reliable methods of age determination. The direct application of the new methods to some of these problems has resulted in the emergence of several significant features. For example, accurate information is needed about the geographic extent and time distribution of orogenic belts in order to evaluate the role orogenies have played in the development of the continents. The information now available leads to certain suggestions about this problem. Specific ages are characteristic of large areas of the North American continent. These times of igneous intrusion and metamorphism are apparently separated by periods during which widespread crystallization did not take place. The same specific age values that are found for North America often occur on several of the other continents as well. It is often possible to determine the age of the basement complexes where they are exposed in orogenic belts. The ages and extent of these basement rocks leave considerable doubt as to whether continents "grow" by successive orogenies.

Recent work on metamorphic rocks is particularly encouraging. The results indicate that micas in metamorphic rocks may be used to determine the time of metamorphism. This will permit detailed studies of the time sequence of metamorphism along and across the strike of single orogenic belts. In addition, zircon and potassium feldspar in certain metamorphic rocks give ages that predate the time of metamorphism as given by the mica in the same rocks. This type of investigation promises to become a powerful method for the study of metamorphic rocks.

The present review is mainly concerned with the accomplishments of geochronology with respect to geological problems; another review by Aldrich and Wetherill (1958) evaluates the methods of age determination and treats the subject of discordant ages in greater detail.

Isotopic Methods of Age Determination

To be useful for age determination a radioactive species must have a half-life within one or two orders of magnitude of the age of the elements from which the earth is made. If the half-life is much shorter than this, the species will have decayed almost completely and be of no use; if it is much longer, the accumulated amount of radiogenic daughter product will be too small to be easily measurable. Five useful systems are listed in table 1. The K^{40}-Ca^{40} system has not

TABLE 1. Decay Systems Useful for Geochronology

Parent	Daughter	Type of Decay	Half-Life, yr	Abundance of Parent Isotope
U^{238}	Pb^{206}	$8\alpha + 6\beta$	4.51×10^9	0.9929 g/g U
U^{235}	Pb^{207}	$7\alpha + 4\beta$	0.71×10^9	0.0071 g/g U
Th^{232}	Pb^{208}	$6\alpha + 4\beta$	13.9×10^9	1.00 g/g Th
Rb^{87}	Sr^{87}	β	50×10^9 *	0.283 g/g Rb
K^{40}	A^{40}	Electron capture	12.4×10^9 *	1.22×10^{-4} g/g K
	Ca^{40}	β	1.47×10^9 *	

* See text for uncertainties in the decay constants of K^{40} and Rb^{87}.

been employed to any extent. Still other systems such as the decay of Re^{187} to Os^{187} remain to be investigated (Hintenberger, Herr, and Voshage, 1954).

Determination of the age of a mineral requires measurement of the ratio of the amount of radioactive parent to the amount of daughter element produced. This ratio is then related to the age through the decay constant of the parent.[1] A number of assumptions must be made in calculating ages by this method. The calculated age will equal the true age of the mineral only if (1) the mineral was formed in an interval of time short compared with its age, (2) there have been no gains or losses either of daughter or parent element in the mineral by processes other than radioactive decay of the parent, (3) proper correction can be made for any amount of daughter product present in the mineral at the time of formation, and (4) the decay constant of the parent element is accurately known.

The validity of these assumptions is adequately established if, when the different methods are applied to a mineral or cogenetic mineral assemblage, concordant age values are found. If the results are not concordant it is evident that some of the assumptions have not been fulfilled. For example, a systematic difference in ages would indicate an error in the half-life of at least one of the parents. Random inconsistencies would probably be related to geologic factors.

Fenner and Piggot (1929) made the first attempt to measure an isotopic age of a mineral. They used the isotopic composition of the lead to distinguish between the uranium-lead and the thorium-lead ages. They had no knowledge of the half-life of U^{235}, and the isotopic composition of the lead as determined by Aston did not include a value for Pb^{204}. The first complete isotopic age determinations based on mass-spectrometric analysis of lead were reported in the classic papers by Nier (1939*b*) and Nier, Thompson, and Murphey (1941). For the first time it was possible to make accurate corrections for the primary lead content of a mineral, and to separate the U^{238}-Pb^{206} age from the U^{235}-Pb^{207} age. This was the beginning of a more precise era in geochronology, although it is well to remember that nonisotopic age determinations by earlier workers had established ages for some areas

[1] The decay constant, λ, is equal to 0.693 divided by the half-life. If N atoms of a radioactive parent are considered,

$$dN/dt = -\lambda N$$

where dN/dt is the instantaneous rate of decay. The number of decays experienced in unit time by a given number of atoms is an expression of the specific activity.

which have not been changed substantially by isotopic methods. An example is the excellent work by Ellsworth (1932) in the Canadian Shield.

The results reported by Nier and his co-workers contain a number of discordant age results; that is, the uranium-lead ages and the thorium-lead age for a single mineral fail to agree. Nier pointed out that when the two uranium-lead ages agree the result is probably the true age of the mineral, since measurable loss or gain of parent or daughter elements would almost certainly affect the U^{238}-Pb^{206} age to a different degree than the U^{235}-Pb^{207} age. The Pb^{207}-Pb^{206} age, which is dependent on the two uranium-lead ages, would be affected to a still different extent. Holmes, Leland, and Nier (1950) published graphical representations of the distribution of ages for a hypothetical mineral that has lost lead or gained uranium at various times. Discordant isotopic ages require interpretation in order to select the best estimate of the age. Nier selected the Pb^{207}-Pb^{206} age as the best, principally on a theoretical basis, since it would be changed the least by such gains or losses. Other factors, however, such as loss of radon or improper correction for the isotopic composition of the lead inherited by the mineral at the time of formation, could cause ages other than the Pb^{207}-Pb^{206} age to be the more accurate.

In an attempt to resolve this uncertainty, work was started about 1950 in several laboratories to apply all the possible methods of age determination to a single mineral assemblage such as a granite or pegmatite. Nier's work was restricted to ores containing amounts of uranium, thorium, and lead that could be determined gravimetrically. In order to determine ages of granites it was necessary to develop procedures capable of determining uranium, thorium, lead, rubidium, strontium, and argon at the parts-per-million level with an error in the range of ± 1 to 3 per cent. The method, that of isotope dilution, has been reviewed by Inghram (1954) and Aldrich (1956).

Another difficulty to be overcome in order to permit comparison of potassium-argon, rubidium-strontium, and isotopic lead ages concerned the decay constants of K^{40} and Rb^{87}. The decay constants of U^{238}, U^{235}, and Th^{232} had been determined by physical experiments within uncertainties of 1 to 2 per cent, but those of K^{40} and Rb^{87} were more uncertain. Until the development of crystal scintillation counting techniques, accurate determination of the specific γ activity of potassium resulting from the decay of K^{40} to A^{40} by orbital electron capture was not possible. Rb^{87} has a β-energy spectrum with a uniquely high proportion of low-energy particles. Even with the thinnest possible sources, the correction for absorbed β particles leaves considerable uncertainty in the determination of the specific β activity.

In the absence of good physical determinations of these decay constants, geologically ascertained values can be used. The geologic method consists of fixing the age of a granite or pegmatite by means of uranium-lead ages, measuring the K^{40}-A^{40} and Rb^{87}-Sr^{87} ratios in minerals from the same assemblage, and calculating the decay constants by assuming no losses or gains of parent or daughter by processes other than radioactive decay. (Since two decay constants must be determined for K^{40}, it is necessary to select a value for the β decay constant from physical measurements. The value of this constant is subject to an error of approximately ± 10 per cent.) If samples of widely differing ages yield the same values for the decay constants, the assumption of closed chemical systems is probably valid. Wasserburg and Hayden (1955) applied this technique to K^{40}, using potassium feldspar-uraninite pairs; they obtained a value for the specific γ activity of 2.5 electron captures per second per gram of potassium, taking a value of 5.07×10^{-10} yr^{-1} for the value of the β decay constant. When it was recognized that micas retain a greater percentage of argon than feldspars do (Wetherill, Aldrich, and Davis, 1955), the work was repeated with micas. Wetherill, Wasserburg, Aldrich, Tilton, and Hayden (1956) reported a value of 3.24 ± 0.15 electron captures per second per gram of potassium ($\lambda_e = 5.57 \times 10^{-11}$ yr^{-1}), using a value of 4.72×10^{-10} yr^{-1} for the β decay constant. Wetherill (1957) has completed a determination of the specific γ activity of K^{40} by scintillation counting and has obtained a value of 3.39 ± 0.12 γ rays per second per gram ($\lambda_e = 5.83 \times 10^{-11}$ yr^{-1}). This value is independent of any choice of values for the β decay constant, but will be in error with regard to the argon production rate if any K^{40} decays directly to the ground state of A^{40}. Comparison of the geological value with that obtained by direct counting shows that argon retention may not be quantitative in micas, although the uncertainties are such that it could be. It does appear that the degree of argon retention in micas is sufficiently high for reliable age determinations. If decay of K^{40} to the ground state of A^{40} were established, the degree of argon retention in micas would have to be lowered.

A geological determination of the half-life of Rb^{87} has been published by Aldrich, Wetherill, Tilton, and Davis (1956), who found a value of $50 \pm 2 \times 10^9$ yr, corresponding to a value of 1.39×10^{-11} yr^{-1} for the decay constant. These authors also summarize values from the literature which range from 40 to 64×10^9 yr. Huster and his co-workers at the University of Marburg have recently obtained a result of 49 billion years, which is in agreement with the geologic value (personal communication to L. T. Aldrich). Another recent determination of the half-life of Rb^{87}, based on thick-source counting, has been published by Libby (1957). Suttle and Libby (1955) found that the specific activity of many β emitters could be determined very simply by taking absorption curves on thick sources with the absorbers placed in close geometry to the source in a cylindrical counter. Empirically, they noted that a plot of log activity against the thickness of absorber gave a nearly straight line. By extrapolating back to zero absorber thickness and evaluating certain constants by using standards of known specific activity, the specific activity of other samples could readily be found. With some refinements Libby later extended the method to rubidium, obtaining a value for the half-life of 50.7 ± 2 billion years. As already noted, the β particles from Rb^{87} have a unique energy spectrum. Whereas a plot of the number of particles of a given energy against energy for a typical β emitter passes through a definite maximum, no maximum has yet been observed for Rb^{87} (Curran, Dixon, and Wilson, 1951). Since Libby's measurement is based on relations derived empirically from β emitters with normal energy spectra, the application of these relationships to Rb^{87} is open to question. The physical measurements of the decay constant of Rb^{87} leave considerable uncertainty as to its value. The geologically determined value is the one currently used for purposes of age determination. Although such an approach is not the best, it should be recalled that Nier (1939*a*) used a method based on the U^{238}-Pb^{206} and U^{235}-Pb^{207} ratios of minerals to obtain a value for the half-life of U^{235} which is within the limits of error assigned to the present-day value obtained by α counting of enriched U^{235} (Fleming, Ghiorso, and Cunningham, 1952).

Table 2 summarizes the results used in the geological evaluation of the decay constants of K^{40} and Rb^{87}. In addition to the pegmatite comparisons, Tilton, Davis, Wetherill, and Aldrich (1957) have reported age comparisons for seven granites, using the newly determined decay constants for K^{40} and Rb^{87}. In general the agreement between the uranium-lead ages of zircon and the potassium-argon and rubidium-strontium ages of mica is highly gratifying. Three granites whose ages appear to be fixed with considerable accuracy are given in table 3. Moreover, since zircon and mica have greatly different physical and chemical properties, the agreement of ages between the two minerals indicates that the ages represent the time of crystallization of the granite as a whole. Until a number of mica-zircon comparisons have

TABLE 2. Summary of Data Used for Geological Determination of the Decay Constants of K^{40} and Rb^{87} *

Locality	Uranium-Lead Ages, million years U^{238}/Pb^{206}	U^{235}/Pb^{207}	Derived Values of Decay Constants in Reciprocal Years K^{40} (λ_e) ($\times 10^{11}$)	Rb^{87} ($\times 10^{11}$)	Mica Ages Calculated Using Selected † Values for Decay Constants, million years K-A	Rb-Sr
Portland, Conn.	268	266	5.52	1.39 ‡	265	267 ‡
Glastonbury, Conn.	251	255	5.73	1.49 ‡	259	273 ‡
Spruce Pine, N. C.	370	375	5.15	1.39	349	375
Branchville, Conn.	367	365	5.83	...	382	...
Parry Sound, Ont.	994	993	5.39	...	970	...
Cardiff Twp., Ont.	1020	1020	5.38	1.36	1000	1030
Wilberforce, Ont.	1040	1050	5.09	1.34	960	1000
Keystone, S. Dak.	1580	1600	5.40 ‡	1.43 §	1520 ‡	1670 §
Viking Lake, Sask.	1850	1880	5.40	1.40	1850	1970
Bikita, S. Rhodesia	2640	2670	5.00	1.39	2550	2680

* These data are taken from results measured or summarized by Wetherill et al. (1956), Aldrich et al. (1956), and Powell et al. (1957).
† λ_β for $Rb^{87} = 1.39 \times 10^{-11}$ yr^{-1}.
λ_β for $K^{40} = 4.72 \times 10^{-10}$ yr^{-1}.
λ_e for $K^{40} = 5.57 \times 10^{-11}$ yr^{-1}.
‡ Average of 2 different minerals.
§ Average of 3 different minerals.

been completed, however, the possibility exists that some zircons may give ages which are older than that of the mica in the same rock. An example will be cited later for which the zircon in a metamorphic rock yields an older age than the mica.

A surprising result has been encountered near Gunnison, Colorado, where mica ages of the Brown Derby pegmatite and the surrounding Quartz Creek granite have a high degree of concordance whereas uranium-lead and thorium-lead ages of other minerals from the same rocks are discordant (Aldrich, Davis, Tilton, and Wetherill, 1956).

TABLE 3. Granites with Concordant Mineral Ages

Locality	Age, million years U^{238}/Pb^{206}	U^{235}/Pb^{207}	Pb^{207}/Pb^{206}	Th^{232}/Pb^{208}	Rb^{87}/Sr^{87}	K^{40}/A^{40}
Redstone, N. H.	187	184	...	190	185	182
Wichita Mts., Okla.	520	527	550	506	500	480
Llano, Tex.	950	990	1070	890	1100	1090

TABLE 4. Mica Ages from the Quartz Creek District, Gunnison County, Colorado *

Mineral	Source	Age, million years	
		Rb-Sr	K-A
Biotite	Granite	1320	1350
Microcline	Granite	1480	. . .
Microcline	Pegmatite	1290	. . .
Muscovite intergrown with microcline	Pegmatite	1390	1270
Lepidolite containing microlite	Pegmatite	1490	1430
Lepidolite, coarse books	Pegmatite	1410	. . .
Lepidolite, medium grained	Pegmatite	1410	. . .
Lepidolite, fine grained	Pegmatite	1370	1370
Lepidolite, coarse, quartz-clevelandite matrix	Pegmatite	1390	1350
Lepidolite, fine, quartz-clevelandite matrix	Pegmatite	1570	1390

* From *Carnegie Institution of Washington Year Book 54.*

Even zircon gives low uranium-lead and thorium-lead ages compared with the micas. These findings are summarized in tables 4 and 5. The mica ages consistently group at 1375 $\pm$ 75 million years. The behavior of the lead ages requires that a mechanism be found whereby these ages can be made discordant by some process or processes that have not seriously affected the mica ages. The Pb^{207}-Pb^{206} ages are in closest agreement with the mica ages, suggesting that recent separation of lead from uranium and thorium by some geologic process was responsible for at least part of the discordance. Tentatively this proc-

TABLE 5. Lead Ages from the Quartz Creek District, Gunnison County, Colorado *

Mineral	Source	Age, million years			
		$\frac{U^{238}}{Pb^{206}}$	$\frac{U^{235}}{Pb^{207}}$	$\frac{Pb^{207}}{Pb^{206}}$	$\frac{Th^{232}}{Pb^{208}}$
Zircon	Granite	925	1130	1540 $\pm$ 140	530
Zircon	Granite	. . .	. . .	1700 $\pm$ 60	. . .
Microlite	Pegmatite	915	1055	1350	. . .
Columbite-tantalite	Pegmatite	1520	1470	1390	. . .
Monazite	Pegmatite	1590	1420	1170	995

* From *C. I. W. Year Book 54.*

TABLE 6. **Granites with Discordant Zircon Ages**

Locality	Age, million years					
	U^{238}/Pb^{206}	U^{235}/Pb^{207}	Pb^{207}/Pb^{206}	Th^{232}/Pb^{208}	Rb^{87}/Sr^{87}	K^{40}/A^{40}
Capetown, S. Africa	330	356	530	238	600	530
Pikes Peak, Colo.	624	707	980	313	1020	1030
Bagdad, Ariz.	630	770	1210	270	1390	1410

ess has been associated with metamorphism during the Laramide orogeny, since the rocks occur in a region that was affected by the orogeny. The fact that the Pb^{207}-Pb^{206} age of the zircon is older than the age of the micas may mean that the zircon is actually older than the mica of the granite. This is the only such example noted for granite so far, but one has been found for the Baltimore gneiss, to be discussed later. Additional examples of granites with discordant zircon ages (Tilton, Davis, Wetherill, and Aldrich, 1957) are given in table 6. The Pb^{207}-Pb^{206} ages agree most closely with the mica ages.

Before the application of the rubidium-strontium and potassium-argon methods to micas, the agreement of the U^{238}-Pb^{206} and U^{235}-Pb^{207} ages was the best indication of absolute age. U^{238} and U^{235} have half-lives differing by a factor of 6; hence loss or gain of measurable amounts of uranium or lead will affect the two ages by different amounts. However, this effect will not be observable for minerals younger than 200 million years, since both uranium-lead ages then closely approach linear dependence on the U^{235}-Pb^{207} and U^{238}-Pb^{206} ratios. Agreement of the rubidium-strontium and potassium-argon ages is perhaps an even better measure of absolute age inasmuch as daughter products with completely different chemical properties are involved. Any processes that alter the K/A and Rb/Sr ratios in a mica might be expected to change the two ratios by very different amounts. One type of alteration might occur that would not destroy the agreement: the addition of potassium and rubidium to a mica in amounts proportional to their concentration in the mica. The potassium-argon and rubidium-strontium ages would then appear to be too low by a uniform amount. In no comparison of uranium-lead ages with mica ages has any indication of this type of alteration been apparent. The agreement of the two mica ages therefore constitutes an acceptable criterion for absolute age.

Current Problems in Geochronology

The previous section has outlined work that serves to evaluate the reliability of age measurements. The present section reports new investigations, including some for which interpretations are tentative. The application of age results to particular geological problems is also discussed. It is worth while examining some of the hypotheses that are being tested by current work in geochronology, even though considerable speculation will thereby be introduced; there is ample justification for such an undertaking because the investigation of promising or partly established hypotheses provides the motivation for much of the work done in research.

Tracing orogenic belts. The use of the criterion of concordant mica ages as a measure of absolute age has led to the discovery of a previously unknown period of crystalline rock formation in a large area of the southwestern United States. In a study of micas from 12 Precambrian granites and pegmatites from Arizona, New Mexico, Colorado, and Wyoming, it was found that all gave nearly concordant ages, with values between 1300 and 1450 million years (Aldrich, Wetherill, and Davis, 1957); see table 7. The areal distribution of these rocks, shown in figure 1, strongly suggests that a large portion of the southwestern United States is underlain by igneous intrusive

TABLE 7. Micas with Ages of about 1400 Million Years from Southwestern United States *

Source	Age, million years	
	Rb-Sr	K-A
Gneiss, Zoroaster Creek, Grand Canyon, Ariz.	1370	1390
Granite, Lawler Peak Area, Bagdad, Ariz.	1390	1410
Pegmatite, Lawler Peak Area, Bagdad, Ariz.	1500	1410
Pegmatite, Wickenberg, Ariz.	1300	1160
Pegmatite, Pidlite Mine, Mora County, N. Mex.	1490	1330
Granite, Sandia Mtn., Albuquerque, N. Mex.	1340	1350
Pegmatite, Harding Mine, Dixon, N. Mex.	1300	1300
Granite, Unaweep Canyon, Mesa County, Colo.	1320	1320
Granite, Quartz Creek District, Gunnison County, Colo.	1310	1320
Pegmatite, Quartz Creek District, Gunnison County, Colo.	1420	1330
Granite, Silver Plume, Colo.	1280	...
Granite, Sherman, Wyo.	1410	1420

* From *C. I. W. Year Book 56*.

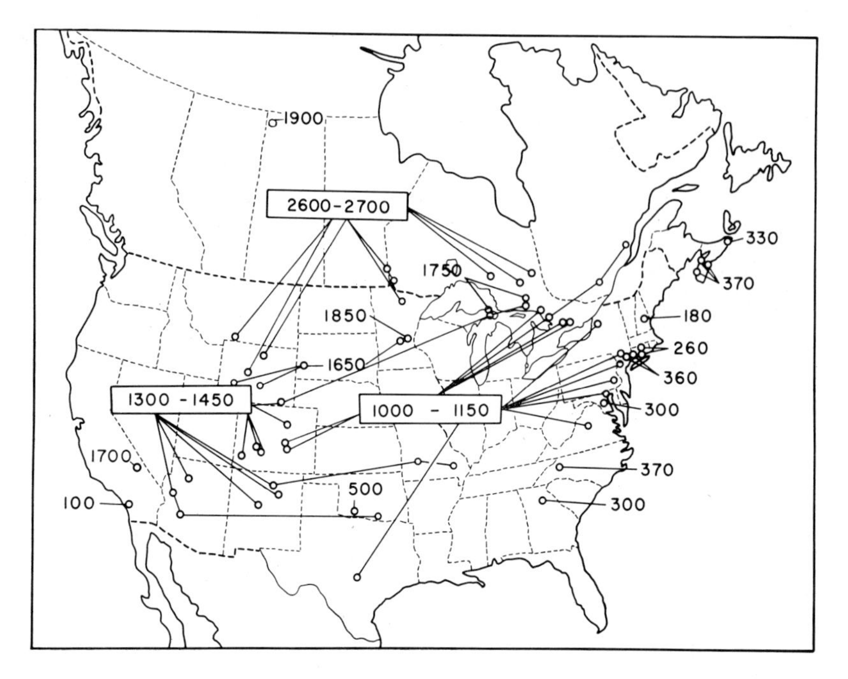

Fig. 1. Reliably dated localities in North America (June 1958).

rocks formed about 1350 million years ago. Further work may extend their geographic occurrence.

This area was affected by the Laramide orogeny, which is considered to have occurred about 60 million years ago. It is striking that all the uranium-lead ages measured in this region have been discordant. The measurements include those on the Bagdad and Quartz Creek granites (Tilton, Davis, Wetherill, and Aldrich, 1957), the Uncompahgre granite (Aldrich, Tilton, Davis, Nicolaysen, and Patterson, 1955), the Las Vegas monazite (Nier, Thompson, and Murphey, 1941), and microlite from the Harding Mine, Dixon, N. Mex. (Carnegie Institution, unpublished data).

Gast, Kulp, and Long (1958) have used micas to establish an age of 2700 million years for the basement rocks in the Bighorn and Beartooth Mountains in Wyoming and Montana. Mica ages and the Pb^{207}-Pb^{206} age of zircon from the granite at the bottom of Pikes Peak, Colorado, are concordant at 1000 million years (Tilton, Davis, Wetherill, and Aldrich, 1957). The Laramide orogeny has also affected the rocks of these areas.

Other work has enlarged the geographic extent of rocks with ages of about 1000 million years which were known in North America only in the Grenville subprovince in Ontario. Ages of 1000 to 1150 million years have been found in Texas at Llano, in Colorado at Pikes Peak, in the Adirondack Mountains at Natural Bridge, N. Y., and in the Catskill Mountains at Bear Mountain, N. Y. These results, all taken from work done at the Carnegie Institution, are shown in table 8. The Pb^{207}-Pb^{206} ages at Natural Bridge and Bear Mountain appear to be distinctly greater than the 1000-million-year Pb^{207}-Pb^{206} ages that have been reported in Ontario. These differences may be reasonable in comparison with the age difference between, say, the Nevadan and Laramide orogenies in western North America which have ages of approximately 100 and 60 million years, respectively. More detailed work may establish ages of 1100 to 1150 million years in Ontario. It is noteworthy that micas taken from the granites at the top and bottom of Pikes Peak have concordant mica ages of 1080 and 1020 million years (see table 8). The relationship of the Colorado and Texas rocks to the rocks of similar age to the north and east will not be discernible until more work has been done in the southern Appalachians and on core samples from basement rocks underlying the sedimentary cover of the central plains. Goldich, Baadsgaard, and Nier (1957) report potassium-argon ages of 1000 to 1100 million years on micas

TABLE 8. 1000- to 1150-Million-Year Rocks of the United States

Rock and Location	Age, million years					
	$\frac{U^{238}}{Pb^{206}}$	$\frac{U^{235}}{Pb^{207}}$	$\frac{Pb^{207}}{Pb^{206}}$	$\frac{Th^{232}}{Pb^{208}}$	$\frac{K^{40}}{A^{40}}$	$\frac{Rb^{87}}{Sr^{87}}$
Zircon crystal, Natural Bridge, N. Y.	1025	1065	1140	...	...	...
Storm King granite, Bear Mt., N. Y.	960	990	1060	850	...	900
Canada Hill gneiss, Bear Mt., N. Y.	1140	1150	1170	1030	930	900
Granite, Petrick Quarry, Llano, Texas	950	990	1070	890	1090	1100
Granite (bottom), Pikes Peak, Colo.	625	710	980	310	1030	1020
Granite (top), Pikes Peak, Colo.	...	...	...	...	1090	1080

from Wisconsin and Minnesota. These ages should be considered tentative until supported by rubidium-strontium measurements.

Space-time relationship of orogenic belts. A major long-range goal of geochronology is to establish the time sequence and geographic extent of orogenic belts with as high a degree of accuracy as possible. Fixing the age and extent of an orogeny within definite limits establishes certain conditions that theories concerning the formation of orogenic belts and their role in the development and structure of the continental masses must explain. Holmes, Leland, and Nier (1950) and Holmes (1955) have attempted studies of this type in South Africa and India, but their work was based on a limited number of age determinations. Holmes and Cahen (1957) have published a more complete study for South Africa. It is now possible to increase greatly the number as well as the reliability of the age results that can be used. The present status of this work is summarized here. Only ages based on at least two methods which give the same result within 5 to 10 per cent are used; that is, either the two uranium-lead ages or the rubidium-strontium and potassium-argon ages must be in agreement. Agreement of a Pb^{207}-Pb^{206} and a rubidium-strontium age is considered satisfactory, but no age based solely on a Pb^{207}-Pb^{206} age is used. When small discordances exist in the uranium-lead ages, the greatest weight is given to the Pb^{207}-Pb^{206} age; for micas, greatest weight is given to the rubidium-strontium age. This conservative approach ignores large quantities of data—discordant uranium-lead ages, samples for which only rubidium-strontium or potassium-argon ages have been measured, nonisotopic ages, and galena ages. Thus is avoided the possible introduction of bias into the results because of uncertain data. A single reliable result is not strengthened by including with it a number of other, less reliable results.

Figures 1, 2, and 3 show the locations and ages of the samples that have been reliably dated. The ages for the figures have been taken from publications by Holmes (1955), Holmes and Cahen (1955), Nier and co-workers (1939, 1941), and the groups at the Lamont Geological Observatory (Gast, Kulp, and Long, 1958), the University of Chicago and the California Institute of Technology (Wasserburg and Hayden, 1955) (Wasserburg, Hayden, and Jensen, 1956), the Massachusetts Institute of Technology (Hurley, Pinson, Fairbairn, and Cormier, 1957) (Pinson, Hurley, Fairbairn, Herzog, and Cormier, 1957), the University of Minnesota (Goldich, Baadsgaard, and Nier, 1957), and the Carnegie Institution of Washington. The U.S.S.R. ages are taken from the papers by Vinogradov (1956) and Starik (1956). Some age values

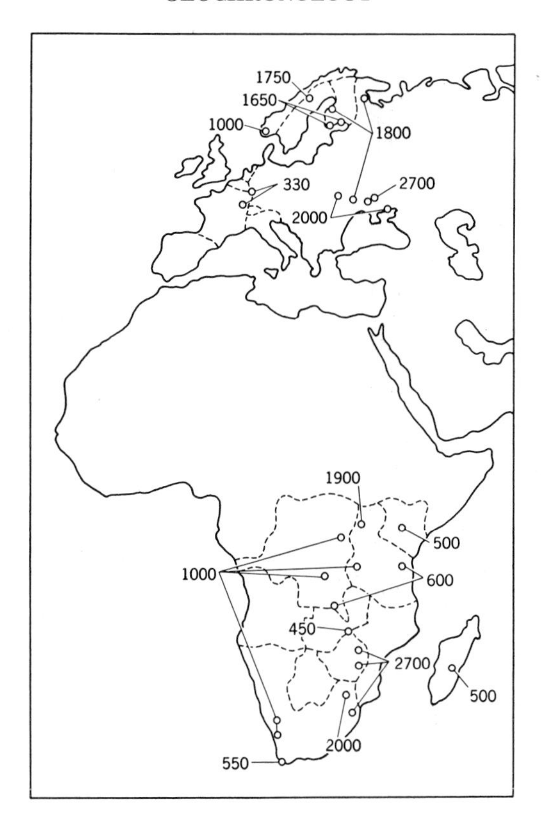

Fig. 2. Reliably dated localities in Europe and Africa (October 1957).

have been rounded off in preparing the figures: Paleozoic Appalachian ages, to the nearest 10 million years; the remaining ones, to the nearest 50 million years. Rounding affects most of the results by less than ± 3 to 5 per cent. To avoid bias as to the grouping of age values, differences in measured ages have been preserved even when such differences might well be within experimental errors. An example is the 1750- and 1800-million-year values given in the Fenno-Scandian shield. The values for the Ukrainian shield in figure 2 are less satisfactory than the rest since they were obtained by selecting a few concordant results from among large numbers of discordant uranium-lead ages. Most of that work was done with monazite and allanite, which commonly give discordant ages.

One interesting feature is the appearance of similar age values on

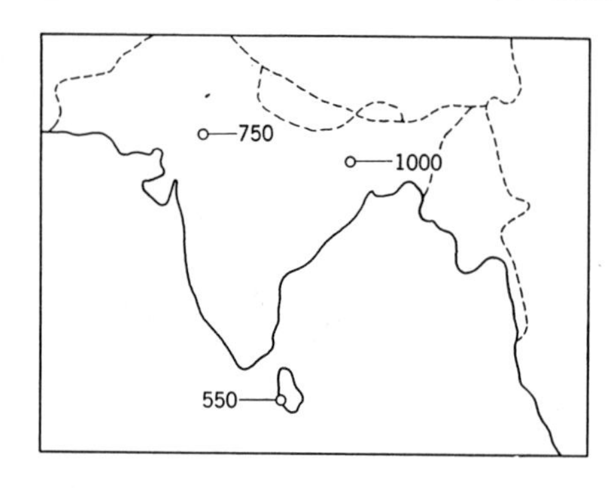

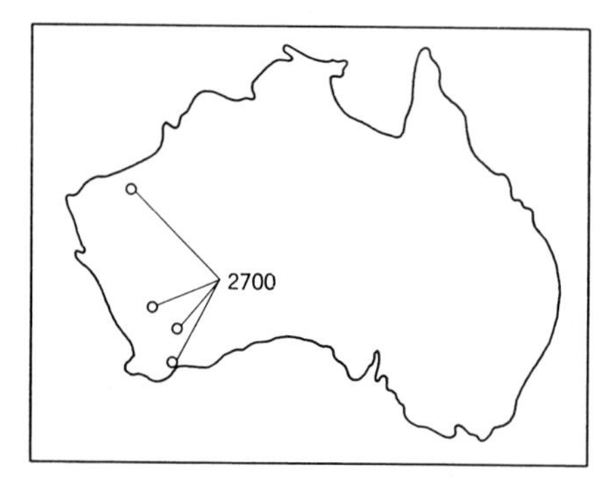

Fig. 3. Reliably dated localities in India and Australia (October 1957).

several continents. Minerals with ages of 2600 to 2700 and 1000 to 1150 million years occur on four continents; those with ages of 1900 to 2000 and 500 to 600 million years have been found on three continents. The manner in which the ages can be fitted into groups suggests that there may have been repeated periods, each 100 to 150 million years long, during which large quantities of intrusive rocks were formed throughout the world. These active periods were separated by inactive periods of about the same duration. Much more sampling, however, is required on all the continents to substantiate this possibility. In particular, more results from Asia, South America, and Australia are needed for a critical test.

When the Precambrian results are compared with knowledge of crustal movements since Precambrian times, it is surprising that the ages in figures 1 to 3 are grouped as distinctly as they seem to be. Many geologists recognize something like twenty periods of worldwide crustal movement since the Precambrian (Umbgrove, 1947). The Appalachian belt contains minerals with reliably established ages of 180, 270, 300, and 370 million years, and it is probable that rocks with still other ages will be found there. The Laramide revolution extended from late Cretaceous to the end of the Oligocene. Gilluly (1949) reviews evidence for some tens of major unconformities in the Tertiary record in California alone. He concludes, reasonably, that paleontological evidence can hardly be used to prove that crustal movements were restricted to a relatively few periods of short duration on a worldwide scale. If the agreement of ages from one continent to another is merely a reflection of the occurrence of the continuous formation of intrusive rocks, however, then the grouping of ages could hardly be expected unless it were due to fortuitous sampling. The implication is that some orogenic epochs are much more important than others with regard to the amount of intrusive rocks formed even if folding and thrusting are more continuous. Folding can take place without the formation of intrusive rocks, as is shown by the fact that intrusive rocks of Paleozoic age have not been recognized in the Wichita and Arbuckle Mountains. There are many other examples. It should be emphasized that ages other than those appearing in figures 1 to 3 will probably be found. Ages will almost certainly be found in the interval between the 1900- to 2000- and the 2600- to 2700-million-year groups. Additional work is essential in order to determine whether the 750-million-year age found in India is of local or general significance.

Certain other points of interest appear from the data. The hypothesis that the continents have grown during geological time by accretion from small "nuclei" through the addition of materials from depth by successive orogenies has aroused considerable interest (see Wilson, 1954). Such a theory must now be altered to allow for the presence of older rocks which appear as basement rocks in younger orogenic belts. The occurrence of rocks with ages of 1000, 1375, and 2700 million years in the Tertiary Laramide belt has already been discussed. Rocks with ages of 1000 to 1150 million years are now known in the Appalachian belt. The 2700-million-year-old rocks in Wyoming and Montana were involved in the Laramide revolution and may have been involved in still earlier orogenies. If the 2600- to 2700-million-year ages found in Wyoming, Montana, southeast Manitoba, and central Ontario are taken to define the strike of an ancient orogenic belt, the strikes of the Nevadan and Laramide belts cut across that of the older belt. In all, the age results serve to complicate the continental accretion hypothesis. Certainly a simple "onion skin" type of growth does not fit the existing age pattern. In order to estimate the extent to which the North American continent may have grown it will be necessary to evaluate the significance of those rocks in the Cordilleran and Appalachian regions with ages that predate the last orogenies in these areas. If the Appalachians are built upon a basement consisting of rocks with ages of 1000 to 1100 million years it is not obvious that the continent has "grown" as a result of the formation of the Appalachian belt.

Still another interesting feature of the data is the occurrence of rocks with ages of 2700 million years near the coast lines of western Australia and southeastern Africa. Present-day theories of orogenic processes generally make use of the boundary between the continental and oceanic types of crust as sites for the development of orogenic belts. To a considerable extent the belts formed since the Precambrian do occur along the margins of continents, with such notable exceptions as the Ural, Pyrenees, and Himalaya Mountains. It is rather striking, then, to find 2700-million-year rocks which would normally be associated with the "stable interior" of a continent occurring on the margins of Australia and Africa. Although several possibilities can be imagined, no definite explanation can be advanced.

The discovery of ages of 2700 million years on four continents, but none older, is suggestive. The 2700-million-year rocks intrude sediments and conglomerates that must have been derived from still older rocks. Wasserburg, Hayden, and Jensen (1956) have, in fact, reported potassium-argon ages of 3000 million years for a pebble from the Manitou conglomerate in the Kenora District of Ontario, and of 3300 million years for a cobble from the Bulawayan basal conglomerate in Southern Rhodesia. As these numbers involve empirical corrections for argon leakage they should be confirmed, if possible, by other methods. The earth is 4500 million years old if it has the same age as meteorites (Patterson, 1956). If this age is accepted, an interval from 4500 to approximately 3300 million years exists for which no record has been found. Two possibilities come to mind—either older rocks have been completely metamorphosed, or else sialic rocks were not formed earlier than 3000 to 3500 million years ago. Did the newly formed earth have continental masses? If it did not, did orogenic processes commence immediately? It is not obvious that this should be true, since the moon exhibits no evidence of orogenic processes to the present day. There is then a need for more age studies which will attempt to close this time gap as much as possible.

Detailed studies of single orogenic belts. In addition to the study of the geographic distribution of orogenic belts in time, detailed studies for single belts are being attempted, aimed at determining the degree of contemporaneity of metamorphism and intrusion both along and across the strike. The number of such periods of mineral crystallization and their distribution in time are also being sought, as well as the age of the basement rocks and the effect of later metamorphism on the ages of the minerals in them.

The Appalachian orogenic zone is almost ideally suited for these studies. It is old enough so that erosion has produced good exposures of rocks of widely different ages. It is also old enough for daughter products to have accumulated from the various radioactive parents in sufficient quantity to allow accurate age determinations. On the other hand it is young enough to enable small time intervals of the order of 10 million years to be distinguished by careful analytical work. In the older Precambrian, differences of this order are lost in analytical errors. Finally, many parts of the Appalachians are well mapped and some control is available from fossil evidence. Comparisons between the Appalachian and the younger Cordilleran systems should provide reasonably complete information on the time sequence of events leading to the formation of a mountain chain.

Several laboratories in the United States have commenced detailed investigations of the ages of the rocks in the Appalachian region. Although the studies are just beginning, more data exist for this than for any other orogenic zone. The following ages, all based on concordant uranium-lead ages, concordant mica ages, or both, are well established: 180 million years for the White Mountain granitic series at Redstone, near Conway, N. H. (Tilton, Davis, Wetherill, and Aldrich, 1957); 260 million years at Spinelli Quarry, Glastonbury, Conn. (Nier, 1939), and at Strickland Quarry, Portland, Conn. (Wasserburg and Hayden, 1955); 360 million years at Branchville, Conn. (Wasserburg, Hayden, and Jensen, 1956), and Kinkel Quarry, Bedford, N. Y. (Nier, 1939); and 370 million years at Spruce Pine, N. C. (Aldrich, Wetherill, Tilton, and Davis, 1956; Eckelmann and Kulp, 1957). Thus there seem to have been at least three periods of intrusion at 180, at 270, and at 360 to 370 million years. Further work will be directed toward ascertaining whether all these ages can be found along the entire chain and whether still other groups of concordant age values will be found. Hurley, Pinson, Fairbairn, and Cormier (1957) have reported three mica ages of 375 million years and one of 330 million years from Nova Scotia, and Pinson, Fairbairn, Hurley, Herzog, and Cormier (1957) have reported mica ages of 290 million years from several granites in the Georgia Piedmont. Additional mica work has been done at other laboratories as well. Although obvious interest attaches to whether the mica ages fall into several distinct age groups or whether a great variety of ages will be found, it seems premature to attempt a discussion of the results. To be of value, analytical errors in the age results must not exceed 10 million years, and, for the present, at least, both the potassium-argon and rubidium-strontium ages should be determined for each mica studied.

A beginning has also been made on studies of the geologically older basement rock in the Appalachian region. As previously mentioned, 1000- to 1150-million-year rocks have been found at Bear Mountain, N. Y. (table 8). In addition, a rubidium-strontium age of 900 million years has been obtained on biotite from a gneiss in Shenandoah National Park, Virginia (Carnegie Institution, unpublished data). Recent work at the Carnegie Institution on the Baltimore gneiss has produced some interesting and promising results. Zircon from two samples of gneiss from the Towson and Phoenix domes near Baltimore has given nearly concordant uranium-lead ages of 1100 million years. Potassium feldspar from the Phoenix dome agrees with the zircon, giving a rubidium-strontium age of 1200 ± 200 million years. Rubidium-strontium ages of the biotite from the same domes are 300 and 320 million years, in agreement with the potassium-argon age of 320 million years reported by Wasserburg, Pettijohn, and Lipson (1957) for the gneiss. The mica ages are presumed to date the time of later metamorphism. In spite of the metamorphism the zircon and potassium feldspar have preserved older ages which probably give the age of the "original" rock. This age is in close agreement with those found for both mica and zircon in granite and gneiss at Bear Mountain, N. Y., in the Catskill Mountains. These results indicate a promising approach to the study of superposed orogenies which will be explored further.

Metamorphic rocks. In addition to the work mentioned above in connection with the Baltimore gneiss, several other studies have been reported on metamorphic rocks. Wasserburg, Pettijohn, and Lipson (1957) published a significant paper which indicates that mica ages from the Glenarm series in Maryland measure the time of metamorphism of the sediments. These authors found that the potassium-argon ages of micas from pegmatites cutting the sediments as well as micas separated from the Cockeysville marble and the Setters quartzite gave ages of 310 to 340 million years. Biotite from the Baltimore gneiss, underlying the Glenarm series, gave an age of 320 million years. The authors infer that the Glenarm sediments were metamorphosed about 350 million years ago and that injection of pegmatites into the sediments took place at that time.

Goldich, Baadsgaard, and Nier (1957) have reported potassium-argon results of possible significance to the study of metamorphic rocks. They compared the potassium-argon ages of feldspar and biotite from granites at Babbitt and Snowbank Lake, Minn. The feldspar ages are older than the biotite ages in each case even if no correction is made for the average amount of argon leakage observed in feldspars. The micas give ages of 1200 million years and the feldspars 1540 and 1650 million years uncorrected for any argon loss. The Duluth gabbro occurs in close proximity to both granites. Mica from a drill core sample of the gabbro taken a few miles from the granite at Babbitt gave a potassium-argon age of 1120 million years. The authors postulate that intrusion of the gabbro is responsible for the age of the biotite in the granites while the feldspars preserve a record of the older age of the granites. The results seem most encouraging, and rubidium-strontium work will help to define the situation further.

Another interesting result was obtained by Wetherill, Davis, and Aldrich (1957) from the Cutler batholith near Sudbury, Ont. See table 9. The rubidium-strontium ages with one exception are about 1750 million years; the potassium-argon ages on the micas are all about 1400 million years. These ages suggest that argon was released from the micas during a period of metamorphism 1400 million years ago and that the rubidium-strontium ages represent either the original age of the rock or else an earlier, more intense period of metamorphism acting on a still older rock (compare these data with those from the Baltimore gneiss). The same authors report ages for micas from other rocks in the region around Sudbury. Many discordances were found. For one mica the potassium-argon age was greater than the rubidium-strontium age. Two more examples of this type of dis-

TABLE 9. Age Determinations from the Cutler, Ontario, Batholith *

Sample		Age, million years	
		Rb-Sr	K-A
Pegmatite 1	Muscovite	1750	1440
	Feldspar	1760	1165
Pegmatite 2	Muscovite	1700	1420
Granite	Biotite	1325	1380

* From *C. I. W. Year Book 56.*

cordance have since been found in micas from this area. Previously potassium-argon ages have always been lower than the rubidium-strontium ages when discordances occur, and loss of argon has been assumed to be the cause. No clear explanation can be offered for the reverse type of discordance. In the present state of knowledge it is impossible to define the histories of these rocks accurately from the mica results alone. If the mica-zircon comparison studies under way on the metamorphic rocks in the Appalachian region are successful, similar studies may serve to unravel the ambiguities that exist at Sudbury.

The fossil time scale. Fossils may be used to establish relative ages in the eras since the Precambrian, but they give little indication of the absolute time scale involved. The "Holmes" fossil time scale, in current use, is based on four points obtained from highly radioactive minerals. Three of the points are obtained from igneous rocks with satisfactory isotopic ages but of somewhat uncertain relation to the sediments. The fourth point is taken from the Swedish kolm, the stratigraphic position of which is accurately known but which has grossly discordant isotopic ages (Nier, 1939; Cobb and Kulp, 1957).

Recent investigations, mostly of the mineral glauconite, have attempted to measure ages of sedimentary materials directly. The potassium-argon method has been used by Wasserburg, Hayden, and Jensen (1956) and by Lipson (1956); the rubidium-strontium method has been used by Cormier, Herzog, Pinson, and Hurley (1956). These workers obtained results in good agreement with the Holmes time scale, but their work is open to objections. The argon retention of glauconite is unknown. Feldspars are well known to have a lower retention of argon than micas. The potassium-argon ages have been calculated by assuming that glauconite retained the same percentage of argon as the average feldspar. All this introduces considerable uncertainty in the results. The difficulty encountered in the rubidium-strontium work is the necessity of making large corrections for primary Sr^{87} in the samples. The fact that the Sr^{87} in the glauconites studied by Cormier et al. was generally 5 to 10 per cent radiogenic places a burden on the analytical accuracy of the data and on the reliability of the isotopic composition of the strontium used to correct for primary strontium. Further problems mentioned by Wasserburg et al. include the possibility that the authigenic minerals may have inherited some radiogenic argon (or strontium), as well as the uncertainty in the time after sedimentation at which the authigenic mineral formed. Losses or gains of parent or daughter after crystallization will, of course, lead to errors. It is possible that similar studies might be made with the uranium-lead and thorium-lead systems by using phosphate minerals from marine sediments. The three difficulties mentioned above would still apply, however. Investigation would be required to ascertain whether the ratios of uranium and thorium to original (common) lead were favorable enough. Shale might be another possibility for lead work, but additional care would have to be exercised to make certain that detrital minerals were not affecting the results.

The amount of evidence obtainable from igneous rocks of known relation to sedimentary horizons can be greatly increased with the recently developed techniques for dating granites. Moreover, these techniques may be applicable to mica-bearing volcanic rocks, which are commonly interstratified with sediments. Possibly the fossil time scale will have to be constructed from several lines of evidence, none of which will have the desired degree of accuracy. If the different approaches are in agreement, a fair amount of confidence in the scale will be justified. At present the situation is far from satisfactory.

Discordant ages. Several types of discordant ages have been mentioned in the previous discussions. In principle, such results contain useful information about the post-crystallization history of rocks. Only a brief summary will be given here of the work that has been started on this problem. Far greater effort has been devoted to problems concerned with the use of concordant ages.

Wetherill (1956*a*, 1956*b*) has shown that, theoretically, groups of discordant U^{238}-Pb^{206}, U^{235}-Pb^{207} ages may be interpreted by means of a simple graphical method to solve for the age of the group of minerals and for the time of loss or gain of lead or uranium, provided that the changes in uranium-lead ratios have taken place in an interval of time which is short compared with the age of the minerals. He has cited several groups of data that fit the theory very closely. In one, four monazites with discordant ages from Rhodesia and Madagascar are interpreted to have an age of 2700 million years. The observed discordances would result if these monazites had lost lead relative to uranium 500 million years ago. The time of these losses coincides with the age values found for a number of rocks occurring in the same area. (See fig. 2 and Holmes and Cahen, 1957.) This suggests that the age discordance may be due to the effects of a later orogeny. Wetherill's method is helpful in solving for the time at which discordant ages were produced in a given locality, but it does not give information about the nature of the process. Loss of lead cannot be distinguished from gain of uranium.

Recently obtained data help to clarify the problem of differences between the thorium-lead and uranium-lead ages from the same mineral. Acid wash studies reported by Tilton and Nicolaysen (1957) and by Tilton (1956) can be related to the age results. Briefly, high uranium-lead ages in monazites were accompanied by excesses of soluble uranium and radiogenic Pb^{206} compared with thorium and radiogenic Pb^{208} in the acid washes. Minerals with low thorium-lead ages gave excesses of soluble thorium and radiogenic Pb^{208} compared with uranium and radiogenic Pb^{206} in the acid washes. A monazite and a uraninite with good agreement between the uranium-lead and thorium-lead ages leached much more uniformly. These data demonstrate inhomogeneous distribution of uranium and thorium and their respective lead daughters within the samples having discordant ages and a more homogeneous distribution within samples having concordant ages. Comparison of acid-extracted lead with that from the parent minerals suggests that the discordant ages are caused by loss of these elements from the minerals rather than by addition from some external source. Although lead loss has always been assumed to be the cause of low uranium-lead and thorium-lead ages, there had previously been no convincing demonstration that this was actually the process involved. Moreover, the data suggest that low thorium-lead or high uranium-lead ages result from a loss of both parent and lead daughter from a mineral, with the loss of daughter predominating in the first case and the loss of parent predominating in the second. Starik (1956), in an extensive study of leaching phenomena with respect to age discordances, has obtained results in general agreement with those of Tilton and Nicolaysen, although his data do not include the isotopic composition of the soluble lead.

Little work has been done in regard to age discrepancies in the potassium-argon and rubidium-strontium systems. Reynolds (1957) has reported data on the diffusion of argon in mica and feldspar that serve to explain the feldspar-mica potassium-argon age discrepancies in a semiquantitative manner. If a comprehensive understanding of the factors producing discordant ages can be gained through experimentation in the laboratory, it may then be possible to specify within certain limits the physical and chemical processes that have acted on a given mineral assemblage to produce discordant ages.

Conclusions

In summing up the accomplishments of the last decade, it is reasonable to say that considerable confidence is justified in age determinations when two different methods give the same result for a mineral or mineral assemblage. Agreement of the potassium-argon and rubidium-strontium ages for mica may be used as well as agreement of the two uranium-lead ages for radioactive minerals such as uraninite or zircon. The situation is most satisfactory when agreement exists between the mica and the uranium-lead ages. For granites this type of agreement indicates that the time of crystallization of the granite as a whole has been measured. Some progress has been made with metamorphic rocks, but much work remains to be done. In the present state of knowledge, there is no justification for accepting any single age method as establishing the absolute age of a mineral or rock; cross checking by two or more independent methods is required to define ages with any degree of certainty.

One of the most engaging aspects of geochronology is the frequent occurrence of unexpected results, indicating that our knowledge of many physical, chemical, and geological phenomena concerning rocks and minerals is inadequate and needs improvement. Examples are the more complete retention of argon by micas than by feldspars, the occurrence of mica with concordant ages and zircon with discordant ages in the same granites in the southwestern United States, and the finding of discordant ages for zircon in the Laramide belt while concordant zircon ages are found in the Baltimore gneiss in the Appalachian belt.

Although the degree of success that geochronology will attain in the future cannot be predicted, it has already contributed greatly to our understanding of rocks, and further accomplishments may be expected. The harboring of any beliefs that are not supported by reliably established data is hazardous.

Note added in proof: Most laboratories now use a value of 5.83×10^{-11} yr^{-1} for λ_e of K^{40} as determined by scintillation counting instead of the geologically determined value. This would have the effect of reducing the potassium-argon ages given in this chapter by about 5 per cent.

References

Aldrich, L. T. 1956. Measurement of radioactive ages of rocks, *Science, 123,* 871–875.

Aldrich, L. T., and G. W. Wetherill. 1958. *Ann. Rev. Nuclear Sci., 8,* Annual Reviews, Inc., Palo Alto, Calif.

Aldrich, L. T., G. W. Wetherill, and G. L. Davis. 1957. Occurrence of 1350 million-year-old granitic rocks in western United States, *Bull. Geol. Soc. Am., 68,* 655–656.

Aldrich, L. T., G. L. Davis, G. R. Tilton, and G. W. Wetherill. 1956. Radioactive ages of minerals from the Brown Derby Mine and the Quartz Creek granite near Gunnison, Colorado, *J. Geophys. Research, 61,* 215–232.

Aldrich, L. T., G. R. Tilton, G. L. Davis, L. O. Nicolaysen, and C. C. Patterson. 1955. Comparison of U-Pb, Pb-Pb, and Rb-Sr ages of Precambrian minerals, *Proc. Geol. Assoc. Can., 7* (pt. II), 7–13.

Aldrich, L. T., G. W. Wetherill, G. R. Tilton, and G. L. Davis. 1956. Half-life of Rb^{87}, *Phys. Rev., 103,* 1045–1047.

Cobb, James C., and J. Laurence Kulp. 1957. Age of the Swedish Kolm (Abstract), *Bull. Geol. Soc. Am., 68,* 1711.

Cormier, R. F., L. F. Herzog, W. H. Pinson, and P. M. Hurley. 1956. Rubidium-strontium age determinations on the mineral glauconite (Abstract), *Bull. Geol. Soc. Am., 67,* 1681.

Curran, S. C., D. Dixon, and H. W. Wilson. 1951. The decay of Rb^{87}, *Phys. Rev., 86,* 420–421.

Eckelmann, Walter R., and J. Laurence Kulp. 1957. Uranium-lead methods of age determination, II, North American localities, *Bull. Geol. Soc. Am., 68,* 1117–1140.

Ellsworth, H. V. 1932. *Rare-Element Minerals of Canada,* Canada, Department of Mines, Economic Geology Series no. 11, 272 pp

Fenner, C. N., and C. S. Piggot. 1929. The mass-spectrum of lead from bröggerite, *Nature, 123,* 793–794.

Fleming, E. H., Jr., A. Ghiorso, and B. B. Cunningham. 1952. The specific alpha-activities and half-lives of U^{234}, U^{235}, and U^{236}, *Phys. Rev., 88,* 642–652.

Gast, P. W., J. L. Kulp, and L. E. Long. 1958. Absolute age of early Precambrian rocks in the Bighorn Basin of Wyoming and Montana, and southeastern Manitoba, *Trans. Am. Geophys. Union, 39,* 322–334.

Gilluly, James. 1949. Distribution of mountain building in geologic time, *Bull. Geol. Soc. Am., 60,* 561–590.

Goldich, S. S., H. Baadsgaard, and A. O. Nier. 1957. Investigations in A^{40}/K^{40} dating, *Trans. Am. Geophys. Union, 38,* 547–551.

Hintenberger, H., W. Herr, and H. Voshage. 1954. Radiogenic osmium from rhenium-containing molybdenite, *Phys. Rev., 95,* 1690–1691.

Holmes, Arthur. 1955. Dating the Precambrian of peninsular India and Ceylon, *Proc. Geol. Assoc. Can., 7,* 81–106.

Holmes, Arthur, and Lucien Cahen. 1955. African geochronology, *Colonial Geol. Mineral Resources Gt. Brit., 5,* 3–38.

Holmes, Arthur, and Lucien Cahen. 1957. Géochronologie africaine 1956, *Mém. acad. roy. sci. Coloniales, 5,* 1–169.

Holmes, Arthur, W. T. Leland, and A. O. Nier. 1950. The age of uraninite from Gordonia, South Africa, *Am. J. Sci., 248,* 81–94.

Hurley, P. M., W. H. Pinson, H. W. Fairbairn, and R. F. Cormier. 1957. Comparison of A^{40}/K^{40} and Sr^{87}/Rb^{87} ages on biotite (Abstract), *Trans. Am. Geophys. Union, 38,* 396.

Inghram, M. G. 1954. Stable isotope dilution analysis, *Ann. Rev. Nuclear Sci., 4,* Annual Reviews, Inc., Palo Alto, Calif.

Libby, W. F. 1957. Simple absolute measurement technique for beta radioactivity, *Anal. Chem., 29,* 1566–1570.

Lipson, Joseph. 1956. K-A dating of sediments, *Geochim. et Cosmochim. Acta, 10,* 149–151.

Nier, Alfred O. 1939*a*. The isotopic constitution of uranium and the half-lives of the uranium isotopes, I, *Phys. Rev., 55,* 150–153.

Nier, A. O. 1939*b*. The isotopic constitution of radiogenic leads and the measurement of geological time, II, *Phys. Rev., 55,* 153–163.

Nier, Alfred O., Robert W. Thompson, and Byron F. Murphey. 1941. The isotopic constitution of lead and the measurement of geological time, III, *Phys. Rev., 60,* 112–116.

Patterson, Claire. 1956. Age of meteorites and the earth, *Geochim. et Cosmochim. Acta, 10,* 230–237.

Pinson, W. H., Jr., H. W. Fairbairn, P. M. Hurley, L. F. Herzog, and R. F. Cormier. 1957. Age study of some crystalline rocks of the Georgia Piedmont (Abstract), *Bull. Geol. Soc. Am., 68,* 1781.

Powell, R. M., W. H. Pinson, Jr., H. W. Fairbairn, and R. F. Cormier. 1957. Test of the half-life of Rb^{87} (Abstract), *Bull. Geol. Soc. Am., 68,* 1782.

Reynolds, John H. 1957. Comparative study of argon content and argon diffusion in mica and feldspar, *Geochim. et Cosmochim. Acta, 12,* 177–184.

Starik, I. E. 1956. The role of secondary processes in age determination by radiometric methods, *Geokhimiya, 1,* 18–29.

Suttle, Andrew D., Jr., and W. F. Libby. 1955. Absolute assay of beta radioactivity in thick solids, *Anal. Chem., 27,* 921–927.

Tilton, George R. 1956. The interpretation of lead-age discrepancies by acid-washing experiments, *Trans. Am. Geophys. Union, 37,* 224–230.

Tilton, G. R., G. L. Davis, G. W. Wetherill, and L. T. Aldrich. 1957. Isotopic ages of zircon from granites and pegmatites, *Trans. Am. Geophys. Union, 38,* 360–371.

Tilton, G. R., and L. O. Nicolaysen. 1957. The use of monazites for age determination. *Geochim. et Cosmochim. Acta, 11,* 28–40.

Umbgrove, J. H. F. 1947. *The Pulse of the Earth,* Martinus Nijhoff, The Hague, Holland, 358 pp.

Vinogradov, A. P. 1956. Comparison of data on the age of rocks obtained by different methods and geologic conclusions, *Geokhimiya, 1,* 3–17.

Wasserburg, G. J., and R. J. Hayden. 1955. A^{40}-K^{40} dating, *Geochim. et Cosmochim. Acta, 7,* 51–60.

Wasserburg, G. J., R. J. Hayden, and Kenneth J. Jensen. 1956. A^{40}-K^{40} dating of igneous rocks and sediments, *Geochim. et Cosmochim. Acta, 10,* 153–165.

Wasserburg, G. J., F. J. Pettijohn, and J. Lipson. 1957. A^{40}/K^{40} ages of micas and feldspars from the Glenarm series near Baltimore, Maryland, *Science, 126,* 355–357.

Wetherill, George W. 1956*a*. An interpretation of the Rhodesia and Witwatersrand age patterns, *Geochim. et Cosmochim. Acta, 9,* 290–292.

Wetherill, George W. 1956*b*. Discordant uranium-lead ages, I, *Trans. Am. Geophys. Union, 37,* 320–326.

Wetherill, G. W. 1957. Radioactivity of potassium and geologic time, *Science, 126,* 545–549.

Wetherill, G. W., L. T. Aldrich, and G. L. Davis. 1955. A^{40}/K^{40} ratios of feldspars and micas from the same rock, *Geochim. et Cosmochim. Acta, 8,* 171–172.

Wetherill, G. W., G. L. Davis, and L. T. Aldrich. 1957. Age measurements on rocks north of Lake Huron (Abstract), *Trans. Am. Geophys. Union, 38,* 412.

Wetherill, G. W., G. J. Wasserburg, L. T. Aldrich, G. R. Tilton, and R. J. Hayden. 1956. Decay constants of K^{40} as determined by the radiogenic argon content of potassium minerals, *Phys. Rev., 103,* 987–989.

Wilson, J. Tuzo. 1954. The development and structure of the crust, in *The Earth as a Planet* (Kuiper, ed.), pp. 138–207, University of Chicago Press, Chicago, Ill.

The Variations of the O^{18}/O^{16} Ratio in Nature and Some Geologic Implications

SAMUEL EPSTEIN

California Institute of Technology

Since the early work of Urey (1947) and his co-workers (Urey and Greiff, 1935), some twenty years ago, it has been understood that variations in the isotopic composition of many of the lighter elements can be expected in naturally occurring materials. Many processes in nature are accompanied by isotopic fractionation. For example, carbonate precipitated in oceans will become enriched in O^{18} relative to the ocean water. Plants are enriched in C^{12} relative to the carbon dioxide in the air. Study of the variations in the abundances of stable isotopes has contributed to our understanding of various processes and should do so to an even greater extent in the future. It is the aim of this paper to discuss a few of the more recent studies on the oxygen-isotope composition of naturally occurring oxygen-containing materials as examples of applying stable isotopes to the study of natural processes, drawing largely from the work of the author and his colleagues.

Theoretical Considerations

Oxygen, the most abundant element of the earth's crust, is composed of three stable isotopes, O^{16}, O^{17}, and O^{18}. The relative abundance varies with the source of the oxygen; in air it is 99.759:0.0374:0.2039 (Nier, 1950). The O^{18}/O^{16} ratios in nature vary by as much as 10 per cent. The lowest ratio so far observed is in glacier ice found near the poles, and the highest in carbon dioxide of the atmosphere.

The various isotopic species of a compound differ slightly in chemical properties from one another. Just as the chemical properties of different compounds determine their formation under various conditions, so the chemical properties of different isotopic species of the compounds determine how the isotopic abundances distribute themselves in the various chemical compounds found in nature. For example, the thermodynamic properties of the isotopic species of quartz, $SiO^{16}O^{16}$, $SiO^{17}O^{16}$, $SiO^{16}O^{18}$, etc., are not identical. The differences are very small and could be ignored in dealing with ordinary chemical reactions where isotope effects are of no particular interest, but they form the basis for the use of stable isotopes in understanding many geochemical processes.

As an example, consider the O^{18}/O^{16} ratio in the components of the carbon dioxide–water vapor system which is in thermodynamic equilibrium. The oxygen isotope distribution among the components can be defined by considering the isotope exchange reaction:

$$CO_2{}^{16}(g) + 2H_2O^{18}(g) \rightleftharpoons CO_2{}^{18}(g) + 2H_2O^{16}(g) \qquad (1)$$

The equilibrium constant for this reaction is [1]

$$K = [CO_2{}^{18}/CO_2{}^{16}]/[H_2O^{18}/H_2O^{16}]^2$$

where the quantities in brackets are the abundance ratios, and

$$\ln K = -\Delta F^\circ/RT$$

where ΔF° = standard Gibbs free-energy change for the reaction; R = gas constant; T = temperature in degrees Kelvin. If the standard free energies for H_2O^{16} and H_2O^{18} were identical, and if the same were true for $CO_2{}^{16}$ and $CO_2{}^{18}$, then $\Delta F^\circ = 0$, $K = 1$, and the O^{18}/O^{16} ratio in both compounds would be identical. Since the standard free energies for different isotopic species of the molecule are not identical, the relation between the O^{18}/O^{16} ratios of the water and carbon dioxide can be specified if ΔF° is known.

Isotopic species of molecules differ in their thermodynamic properties because the masses of the atoms that constitute them affect the energy

[1] In dealing with natural variations in the isotopic abundances of oxygen only the O^{18}/O^{16} ratios are measured. The isotope ratios O^{18}/O^{17} and O^{17}/O^{16} can be inferred. For two oxygen compounds A and B in isotopic equilibrium, if $K_1 = (O^{17}/O^{16})_A/(O^{17}/O^{16})_B$ and $K_2 = (O^{18}/O^{17})_A/(O^{18}/O^{17})_B$, then $K_1 = K_2$ and $K_3 = (O^{18}/O^{16})_A/(O^{18}/O^{16})_B = K_1 \times K_2 = K_1{}^2 = K_2{}^2$. Since isotope equilibrium constants usually have values very close to 1,

$$K_3 - 1 \approx (K_2 - 1) + (K_1 - 1)$$

The difference in the O^{18}/O^{16} ratios between compounds A and B is about twice the differences for the O^{17}/O^{16} and O^{18}/O^{17} ratios.

From a practical aspect the O^{18}/O^{16} ratio is much simpler than the O^{17}/O^{16} ratio to measure by means of a mass spectrometer using carbon dioxide as the working gas.

states of the molecules, the moments of inertia and the fundamental frequencies of vibration of the molecules being mass-dependent.

The ability to calculate K for isotopic exchange reactions (Urey, 1947) provides the basis for estimating the equilibrium distribution of the O^{18}/O^{16} ratio among different components in a system. Usually we are interested in the fractionation factor α rather than in the equilibrium constant. The fractionation factor is defined as the over-all ratio of the isotopes of an element in one chemical compound as compared with the same ratio in a second chemical compound.

For reaction 1,

$$\alpha = \frac{(O^{18}/O^{16})_{CO_2}}{(O^{18}/O^{16})_{H_2O}} = \frac{[2(CO_2{}^{18}) + CO^{16}O^{18}]/[CO^{16}O^{18} + 2(CO_2{}^{16})]}{H_2O^{18}/H_2O^{16}}$$

Generally,

$$\alpha = K^{1/n} \tag{2}$$

where n is the maximum number of exchangeable oxygen in any one of the molecules under consideration ($n = 2$ in reaction 1); that is,

$$\frac{[2(CO_2{}^{18}) + CO^{16}O^{18}]/[CO^{16}O^{18} + 2(CO_2{}^{16})]}{H_2O^{18}/H_2O^{16}} = \left[\frac{CO_2{}^{18}/CO_2{}^{16}}{(H_2O^{18}/H_2O^{16})^2}\right]^{1/2}$$

if the relative abundances of the different isotopic species of carbon dioxide, $CO^{16}O^{18}$, $CO^{16}O^{16}$, and $CO^{18}O^{18}$, are determined by random distribution of the different isotopes, that is, if the abundance of $CO^{16}O^{18}$ $= 2 \times$ atom abundance of $O^{16} \times$ atom abundance of O^{18}, and that of $CO^{16}O^{16}$ = (atom abundance of $O^{16})^2$, and that of $CO^{18}O^{18}$ = (atom abundance of $O^{18})^2$.

Similarly for the $CO_3{}^{=}$–H_2O system,

$$\alpha = (CO_3{}^{=18}/CO_3{}^{=16})^{1/3}/(H_2O^{18}/H_2O^{16})$$

if the different isotopic species of $CO_3{}^{=}$ are determined randomly.

Equation 2 does not hold true in compounds where the isotopes of hydrogen are considered or where the different positions of the several atoms of a single element are not equivalent, as in N_2O, where only one of the nitrogen atoms is bound to the oxygen NNO.

The change of α with temperature can be calculated approximately by the methods of statistical mechanics. For a detailed discussion of the procedure the reader is referred to the paper by Urey (1947). In many cases α is very sensitive to temperature and approaches the value of unity at elevated temperatures. For example, Urey's calculated α values for the O^{18}/O^{16} ratios in the $(CO_2)_{gas}$–$(H_2O)_{gas}$ system are 1.055,

1.047, 1.027, and 1.017 at 273.1°, 298.1°, 400°, and 500° K, respectively. Between temperatures 273° and 298° K, α changes by 0.0003 per degree. Since present-day mass spectrometers can measure α variations to ∓ 0.0001, such temperature effects are quite large.

Usually the calculated α's are only approximate. In some cases the calculated and the experimental values for α are very close. An interesting example is the calculation of α by Urey for the $(CO_2)_{gas}$–$(H_2O)_{gas}$ system, which yielded the value 1.047 at 25° C. Current data in our laboratories give the result 1.048. In the early stable isotope researches, the calculated fractionation factors were usually more accurate than values determined experimentally, particularly where gases were involved. With new methods of measuring variations in isotope abundances of certain elements, this is no longer true. In any event, the calculated fractionation factors serve as excellent guides in planning and interpreting isotope experiments in natural materials when fractionation factors have not been determined experimentally. The preceding considerations are equally applicable, in principle at least, to all elements composed of isotopes, whether they are stable or radioactive.

The Effect on α of Factors Other Than Temperature

In considering chemical equilibrium between assemblages of minerals it is necessary to take into account not only the effect of temperature but also the effects of all the factors influencing the chemical behavior of the system, such as pressure, chemical composition, and activity coefficients of the solutions from which minerals form. A great deal of information about the conditions of formation of mineral assemblages has been obtained from thermodynamic considerations. At the same time such studies have been handicapped by the lack of information about volatile constituents, the activity of solutions, and the pressure. Many of these complicating aspects can be ignored (for all practical purposes) or can be investigated experimentally in a relatively simple manner when applying isotope studies to problems of geologic interest. The simplifying aspects are due to the ideality of the solutions of isotopic molecules of a compound and to the fact that a fractionation factor deals with exchange reactions in which the two sides of the equation are nearly identical in terms of molar volumes.

In addition, α between oxygen isotopes in minerals is independent of the concentration of any other constituents as long as the chemical nature of the minerals in question is not altered appreciably. It therefore seems reasonable to assume that within the scope of present-day measurements the fractionation factor is only temperature-dependent.

For example, it has been shown that α for the $CaCO_3$–H_2O system is independent of whether the water is ocean water or fresh water, is independent of *p*H and relative amount of each phase, and appears to be independent of pressure or of small amounts of Mg and Sr ions in the carbonate lattice; it is the same, moreover, whether calcium carbonate is in the form of calcite or aragonite. The insensitivity of the fractionation factor to the effects mentioned, other than temperature, greatly simplifies the application of oxygen-isotope methods to studies on temperature and equilibrium conditions in the formation of rocks.

Kinetic Effects

Although we have discussed the effect of the difference in chemical properties of different isotopic molecules of a compound as an example of how heterogeneities in nature can occur, there are other stable isotope effects which lead to isotope fractionation. The process of diffusion undoubtedly causes heterogeneities in isotopic composition of the lighter elements in nature, since the lighter isotopic species of a molecule can be expected to diffuse more rapidly through concentration gradients than the heavier ones. The relative velocities of gas molecules, which are inversely proportional to the square roots of the masses, are a factor in the distribution of isotopes of some of the elements. For example, the fact that the C^{13}/C^{12} ratio in plants is some 2 per cent lower than that of atmospheric carbon dioxide is due in part to the more frequent collision of $C^{12}O_2{}^{16}$ with the photosynthesizing leaf as compared with $C^{13}O_2{}^{16}$.

There are isotope effects in the rates of chemical reactions where different isotopic molecules of a compound react at different rates. For example, oxalic acid (HOOC—COOH) decomposes so that the carboxyl groups (COOH) containing C^{12} decompose more rapidly than the C^{13} carboxyl (Lindsay et al., 1949). Rakestraw et al. (1951) found that the oxidation of organic material in the oceans by the dissolved oxygen preferentially uses the O^{16}. Bigeleisen (1949) has treated the problem of the kinetics of chemical reactions of different isotope molecules theoretically, and other workers have done considerable experimentation on this subject.

The Measurement of the O^{18}/O^{16} Ratios

In the early works on oxygen-isotope variation a density method was used, based on the fact that the density of pure water could reflect the concentration of H_2O^{17}, HDO, and H_2O^{18}. Because H_2O^{18} constitutes only 0.2 per cent of the total water, this method requires that the density of water be measured to a precision of 0.1 to 1 part per million. The method is subject to considerable error, particularly if samples require chemical steps to convert them into water. Nevertheless, many excellent experiments were done. Riesenfeld and Chang (1936) determined the equilibrium fractionation factor for oxygen isotopes between the liquid and vapor phase of water at several temperatures. Their results are essentially correct within about 0.1 per cent of the O^{18}/O^{16} ratio. Dole (1935, 1936) established that there are important differences between the oxygen-isotope ratios in air, water, and some oxides.

The advent of modern mass spectrometry greatly enlarged the scope for oxygen-isotope research. At present, variations of the O^{18}/O^{16} ratio can be measured within ± 0.01 per cent, and in most experiments it is the handling and preparation of the samples for the spectrometer that is the limiting factor in the accuracy of the measurements.

The modern mass spectrometer commonly used for oxygen-isotope research is basically the design of A. O. Nier (1947). Carbon dioxide is the gas best suited for the analysis. The O^{18}/O^{16} ratio is measured by comparing mass 46 ($C^{12}O^{16}O^{18}$) with mass 44 ($C^{12}O^{16}O^{16}$). The gas is introduced into the spectrometer through a small gas leak (to reduce the pressure from centimeters to less than a micron) into a source which ionizes the gas to CO_2^+. The ions, while passing through collimating slits, are accelerated by means of an electrostatic field of some 1500 volts, and emerge from the final slit of the source as a well defined beam of CO_2^+ ions of nearly constant energy. The ions pass through a magnetic analyzer and are deflected into paths determined by their mass. The single ion beam cutting the magnetic lines of force separates into several discrete ion beams, each composed of ions of a single mass and charge. Collectors for each desired mass are mounted at the point of best focus of the resolved beams. On hitting the collectors the ions are neutralized, imparting an electric current to the collectors and their electronic components.

The currents from the collectors pass through high-value resistors across which are developed voltages proportional to the ion intensities hitting the collectors. The voltages developed by the different signals are balanced and compared with one another in a bridge circuit. The output of the circuit gives a null point which is recorded on a sensitive potentiometer. Simultaneous collection of the beams is important, because then considerable fluctuations in the intensity of the ion beams due to instabilities in the source can be tolerated without causing fluctuations in recorded output of the bridge circuit.

McKinney et al. (1950) modified Nier's mass spectrometer for the

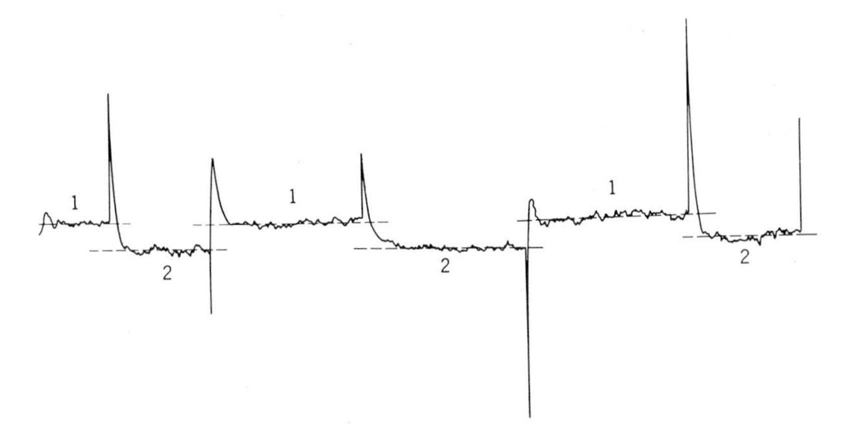

Fig. 1. Sample potentiometer record for measuring δ values.

purpose of measuring small variations in the 46/44 ratio very accurately. In addition to the necessary changes in the electronics and the installation of a vibrating-reed electrometer, they introduced a magnetically operated valve into the gas feed system. The valve permits the switchover from a standard gas to the unknown in a matter of seconds and the rapid comparison of the O^{18}/O^{16} ratio of the gases at a time when the conditions in the mass spectrometer source are essentially the same for both gases. The difference in trace levels of gas 2 and gas 1 in figure 1 represents a change of only 0.06 per cent of the ratio. It is evident that the sensitivity of the method is about ± 0.01 per cent. The comparative method nullifies the effect of background impurities in the tube of the mass spectrometer and the effect of mass discrimination as long as the differences between the O^{18}/O^{16} ratios of the standard and the sample are only a few per cent.

Reporting the absolute isotope ratio is of little significance when it is the changes of the ratio that are of interest. The variations of the O^{18}/O^{16} ratio are therefore recorded as deviations from a standard, δ. In this paper the δ values are given in parts per thousand and are relative to mean ocean water

$$\delta = \left[\frac{(O^{18}/O^{16})_{\text{sample}}}{(O^{18}/O^{16})_{\text{ocean water}}} - 1 \right] 1000$$

Thus, when the O^{18}/O^{16} ratio of the sample is smaller than that of mean ocean water by 1 per cent or 10 per mil, the value of δ is -10 per mil, or if it is greater by 1 per cent, $\delta = +10$ per mil. The nature of the standard used has in the past depended on the problem under consideration. Craig (1957) has discussed the choice of standards, the relationship between measurements of the 46/44 ratio to the actual O^{18}/O^{16} ratio, and related problems.

The Variation of O^{18}/O^{16} Ratio in Natural Waters

The variation of the isotopic composition of water in the meteorological cycle is pertinent to many fields, being of interest to the meteorologist, the hydrologist, and the geologist. Although water itself cannot be put into the mass spectrometer for analysis, the oxygen can be analyzed by analyzing carbon dioxide equilibrated with the water. As long as the samples of water including the standard ocean sample are treated identically, the O^{18}/O^{16} ratio of the equilibrated carbon dioxide is related to that of the water as follows:

$$(O^{18}/O^{16})_{\text{water}} = \alpha(O^{18}/O^{16})_{CO_2}$$

and the δ relative to mean ocean water is identical to the δ values obtained using the equilibration method. That is,

$$\left[\frac{(O^{18}/O^{16})_{\text{sample}} - (O^{18}/O^{16})_{\text{standard}}}{(O^{18}/O^{16})_{\text{standard}}}\right] 1000$$

$$= 1000\left[\frac{\alpha(O^{18}/O^{16})_{CO_2} - \alpha(O^{18}/O^{16})_{CO_2\ \text{standard}}}{\alpha(O^{18}/O^{16})_{CO_2\ \text{standard}}}\right]$$

thus $\delta_{\text{water}} = \delta_{CO_2\ \text{equilibrated with water}}$.

The O^{18}/O^{16} variation in waters in the meteorological cycle is due to the fact that at any one temperature the vapor pressure of H_2O^{16} is greater than that of H_2O^{18}.

The vapor-pressure differences are such that the fractionation factor

$$\alpha = (H_2O^{18}/H_2O^{16})_{\text{liquid}}/(H_2O^{18}/H_2O^{16})_{\text{vapor}}$$

is approximately 1.005 at 100° C, 1.008 at 25° C, and 1.010 at 0° C (Riesenfeld and Chang, 1936).

The above information permits some understanding of the distribution of the H_2O^{18}/H_2O^{16} ratio in natural waters.

Measurements of the O^{18}/O^{16} variation in a large number of samples of ocean water (Epstein and Mayeda, 1953) indicate the extent and sources of the variations in ocean waters and in the whole meteorological cycle. The O^{18}/O^{16} ratio of most ocean water falls in a range of less than 1 per mil. Water of high salinity has the greatest O^{18} abundance. The relationship between the O^{18} abundance and salinity indicates that the water removed from the ocean has a lower O^{18}/O^{16} ratio than the vapor in equilibrium with the oceans. To explain this, Epstein and Mayeda (1953) suggested that the meteorological cycle is much like a multiple-stage still with reflux. A marine air mass containing water vapor initially in isotope equilibrium with ocean preferentially loses H_2O^{18} when it loses water through rain. The H_2O^{18}-richer rain formed in this way returns to the ocean (reflux). The H_2O^{18}-depleted water vapor is eventually condensed to form snow in the high latitudes and altitudes. Apparently the increase in the O^{18}/O^{16} ratios of the warm ocean water is effected primarily by the loss of O^{18}-poor water to the permanent snow and ice regions and the decrease in the O^{18}/O^{16} in the cold ocean currents by the addition of melt water from the ice region.

The multiple-plate still model has many implications. For example, it suggests that the values of the O^{18}/O^{16} ratio of fresh waters should range anywhere from those of mean ocean water to minimum values in the coldest regions of the earth. Isotope analyses on fresh water entering into cold ocean streams such as the Alaska and Labrador currents showed an average $\delta = -20$ per mil compared to $\delta = -8$ per mil for vapor in equilibrium with ocean water. Chicago snow gave a $\delta = -17$ per mil; a Chicago rain, $\delta = -7$; water from Lake Michigan had a $\delta = -7$; water from near the mouth of the Mississippi River had a $\delta = -4$. The O^{18}/O^{16} ratio is affected by such factors as latitude, altitude, climate, and temperatures. The effect of temperature would suggest seasonal variation in the O^{18}/O^{16} of rain and snow, which has also been observed (Epstein, 1957). The author obtained a value of $\delta = -50$ per mil for snow at the South Pole, probably the lowest O^{18}/O^{16} ratio measured to date. Assuming that evaporation and condensation in the meteorological cycle are equilibrium processes, this value would mean that the meteorological cycle has about 6 to 7 theoretical distillation plates.

Dansgaard (1953) used the Raleigh distillation formula to show how the O^{18}/O^{16} ratio of rain and snow can acquire a large range of values. The Raleigh distillation formula can be written in the form

$$R/R_0 = f^{(1-\alpha)} \qquad (a)$$

where f = fraction of the initial liquid water remaining; f is 1 at the start of the distillation and approaches 0 as distillation progresses.

α = fractionation factor
$= (H_2O^{18}/H_2O^{16})_{\text{liquid}}/(H_2O^{18}/H_2O^{16})_{\text{vapor}}$.

R = H_2O^{18}/H_2O^{16} ratio of the residual liquid water.

R_0 = H_2O^{18}/H_2O^{16} of the liquid water before distillation is initiated.

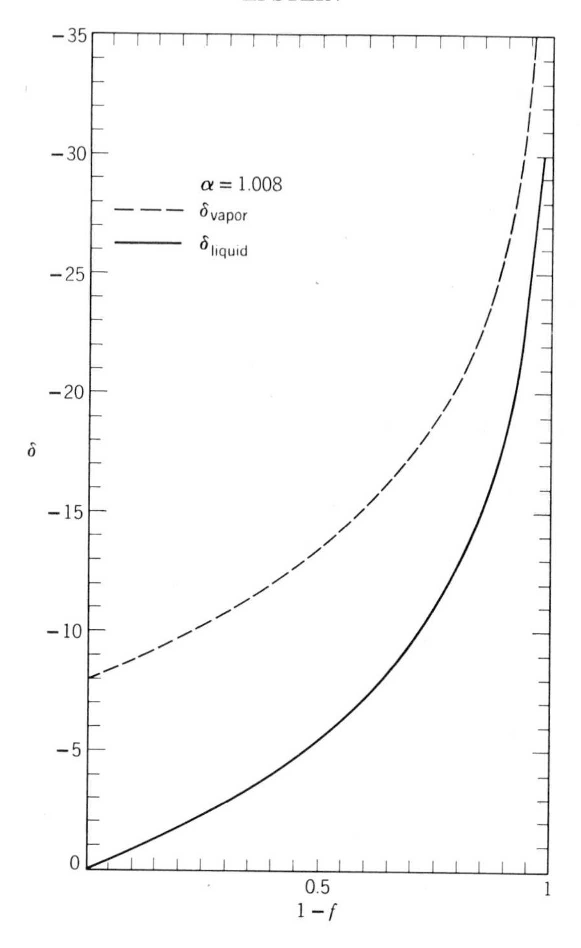

Fig. 2. A plot of the Raleigh equation: Variation of the O^{18}/O^{16} ratio of water and vapor, with degree of condensation of a water vapor system. The condensed phase is continuously removed from the system.

Formula (*a*) describes the change in the O^{18}/O^{16} ratio of a system of liquid water as the system is subjected to distillation and the vapor is removed from the system as it is formed. It is assumed here that α remains constant: the distillation is an equilibrium one, performed at a constant temperature.

The Raleigh equation can also be applied to a system of water vapor. Here the formula would be

$$R/R_0 = f^{(\alpha-1)} \qquad (b)$$

where R_0 and R are the H_2O^{18}/H_2O^{16} ratios of the initial water vapor and of the water vapor after partial condensation, respectively; f is the fraction of vapor remaining in the system.

For the purpose of explaining the variation in the O^{18}/O^{16} ratios of rain and snow, formula (*b*) is of interest. Figure 2 is a plot of δ against $(1 - f)$ where the initial air mass has a water vapor of $\delta = -8$, which is the δ value for water vapor in equilibrium with ocean water. The dotted curve shows the relation between the fraction of water vapor condensed $(1 - f)$ and the δ of the remaining vapor. The solid curve gives the δ values of the condensed liquid at the moment it is formed. As was indicated by Dansgaard (1953, 1954), this curve explains how the δ values of some natural precipitation can acquire such low values: a vapor-laden air mass will precipitate water of decreasing O^{18}/O^{16} ratios as it is progressively depleted of water vapor by condensation.

The Raleigh equation can be used in the evaluation of the relation between the isotopic composition of water and the condition of formation of rain and snow provided that the evaporation-condensation processes in the meteorological cycle are equilibrium ones. It is possible to determine from a comparison of the O^{18}/O^{16} and the DH/H_2 ratios whether rain and snow were formed under equilibrium conditions. For the water-vapor system, the oxygen fractionation factor

$$\alpha_O = (H_2O^{18}/H_2O^{16})_{\text{liquid}}/(H_2O^{18}/H_2O^{16})_{\text{vapor}}$$

is about $\frac{1}{9}$ of the hydrogen fractionation factor

$$\alpha_H = (HDO/H_2O)_{\text{liquid}}/(HDO/H_2O)_{\text{vapor}}$$

at about 20° C when equilibrium conditions exist. Under nonequilibrium conditions α_O/α_H can have values that are much greater (up to approximately 2). The combined data of Friedman (1953) and Epstein and Mayeda (1953) on the same samples showed that for rain and snow the value of the α_O/α_H is approximately $\frac{1}{9}$.[2] The apparent existence of isotopic equilibrium in the condensation-evaporation processes in the meteorological cycle should simplify the treatment and interpretation of isotope data of waters.

It is possible to calculate many models for different processes involving evaporation and condensation, specifying the degree of recycling and mixing of different air masses containing water vapor of different O^{18}/O^{16} ratio (Dansgaard, 1954).

[2] Craig (unpublished data), who analyzed many samples for their HD/H_2 and O^{18}/O^{16} ratios, found that equilibrium evaporation and condensation did occur in nearly all rain and snow that he analyzed. There are marked deviations from equilibrium in stagnant water from lakes and hot springs.

In summary, the O^{18}/O^{16} and HDO/H_2O ratios are properties of water characteristic of the processes to which they have been subjected. As such, measurements of this type should be valuable in studies of natural processes associated with movements of water and water vapor.

Paleotemperatures by the Oxygen-Isotope Thermometer

The literature contains many interesting examples of the application of oxygen-isotope studies to geological problems. Among them are the researches utilizing the oxygen-isotope temperature scale developed by Urey and his colleagues (1951).

In the $CaCO_3(s)$–$H_2O(l)$ system

$$\alpha = (CO_3{}^{18}/CO_3{}^{16})^{1/3}/H_2O^{18}/H_2O^{16} = 1.025 \text{ at } 0° \text{ C} \qquad \text{(McCrea, 1950)}$$

decreasing with increasing temperature. In the oceans the amount of water is so much greater than the amount of calcium carbonate that any redistribution of the oxygen isotopes among the two phases, to accommodate a change in α, will not appreciably affect the O^{18}/O^{16} ratio of the ocean water. Thus only the O^{18}/O^{16} ratio of the calcium carbonate will be temperature-dependent.

It follows that, if marine carbonate skeletons are grown in isotopic equilibrium with the surrounding water, it will be possible to measure the temperatures at which the carbonate was laid down by the organism by measuring the O^{18}/O^{16} ratios of the carbonates. It is also evident from the above equation that the O^{18}/O^{16} ratio of the carbonate will change if the O^{18}/O^{16} ratio of the water is changed.

The temperature dependence of the O^{18}/O^{16} ratio of the carbonate was experimentally determined, for both organically (Epstein et al., 1953) and inorganically (McCrea, 1950) precipitated carbonate, by analyzing carbonate skeletal material grown under known temperature conditions as well as by analyzing slowly precipitated inorganic carbonate in water of known O^{18}/O^{16} ratios. Both these methods gave the same relation for the change in the O^{18}/O^{16} ratio in carbonate with temperature. If the isotopic composition of ocean water were homogeneous (within $\delta = \pm 0.1$ per mil for oxygen) and did not change with time, the precision of the scale is such that it would be possible to determine temperatures of the oceans as far back as the Paleozoic to within 1° C. For present-day marine invertebrate organisms whose habitat waters can be analyzed it is possible to obtain such precise temperature measurements. The existence of heterogeneities in the oxygen isotopic composition in the oceans represents the most serious limitation to the usefulness of the temperature scale for measuring temperatures of the past. There are other problems associated with the preservation of fossil material that must be considered, but they can be surmounted with various degrees of success by intelligent choice of materials. In spite of the afore-mentioned difficulties it is still possible, by proper choice of materials, to make studies of the climates of the past.

Studies of present-day ocean waters indicate that the main reasons for variations in the O^{18}/O^{16} ratio in oceans is associated with the presence of regions of very low temperatures. The water composing snow and glaciers is isotopically very different from ocean water. It has been estimated (Epstein and Mayeda, 1953) that variations in salinities of 1 unit in 35, where the salinity of average ocean water is 35 per mil, would be accompanied by a 1° C error in temperature determinations in a nonglacial period of the history of the earth. Since variations in salinity would probably be less in open oceans in the absence of melting snow and ice, considerable confidence could be felt in temperatures determined from the O^{18}/O^{16} ratio for most of the history of the earth for which unaltered fossils exist.

A thorough study of the temperature of the Upper Cretaceous period (Urey et al., 1951; Lowenstam and Epstein, 1954) has been made; to judge from the consistency in distribution of the temperatures from a large variety of localities, there is reason for confidence in the temperatures determined. For example, using well preserved samples (belemnites) from the United States, Sweden, Denmark, England, France, Holland, and Germany, temperatures were obtained that seem reasonable and vary in the expected way with latitude. If brackish (contaminated by fresh water) marine waters were present, temperatures would be unreasonably high. The comparative history in the Upper Cretaceous showed a maximum temperature in the middle Upper Cretaceous and lower temperatures in the late Upper and early Upper Cretaceous. Such a trend was observed whether the series of samples were from a geographically restricted area (Sweden, England) or whether both European and United States samples were included. In addition, a latitudinal effect was observed for a single subperiod over a wide geographical area. In general, the Upper Cretaceous isotope temperature fell in a range of about 12° to 28° C. For the middle Upper Cretaceous the lowest temperatures were observed for an Alaskan and a Siberian sample—about 14° C. This showed, what has largely been known, that the climate in the Upper Cretaceous was relatively mild and much more uniform than the present climate. Moreover, the temperature of the oceans in the northern region, and thus probably at depth, was about 14° C, which is higher than the temperature of the present ocean depths.

Sometimes ocean-surface temperatures fluctuated greatly in a relatively short period, as during the glacial and interglacial periods of the Pleistocene. These temperatures were measured by Emiliani (1955) using foraminifera from ocean-bottom cores. He found very large temperature variations compatible with other lines of evidence. His research appears to be extremely useful for studying the Pleistocene history of the earth. As has been pointed out by Urey et al. (1951), the development of another temperature scale using calcium carbonate and another oxygen compound (phosphate) precipitated by organisms would permit a temperature scale independent of the O^{18}/O^{16} ratio of ocean waters. Such a scale not only would eliminate the difficulties introduced by variations in the O^{18}/O^{16} ratio of water but also would permit the determination of the O^{18}/O^{16} ratio of the waters of the past. Such data would give information about locations of river mouths, about the general circulation of the ocean, and any other information that can be obtained from isotopic studies of present-day ocean water.

The O^{18}/O^{16} Ratio in Minerals and Rocks

One of the promising applications of oxygen-isotope research is in the field of igneous and metamorphic petrology, including low- and high-temperature diagenesis and ore formation. The applicability of oxygen-isotope research to such problems is due to the fact that common rock systems are usually composed of two or more coexisting minerals. If these minerals were in isotopic equilibrium with one another at the time of crystallization, it is possible to determine the temperature of equilibration by using the temperature dependence of several fractionation factors simultaneously. If the minerals are not all in equilibrium, it is possible from the oxygen-isotope data to draw conclusions about the paragenesis, degree of low- and high-temperature diagenesis, and other interesting aspects of petrology. Laboratory experiments in conjunction with the analyses of natural materials are necessary to establish the variation with temperature of the isotopic fractionation factors among the different minerals. The experiments can be simplified by choosing simple systems, like one mineral plus water. Once the fractionation factors at different temperatures for mineral–water systems are known, fractionation factors for different mineral pairs can be calculated.[3] At present we know the approximate values and temperature dependence of the isotopic fractionation factors for oxygen between carbonate (McCrea, 1950), quartz (Silverman, 1951), iron oxides, and water. With

[3] $\alpha_1 = \dfrac{(O^{18}/O^{16})_{\text{mineral A}}}{(O^{18}/O^{16})_{\text{water}}}, \quad \alpha_2 = \dfrac{(O^{18}/O^{16})_{\text{mineral B}}}{(O^{18}/O^{16})_{\text{water}}}, \quad \alpha_3 = \dfrac{\alpha_2}{\alpha_1} = \dfrac{(O^{18}/O^{16})_{\text{mineral B}}}{(O^{18}/O^{16})_{\text{mineral A}}}.$

this information it has been possible to attack a problem of some petrologic significance.

The amount of the variation in the O^{18}/O^{16} ratio in silicates, carbonates, and oxides in igneous and metamorphic rocks is not very well known. The extraction of oxygen for isotope analysis from many of the minerals composing the rocks is difficult. The early attempts showed that such variations existed, but measurements were relatively crude so that it is difficult to assess whether they were real or were caused by the chemical procedures involved in the measurements. The first to succeed in obtaining precise and reliable data on oxygen isotopes were Baertschi and Silverman (1951) and Silverman (1951). They analyzed complete silicate rocks, finding that in general the rocks that contained the greatest percentage of free quartz were richest in O^{18}. The greatest concentration of O^{18} was found in quartz that formed at relatively low temperatures. Silverman, who analyzed a sequence of igneous rocks from Wisconsin, found the highest O^{18}/O^{16} ratios in the more siliceous rocks and the lowest in the more basic rocks. He attributed the variations in isotopic composition to diffusion processes. Although his interpretation may be subject to question, the variations he observed are correct and as such represented the most accurate data on oxygen-isotope variations in silicates at that time.

Baertschi and Schwander (1952) and Schwander (1953) extracted oxygen from silicate rocks by reacting them at high temperatures with graphite. The resultant carbon monoxide, obtained in variable yields, was used for mass-spectrometric analysis. These workers, in contrast to Silverman, found that in general the O^{18}/O^{16} ratio is higher for basic igneous rocks than for the more siliceous ones. Clayton and Epstein (1958) later discovered that the reduction method fails to yield a carbon monoxide gas whose oxygen isotopic composition is representative of the rock sample. The reduction procedure is valid only for those chemical compounds that react to give nearly 100 per cent yields of carbon monoxide. The O^{18}/O^{16} ratio of the carbon monoxide produced in the lower-yield reactions is variable and subject to considerable error. Clayton and Epstein (1958) found that oxygen in quartz, iron oxide, and zircon can be studied by reduction methods. Mass-spectrometer analyses are much simpler and less subject to error if the carbon monoxide is converted to carbon dioxide in the presence of a nickel catalyst by the reaction

$$2CO \rightleftharpoons CO_2 + C$$

Although the reduction method permitted the extraction of oxygen for isotope analyses of only quartz, magnetite, and a few of the rarer minerals, it was still possible to attack some interesting petrological problems using the oxygen-isotope data. The minerals considered were quartz, dolomite, calcite, and magnetite. The oxygen was extracted from the carbonate by acidifying the carbonate and using the carbon dioxide thus released (McCrea, 1950).

In discussing the results of the above work (Clayton and Epstein, 1958) the following relationships should be emphasized.

1. All data are reported relative to mean ocean water in terms of δ, which has been defined previously.

2. The fractionation factor

$$\alpha = (O^{18}/O^{16})_{\text{mineral}}/(O^{18}/O^{16})_{\text{water}}$$

can be put in terms of δ as $\alpha = 1 + (\delta_{\text{mineral}}/1000)$.

For fractionation factor α_3,

$$\alpha_3 = \frac{(O^{18}/O^{16})_{\text{mineral A}}}{(O^{18}/O^{16})_{\text{mineral B}}} = \frac{1 + (\delta_A/1000)}{1 + (\delta_B/1000)}$$

$$= 1 + (\delta_A - \delta_B)/1000 = 1 + (\Delta_{AB}/1000)$$

where $\Delta_{AB} = \delta_A - \delta_B$.

The last relationship between α_3 and Δ_{AB} is nearly correct because the α's under consideration are between 1.00 and 1.04 and not greater.

From the above considerations, changes in δ values or Δ values represent the changes in the fractionation factor α for the mineral–water system or the mineral A–mineral B system, respectively.

3. Comparison of the O^{18}/O^{16} ratio of the oxygen extracted by the reduction method (100 per cent yields) with that by the acid method (⅔ of oxygen of carbonate) is possible only if direct comparison can be made of oxygen of a carbonate extracted by both methods. The reduction method does not work for $CaCO_3$ but does for $MnCO_3$. All δ_{CO_2} are greater than the $\delta_{\text{total oxygen in carbonates}}$ by 10 per mil. This correction has been applied to all carbonate data.

The O^{18}/O^{16} Ratio in Coexisting Minerals

In evaluating the O^{18}/O^{16} ratio variations in mineral systems it is usually helpful to set up predictions from known information as to how the O^{18}/O^{16} ratio would be expected to distribute itself among the different minerals under various thermodynamic conditions of mineral formation. Let us consider the system quartz, calcite, and water. Although it is not known exactly what the ratios $(O^{18}/O^{16})_{\text{quartz}}/(O^{18}/O^{16})_{\text{calcite}}/(O^{18}/O^{16})_{\text{water}}$ would be under various temperatures, we can make certain approximations. It is estimated that the $(O^{18}/O^{16})_{quartz}/(O^{18}/O^{16})_{water}$ ratio is approximately 1.04 (Silverman, 1951) at room temperatures and should approach 1 at very high temperatures. The $(O^{18}/O^{16})_{calcite}/(O^{18}/O^{16})_{water}$ ratio is approximately 1.03 (McCrea, 1950) at room temperatures and approaches 1.00 at very high temperatures. There are many calculated α's for different oxygen compound systems that behave similarly, and they can be used to illustrate some models.

Consider geologic deposits where calcite and quartz formed in isotopic equilibrium in the presence of a large excess of water (amount water $\gg$ amount quartz + calcite), a possible condition in hydrothermal deposits, and where the O^{18}/O^{16} ratio of the water is the same in all systems. Since we do not have the calculated data for the calcite–quartz–water system, let us use the data by Urey (1947) for the systems CO_2–$CO_3^{=}$–H_2O and CO–O_2–H_2O to illustrate certain relationships. The CO_2 and CO are substituted for the quartz, and the $CO_3^{=}$ and O_2 for the calcite, in the respective systems. If δ_{CO_2} is plotted against the $\Delta_{CO_2\text{-}CO_3^{=}}$ and δ_{CO} against $\Delta_{CO\text{-}O_2}$, curves are obtained in which the δ_{CO_2} or δ_{CO} varies as the $\Delta_{CO_2\text{-}CO_3^{=}}$ and $\Delta_{CO\text{-}O_2}$, respectively (fig. 3). The equilibrium temperatures increase with decrease in Δ's and δ's, and at very high temperatures the δ's of all the components are identical.

The relationships shown in figure 3 are true only under very stringent conditions: (1) the existence of isotopic equilibrium, (2) the presence of a large excess of water, and (3) the same O^{18}/O^{16} ratios for water in all deposits. Suppose, now, that these conditions do not prevail. In the absence of isotopic equilibrium no relationship between δ values of the minerals will exist, and so points would fall randomly in a plot of the type in figure 3. If a large excess of water does not exist or if the isotopic composition of the waters is not uniform, a variety of δ values for quartz and carbonate can be obtained, depending on what the δ_{water} would be and on the temperature of equilibrium. On the other hand, the value for $\Delta_{quartz\text{-}calcite}$ would be independent of the isotopic composition of the water. Therefore pairs of quartz and calcite formed at the same temperature in isotopic equilibrium but in the presence of water of different isotopic composition would form a series of points following a line parallel to the ordinate.

The fractionation factor of the quartz–calcite–water system can be determined by laboratory experiments. Once this is known, for any equilibrium mineral assemblage which includes calcite and quartz the temperature of formation and the δ value for water can be determined from the O^{18}/O^{16} analyses of calcite and quartz. If another coexisting oxygen-containing mineral is analyzed and its fractionation factor rela-

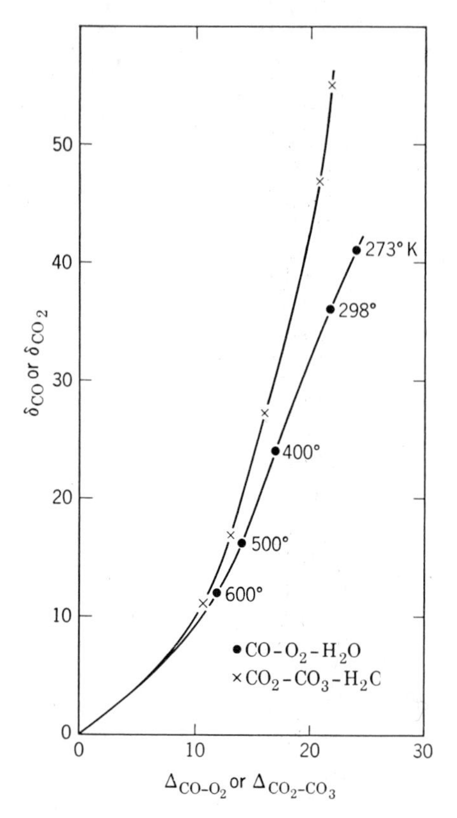

Fig. 3. Two examples of the temperature relationship of the O^{18}/O^{16} ratio between components of a system when the $\delta_{water} = 0$ and when the amount of water is in large excess over the other components of the system. The curves are calculated using the data of Urey (1947). (From Clayton and Epstein, 1958, by permission.)

tive to water is known, two temperature scales will be available for determining the temperatures of formation of the three minerals. Consistency in temperature values using the two temperature scales can serve as an excellent criterion for the existence of isotopic equilibrium. Thus with three coexisting minerals available for oxygen-isotope analyses the following can be determined: (1) the presence or absence of oxygen isotopic equilibrium between the minerals; (2) if equilibrium exists, the temperature at which equilibrium was attained; and (3) the oxygen isotopic composition of the water with which the minerals equilibrated. Incidentally, oxygen isotopic equilibrium between minerals is an excellent indication that chemical equilibrium existed between them at the temperatures at which isotopic equilibrium was established. The greater the number of mineral pairs that can be examined for the O^{18}/O^{16} ratio, the more reliable will be the temperature information obtained.

The data obtained by Clayton and Epstein were for a series of calcite–quartz pairs from a variety of localities as described in table 1.

TABLE 1. The δ Values of Cogenetic Quartz and Calcites

Sample No.	Description	Collector	Locality	Mineral	δ, ‰	$\Delta_{quartz-calcite}$, ‰
1	Hard black chert (microcrystalline quartz) in a white calcareous chalk. Cretaceous age	A. E. J. Engel	France	Quartz Calcite	34.1 26.7	7.4
2	Black chert in fine-grained limestone. Mississippian age	A. E. J. Engel	Fulford, Colo.	Quartz Calcite	29.2 22.6	6.6
3	"Herkimer diamonds"—quartz crystals in cavities in sandstone. Small calcite crystals partly embedded in the quartz	A. E. J. Engel	Herkimer County, N. Y.	Quartz Calcite	23.8 18.5	5.3
4	Recrystallized chert nodule in calcite marble. Wollastonite surrounds the chert	C. W. Burnham	Crestmore, Calif.	Quartz Calcite	23.8 19.6	4.2
5	Chert from same bed as sample 2, but here limestone recrystallized to coarse calcite	A. E. J. Engel	Fulford, Colo.	Quartz Calcite	22.1 17.6	4.5
6	Hydrothermal vein containing coarsely crystalline intergrown quartz and calcite	A. E. J. Engel	Hot Springs, Ark.	Quartz Calcite	18.6 15.2	3.4
7	Hydrothermal zinc ore containing sphalerite, chalcopyrite, calcite, and quartz	C. W. Burnham	Santa Eulalia, Chihuahua, Mexico	Quartz Calcite	17.0 12.5	4.5
8	High-temperature hematite-calcite-quartz occurrence	H. L. James	...	Quartz Calcite	10.4 7.4	3.0
9	Quartz and calcite from core of a pegmatite	C. W. Burnham	Crestmore, Calif.	Quartz Calcite	11.2 8.6	2.6
10	Scheelite ore containing quartz and calcite	J. A. Noble	Hermosillo, Sonora, Mexico	Quartz Calcite	11.9 10.0	1.9

The δ_{quartz} vs. $\Delta_{quartz-calcite}$ relation obtained for the above samples is shown in figure 4. The most reasonable conclusion to be drawn from these data is that all the above mineral pairs had formed under conditions simulating large excess of water where the $\delta_{water} = 2$ per mil and that the quartz, calcite, and water were in isotopic equilibrium. In addition, the geologic estimate of relative temperatures of formation is consistent with the relative temperatures indicated by the δ and Δ values. The higher the temperatures of formation, the lower are the δ and Δ values. In spite of the fact that these mineral pairs were chosen as samples where the conditions of excess water and chemical equilibrium had the best chance of existing during their formation it is still surprising

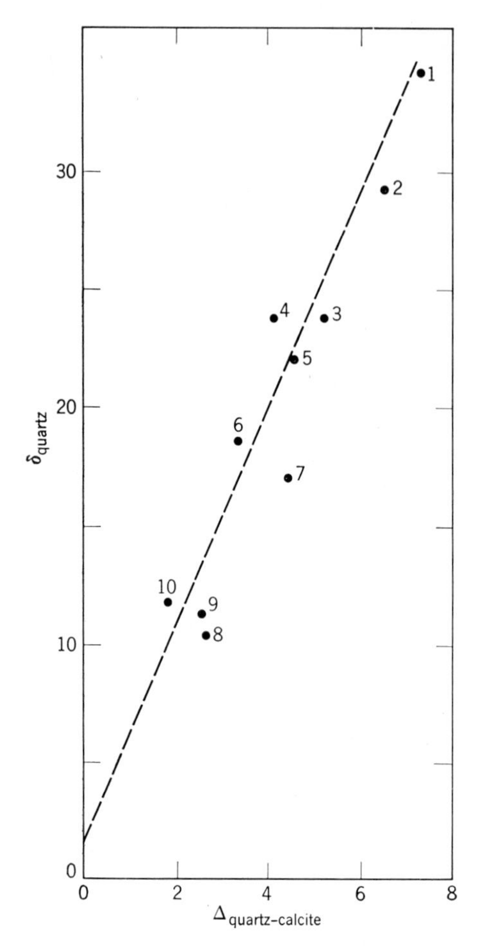

Fig. 4. The relationship between the O^{18}/O^{16} ratios of quartz and calcite for a series of naturally occurring coexisting quartz–calcite pairs (from Clayton and Epstein, 1958, by permission).

that the O^{18}/O^{16} ratios of their oxygens should fall into such a regular curve. The extrapolation of the curve to $\Delta_{\text{quartz-calcite}} = 0$ suggests that the δ_{water} in which they formed is 2.0 per mil. This would be a reasonable value for magmatic water, for several reasons. First, the δ value for magmatic water should be positive relative to ocean water. This is so because the low-temperature sedimentary processes transfer O^{18} from the water to the carbonates and re-equilibrated silicates. Since the $\delta_{\text{mean ocean}} = 0$, juvenile waters which have not participated in a low-temperature sedimentary cycle should have δ values that are positive. Second, as will be seen subsequently, there appears to be no oxygen isotopic fractionation between magnetite and water, and the δ values for magnetite from metamorphic and igneous rocks are on the average +2.0 per mil, without large variation in this value.

Several quartz–calcite pairs from open vugs have been analyzed. The geologic evidence indicates that the quartz formed first and that the calcite was deposited on top of the quartz at some subsequent time and under different conditions. As shown in table 2, all the $\delta_{carbonate}$ values are greater than δ_{quartz} values. This would indicate α values (as defined previously) much less than 1.0, which is unreasonable on theoretical grounds. Thus, as the geological information predicts, the calcite–quartz pairs were not equilibrium pairs.

Comparison of $\delta_{dolomite}$ and δ_{quartz} values of coexisting quartz–dolomite pairs shows in all cases that there is little isotope fractionation in the oxygen between these mineral pairs (table 3).

Oxygen-isotope analyses of quartz–magnetite pairs also showed interesting relations (table 4). All the magnetite of metamorphic and igneous origin gave values of about 2 per mil. One magnetite assemblage formed under supergene conditions in a vug in the Great Lake area gave a δ value of −7.0 per mil, and the δ_{water} of the Great Lakes is also approximately −7.0 per mil. In the coexisting quartz–magnetite pairs the quartz–magnetite varied as expected with relative temperatures of formation, whereas the $\delta_{magnetite}$ varied over a narrow range of values and appears to be independent of temperatures, indicating only very little difference between the O^{18}/O^{16} ratios of magnetite and coexisting water. This interpretation is reasonable and in agreement with

TABLE 2. The δ Values of Quartz and Calcite Formed under Different Conditions

Sample No.	Description	Collector	Locality	Mineral	δ, ‰	$\Delta_{quartz\text{-}calcite}$, ‰
11	Quartz and calcite in an open cavity	Calif. Inst. of Tech. collection	St. Gothard, Switzerland	Quartz Calcite	9.7 16.7	−7.0
12	Quartz and calcite with native copper	Calif. Inst. of Tech. collection	Northern Michigan	Quartz Calcite	16.3 19.4	−3.1
13	Amethyst (quartz crystals) overgrown with small white calcite crystals, open cavity	Calif. Inst. of Tech. collection	Quanajusto, Mexico	Quartz Calcite	11.6 15.1	−3.5
14	Zinc ore with coarsely crystalline sphalerite, open-cavity coatings of quartz and calcite crystals	C. W. Burnham	Hanover, N. Mex.	Quartz Calcite	12.9 21.6	−8.7

TABLE 3. The δ Values of Coexisting Dolomite and Quartz

Sample No.	Description	Collector	Locality	Mineral	δ, ‰	$\Delta_{quartz\text{-}calcite}$, ‰
17	Quartz and dolomite in a marble	Calif. Inst. of Tech. collection	Palos Verdes, Calif.	Quartz Dolomite	23.3 23.0	0.3
18	Quartz and coexisting dolomite	A. E. J. Engel	Marble, Colo.	Quartz Dolomite	22.9 22.9	0
19	Quartz recrystallized from detrital sand grain in crystalline dolomite	A. E. J. Engel	Leadville, Colo.	Quartz Dolomite	17.0 16.5	0.5
20	Chert and dolomite from "unaltered" Leadville formation	A. E. J. Engel	Meeker, Colo.	Quartz Dolomite	27.6 28.6	−1.0
21	Intergrown quartz and dolomite at ore in Gilman mine	A. E. J. Engel	Gilman, Colo.	Quartz Dolomite	16.2 16.4	−0.2

the similarity in δ_{water} estimated from the calcite–quartz data and $\delta_{magnetite}$ for the metamorphic and igneous magnetites. Thus a new method may be available for studying the O^{18}/O^{16} ratios of waters in igneous, metamorphic, and hydrothermal processes without actually having a water sample. If so, it may be one of the few ways of studying these waters, since water from hot springs and volcanoes is usually highly contaminated with ground water.

Many other aspects of oxygen isotope research as applied to igneous and metamorphic processes could be discussed. One interesting study

TABLE 4. δ_{quartz} and $\delta_{magnetite}$ for Igneous Rocks

Sample No.	Sample	δ_{quartz}	$\delta_{magnetite}$	$\Delta_{quartz\text{-}magnetite}$
36	Alaskite	13.6	0.3	13.3
37	Granite gneiss	11.9	3.3	8.6
38	Granite	10.4	2.2	8.2
39	Granodiorite	9.6	1.7	7.9
40	Granodiorite	8.9	1.4	7.5
41	Rhyolite	8.0	0.6	7.4
42	Gabbro		1.1	
43	Tonalite		0.3	
44	Anorthosite		1.5	
45	Augite syenite		0.9	
46	Quartz monzonite		1.5	
47	Oranite aplite		1.7	

deserving brief mention is that of Engel, Clayton, and Epstein (1958) on the oxygen-isotope distribution in quartz, calcite, and dolomite in a series of carbonates in the Mississippian Leadville formation in Colorado which are associated with the sulfide mineral deposits. Hydrothermal alteration associated with the deposition of the sulfides could be detected by the O^{18}/O^{16} ratio measurements of associated calcite–quartz and dolomite. The data show that there is a gradient in δ values and in Δ values with distance from the ore body, the ore body representing the hottest point in the carbonate beds. Also, various stages in the alteration of the original carbonate bed could be differentiated as to whether they were associated with hydrothermal activity or were due to supergene diagenesis.

References

Baertschi, P., and H. Schwander. 1952. A new method for measuring differences in O^{18} content of silicate rocks, *Helv. Chim. Acta, 35,* 1748–1751.

Baertschi, P., and S. R. Silverman. 1951. The determination of relative abundances of the oxygen isotopes in silicate rocks, *Geochim. et Cosmochim. Acta, 1,* 317–328.

Bigeleisen, J. 1949. The relative reaction velocities of isotopic molecules, *J. Chem. Phys., 17,* 675–678.

Clayton, R. N., and S. Epstein. 1958. The relationship between O^{18}/O^{16} ratios in coexisting quartz, carbonate, and iron oxides from various geological deposits, *J. Geol., 66,* 352–373.

Craig, H. 1957. Isotopic standards for carbon and oxygen and correction factors for mass-spectrometric analysis of carbon dioxide, *Geochim. et Cosmochim. Acta, 12,* 133–149.

Dansgaard, W. 1953. The abundance of O^{18} in atmospheric water and water vapor, *Tellus, 5,* 461–476.

Dansgaard, W. 1954. The O^{18} abundance in fresh water, *Geochim. et Cosmochim. Acta, 6,* 241–260.

Dole, M. 1935. The relative atomic weight of oxygen in water and in air, *J. Am. Chem. Soc., 57,* 2731.

Dole, M. 1936. The relative atomic weight of oxygen in water and air, *J. Chem. Phys., 4,* 268–275.

Emiliani, C. 1955. Pleistocene temperatures, *J. Geol., 63,* 538–578.

Engel, A. E. J., R. N. Clayton, and S. Epstein. 1958. Variations in isotopic composition of oxygen and carbon in Leadville limestone (Mississippian, Colorado) and in its hydrothermal and metamorphic phases, *J. Geol., 66,* 374–393.

Epstein, S. 1957. *Nuclear Processes in Geologic Settings, Publ.* 400, Natl. Acad. Sci. U. S.–Natl. Research Council, Washington, D. C.

Epstein, S., R. Buchsbaum, H. A. Lowenstam, and H. C. Urey. 1953. Revised carbonate–water isotopic temperature scale, *Bull. Geol. Soc. Am., 64,* 1315–1326.

Epstein, S., and T. Mayeda. 1953. Variation of O^{18} content of waters from natural sources, *Geochim. et Cosmochim. Acta, 4,* 213–224.

Friedman, I. 1953. Deuterium content of natural waters and other substances, *Geochim. et Cosmochim. Acta, 4,* 89–103.

Lindsay, J. G., D. E. McElcheran, and H. G. Thode. 1949. The isotope effect in the decomposition of oxalic acid, *J. Chem. Phys., 17,* 589.

Lowenstam, H. A., and S. Epstein. 1954. Paleotemperatures of the post-Aptian Cretaceous as determined by the oxygen isotope method, *J. Geol., 62,* 207–248.

McCrea, J. M. 1950. On the isotopic chemistry of carbonates and a paleotemperature scale, *J. Chem. Phys., 18,* 849–857.

McKinney, C. R., J. M. McCrea, S. Epstein, H. A. Allen, and H. C. Urey. 1950. Improvements in mass spectrometers for the measurement of small differences in isotope abundance ratios, *Rev. Sci. Instr., 21,* 724–730.

Nier, A. O. 1947. A mass spectrometer for isotope and gas analysis, *Rev. Sci. Instr., 18,* 398–411.

Nier, A. O. 1950. A redetermination of the relative abundances of the isotopes of carbon, nitrogen, oxygen, argon, and potassium, *Phys. Rev., 77,* 789–793.

Rakestraw, N. M., D. F. P. Rudd, and M. Dole. 1951. Isotopic composition of oxygen in air dissolved in Pacific Ocean as a function of depth, *J. Am. Chem. Soc., 73,* 2976.

Riesenfeld, E. H., and T. L. Chang. 1936. Dampfdruck, Siedepunkt und Verdampfungswärme von HDO und H_2O^{18}, *Z. physik. Chem., B, 33,* 127–132.

Schwander, H. 1953. Bestimmung des relativen Sauerstoffisotopen-Verhältnisses in Silikatgesteinen und -Mineralien, *Geochim. et Cosmochim. Acta, 4,* 261–291.

Silverman, S. R. 1951. The isotope geology of oxygen, *Geochim. et Cosmochim. Acta, 2,* 26–42.

Urey, H. C. 1947. The thermodynamic properties of isotopic substances, *J. Chem. Soc., 1947,* 562–581.

Urey, H. C., and L. J. Greiff. 1935. Isotopic exchange equilibria, *J. Am. Chem. Soc., 57,* 321–327.

Urey, H. C., H. A. Lowenstam, S. Epstein, and C. R. McKinney. 1951. Measurement of paleotemperatures and temperatures of the Upper Cretaceous of England, Denmark, and the southeastern United States, *Bull. Geol. Soc. Am., 62,* 399–416.

Isotopic Fractionation of Sulfur in Geochemical Processes[1]

WAYNE U. AULT

U. S. Geological Survey

Because of the large variations in the isotopic composition of sulfur in various phases of the lithosphere and hydrosphere, the stable isotopes of sulfur are important as natural tracers for studying geochemical processes. Knowledge of the extent of isotopic fractionation in important processes may place limitations on the theories of origin of the crust of the earth and of ore deposits, and may aid in the study of regional geology.

Sulfur undergoes a valence change of -2 to $+6$ during oxidation-reduction processes, and it also has two stable isotopes, S^{32} and S^{34}, with a 6 per cent mass difference, which are abundant enough to be readily detected with an accuracy (± 0.02 per cent) sufficient for geologic applications. Sulfur isotopes, in geochemical and biochemical processes involving a valence change such as that between sulfate and sulfide, are fractionated with the lighter, more energetic isotope favoring the sulfide, and the heavier, less energetic isotope being concentrated in the more tightly bound sulfate. Urey (1947) and Tudge and Thode (1950) have shown that the energy, entropy, and free energy of isotopic substances depend largely on the vibrational frequencies of the molecules, which in turn depend on the masses of the atoms in the molecules.

The ratio of S^{32}/S^{34} in nature has been found to vary from 20.8 for sulfate in the cap rock of salt domes to 23.3 for sulfide in shales, or a total variation of 11 per cent.

[1] Publication authorized by the Director, U. S. Geological Survey.

Research Technique

Methods of preparing and analyzing sulfur mineral samples isotopically are presented in detail in Thode et al. (1954), Vinogradov et al. (1956), and Feely and Kulp (1957). Sulfur is converted to SO_2 gas and analyzed by a mass spectrometer. For most analyses double collecting mass spectrometers of 60°, 90°, or 180° design are used. There are numerous interlaboratory checks on various types of samples. Caution must be exercised in preparation of SO_2 from galena, because stable $PbSO_4$ will form at temperatures below 1000° C and can cause a fractionation of about 0.1 per cent. Precision for interlaboratory work seems to be ± 0.1 per cent or better, whereas analyses within a laboratory are generally at least twice as precise at a confidence level of 2σ.

Isotopic ratios are reported relative to the primary standard, Cañon Diablo troilite, which is assumed after Macnamara and Thode (1950) to have the ratio 22.21. Variation in parts per thousand (δ, ‰) is also given. Positive and negative δ values indicate, respectively, heavier and lighter sulfur than that of meteoritic troilite.

Historical Survey

By 1927, Aston (1933) was able to show that sulfur consisted of the isotopes S^{32}, S^{33}, and S^{34} in the approximate proportions of 96:1:3. About ten years later Nier (1938) detected S^{36} and determined its approximate proportion as about 1:5000. Macnamara and Thode (1950) gave the following relative percentage abundances for sulfur of meteoritic troilite: $S^{32} = 95.081$, $S^{33} = 0.750$, $S^{34} = 4.215$, and $S^{36} = 0.017$. Thode (1949) and Tudge and Thode (1950) reported the abundance of S^{33} to vary half as much and S^{36} to vary twice as much as S^{34}. Therefore, if the isotope S^{36} were abundant enough so that the S^{36}/S^{32} ratio could be determined with a precision of ± 0.02 per cent or better, its variation would be twice as sensitive as that of the S^{32}/S^{34} ratio.

Investigations of the sulfur isotopes in naturally occurring materials were first reported in 1949 by Thode and co-workers and by Trofimov. Since then many investigations have given many consistent, confirmatory isotopic data on sulfur in its various phases in the earth's crust.

The isotopic content of some important natural occurrences of sulfur is summarized and discussed in the following sections.

1. *Sulfur in the troilite phase* (perfect FeS lattice with no iron de-

TABLE 1. **Sulfur Isotopic Ratios of Meteorites**

Type	Locality	S^{32}/S^{34}	δS^{34}, ‰
Siderite	Cañon Diablo, Ariz.[1,2,3]	22.21 *	0.0
Siderite	Xiquipilco, Mexico	22.20	+0.5
Siderite	Toluca, Mexico [1,4]	22.23	−0.9
Siderite	Richland, Tex.	22.23	−0.9
Siderite	Odessa, Tex.	22.18	+1.3
Siderite	Waterville, Douglas County, Wash.[3]	22.20	+0.5
Siderite	Duchesne County, Utah [3]	22.235	−1.2
Siderite	El Toba, Argentina [3]	22.22	−0.5
Siderite	Goamus, Southwest Africa [4]	22.22	−0.5
Aerolite	"Beenham," Union County, New Mexico [3]	22.20	+0.5
Siderolite	Brenham, Kiowa County, Kansas [3]	22.23	−0.9
Average (equal weight each locality)		22.21	
Troilite (terrestrial)	Del Norte County, Calif.[1]	22.26	−2.3

* Average of 12 complete analyses, some on different portions of Cañon Diablo meteorite by different laboratories.

1. Ault and Kulp (1958*a*).
2. Feely and Kulp (1957).
3. Macnamara and Thode (1950).
4. Rankama (1954); quoting ratios by the McMaster group.

ficiency as in pyrrhotite) of meteorites was first investigated by Trofimov (1949) and by Macnamara and Thode (1950). Trofimov's results are of doubtful value, owing to the lack of agreement with subsequent work, and were later pointed out as aberrant by Vinogradov et al. (1956*a*). The data on meteoritic sulfur are summarized in table 1. To these could be added the analyses of troilite from nine stony chondrites and one stony achondrite (Vinogradov et al., 1957) all of which had the ratio 22.20 without any reported variation. All other analyses of meteorites vary between the limits 22.18 and 22.24. Vinogradov's constant ratio for stony meteorites may be unreal, and their inclusion would not affect the average value. Because the isotopic ratios of meteoritic sulfur were essentially constant and because they appeared to coincide roughly with the median value for terrestrial sulfur, Macnamara and Thode suggested that initially terrestrial and troilite sulfur were isotopically identical.

2. *Sulfide minerals in igneous rocks* were investigated by Macnamara et al. (1952), who assumed that sulfide minerals from igneous rock

TABLE 2. **Sulfides from Igneous Rocks**

Type	Range of Ratios	Number of Samples Averaged	Average S^{32}/S^{34} Ratio
	Mafic igneous rocks [1,2,3]		
Diabase and basalt	22.05 to 22.21	5	22.16
Gabbro	22.07 to 22.26	5	22.15
Pyroxenite	22.11 to 22.20	2	22.16
Peridotite	...	2	22.22
Norite	...	1	22.11
Dunite	...	1	22.20
Andesite lava	...	1	22.13
(Average, all available data, mafic igneous rocks, 22.16)			
	Silicic igneous rocks [1,4]		
Diorite		1	22.11
Granodiorite		1	22.24
Monzonite		2	22.09
Syenite	21.99 to 22.16	2	22.08
Phonolite		1	22.14
(Average, all available data, silicic igneous rocks, 22.13)			

1. Ault and Kulp (1958*a*).
2. Macnamara et al. (1952).
3. Vinogradov et al. (1957).
4. Thode et al. (1949).

represented terrestrial sulfur unaltered isotopically. Additional sulfur data on igneous rocks appear in Vinogradov et al. (1957) and Ault and Kulp (1958*a*) and are summarized in table 2. The range of S^{32}/S^{34} ratios of sulfur in mafic igneous rocks is 22.05 to 22.26, or a 1 per cent variation, with an average sulfur isotopic composition distinctly heavier (22.16) than meteoritic troilite sulfur. If only the results from the apparently larger bodies of rock are averaged a value of 22.12 is obtained. Smaller intrusive bodies are subject to more variation either by contamination or by loss of isotopically lighter volatiles.

Also to be considered are seven sulfide samples from large silicic bodies not including pegmatites but including syenite, granodiorite, phonolite (Devil's Tower), and quartz-monzonite (Boulder batholith) having an average ratio of 22.13. If large silicic rock bodies are due to granitization, and if they can be considered to be the homogenization of a large sample of metasediments, the average sulfur isotopic composition in such occurrences would be expected to be similar to that of the average crust.

3. *Volcanic native sulfur* was studied by Macnamara and Thode (1951) to establish isotopic criteria for distinguishing it from native sulfur of bacterial origin. But the ratios for native volcanic and biogenic sulfur are seen from figure 5 to overlap, and they cannot be used as a criterion for distinguishing the two types as Macnamara and Thode (1951) have done. Vinogradov et al. (1957) also report analyses of six museum specimens of volcanic sulfur which average the same as the meteoritic value (22.20), but volcanic sulfur ratios as reported by three different laboratories (table 3 and figure 5) range from 22.10 to 22.57 with an average ratio of 22.32.

TABLE 3. Isotopic Composition of Volcanic Exhalations

Location	Range of Ratios	Number of Samples Averaged	Average S^{32}/S^{34} Ratio
	Native sulfur		
Hawaii [1]	22.10 to 22.57	3	22.38
Andes of S. America [1,2]	22.16 to 22.55	13	22.34
West Indies [3]	...	1	22.14
Italy [3]	...	1	22.30
New Hebrides [3]	...	1	22.30
Japan and Kuriles [4]	22.14 to 22.42	15	22.30
(Average, all available data, native sulfur, 22.32)			
	Hydrogen sulfide		
Japan [4]	22.27 to 22.42	7	22.33
	Sulfur dioxide		
Hawaii	22.23 to 22.39	2	22.31
Japan [4]	22.33 (and 21.81 *)	1	22.33

* May be contaminated by bacterial activity in Crater Lake.
1. Ault and Kulp (1958*a*).
2. Noetzlin (1956), private conversation.
3. Rankama (1954).
4. Sakai (1957).

Volcanic sulfur gases were isotopically similar to native sulfur. When sampled in genetically related suites the sulfur dioxide was heavier and the hydrogen sulfide lighter than the native sulfur. Isotopic exchange equilibrium between the gaseous emanations has been discussed by Sakai (1957) and Sakai and Nagasawa (1958). They observe up to 2.3 per cent difference for the S^{34} enrichment between volcanic H_2S and SO_2.

The wide range of ratios of the transient volcanic sulfur types is attributed to oxidation-reduction and volatilization processes which take place in volcanic channels. These processes, which are often not quantitative, lead to variable isotopic effects.

4. *Hydrothermal sulfide deposits* have been studied as an indirect means of investigating mineralizing solutions. A variety of deposits have been studied by Thode et al. (1949), Kulp et al. (1956), Vinogradov et al. (1956*b*), Jensen (1957), and Ault and Kulp (1958*b*). The data are summarized in figure 1. In general the average for hydrothermal sulfides, determined by giving equal weight to each locality, gives S^{32}/S^{34} equal to 22.13, a ratio equivalent to sulfur which is heavier than meteoritic. Some mineral deposits show a surprisingly narrow spread of isotopic ratios; others have a spread of several per cent. Ault and Kulp (1958*b*) have shown that such changes are probably due to changes in the isotopic composition of the mineralizing solutions. Sulfide deposits that show little sulfur isotopic variation are probably derived from homogeneous sources such as magmatic solutions with slight contamination. Minerals associated with pegmatites which were derived from metasediments are likely to reflect the sulfur isotopic ratios of sedimentary rocks. Sulfides showing a large range in sulfur ratios as at southeast Missouri (21.47 to 22.44), Sterling Hill, N. J. (21.61 to 22.43), and Ivigtut, Greenland (21.55 to 22.23), may indicate inhomogeneous source and the mechanism of mobilization. Up to 3 per cent difference in S^{32}/S^{34} ratios has been observed between contemporaneous hydrothermal sulfate and sulfide minerals (Sakai, 1957; Ault, 1957), in agreement with the prediction by equilibrium theory. If equilibrium could be demonstrated for such cogenetic minerals, the fractionation of the isotopes between the sulfate and sulfide would indicate the temperature of the process.

5. *Sedimentary sulfides and sulfates* are summarized in table 4 and figures 2 and 5. Shale dominates over the other sediments in importance because of its abundance and sulfur content (discussed later). The average S^{32}/S^{34} ratio for sedimentary sulfide is 22.49, or the sulfur is about 1½ per cent lighter than meteoritic sulfur. In selecting sulfides

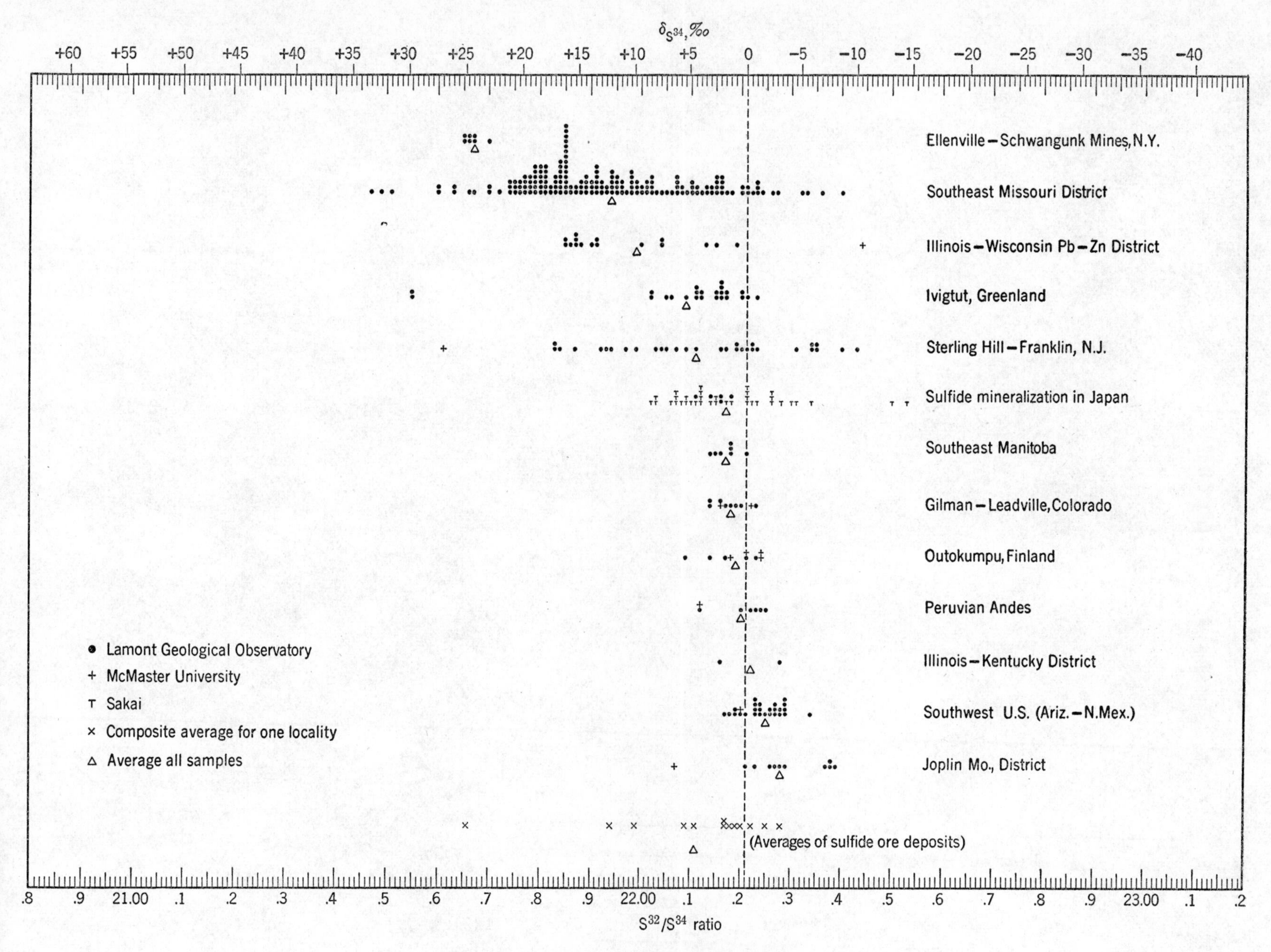

Fig. 1. Sulfides from hydrothermal ore deposits.

TABLE 4. Sulfides in Sedimentary Rocks

Location	Range of Ratios for Localities	Number of Localities Averaged	Average S^{32}/S^{34} Ratio
Canada and United States	21.58 to 23.20	33	22.55
England, Finland, and France	22.14 to 23.00	11	22.54
Russia	21.28 to 23.21	30	22.40
(Average * for sedimentary sulfides, 22.49)			

* Average of all available data obtained by using one average value from each locality (Ault and Kulp, 1958*a*).

of this category the designation as sedimentary by the various researchers was accepted by the present author. The best criteria for identification of sulfides as being sedimentary in origin contemporaneous with the geologic formations are sulfide concretions and iron sulfide crystals disseminated throughout the strata with no evidence of hydrothermal activity. With the inclusion of recent data from sandstone-

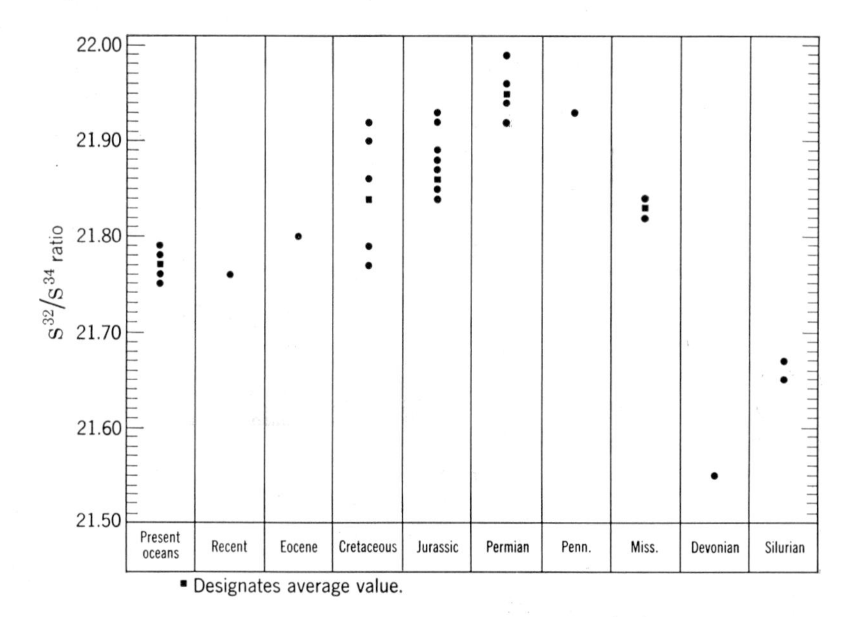

Fig. 2. S^{32}/S^{34} ratios in sulfate deposits of known age (Ault and Kulp, 1958*a*).

type uranium deposits (Jensen, 1958) the average ratio for sedimentary sulfides (22.49) is not likely to be low. The average was obtained by giving each locality equal weight since the data are too varied and limited to allow quantitative weighting by geologic formation or period. Sulfate from evaporite beds has received little attention. Feely and Kulp (1957) found a ratio of 21.87 ± 0.02 for 20 samples of Jurassic anhydrite from the Gulf Coast. Recent data on evaporite beds in the United States (Ault and Kulp, 1958*a*) have shown that there is no simple trend in the change of the ratios with time (fig. 2). The ratios from evaporites trend toward isotopically lighter sulfur back to the Permian, but a few samples from early Paleozoic were heavier than those from Recent evaporites or sea-water sulfate. Silurian evaporites from widely separated localities such as Montana, the Michigan Basin, and New York State have isotopically similar sulfur, which suggests that these deposits were derived from a common body of sea water.

The oceans, by early Paleozoic time, had already reached a dynamic equilibrium between the factors of sulfur addition by the rivers, removal by deposition, and the activity of sulfate-reducing bacteria (discussed later) during these processes. Analyses of any Precambrian evaporites would indicate how much earlier such balance was achieved. These investigations need to be more detailed for various periods and on a world-wide basis to determine whether sulfur isotopic studies of evaporite deposits are useful for correlation from one continent to another. On the other hand, if limited communication prevailed between the basins depositing sulfates and the oceans, such variations may be useful as a paleoclimatic indication.

Thode et al. (1953) and Thode and Macnamara (1953) reported a divergence of the sulfur ratios between sedimentary sulfide and sulfate which began about 800 million years ago and became accumulative with time until the present. However, it has been shown (Ault and Kulp, 1958*a*) that the S^{32}/S^{34} ratios of sedimentary sulfate and sulfide do not converge isotopically at 800 million years and that bacterial activity has probably been important for the last 2000 million years. Important to this argument is the above observation that the sulfur in evaporites does not show a simple variation with time and that sulfides from very old deposits show large variations. Sedimentary pyrite from Karhunsaari, Finland, in shale dated older than 1800 million years, has a ratio 22.65. Hydrothermal sulfide minerals, which are believed to reflect the source isotopically, show large variations (21.5 to 22.44) in old deposits, e.g., Sterling Hill, N. J., and Ivigtut, Greenland, discussed earlier. Vinogradov et al. (1956*a*) reported a rather constant range of ratios 21.3 to 23.2, or 8 per cent, for sedimentary sulfide and three sulfates from Mesozoic and Paleozoic rocks.

It must be concluded that there is no simple correlation between geologic age and extent of fractionation.

6. *Sea-water sulfate* is the second most abundant anion in the oceans, which therefore contain a quantitatively important amount of sulfur. Szabo et al. (1950) presented several analyses of sea-water sulfate which average 21.75 and observed that the "ratios obtained are remarkably constant for the three different oceans" (Arctic, Atlantic, and Pacific) but that the available data show "some significant difference between [the] Pacific and Atlantic." Subsequently Macnamara and Thode (1951) published ratios having a 1 per cent spread and an average 21.80, but later, Thode et al. (1953) stated that a more accurate investigation of sea-water sulfate gave an average value of 21.8 and a much smaller spread. Feely and Kulp (1957) gave sea-water values averaging 21.76. Sakai (1957) reported 21.75 for Pacific Ocean "standard sea water." Ault and Kulp (1958*a*) report data on depth profiles from a number of ocean basins, the Gulf of Mexico, and a lagoon where gypsum is forming in the water. Twenty-five sulfate sulfur samples from the Pacific and Atlantic sea water gave remarkably constant ratios averaging 21.76 $\pm$ 0.02 (table 5 and fig. 5).

Szabo et al. (1950) suggested that isotopic equilibrium or partial equilibrium may prevail in the sulfur cycle in nature. Anaerobic bacteria, *Desulfovibrio desulfuricans* in particular, are known to reduce sulfate in solution, generating H_2S, which is depleted in S^{34}, and

TABLE 5. Sulfur Isotopic Ratios from Sea-Water Sulfate

Location	Range of Ratios	Number of Localities Averaged	Average S^{32}/S^{34} Ratio
N. Pacific Basin	21.75 to 21.77	3	21.76
N. Atlantic Basin	21.75 to 21.79	7	21.77
N. Canary Basin	21.75 to 21.78	6	21.76
Cape Basin	21.75 to 21.78	4	21.76
Gulf of Mexico	. . .	2	21.76
Laguna Madre, Texas coast	21.76 to 21.78	2	21.77
(Average for sea-water sulfate, 21.76)			

Values compiled from Ault and Kulp (1958*a*) and Thode et al. (1951).

thus leaving the residual sulfate enriched in this isotope. Thode et al. (1953) found a considerable variation, 21.8 to 22.1, or 1.5 per cent, in the sulfate contained in limestones. This variation may be caused by bacterial activity on the sulfate present in the period following deposition and during diagenesis.

7. *Biogenic sulfur*. The heaviest sulfur found in nature is in anhydrite from calcite cap rock of salt domes. Feely and Kulp (1957) report ratios as low as 20.84. Thode et al. (1951) first investigated salt domes and proposed a bacterial origin for the deposits of native sulfur. They were able to obtain 1 per cent fractionation in laboratory experiments with anaerobic bacteria whereas Macnamara and Thode (1951) found 3.2 per cent difference between native sulfur and sulfate from a lagoon in Cyrenaica, North Africa. The fractionation was only about half that predicted for oxidation-reduction by isotopic equilibrium theory. Jones et al. (1956) were able to detect a maximum fractionation of 2.7 per cent by the bacterium *Desulfovibrio desulfuricans*. The greatest fractionation was observed for incubation temperatures between 10° and 20° C and for a high concentration of soluble sulfate and for conditions such that only a small part of the total sulfate was reduced. Also Feely and Kulp (1957) report that apparently some strains of *Desulfovibrio* found associated with petroliferous materials on the Gulf Coast can utilize petroleum as a source of metabolic energy.

The genesis of the Gulf Coast native sulfur deposits is reviewed by Feely and Kulp (1957). The anhydrite was originally laid down in evaporite beds and was subsequently mobilized by the great pressures of the overlying sediments so that it flowed upward in dome or piercement structures. Ground waters dissolved and carried away the more soluble salts, and bacteria acted upon the sulfate, generating isotopically light H_2S which was subsequently oxidized to native sulfur. The residual sulfate forming the anhydrite and gypsum cap rock is characteristically heavy isotopically. As an energy source for reducing the sulfate the bacteria could have oxidized the petroliferous materials associated with the salt domes and generated CO_2 which with the calcium from the reduced anhydrite would produce the calcite cap rock. The calcite of the cap rock was found to have C^{12}/C^{13} ratios of about 92 to 94 (Thode et al., 1954; Feely and Kulp, 1957) typical of petroleum and not like that of marine limestones, which is about 89. This is additional confirmation of the biogenic origin of native sulfur in salt domes.

Establishing the bacterial origin of the native sulfur deposits of the Gulf Coast, where millions of tons of elemental sulfur have been produced by biogenic processes, is a triumph for isotopic geology and sulfur isotopic studies.

Importance of Fractionation Processes

In order to interpret the data available on the variation of sulfur isotopes it was desirable to determine the extent of fractionation due to various geochemical processes and to determine more adequately the isotopic composition of the sulfur in the important sulfur reservoirs in nature. Though laboratory tracer experiments may aid greatly in evaluating the various fractionation processes in nature, geologic conditions are complex and probably never quite reproducible. Therefore, when naturally occurring samples can be found that are products of these processes the limits of fractionation due to the processes can be determined. It was known from the studies above that reducing bacteria were perhaps the dominant factor in producing large isotopic variation of sulfur. Under optimum conditions they may cause a fractionation of 3 per cent or more between the hydrogen sulfide and the original sulfate, and the effect can be cumulative.

Recent studies have been directed toward selecting samples produced by precipitation, oxidation during weathering, possible diffusion, or temperature changes, and samples that could reflect the changes of mineralizing solutions with time. These data are presented in detail by Ault and Kulp (1958*b*). Isotopic exchange during oxidation-reduction is theoretically capable of producing fractionation, as shown by a plot of the equilibrium constant as a function of temperature (fig. 3) based on calculations made after the method of Tudge and Thode (1950). Should this relationship be refined as a paleotemperature method, the precision of the isotope ratio indicates that it could have a sensitivity of about ± 2 per cent of the temperature of mineralization provided that equilibrium is obtained. Barite-galena mineral pairs from Japan (Sakai, 1957) and from southeast Missouri (Ault and Kulp, 1958*b*) have shown isotopic ratio differences up to 3 and 4.5 per cent which would correspond to temperatures of 260° and 150° C, respectively. Hydrogen sulfide and sulfur dioxide gas at fumarolic vents also have shown differences up to 2.5 per cent (Sakai, 1957). This spread readily accounts for the 2 per cent range of ratios shown by native volcanic sulfur from Hawaii and Peru mentioned earlier.

Precipitation of sulfate from sea water apparently does not produce detectable fractionation, since at least the sulfate in the sea water

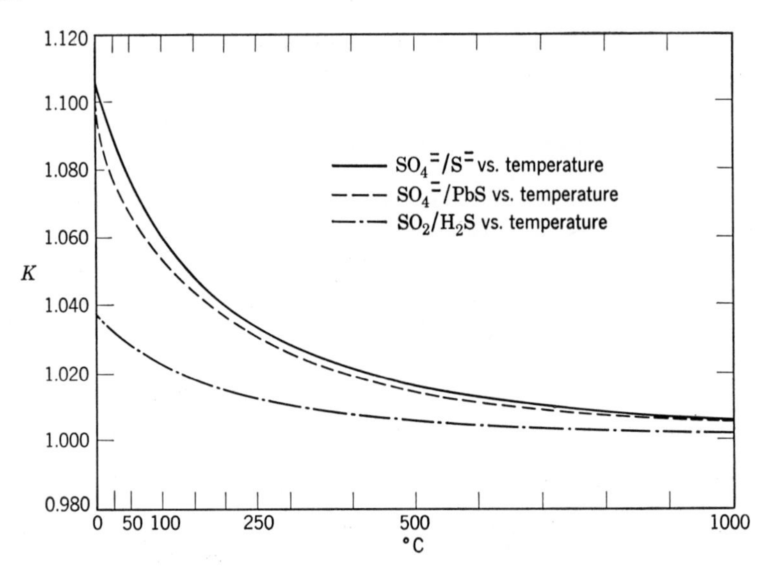

Fig. 3. Equilibrium constants vs. temperature.

from Laguna Madre, Texas, was identical isotopically with that in gypsum crystals growing in the water.

Weathering processes involving oxidation of sulfide and growth of selenite on the surface of two pyrite-containing boulders from the New Jersey–New York Highlands gave isotopic ratios for the sulfate only 0.03 lower than the sulfide. Since this variation is within the experimental error, the oxidation, solution, and selective precipitation must be essentially quantitative in such situations.

Diffusion can be effective as a mechanism for isotopic fractionation, as has been shown by theory and simplified laboratory experiments. Examples of diffusion, and its extent in nature as a cause of fractionation, however, are still open to question. The examples in the literature were reviewed by Ault and Kulp (1958*a*), who concluded that no really definitive examples of isotopic fractionation by diffusion have yet been found.

There are, however, data indicating a change with time in the isotopic composition of hydrothermal solutions during mineralization. Figure 4 is a sketch of a galena crystal, about 5 cm on an edge, which was attached to a vug wall. Some smaller (1 cm) galena crystals also attached to the vug walls penetrated the larger cube. The wall contacts and small cubes have low sulfur ratios and are considered to have been formed early. Extremities of growth (last-forming free edges and surfaces) gave higher ratios, and a profile diagonally across the cube showed a consistent trend or compositional variation of 0.75 per cent. Jensen (1957) detected a comparable change in several sequences of sulfides.

When valence change of the sulfur is not involved the effect of temperature and crystal habit appears to be very small. Theoretically one would not expect detectable variations due to temperature difference alone, as suggested by Vinogradov et al. (1956*b*) for paragenetic sulfides, because at elevated temperatures the equilibrium constant, which is already very similar for sulfide species, approaches unity. In table 6 are assembled data on sulfide suites from single hand specimens which, from all appearances, are contemporaneous,

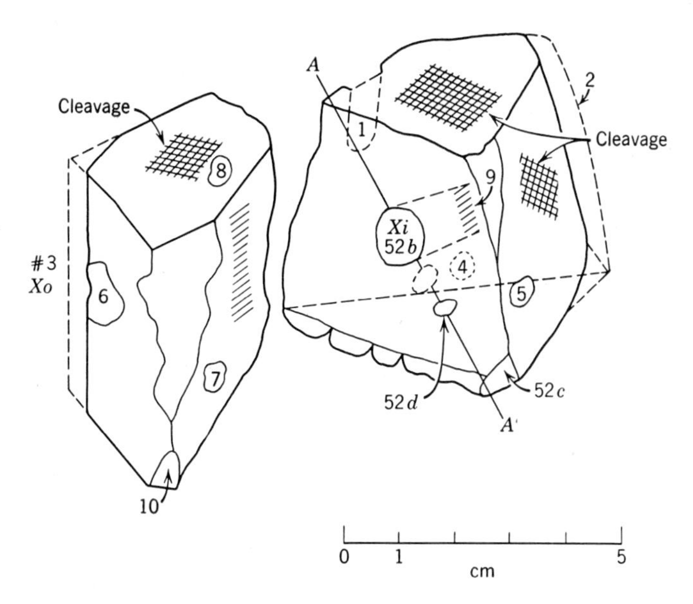

Fig. 4. Sketch of galena crystal from Indian Creek Mine, southeast Missouri, and the S^{32}/S^{34} values at the following positions:

Wall contact: #4 nodule, 21.98; #6 nodule, 21.99; #5 nodule, 22.06; #1 crystal face, 22.07.

Extremities of growth: #2, 22.20; #3, 22.21; *Xo*, 22.21; #10 and 52*c*, 22.23; #8, 22.24.

Profile *AA'*: #1 wall contact, 22.07; *Xi* and 52*b*, 22.10; #7 and 52*d*, 22.15; #10 and 52*c*, 22.23.

Sample #9 was taken intermediate between *Xi* and 52*b* and #2, 22.08.

TABLE 6. Sulfides Occurring Together in Single Hand Specimens

Locality	S^{32}/S^{34}				
	Pyrite	Sphal-erite	Chalco-pyrite	Molyb-denite	Galena
Ivigtut, Greenland					
In massive quartz, from "chimney area"		22.17	22.20		22.20
In white cryolite		22.15			22.05
In siderite, some cryolite	22.09	22.12	22.15		22.11
Between siderite rich and poor zones			22.16		22.21
In cryolite siderite assemblage			22.12		22.11
In cryolite siderite assemblage			21.55		21.55
In cryolite siderite assemblage	22.11		22.16		22.23
Three Found Claims, Manitoba, Canada					
From pegmatite	22.18			22.21	
From pegmatite	22.18			22.18	
Santa Rita, N. Mex.					
Ground Hog Mine	22.20		22.24		22.28
Kearney Mine	22.19	22.20			
		22.24			
Miami Copper Co. Mine, Miami, Ariz.					
In porphyry			22.29		22.24
Minnie Moore Mine, Wood River District, Idaho					
"Velvet galena," fine-grained, showing flow structure					21.92
Large cube of galena enmeshed in preceding sample					21.94

but which do not indicate an effect of temperature, species, or crystal habit greater than the precision of the measurements. Galena shows ratios higher than, equal to, and lower than, other sulfides.

It is interesting to note that in the Arizona–New Mexico–Mexico metallogenic province, where sulfide mineralization has a remarkably constant range of about 0.8 per cent (Ault and Kulp, 1958*b*), the sulfur of galena at Ground Hog Mine, New Mexico, of sphalerite at

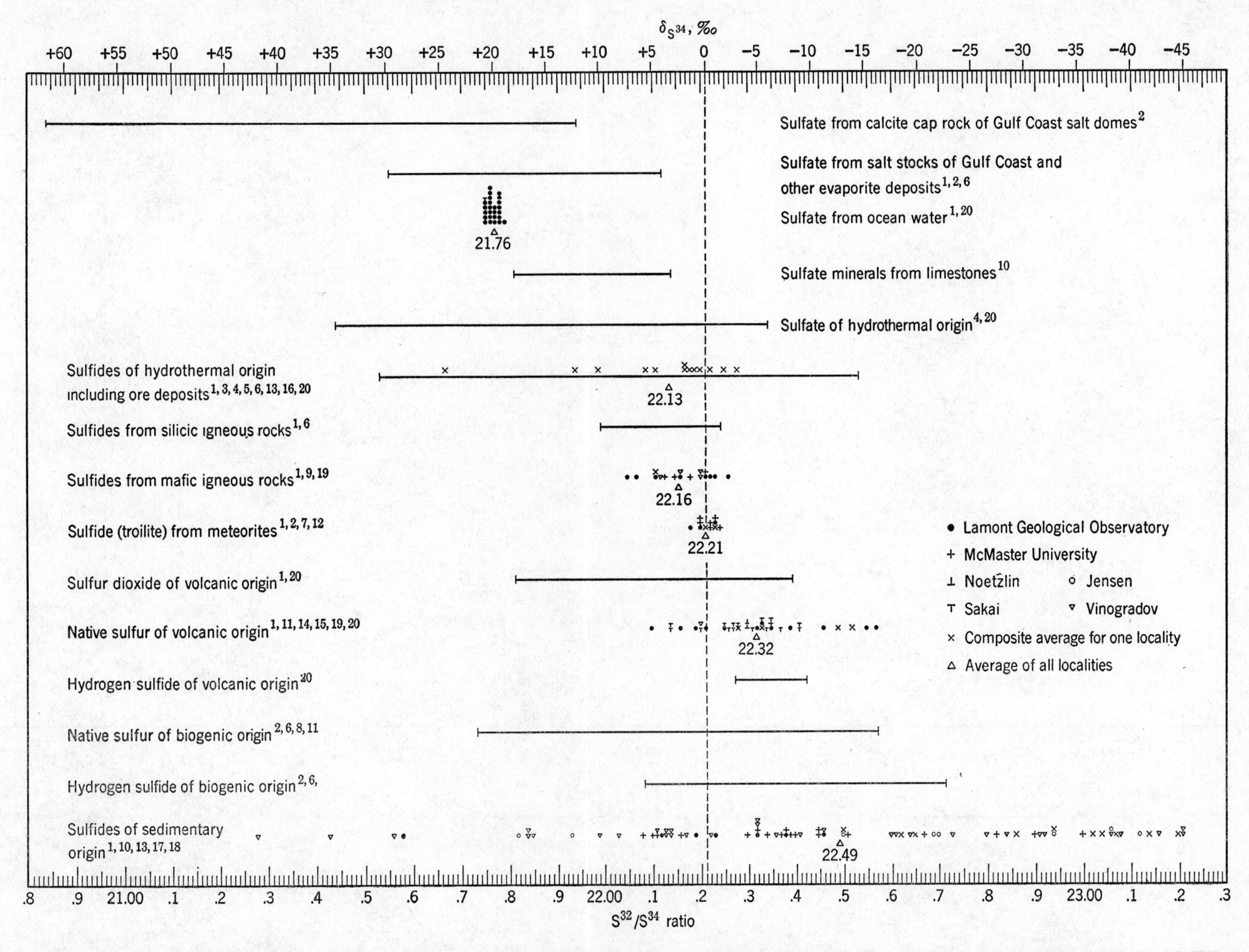

Fig. 5. Sulfur isotopic abundance in nature. References: (1) Ault and Kulp (1958*a*); (2) Feely and Kulp (1957); (3) Kulp et al. (1956); (4) Ault and Kulp 1958*b*); (5) Eckelmann et al. (1958); (6) Thode et al. (1949); (7) Macnamara and Thode (1950); (8) Macnamara and Thode (1951); (9) Macnamara et al. (1952); (10) Thode et al. (1953); (11) Thode et al. (1954); (12) Rankama (1954); ratios by McMaster group; (13) O. Kouvo, personal communication, 1956; ratios by McMaster group; (14) Noetzlin (1952); (15) J. Noetzlin, personal communication, 1956; (16) Jensen (1957); (17) M. L. Jensen, personal communication, 1958; (18) Vinogradov et al. (1956*a*); (19) Vinogradov et al. (1957); (20) Sakai (1957).

Kearney Mine, New Mexico, and of copper sulfides at Miami, Arizona, is isotopically similar.

It is concluded that equilibrium oxidation-reduction processes, both biochemical and geochemical, constitute mechanisms producing primary fractionation of several per cent which can be cumulative. Other mechanisms probably play a very minor or local role in the separation of isotopes.

Summary of Sulfur Occurrences

In figure 5 are summarized important occurrences of sulfur in the earth's crust. Data on the samples used in this graph have already been given in tables 1 to 6. Types of sulfur occurrence for which an average value is fairly well established and which are necessary for a material balance are plotted in detail, the different symbols representing various investigators, as indicated also by the references in the tables. Wherever practical, in order to obtain a weighted average of the ratios for all localities, the average value for each locality was plotted instead of each individual analysis, as the same number of samples has not been analyzed from each locality.

The bases for selection of data were descriptions permitting them to be classified as to type and indicated precision. Some 395 samples of hydrothermal sulfides from 25 localities averaged 22.13 when weighted by using one average value per locality and 22.12 when including only those localities where 5 or more samples are reported. It is significant that sulfides from hydrothermal deposits and from silicic and mafic igneous rocks are all heavier isotopically than meteoritic sulfur.

Sea-water sulfate gave remarkably constant ratios averaging 21.76 $\pm$ 0.02. Evaporite deposits, if averaged for each geologic period and weighted by the length of the period, give 21.80. This value assumes that the rate of deposition is the same during each geologic period. At present the data are too scanty to verify the assumption.

Sedimentary sulfides show a very wide range of ratios, as would be expected from the many sources and processes involved. The heaviest are, very likely, derived from sulfates; the lightest may be the result of successive fractionations from magmatic, volcanic, or even previously existing sedimentary sulfides.

Material Balance

With the extensive data now available on sulfur an isotopic material balance is possible. Such a calculation, made by Ault and Kulp (1958*a*), will be summarized briefly. The important reservoirs of sulfate are sea water containing on the order of 1.44×10^{21} grams sulfur and evaporite deposits containing an estimated 10^{21} grams sulfur, which estimate is believed to be conservative and is based on a summary by Krumbein (1951). Quantitatively important sulfide reservoirs are sandstones and shale. Limestone, which has been variously estimated to be 1 to 4 times as abundant as sandstone, contains both sulfate and sulfide, which it is assumed will balance each other quantitatively with respect to light and heavy sulfur. Material balance calculations and estimates on shale indicate it to be 8 to 10 times as abundant as sandstone, or about 10^{24} grams. Sulfur abundance in shale and sandstone is accepted as 0.26 and 0.05 per cent or 2.6×10^{21} grams and 0.05×10^{21} grams respectively. If from figure 5 the values 22.49, 21.76, and 21.80 are used as the average sulfur isotopic ratios for sedimentary sulfide, sea-water sulfate, and evaporite sulfate, respectively, and the total mass of sulfur in each as indicated above, the value of 22.14 is obtained for average crustal sulfur. This ratio indicates that terrestrial sulfur is heavier than meteoritic.

This conclusion is in disagreement with Vinogradov et al. (1956*b*, 1957), who assume that meteoritic and terrestrial sulfur are isotopically similar. Then, because magmatic and high-temperature sulfides contain sulfur that is heavier than that of meteoritic troilite, they conclude that such sulfur is a product associated with the differentiation of crustal material to the shell. Also, because stony and iron meteorites have sulfur of isotopically the same composition, they conclude that there may be a different origin for these two types of meteorites. Rather, this conclusion should cause one to question the initial assumption.

It might be argued that average terrestrial sulfur is different from crustal sulfur since sampling has necessarily been limited to the crust. Sulfur in mafic rocks, however, should isotopically approximate that in the mantle, since at the high temperatures at which such rocks are formed no process is known that would concentrate heavier sulfur. Variation in igneous sulfur ratios are probably due to assimilation of sulfur from crustal sources and loss by volatilization which could affect the sulfur composition of small bodies. The transient volatiles and native sulfur soon find their way into oceanic and sedimentary reservoirs and are averaged out in the material balance.

Although the uncertainties involved in the above balance calculation are large, nevertheless the direction of the most critical additional research is indicated. The data on the average content of sulfur in sediments, especially shales, are not the best. The abundance of evaporite deposits, and the abundance and mode of occurrence of sulfur in the continental-slope deposits, are important to the calculation. Increasing the mass of sedimentary sulfide by 50 per cent would make the average terrestrial sulfur approach the meteoritic value.

Summary

The processes most effective in causing sulfur isotopic fractionation are those involving oxidation-reduction, both biochemical and geochemical. Further evidence is necessary to demonstrate that the effectiveness of diffusion is quantitatively important. An empirical temperature scale and indications of equilibrium are problems yet to be solved in using sulfate-sulfide mineral pairs to indicate mineralizing temperatures. The amount of variation of ratios in sulfide deposits is interpreted as an indication of the nature of the sulfur source.

Sulfur abundance data in all types of rocks are very meager. Many more isotopic ratio measurements are needed from sedimentary, igneous, and metamorphic sulfides and from evaporite deposits on a world-wide distribution and representing the various geologic periods. More stratigraphic data are needed on sulfates. Sulfur isotopes are well suited to tracer experiments involving complex-ion transport and certainly would add to our understanding of mineralizing processes.

The large sulfur isotopic variations seen in evaporites, if due to local conditions, may give information on paleoclimatic conditions. Finally, from several lines of evidence—the average isotopic ratio for sulfur from silicic and mafic rocks, from hydrothermal sulfides, and from the material balance—it seems that terrestrial sulfur (22.14) is heavier than meteoritic sulfur (22.21). Just as some of the conclusions in the past have become untenable after much more work, so these may need to be modified when sufficient new data are available.

References

Aston, F. W. 1933. *Mass Spectra and Isotopes,* Edward Arnold, London (2d ed., 1942).

Ault, W. U. 1957. Isotopic geochemistry of sulfur. Ph.D. dissertation, Lamont Geological Observatory, Columbia University, unpublished.

Ault, W. U., and J. L. Kulp. 1958*a*. Isotopic geochemistry of sulfur, *Geochim. et Cosmochim. Acta* (in press).

Ault, W. U., and J. L. Kulp. 1958*b*. Sulfur isotopes and ore deposits, *Econ. Geol.* (in press).

Eckelmann, F. D., J. L. Kulp, J. S. Brown, F. Snyder, and W. U. Ault. 1958. Lead and sulfur isotopes and the history of mineralization in Southeast Missouri, *Bull. Geol. Soc. Am.* (in press).

Feely, H. W., and J. L. Kulp. 1957. The origin of Gulf Coast salt dome sulfur deposits, *Am. Assoc. Petrol. Geologists, 41,* 1802–1853.

Jensen, M. L. 1957. Sulfur isotopes and mineral paragenesis, *Econ. Geol., 52,* 269–281.

Jensen, M. L. 1958. Sulfur isotopes and the origin of sandstone type uranium deposits, *Econ. Geol., 53,* 598–616.

Jones, G. E., R. L. Starkey, H. W. Feely, and J. L. Kulp. 1956. Biological origin of native sulfur in salt domes of Texas and Louisiana, *Science, 123,* 1124–1125.

Krumbein, W. C. 1951. Occurrence and lithologic associations of evaporites in the U. S., *J. Sediment. Petrol., 21,* 63–81.

Kulp, J. L., W. U. Ault, and H. W. Feely. 1956. Sulfur isotope abundances in sulfide minerals, *Econ. Geol., 51,* 139–149.

Macnamara, J., W. Fleming, A. Szabo, and H. G. Thode. 1952. The isotopic constitution of igneous sulphur and the primordial abundance of the terrestrial sulphur isotopes, *Can. J. Chem., 30,* 73–76.

Macnamara, J., and H. G. Thode. 1950. Comparison of the isotopic constitution of terrestrial and meteoritic sulfur, *Phys. Rev., 78,* 307–308.

Macnamara, J., and H. G. Thode. 1951. The distribution of S^{34} in nature and the origin of native sulphur deposits, *Research (London), 4,* 582–583.

Nier, A. O. C. 1938. The isotopic constitution of calcium, titanium, sulfur, and argon, *Phys. Rev., 53,* 282–286.

Noetzlin, J. 1952. Measurement of isotopic ratios and its possible applications to volcanology, *Bull. volcanol., 12,* 115–125.

Rankama, K. 1954. *Isotope Geology,* McGraw-Hill Book Company, New York, p. 276.

Sakai, H. 1957. Fractionation of sulphur isotopes in nature, *Geochim. et Cosmochim. Acta, 12,* 150–169.

Sakai, H., and H. Nagasawa. 1958. Fractionation of sulphur isotopes in volcanic gases, *Geochim. et Cosmochim. Acta, 15,* 32–39.

Szabo, A., A. Tudge, J. Macnamara, and H. G. Thode. 1950. The distribution of S^{34} in nature and the sulfur cycle, *Science, 111,* 464–465.

Thode, H. G. 1949. Variations in abundances of isotopes in nature, *Research (London), 2,* 154–161.

Thode, H. G., H. Kleerekoper, and D. McElcheran. 1951. Isotope fractionation in the bacterial reduction of sulphate, *Reasearch (London), 4,* 581–582.

Thode, H. G., and J. Macnamara. 1953. The distribution of S^{34} in nature, *Natl. Bur. Standards Circ. 522,* 235–241.

Thode, H. G., J. Macnamara, and C. B. Collins. 1949. Natural variations in the isotopic content of sulphur and their significance, *Can. J. Research, B27,* 361–373.

Thode, H. G., J. Macnamara, and W. H. Fleming. 1953. Sulphur isotope fractionation in nature and geological and biological time scales, *Geochim. et Cosmochim. Acta, 3,* 235–243.

Thode, H. G., R. K. Wanless, and R. Wallouch. 1954. The origin of native sulphur deposits from isotope fractionation studies, *Geochim. et Cosmochim. Acta, 5,* 286–298.

Trofimov, A. 1949. Isotopic composition of sulfur in meteorites and terrestrial objects, *Doklady Akad. Nauk S. S. S. R., 66,* 181–184.

Tudge, A. P., and H. G. Thode. 1950. Thermodynamic properties of isotopic compounds of sulphur, *Can. J. Research, B28,* 567–578.

Urey, H. C. 1947. The thermodynamic properties of isotopic substances, *J. Chem. Soc., 1947,* 562–581.

Vinogradov, A. P., M. S. Chupakhin, V. A. Grinenko, and A. V. Trofimov. 1956*a*. The isotopic composition of sulfur in connection with the growth of pyrites of sedimentary origin, *Geokhimiya, 1,* 96–105.

Vinogradov, A. P., M. S. Chupakhin, and V. A. Grinenko. 1956*b*. Isotopic ratios S^{32}/S^{34} in sulfides, *Geokhimiya, 4,* 3–9.

Vinogradov, A. P., M. S. Chupakhin, and V. A. Grinenko. 1957. Some data on the isotopic composition of the sulfur of sulfides, *Geokhimiya, 3,* 183–186.

The Use of Equilibrium Calculations in Finding the Composition of a Magmatic Gas Phase

KONRAD B. KRAUSKOPF
Stanford University

The nature of the volatile material associated with crystallizing magma is a problem of great geologic interest, inasmuch as this material is commonly held responsible for the origin of many pegmatite dikes, quartz-sulfide veins, and the substances introduced into wall rocks during additive metamorphism. At active volcanoes, where we have our only opportunity to observe volatile materials in natural association with fluid magma, the volatile compounds are in large part gases. This is no guarantee, of course, that the same substances are in gaseous form at depth, where pressures are much higher, but a gas phase is often postulated even at depths of several kilometers. If such a phase is assumed, on what basis can we set limits to its possible composition?

Analyses of volcanic gases provide one obvious source of information, but their use is open to question. Contamination is almost impossible to avoid in collecting samples of volcanic gas, and even uncontaminated samples may have a different composition from the original magmatic gas formed at depth under high pressure. A second source of data would be gases obtained by heating in the laboratory samples of fresh igneous rock, but again the danger of contamination and the dubious correlation between gases retained and gases originally present make this procedure questionable. A third way to estimate an average composition of magmatic gas is to calculate the amounts of volatile materials that have been added from the earth's interior to the atmosphere, the oceans, and the products of weathering during geologic time; but clearly this method also depends on so many assumptions and speculative correlations that its value is doubtful.

Another possible procedure is to study equilibrium relationships between a hypothetical magmatic gas and mineral assemblages that once were in contact with it. Mineral assemblages most likely to have been associated with a gas are those of high-temperature deposits—the minerals of pegmatites, contact deposits, and hypothermal veins. Such assemblages show sufficient uniformity of composition to suggest that their conditions of formation, including the nature of an associated fluid phase, were reasonably similar from one deposit to another. Hence it should be possible to make guesses as to the kinds of gases which at one time were in equilibrium with the coexisting minerals of these high-temperature deposits. The procedure is to set up hypothetical chemical reactions involving coexisting minerals and possible gaseous compounds, and then from thermochemical data to calculate the equilibrium pressures of the gases. For any single gas or any one pair of minerals the result would have little significance, but if similar gas compositions are indicated by various combinations of minerals the result will have some claim to reliability.

Similar calculations for equilibria among gases have been used by Ellis (1957) to predict changes in magmatic gas with temperature and pressure and to show that analyzed samples of volcanic gas represent approximate equilibrium. Holland (1957) has made use of thermochemical data to calculate conditions of equilibrium between ore minerals and gases at various temperatures. Similar reasoning underlies the work of Barton (1957) on equilibria between ore minerals and common constituents of solutions at ordinary temperatures and under low-temperature hydrothermal conditions.

Most of the calculations to be outlined below have been described more fully in another place (Krauskopf, 1957). Disagreement between some of the earlier figures and those in this paper reflects chiefly the recent appearance of additional data, particularly a revised edition of Kubaschewski and Evans (1956). The author has also benefited in the interim from conversations with other workers in this field, especially Holland and Barton. To these conversations the author is indebted for clarification and extension of his ideas, but he, of course, assumes sole responsibility for opinions expressed below.

Assumptions

Existence of a gas phase. Whether a fluid phase that can properly be called a gas exists at the temperatures and pressures of plutonic crystallization remains a debatable question. In some volatile-poor magmas a free gas phase may never form; others may give rise to a supercritical residual fluid; from still others both a gas and a liquid may separate. The various possibilities have been explored from a theoretical standpoint by Verhoogen (1949); pertinent experimental data have been well summarized in recent papers by Morey (1957) and by Roy and Tuttle (1956). Without going into details of the argument, we shall assume for present purposes that separation of gas from crystallizing magma is a reasonably common phenomenon; whether the gas is a supercritical fluid or a vapor in equilibrium with a small amount of liquid does not affect the calculations.

Maintenance of equilibrium. Approximate equilibrium must be assumed at the temperatures under which the observed mineral assemblages were formed. Many of the reactions to be considered are between two gases, or between gases and solids; such reactions are often slow at room temperatures, but presumably would be fast enough at the temperature of a freezing magma to ensure attainment of equilibrium.

Validity of the perfect-gas laws. Gas pressures are calculated on the assumption that each constituent of the fluid behaves as a perfect gas. Clearly this cannot be accurate, because gas molecules under pressures of hundreds or thousands of atmospheres are almost as close together as the molecules in ordinary liquids, hence must exert large forces on one another. The amount of deviation from the perfect-gas laws cannot be calculated from available data.

Accuracy of chemical data. Thermodynamic data for the calculations are taken chiefly from Kubaschewski and Evans (1956), supplemented by figures from Latimer (1952) and Kelley (1935, 1937, 1949). Uncertainties in some of the free-energy figures are considerable; since the calculations require finding relatively small numbers as differences of large ones, even small uncertainties in the original figures become magnified into large ones in the results. Some of the free energies are uncertain by amounts as large as the figures themselves. Additional sources of uncertainty in the calculations inhere in the necessity of extrapolating some of the thermal data and the necessity of estimating a few of the heats of fusion.

Assumed conditions of temperature and pressure. The calculations are referred to an assumed total pressure of roughly 1000 atm (corresponding to a depth of 10 km based on hydrostatic pressure, or 4 km based on lithostatic pressure), and a temperature of 600° C. The figure for temperature is chosen as a reasonable average for (1) the temperature of final crystallization of a granitic melt, (2) the temperature of formation of pegmatite dikes and hypothermal veins, (3) the temperature of formation of many contact-metamorphic deposits. The mineral associations common to these several environments are used as basic data for the equilibrium calculations.

The Major Gases

Ideally the calculations should begin with an assumed pressure for some one gas, say water, and then the relative amount of each major constituent of the gas should be worked out from an equilibrium reaction involving two coexisting minerals. Unfortunately this can be accomplished for only a few of the gas constituents, chiefly because the others are inert toward the common minerals of high-temperature deposits.

Hydrogen sulfide. For H_2S the calculation is straightforward. We assume first that the pressure of water vapor is 1000 atm; since water is the dominant constituent of practically all volcanic gases, this figure should not be far from the total pressure of all the gases combined. To find the pressure of H_2S, we note that pyrrhotite and ferrous silicate minerals commonly occur together at igneous contacts. When these minerals were being formed, H_2O and H_2S must have taken part in an equilibrium reaction of the form

$$FeSiO_3 + H_2S = FeS + SiO_2 + H_2O \tag{1}$$

The hypothetical $FeSiO_3$ stands for such minerals as hedenbergite or diopside; heat effects on mixing silicates are not large, so that the equilibrium should not be greatly affected by this substitution. Unfortunately the necessary thermal data are not available for calculating the equilibrium constant at 600° for equation 1, so that we must substitute a different reaction:

$$Fe_2SiO_4 + 2H_2S = 2FeS + SiO_2 + 2H_2O \tag{2}$$

Again the substitution is partly justified by the fact that heat effects are generally small for reactions between silicates, metal oxides, and silica.

The equilibrium constant for equation 2 is calculated from the free-energy change, and this in turn is obtained from data in Kubaschewski and Evans or other standard sources. Ordinarily two methods are available for finding free energies at high temperatures. One is a simple matter of adding together equations giving free energies of formation expressed as functions of temperature (e.g., Kubaschewski and Evans, pp. 331–338). A second method, useful when such equations are not available, is to calculate changes of enthalpy and entropy for the temperature change from 25° to 600° (from the data of Kelley, 1949, and Kubaschewski and Evans, pp. 228–280), and then set up the relation

$$\Delta F = \Delta H - T\,\Delta S \tag{3}$$

where ΔH is the change in enthalpy and ΔS the change in entropy for the reaction at 600°. For equation 2 the first method of calculation gives for ΔF at 600° a value −16.1 kcal, the second method a value −15.8. Since the uncertainty in both figures amounts to several kilocalories, the agreement between them is excellent. We may take −16 kcal as an approximate average value.

From the free-energy change the equilibrium constant may be computed by means of the standard equation

$$\log K = -\Delta F/2.303RT \tag{4}$$

where K is the constant, ΔF is the free-energy change, 2.303 is the conversion factor from natural to decimal logarithms, R is the gas-law constant (1.99 cal/mole), and T is absolute temperature. For equation 2:

$$\log K = -(-16)/(2.303 \times 1.99 \times 10^{-3} \times 873) = 16/4.0 = 4$$

and therefore K is 10^4. In equation 2 only two of the five substances are gases, and so the expression for the equilibrium constant will be a quotient involving only the pressures of these two:

$$K = (H_2O)^2/(H_2S)^2 = 10^4$$

whence

$$(H_2S) = (H_2O)/10^2 = 1000/100 = 10 \text{ atm}$$

for equilibrium with an H_2O pressure of 1000 atm. The figure 10 atm is probably a lower limit for the pressure of H_2S, inasmuch as the ferrous silicate minerals actually found in contact deposits are presumably more stable than Fe_2SiO_4, hence would displace the equilibrium of equation 2 farther toward H_2S.

Oxygen. The amount of free oxygen in magmatic gas can also be fixed by a simple calculation. We note that hematite and magnetite coexist in many high-temperature deposits, suggesting an equilibrium

$$3Fe_2O_3 = \tfrac{1}{2}O_2 + 2Fe_3O_4 \tag{5}$$

Calculation of the free-energy change at 600° leads to a value of $10^{-7.6}$ for K, hence $10^{-15.2}$ atm for the equilibrium pressure of O_2. This is an upper limit for oxygen in most magmatic gas, for a greater pressure would lead to conversion of all iron to ferric oxide, a situation not common in high-temperature deposits. Where ferric oxides are completely absent the O_2 pressure is presumably much lower. An extreme lower limit is set by the nonoccurrence of metallic iron, hence by equilibrium in the reaction

$$Fe_3O_4 = 3Fe + 2O_2 \tag{6}$$

At 600° the equilibrium pressure would be 10^{-24} atm. For various reasons to be explained below it seems doubtful that the O_2 pressure would even approach so low a figure; a more reasonable lower limit for most magmatic gases would be about 10^{-21} atm. Thus free oxygen has a millionfold range in different samples of magmatic gas, from 10^{-15} to 10^{-21} atm, and the state of oxidation of a given sample of gas can be expressed by the position of the O_2 pressure in this range.

Other gases. Equilibrium calculations are much less satisfactory for other gases. One might expect to obtain a pressure for *hydrogen fluoride* from the reaction

$$CaF_2 + H_2O + SiO_2 = CaSiO_3 + 2HF \tag{7}$$

inasmuch as fluorite and calcium silicates are common in contact deposits. Unfortunately two different values are given for S_{298} for HF (Kubaschewski and Evans, p. 248), and these lead to widely different equilibrium pressures of HF: 10^{-5} and 10^{-1} atm. Evidently the pressure of HF is low, but a definite figure cannot be given. For *hydrogen chloride* the difficulty is the lack of minerals containing chlorine in high-temperature deposits. It may be noted that, if they were not so soluble, the absence of metal chlorides would set a possible upper limit to HCl pressures; for example, the equilibrium

$$2HCl + MnSiO_3 = H_2O + SiO_2 + MnCl_2 \tag{8}$$

would be displaced to the right if HCl exceeds its equilibrium pressure of 12 atm, and the absence of scacchite ($MnCl_2$) from high-temperature deposits may indicate that this is an upper limit for expectable HCl pressures. This conclusion does not seem well founded, however, because scacchite, even if formed at high temperatures, is so soluble that subsequent cool solutions would be expected to remove it. Pressures of *carbon dioxide* could perhaps be limited by the observation that graphite is an uncommon mineral in contact deposits except where a local source of abundant carbon (carbonate rock or rocks rich in organic matter) is evident. But the reaction

$$C(\text{graphite}) + O_2 = CO_2 \tag{9}$$

permits the equilibrium pressure of CO_2 to vary within such wide limits (up to 700 atm even for O_2 as low as 10^{-21} atm) that the restriction is not significant. None of the *nitrogen gases* can be assigned limiting pressures by means of solid-gas equilibria, because no minerals of nitrogen are known in high-temperature deposits.

Data from volcanic gases and "excess volatiles." Because equilibrium calculations set only partial limits on the amounts of the major substances in magmatic gas, we turn to analyses of volcanic gases as a source of data, despite the uncertainties in such analyses mentioned earlier. Representative data are given in table 1.

This table is taken from Rubey (1951), with the figures converted to volume percentages (which are proportional to partial pressures) and then recalculated on the basis of an arbitrary figure of 1000 atm for water-vapor pressure. The first column is derived from Shepherd's analyses of volcanic gases from Kilauea; the next two columns are Shepherd's data on gases obtained by heating igneous rocks; the last

TABLE 1. Analyses of Gases and "Excess Volatiles"

Recalculated from Rubey's (1951) table 5, page 1136. Water-vapor pressure assumed 1000 atm. All pressures in atmospheres.

	Volcanic Gases from Kilauea and Mauna Loa	Gases from Heated Diabase and Basalt	Gases from Obsidian, Andesite, and Granite	Excess Volatiles
C as CO_2	167	99	27	22
Cl as HCl	1	12	11	5
F as HF	...	91	50	Trace
S as H_2S	124	26	4	0.8
N as N_2	64	24	13	2

column is Rubey's estimate of the average composition of volatile materials that have come to the earth's surface from the interior during geologic time. Rough averaging and rounding off gives the following estimate for an average composition of magmatic gas:

Water vapor	10^3	(1000) atm
Total carbon as CO_2	$10^{1.7}$	(50) atm
Total sulfur as H_2S	$10^{1.5}$	(30) atm
Total chlorine as HCl	10^1	(10) atm
Total nitrogen as N_2	10^1	(10) atm
Total fluorine as HF	10^{-1}	(0.1) atm

The last figure is arbitrarily made less than the average from table 1 because of the equilibrium requirements of equation 7. The other figures agree with the equilibrium restrictions imposed by equations 2, 8, and 9.

No accuracy can be claimed for these pressures, of course, and they will certainly vary from one sample of magmatic gas to another. The only reason for attaching any significance to them is their internal consistency when applied to many equilibria involving common mineral associations, as will appear in subsequent calculations.

Equilibria in the Gas Phase

Having estimated the amounts of the major constituents from gas analyses, and having shown that these estimates are consistent with the few calculations that can be made on the basis of mineral associations, we now turn to a study of the various compounds among which the major constituents distribute themselves in the gas phase. This involves calculations of equilibria among gases, checked wherever possible by calculations of equilibria with known mineral associations.

Hydrogen. The pressure of hydrogen is fixed by the equilibrium

$$2H_2O = 2H_2 + O_2 \tag{10}$$

for which log K at 600° is -23.8. If the H_2O pressure is 1000 atm and the O_2 pressure is in the range 10^{-15} to 10^{-21} atm, H_2 pressures fall within the limits $10^{-1.4}$ and 40 atm.

Carbon gases. The equilibrium constant for the reaction

$$2CO + O_2 = 2CO_2 \tag{11}$$

is $10^{24.7}$, which means that for any O_2 pressure between 10^{-15} and 10^{-21} atm the dominant carbon oxide is CO_2. If this gas is assigned the pressure $10^{1.7}$ atm (see above), the possible pressures of *carbon monoxide* fall between the extremes $10^{-3.1}$ and 0.2 atm. *Methane* must take part in the equilibrium

$$CH_4 + 2O_2 = CO_2 + 2H_2O \tag{12}$$

for which the quotient $(CO_2)(H_2O)^2/(CH_4)(O_2)^2$ is $10^{47.3}$. With the pressure of H_2O 1000 atm and of CO_2 50 atm, this reaction gives extreme values for CH_4 of $10^{-9.6}$ atm at $O_2 = 10^{-15}$ and $10^{2.4}$ atm at $O_2 = 10^{-21}$. So high a value as this last is impossible as long as the total pressure of carbon gases is $10^{1.7}$. To find a more reasonable figure we note that the ratio $(CO_2)/(CH_4)$ must be $10^{-0.7}$ or 0.2, so that the 50 atm total is divided roughly into 10 atm CO_2 and 40 atm CH_4. In other words, carbon dioxide is the principal carbon compound in magmatic gas at 600° for oxygen pressures of 10^{-20} and greater, but methane becomes dominant when oxygen falls as low as 10^{-21} atm.

Sulfur. The equilibrium constant for the reaction

$$2H_2 + S_2(\text{gas}) = 2H_2S \tag{13}$$

is $10^{5.7}$ at 600°, so that for H_2 in the range $10^{-1.4}$ to 40 atm the pressure of H_2S is higher than the pressure of gaseous sulfur. If the total pressure of sulfur gases is assigned the value $10^{1.5}$ atm (see last section), the pressure of S_2 gas has a possible range from 1 to 10^{-6} atm.

Several equilibrium reactions involving minerals of high-temperature deposits are available for checking the general correctness of this range for sulfur pressures. Where both pyrite and pyrrhotite are present, the equilibrium pressure of S_2 is determined by

$$2FeS_2 = 2FeS + S_2 \tag{14}$$

from which $S_2 = 10^{-2.0}$ atm at 600°, a figure within the range just calculated. Where pyrite is present together with ferrous silicates, a value for S_2 may be computed from

$$Fe_2SiO_4 + 2H_2S + S_2 = 2FeS_2 + 2H_2O + SiO_2 \tag{15}$$

This gives $S_2 = 10^{-2.8}$ atm, again within the estimated limits. The mineral association pyrrhotite plus magnetite means equilibrium in the reaction

$$3FeS + 2O_2 = Fe_3O_4 + \tfrac{3}{2}S_2 \tag{16}$$

for which S_2 pressures have a range from 1 to 10^{-8} atm, a range similar to that found from equation 13 except at low O_2 pressures.

Further checks on the validity of the calculated range of S_2 pressures are provided by minerals of molybdenum, tungsten, and tin. Molybdenum in contact deposits occurs always as the sulfide, never as a primary molybdate. Therefore, equilibrium must be displaced to the left in the reaction

$$MoS_2 + \tfrac{3}{2}O_2 = MoO_3 + S_2 \qquad (17)$$

(MoO_3 is used in place of a molybdate, for which thermal data are not available.) Calculation gives 18.7 as the value of log K for this reaction, hence $10^{+18.7}$ as the equilibrium quotient $(S_2)/(O_2)^{3/2}$. The S_2 pressures corresponding to extremes of O_2 are then $10^{-3.8}$ and $10^{-12.8}$ atm. The condition that MoO_3 not form means that actual S_2 concentrations must be greater than these figures; and this condition is fulfilled by the values calculated above from equation 13. Tungsten, unlike molybdenum, nearly always occurs in contact zones as tungstates rather than as a sulfide, meaning that the equilibrium

$$WS_2 + \tfrac{3}{2}O_2 = WO_3 + S_2 \qquad (18)$$

must be displaced to the right. Equilibrium values for S_2 from equation 18 range from $10^{3.5}$ to $10^{-5.5}$ atm; the condition that WS_2 not form means that actual S_2 pressures must remain below these values, a condition that is met for O_2 pressures down to about 10^{-22} atm. Tin is found almost exclusively as the dioxide, so that the equilibrium

$$SnS + O_2 = SnO_2 + \tfrac{1}{2}S_2 \qquad (19)$$

must be displaced to the right. Since calculated equilibrium pressures for S_2 lie in the range 10^{8} to 10^{-4} atm, well above those found from equation 13, the proper displacement of equilibrium is assured for O_2 pressures down to 10^{-22} atm.

Sulfur dioxide. Equilibrium must be established between H_2S and SO_2 according to the reaction

$$H_2S + \tfrac{3}{2}O_2 = SO_2 + H_2O \qquad (20)$$

Calculation gives log $K = 26.9$, hence a range of SO_2 pressures from $10^{2.9}$ to $10^{-6.1}$ atm. The higher of these figures is impossible if the total pressure of sulfur gases is only $10^{1.5}$ atm (last section); hence we note that the ratio $(SO_2)/(H_2S)$ must be $10^{1.4}$ at an O_2 pressure of 10^{-15} atm, so that the total $10^{1.5}$ atm is distributed between roughly 30 atm of SO_2 and 1 atm of H_2S. Thus H_2S is the dominant sulfur gas at 600° for oxygen pressures up to 10^{-16} atm, but SO_2 becomes the chief gas for conditions more oxidizing than this.

Checks on the correctness of these SO_2 pressures are provided by equilibria involving anhydrite and barite. The formation of hypogene anhydrite requires that the equilibrium

$$CaSiO_3 + SO_2 + \tfrac{1}{2}O_2 = CaSO_4 + SiO_2 \qquad (21)$$

should be displaced to the right. The constant for this reaction is $10^{10.0}$, and the range of equilibrium pressures of SO_2 is therefore $10^{-2.5}$ to 3 atm; displacement of the reaction toward the right can occur only when the actual SO_2 pressures calculated from equation 20 are greater than these figures. This condition is met at O_2 pressures in the range 10^{-17} to 10^{-15} atm. Hence hypogene anhydrite would be expected in some high-temperature deposits but not in all; its presence demands no special explanation, but means only that the associated gas was somewhat more oxidizing than usual. The association of primary anhydrite with primary sulfides need not be regarded as unusual, for the figures from equations 14, 15, 16, and 21 indicate that iron sulfides are stable through part of the oxidizing range that permits the formation of anhydrite.

Barite is clearly more stable than anhydrite in high-temperature deposits, since barium silicate minerals are rare. Therefore, equilibrium in the reaction

$$BaSiO_3 + SO_2 + \tfrac{1}{2}O_2 = BaSO_4 + SiO_2 \qquad (22)$$

should be displaced to the right through the whole range of O_2 pressures. Equilibrium SO_2 pressures fall in the range $10^{-9.7}$ to $10^{-6.7}$ atm, safely under the actual pressures calculated from equation 20; hence the equilibrium is indeed displaced to the right, provided that the O_2 pressure does not fall below 10^{-21} atm.

Ammonia. Equilibrium in the reaction

$$2NH_3 = N_2 + 3H_2 \qquad (23)$$

fixes limits for NH_3 pressures at $10^{-4.5}$ and 1 atm. In other words, ammonia becomes important in magmatic gases only when conditions are unusually reducing. This calculation and the calculation for equation 12 indicate that ammonia and methane should be normal constituents of some magmatic gases purely as a result of shifting equilibria, regardless of whether the gas has come in contact with organic material. It remains true, of course, that organic matter, in many instances, may provide the reducing conditions necessary to cause the gas equilibria to shift in the direction of these compounds.

Summary. The amounts of the major constituents of a magmatic gas phase can be guessed from analyses of volcanic gases and gases given off by heated igneous rocks. Figures so obtained, with the exception of that for hydrogen fluoride, agree with rough inferences based on data for equilibrium with minerals of high-temperature deposits. The separate compounds among which the major constituents distribute themselves can then be worked out from equilibria in the gas phase, starting with the basic assumption that the amount of free oxygen is determined by equilibrium with iron minerals. The pressures calculated for various gases can be shown to be consistent with the occurrences of many common minerals in high-temperature deposits, and this consistency forms the principal justification for the many assumptions on which the calculations are based.

Different magmatic gases doubtless have widely different compositions, but the results of these calculations suggest that the most important difference is in the state of oxidation. In defining the oxidation state, the partial pressure of free oxygen serves much the same purpose as redox potential in defining the oxidation state of a solution. Geologic factors that determine the oxidation states of contact deposits and high-temperature veins are little known.

A summary of numerical results from the equilibrium calculations is given in table 2.

TABLE 2. Possible Equilibrium Compositions of a Magmatic Gas Phase at 600° C

Each vertical column shows the composition corresponding to the oxygen pressure at the head of the column. Assumed total pressures: H_2O 1000 atm, Cl 10 atm, F 0.1 atm, S 30 atm, N 10 atm, C 50 atm. All pressures in atmospheres.

	Oxidizing Conditions		Reducing Conditions	
O_2	10^{-15}	10^{-17}	10^{-19}	10^{-21}
H_2	0.04	0.4	4	40
HCl	10	10	10	10
Cl_2	$10^{-8.5}$	$10^{-9.5}$	$10^{-10.5}$	$10^{-11.5}$
HF	0.1	0.1	0.1	0.1
CO_2	50	50	50	10
CO	$10^{-3.1}$	$10^{-2.1}$	$10^{-1.1}$	0.2
CH_4	$10^{-9.6}$	$10^{-5.6}$	$10^{-1.6}$	40
N_2	10	10	10	9
NH_3	$10^{-4.5}$	$10^{-3.0}$	$10^{-1.5}$	1
H_2S	1	29	30	30
S_2	$10^{-1.4}$	10^{-2}	10^{-4}	10^{-6}
SO_2	29	0.8	$10^{-3.1}$	$10^{-6.1}$

Compounds of the Heavy Metals

In addition to the volatile compounds so far considered, magmatic gases may contain small amounts of compounds of metals, which can be estimated by the same sort of equilibrium calculations we have used hitherto. Such calculations are of interest because of their bearing on hypotheses of ore formation.

According to the currently favored ("hydrothermal") hypothesis, ore-forming metals are transported from a crystallizing magma into veins or wall rocks as dissolved compounds in a hot aqueous liquid. A serious difficulty with this hypothesis is the low solubility of many common ore minerals in such a liquid. So troublesome is the problem of solubility that several authors in recent years have suggested abandonment of the hydrothermal hypothesis in favor of transportation of the metals in volatile form. In particular, Brown (1948) has suggested movement of volatile sulfides, Sullivan (1954) volatile metals, and Walker (1956) volatile chlorides. The feasibility of these suggestions can be studied by calculating the amounts of the metals and their compounds that can exist at equilibrium in a magmatic gas at 600°.

Volatilities. The volatility of a compound, say $ZnCl_2$, as recorded in tables, is the amount of $ZnCl_2$ that will vaporize at a specified temperature from the solid or liquid salt into an evacuated space or a space filled with an inert gas at low pressure. This amount may be quite different from the amount that can exist in a magmatic gas at the same temperature. There are several reasons for the difference, but we need mention here only the two most important: (1) The $ZnCl_2$ in magmatic gas is not in equilibrium with the pure solid or liquid compound, but takes part in more complex equilibria like

$$ZnS + 2HCl = ZnCl_2(gas) + H_2S \quad (24)$$

The amount of $ZnCl_2$ in the gas phase thus depends not only on its volatility but also on its stability relative to ZnS and on the ratio of HCl to H_2S in the gas. (2) Water molecules in magmatic gas under high pressure are so close together that the gas acts as a solvent, taking more of a substance into the fluid phase than would be expected from volatility alone (Morey, 1957). The few experimental data available suggest, in fact, that the solubility of a compound like $ZnCl_2$ in compressed water gas is very much greater than its simple volatility; but how this solubility would be influenced by the presence of H_2S is completely unknown. Thermochemical data permit an examination of the first of these two effects on volatility but not of the second. The figures obtained below are thus *minimum* values for the amounts of heavy metals in magmatic gases; they are obtained simply by considering the effects of various equilibria on volatilities, disregarding possible additional amounts added to the gas phase by solution.

Calculations. The first step is to determine what solid compound of each metal would be most stable in contact with magmatic gas. This is a straightforward matter of calculating constants for equilibria involving the various possible solid compounds. For example, the reaction

$$PbSiO_3 + H_2S = H_2O + SiO_2 + PbS \tag{25}$$

gives for the equilibrium ratio $(H_2O)/(H_2S)$ at 600° a value $10^{6.1}$. This is more than 1000 times the ratio calculated for magmatic gas ($10^{1.5}$, from equation 2 and table 1), showing that the reaction of equation 25 would be displaced far to the right and that PbS is therefore much more stable than $PbSiO_3$. Similar computations indicate that most of the ore-forming metals under magmatic conditions are most stable as sulfides, as might be expected from their geologic occurrence; manganese is most stable as the silicate, tin as the oxide, and gold as the native metal.

For any metal whose sulfide is its most stable solid, the amount of vaporized sulfide in the gas can be read directly from vapor-pressure tables (e.g., Hsiao and Schlechten, 1952). It turns out that the vapor pressures of all sulfides except arsenic sulfide are very low at 600°, so low that little transportation of heavy metals could take place in this manner (table 3, column 2). Brown's (1948) hypothesis of ore genesis by deposition of volatile sulfides is therefore eliminated.

The amount of each metal in the gas as the vapor of the metal itself can be calculated from reactions of the form

$$PbS = Pb(gas) + \tfrac{1}{2}S_2 \tag{26}$$

For an S_2 pressure of 10^{-6} atm (the lower limit of sulfur pressures from table 2, hence the most favorable condition for volatilization of the metals) only four metals show appreciable vapor pressures: mercury, antimony, bismuth, and cadmium (table 3, column 3). Hence Sullivan's (1954) hypothesis that ores are transported as metallic vapors is very unlikely.

TABLE 3. Volatilities of Metals and Metal Compounds in Equilibrium with Solid Sulfides, Silicates, and Oxides at 600° C

All pressures in atmospheres. The metals are arranged in the order of decreasing total volatility.

Metal	Vapor Pressure of Sulfide	Metal Vapor in Equilibrium with Sulfide if $(S_2) = 10^{-6}$	Vapor Pressure of Oxide	Vapor Pressure of Chloride in Equilibrium with Most Stable Solid if $(H_2S) = 30$ and $(HCl) = 10$
Hg	Decomposed	>10	Decomposed	>10
Sb	$10^{-4.9}$	$10^{-5.3}$	$10^{-2.5}$	0.7
As	ca. 0.1	No data	>10	0.1
Bi	No data	$10^{-5.2}$	No data	$10^{-2.2}$
Pb	$10^{-6.3}$	$10^{-8.3}$	$10^{-7.0}$	$10^{-2.3}$
Sn	$10^{-5.7}$	$10^{-7.4}$	No data	$10^{-2.9}$
Mn	$10^{-11.9}$	$10^{-18.8}$	$<10^{-7}$	$10^{-3.4}$
Zn	$10^{-9.9}$	$10^{-8.0}$	$<10^{-7}$	$10^{-3.8}$
Fe	$10^{-11.3}$	$10^{-20.6}$	$<10^{-7}$	$10^{-3.9}$
Cd	$10^{-7.3}$	$10^{-5.6}$	$10^{-7.3}$	$10^{-4.6}$
Co	$10^{-10.6}$	No data	$<10^{-7}$	$10^{-5.0}$
Cu	$10^{-5.7}$	$10^{-20.6}$	$<10^{-7}$	$10^{-10.8}$
Ni	$10^{-7.6}$	No data	No data	$10^{-6.2}$
Ag	No data	$10^{-10.8}$	Decomposed	$10^{-7.3}$
Au	Decomposed	10^{-16}	Decomposed	Decomposed

For all the metals in table 3 except arsenic, copper, and gold the chlorides are the most volatile compounds under plutonic conditions. The figures in the table (last column) are obtained by calculating equilibrium constants for reactions like equation 24. For most metals the amounts are considerably smaller than the vapor pressures of the chlorides themselves, but are still large enough so that volatile chlorides must be considered as a possible means of transportation. This mechanism cannot serve as a general explanation for ore deposits, however, because the volatilities of the chlorides of a few common metals (notably copper and silver) are so low that the amount transported by a magmatic gas would be negligible.

Discussion. The total amount of any metal to be expected in a magmatic gas at 600° may be obtained by adding together the figures in table 3; in effect, this means simply selecting the highest volatility shown for each metal. Now if transportation in a gas plays any role, even indirectly, in the formation of ore deposits, one might expect that the order of volatilities would show some relation to the order in which metals are emplaced during deposition—in other words, to zonal and paragenetic sequences. Such a relationship is vaguely indicated by some aspects of the table, but is not borne out in detail. The appearance of mercury, arsenic, and antimony at the top of the table, for example, may be correlated with the common occurrence of these metals in low-temperature deposits far from an intrusive center. The greater volatility of lead than zinc is suggestive of the normal order of the two metals in mineral sequences. The fact that lead, zinc, cadmium, and iron have comparable volatilities may be linked to the common association of these metals in sulfide ores. On the other hand, manganese is generally found above zinc and lead in zonal sequences, instead of between them as table 3 would suggest; and copper, gold, and silver seem completely out of place in the table in view of their widespread occurrence in medium- and low-temperature deposits.

The discrepancies between table 3 and common successions of metals in ore deposits are so serious that these simple volatilities must be abandoned as a general explanation for the transportation of metals in magmatic fluids. This means that *no* hypothesis of simple volatile transport can serve as a complete explanation, for in compiling table 3 all reasonable possibilities have been explored. On the other hand, the table indicates clearly that considerable amounts of heavy metals *must* be present in magmatic gas at 600°—provided, of course, that a gas phase is present and that the metals were originally contained in the silicate melt.

To explain the discrepancies, it is reasonable to assume that solubility effects are added to the effects of volatility. A highly compressed, water-rich gas at 600° might be expected to serve not only as a gas into which metal compounds could evaporate, but also as an active solvent forcing them into solution. The magnitude of the solvent effect cannot be predicted from present knowledge. To consider the solvent action, in fact, is to go back to all the unresolved difficulties of the hydrothermal hypothesis, and to abandon the sort of phenomena usually envisaged in hypotheses of vapor transport.

In summary, a study of the possibilities of transport in a gas phase by means of equilibrium calculations shows clearly that many of the heavy metals can be volatilized in considerable quantity at 600°. On the other hand, a few common metals are practically nonvolatile in any form that might be found in a magmatic environment, and the order of volatilities shows several discrepancies with sequences of metals in ore deposits. The difficulties are so intractable as to justify the statement that *any* hypothesis depending on simple vapor transport cannot serve as a general explanation for the origin of ore deposits. Solubility must be called on to supplement volatility, but considerations of solubility belong more to the hydrothermal hypothesis than to the hypothesis of volatile transport.

Suggestions for Further Research

The central purpose of this discussion has been to show how the methods of theoretical chemistry, applied to recent compilations of thermochemical data, can be used to shed light on geologic problems. The principal problems examined here are (1) the probable composition of a magmatic gas phase and (2) the adequacy of such a gas to transport the heavy metals that are concentrated in ore deposits. Neither problem has been fully solved by the application of chemical theory, but limitations have been established for geologic speculations regarding them. The first problem is attacked by setting up equilibrium requirements for a gas in contact with common mineral associations in high-temperature deposits; data regarding such associations permit calculation of limiting ratios for a few gases, but cannot be used to specify closely the amounts of carbon, nitrogen, and halogen gases. The second problem is handled by calculating equilibria involving volatile compounds of the heavy metals and the major constituents of the gas phase. These equilibria show clearly that volatility alone cannot be a complete explanation for the transportation of metals in forming an ore deposit, but leave unsettled the question of just how important volatility may be in relation to solubility. Thus the application of chemical theory to these two major problems gives useful information but falls far short of solving them completely.

As a by-product of the calculations, several minor problems have been clarified: (1) the coexistence of magnetite and hematite in contact deposits may be regarded as a consequence of a particular oxidation state in the associated gas; (2) the existence of hypogene anhydrite implies a certain range of oxidizing conditions; (3) the association of metal sulfides with calcium and barium sulfates is fully in accord with equilibrium requirements; (4) the fact that molybdenum occurs as a sulfide and tungsten as a tungstate is consistent with a certain sulfur-oxygen ratio in the gas; (5) the existence of methane and ammonia in volcanic gases is explainable as a consequence of shifting equilibria and does not require contact of the lava with organic matter.

This application of chemistry to geologic problems is sufficiently promising to warrant its extension in various directions. Equilibria involving other metals (e.g., titanium, uranium, chromium) can be studied in the same manner; not all the necessary thermal data are available, but some headway can be made by using estimated values. The volatility of fluorine compounds should be investigated, but again some of the data are lacking or contradictory. Equilibria involving the chlorides of the alkali metals and the alkaline earths could be profitably studied, particularly in the light of White's (1957) recent suggestion that NaCl is the principal chloride in hot supercritical fluids, HCl becoming prominent only at the low pressures of volcanic outlets. An obvious extension of the calculations would be to other pressures and temperatures; some of the necessary calculations have been made by Ellis (1957), and the problem will be treated more fully in a forthcoming paper by Holland.

The greatest need in the way of additional research, however, is not further calculations but observational checks. One kind of check would be provided by field studies of the mineral assemblages of individual high-temperature deposits, to see whether predictions from the calculations are borne out in general, and whether differences of detail can be spotted from which variations in the composition of the original gases might be inferred. A second way to test the calculations would be to set up experiments in which some of the equilibria could be studied under conditions simulating as far as possible the original environment of magmatic gases. Until such field and laboratory checks have been made, the results of the theoretical study must remain somewhat speculative because of the numerous assumptions and the often inadequate data on which the calculations are based.

References

Barton, P. B. 1957. Some limitations on the possible composition of the ore-forming fluid, *Econ. Geol., 52,* 333–353.

Brown, J. S. 1948. *Ore Genesis,* Hopewell Press, Hopewell, N. J.

Ellis, A. J. 1957. Chemical equilibrium in magmatic gases, *Am. J. Sci., 255,* 416–431.

Holland, H. D. 1957. Thermochemical data, mineral associations, and the Lindgren classification of ore deposits (Abstract), *Bull. Geol. Soc. Am., 68,* 1745.

Hsiao, C. M., and A. W. Schlechten. 1952. Volatility and stability of metallic sulfides, *J. Metals* (A.I.M.E.), *4,* 65–69.

Kelley, K. K. 1935. Contributions to the data on theoretical metallurgy, III, The free energies of vaporization and vapor pressures of inorganic substances, *U. S. Bur. Mines, Bull. 383,* 132 pp.

Kelley, K. K. 1937. Contributions to the data on theoretical metallurgy, VII, The thermodynamic properties of sulfur and its inorganic compounds, *U. S. Bur. Mines, Bull. 406,* 154 pp.

Kelley, K. K. 1949. Contributions to the data on theoretical metallurgy, X, High-temperature heat-content, heat-capacity, and entropy data for inorganic compounds, *U. S. Bur. Mines, Bull. 476,* 241 pp.

Krauskopf, K. B. 1957. Heavy metal content of magmatic vapor, *Econ. Geol., 52,* 786–807.

Kubaschewski, O., and E. Ll. Evans. 1956. *Metallurgical Thermochemistry,* revised edition, Butterworth-Springer, Ltd., London.

Latimer, W. M. 1952. *Oxidation Potentials,* Prentice-Hall, New York.

Morey, G. W. 1957. The solubility of solids in gases, *Econ. Geol., 52,* 225–251.

Roy, R., and O. F. Tuttle. 1956. Investigations under hydrothermal conditions, *Physics and Chemistry of the Earth, 1,* 138–180, McGraw-Hill Book Co., New York.

Rubey, W. W. 1951. Geologic history of sea water, *Bull. Geol. Soc. Am., 62,* 1111–1147.

Sullivan, C. J. 1954. Metallic melting point and ore deposition, *Econ. Geol., 49,* 555–574.

Verhoogen, J. 1949. Thermodynamics of a magmatic gas phase, *Univ. Calif. Publs. Geol. Sciences, 28,* 91–136.

Walker, R. T. and W. J. 1956. *The Origin and Nature of Ore Deposits,* Walker Associates, Colorado Springs.

White, D. E. 1957. Thermal waters of volcanic origin, *Bull. Geol. Soc. Am., 68,* 1637–1658.

The Chemical Environment of Ore Deposition and the Problem of Low-Temperature Ore Transport[1]

PAUL B. BARTON, JR.
U. S. Geological Survey

One of the major challenges to modern geochemistry is presented by the processes leading to the formation of hydrothermal[2] ore deposits.

The ore minerals, principally the heavy-metal sulfides, are extremely insoluble in nearly pure water at high as well as at low temperatures; thus it is difficult to explain how the elements that constitute the ore minerals were transported. This chapter deals with two aspects of the problem—the chemical environment of ore deposition and low-temperature ore transport. As ore formation must be intimately related to the physical-chemical nature of the ore-forming fluid, we must review current ideas about the conditions of ore deposition. To define physical conditions there are a few manometers and geologic thermometers (Ingerson, 1955*a*, *b*) which indicate that hydrothermal ores form at temperatures from just a few degrees above room temperatures to 500° or 600° C or higher, and at pressures from close to atmospheric to several thousand atmospheres. This discussion will be primarily concerned with the chemistry of low-temperature environments where the extrapolation of thermodynamic data from aqueous systems at 25° C is not unreasonable.[3] Many deposits ap-

[1] Publication authorized by Director, U. S. Geological Survey.
[2] Hydrothermal here means hot or warm water, with no implication as to origin of solution.
[3] The point at which the thermodynamic calculations in this paper become invalid is not known, but a deposit formed above 150° to 200° C is probably beyond the "low-temperature" range as used here.

parently were formed under such conditions; some examples of low-temperature deposits are: (1) the Mississippi Valley type lead-zinc deposits; (2) the Kentucky-Illinois fluorspar deposits and other fluorspar ores more closely related to hot springs; (3) the redbed copper deposits; (4) the Colorado Plateau type uranium-vanadium deposits; (5) most, if not all, mercury deposits; (6) perhaps many of the shallow base-metal ore deposits such as Creede, Colo., or precious-metal deposits such as Goldfield, Tonopah, or Getchel, Nev.; (7) hot-spring manganese-tungsten deposits such as Golconda, Nev.

In treating ore deposits the geologist is dealing with some extremely complicated processes about which very little is known and for which adequate experimental data are practically nonexistent. We shall be pleased to learn anything at all about these phenomena. With this situation in mind we shall consider first the criteria for defining the chemical environment of ore deposition and shall finish with a discussion of various ore-transport mechanisms leading to the conclusion that complex ions provide the most probable answer to the problem of low-temperature ore transport.

The Chemical Environment

There are three principal types of information on chemical environment: thermal springs and fumaroles; fluid inclusions from minerals in ore deposits; and phase relations of minerals in the ore or wall rocks.

Information from thermal springs and fumaroles

Thermal springs and fumaroles provide the closest approach to a direct look at the processes of ore deposition because some ore and gangue minerals form within the range of direct observation. The solutions from these springs give diluted, and possibly contaminated, partly oxidized and partly devolatilized samples of the sort of fluid that presumably forms ore bodies at greater depths. As shown by isotopic studies cited by White (1957*a*, p. 1643), and as inferred on the basis of less quantitative evidence by other investigators, solutions of volcanic origin usually have been diluted by local meteoric water until less than 5 or 10 per cent of the fluid emitted at the surface is of deep-seated origin.

White (1957*a*, *b*) has shown that the typical thermal springs associated with volcanic activity, which often deposit ore or gangue minerals, are of the sodium chloride type. This kind of water often originates through the condensation (and mixing with meteoric water) of supercritical magmatic gases which are under high pressure and are correspondingly relatively dense. These gases have an appreciable solvent capacity for many compounds of low volatility, for example, the alkali halides. Reaction with the wall rocks may enrich the fluids in some elements such as sodium and calcium and may deplete the fluid in others such as potassium and fluorine; and, of course, the formation of mineral deposits removes part or most of the ore elements from solution. Some oxidation of sulfide to higher valencies, especially to sulfate, by the oxygen dissolved in the diluting meteoric solutions is likely. The solutions may also lose volatiles by boiling. The fact that common hydrothermal minerals (like pyrite, stibnite, cinnabar, quartz, calcite, barite, and fluorite) are found in or near thermal springs suggests that, despite the many changes that may take place as the solutions approach the surface, useful information on the nature of the ore-forming fluids can be obtained by analysis of these liquids. Table 1 is a partial summary, taken from White (1957*a*), of the composition of volcanic thermal springs of the sodium chloride type.

TABLE 1. Partial Composition of Typical Sodium Chloride Type Thermal Springs of Volcanic Affiliation

Data from White (1957*a*)

	Steamboat Springs, Washoe County, Nev.	Morgan Springs, Tehama County, Calif.	Norris Basin, Yellowstone Park, Wyo.	Upper Basin, Yellowstone Park, Wyo.	Well A, Wairakei, New Zealand
Temperature, °C	89.2	95.4	84	94.5	100
*p*H *	7.9	7.8	7.5	8.7	8.6
Ca	5.0 ppm	79 ppm	5.8 ppm	4 ppm	26 ppm
Na	653	1398	939	453	1130
K	71	196	74	17	146
ΣCO_2	305	52	27	532	46
$SO_4^{=}$	100	79	38	15	35
Cl^-	865	2427	744	307	1927
F^-	1.8	1.5	4.9	21.5	6.2
ΣH_2S	4.7	0.7	0	0	1.1
B	49	88	11.5	3.7	26
As	2.7	2.2	3.1		
Sb	0.4	0.0	0.1		
Total †	2359	4577	1885	1676	3742

* See text for discussion of *p*H measurements. White does not give temperature of measurement.

† Total includes SiO_2 and minor amounts of many other elements.

Under conditions of relatively low pressure magmatic gases have relatively low densities, and the solubility of nonvolatiles in them is small. White (1957*a*) has shown that the low-pressure (low-density) gases tend to be enriched in acid components. This enrichment leads to the formation of the acid sulfate and sodium bicarbonate types of thermal springs when the gases are mixed with and condensed by cooler meteoric waters near the surface. If the meteoric water is not sufficiently abundant to condense the gases, a fumarole results. Although some ore minerals are known to form from low-density fumarolic gases (for example, see Zies, 1929), Krauskopf (1957, and this volume) has shown that simple volatility is an inadequate transport mechanism for many minerals commonly found in ore deposits.

As shown in table 1, waters of the sodium chloride type are slightly alkaline at room temperature. There are also some moderately acid (*p*H 2 or 3) thermal springs, but very few are either strongly acid or strongly alkaline.

Some caution is advisable in the interpretation of *p*H measurements from natural liquids. It is common practice to discuss the acidity of a solution in terms of *p*H ($p\text{H} = -\log a_{\text{H}^+}$). At 25° C and unit H_2O activity the *p*H of a neutral solution ($a_{\text{H}^+} = a_{\text{OH}^-}$) is close to 7.00. If the solution is put under pressure the $a_{\text{H}_2\text{O}}$ increases and a neutral solution would have a *p*H of less than 7 (Owen and Brinkley, 1941). Conversely, if a salt is dissolved in the water the $a_{\text{H}_2\text{O}}$ decreases and the neutral point is at a *p*H greater than 7. Neither the salt nor the pressure has a large effect, however (at most only a few tenths of a *p*H unit). On the other hand, temperature has a pronounced influence. Figure 1 shows the variation in the *p*H of neutrality as a function of temperature. Thus at 250° C a neutral solution has a *p*H of 5.6, and a solution 1 normal in OH^- would have a *p*H of only 11.2. It is difficult to predict the effect of temperature changes on complex solutions such as those of interest to the geologist. For example, a solution containing equal amounts of CO_2 and HCO_3^- is weakly acid at 25° C; but if it is heated to 125° C (with sufficient pressure maintained to prevent the loss of CO_2) it becomes weakly alkaline. Thus *p*H measurements made at room temperature on samples of thermal-spring water, or of fluid-inclusion liquids, or of laboratory solutions from hydrothermal studies, do not necessarily indicate the *p*H of the solutions at higher temperatures.

Information from fluid inclusions

Studies, summarized by Smith (1953, 1954), on the composition of fluid inclusions in minerals (mostly gangues) from ore deposits, show

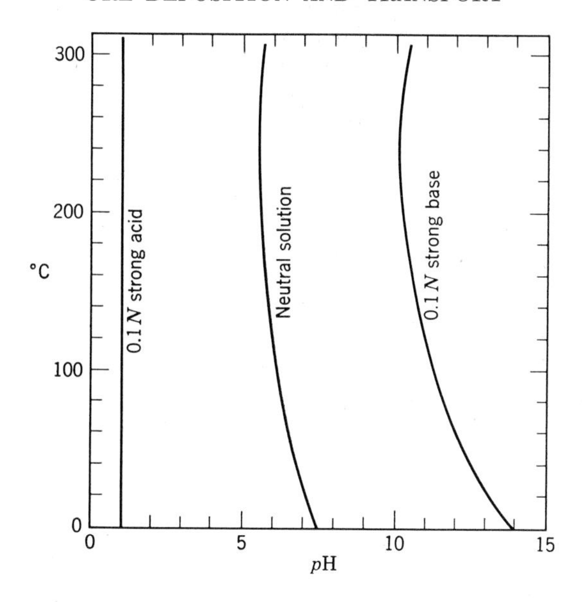

Fig. 1. The effect of temperature on pH in some unbuffered solutions. Data from Bjerrum (1929).

that ore-forming fluids trapped as inclusions may vary widely, but generally contain much sodium chloride with important amounts of potassium and calcium with chloride, sulfate, and carbonate (bicarbonate). The concentration of these salts is often from 5 to 20 weight per cent, and some inclusions show saturation in cubic crystals (probably NaCl), indicating concentration in excess of 30 weight per cent. In addition, there are small amounts of many other components, for example, B, P, Li, Rb, Cs, F, N, hydrocarbons, Si, I, and Br. After losing some CO_2 and H_2S through release of pressure and oxidation when the inclusions are opened, the solutions are neither strongly acid nor strongly alkaline. Inclusions from high-temperature veins and pegmatites sometimes show liquid CO_2 as an immiscible phase (below 31° C, the critical temperature of CO_2). However, inclusions from low-temperature deposits seldom if ever contain liquid CO_2. Some inclusions contain "smellable" amounts of H_2S in the aqueous solution, but liquid H_2S has never been reported, though it is only about three times more soluble in water than CO_2 and the critical temperature of H_2S is 100.4° C.

That heavy metals have not been detected may be partly due to the difficulty of removing and analyzing the fluids (Roedder, 1958), but there are certainly not gram-per-liter quantities of ore metals still in solution at the time of analysis. E. Roedder (oral communication), who has examined numerous fluid inclusions from ore deposits microscopically, has carefully noted the absence of any detectable amount of sulfide precipitate inside most of them. This observation shows that it is unlikely that the metals were originally present in high concentration and have precipitated in the time between the formation of the inclusion and its opening for the analysis. To summarize, the samples of fluid from vein minerals are highly concentrated in salts, especially alkali chlorides, but are dilute in terms of heavy-metal and H_2S content. The solutions are within 2 or 3 *p*H units of neutral, and the CO_2 content is sufficiently low that a water-poor, CO_2-rich phase is unlikely.

Information from phase relations

The mineral assemblage in a deposit provides certain limits to the possible variations in conditions that prevailed during ore deposition. Phase relations also provide geological thermometers and manometers (Ingerson, 1955*a*, *b*; Kullerud, this volume).

Studies of wall-rock alteration (Morey and Ingerson, 1937; Folk, 1947; and Ingerson, 1955*a*, *b*) have given some indication of the environment of ore deposition and potentially can give much more information on the temperature, pressure, and composition of the ore-forming solutions. The clays are indicative of lower temperatures and higher water pressures. The montmorillonites are favored by and probably indicative of higher alkaline-earth concentrations and relatively high *p*H. Kaolinite forms under relatively low alkali concentrations and at a lower *p*H than montmorillonite. Garrels and Howard (Garrels, 1957) have shown that sericite (white K mica) is stable in a narrow *p*H range between *p*H 9.5 and 10.5 at K^+ activity of 10^{-3} at room temperature. Above *p*H 10.5, feldspar is stable, and below *p*H 9.5 kaolinite forms. Higher K^+ concentrations shift the *p*H boundaries to lower values; higher Al^{+3} concentration acts in the opposite direction (Folk, 1947). Increasing temperature shifts the fields of sericite and K feldspar to lower *p*H values, as indicated by experiments of Gruner (1944) which produced sericite in very acid solutions (*p*H ~1 when cold) at temperatures above about 350° C as well as by more quantitative recent work by J. Hemley (oral communication). Roy and Osborn (1952) show that kaolinite can exist to slightly above 400° C, and Yoder and Eugster (1955) show that sericite is stable to above 600° C in the significant P_{H_2O} range. An example of the application of the study of wall-rock alteration would be the kaolinite–alunite–quartz–pyrite alteration at the low-temperature Goldfield, Nev., deposits (Ransome, 1907). The presence of this mineral assemblage indicates that the a_{H^+}/a_{K^+} was greater than that compatible with sericite.

The presence of carbonate minerals in deposits formed under relatively low confining pressures indicates that the depositing solutions were not strongly acid; otherwise the CO_2 pressure could not have been contained.

The phases present in an ore body can be used to calculate much about the chemical nature of the environment of ore deposition, but until very recently no one had attempted to apply the available thermodynamic data to the study of ore deposition. In 1933 Lindgren (pp. 206–207) suggested that such an approach might be possible, but made no attempt at quantitative evaluation. Kordes (1935) employed P_{S_2}–T diagrams for heavy-metal sulfides to show that the sulfides with similar vapor pressures occurred together, rather than using the data to define P_{S_2} during ore deposition. Kennedy's paper on the relation of the partial pressure of oxygen to the ferrous-ferric ratio in basalts appeared in 1948, but nothing further happened until the last year or two when independently, and almost simultaneously, several investigators came forth with variations of the same approach.

Krauskopf (1957, and this volume) has presented calculations on the composition of magmatic vapor at 600° C and has shown that simple vapor transport of ore-forming elements is not adequate to explain most ores. Holland (1957, and oral communication, 1958) has calculated the partial pressures of the quantitatively important hydrothermal gases over a range of temperatures. Ellis (1957) has made similar calculations and reached similar conclusions to Holland and Krauskopf, but, instead of using phase relations from mineral assemblages, he calculated the equilibrium composition that the volatile components of typical magmatic fluids from thermal springs would have at temperatures up to 1000° C. Holland (1956) has shown that the distribution of various major, minor, and trace elements between coexisting minerals might be used to set up simultaneous equations to solve for many of the physical and chemical properties of the ore fluid. R. M. Garrels (written communication, 1957) has calculated P_{O_2} vs. P_{S_2} isotherms for the system Cu–Fe–O–S and, on the basis of naturally occurring mineral assemblages, has estimated values for the standard free energies of chalcopyrite, bornite, and digenite.

Barton (1956, 1957) has used phase equilibria to calculate the relative activities (thermodynamic concentrations) of various anions in low-temperature, ore-forming solutions. The fundamental data are summarized in figure 2, which shows the calculated boundaries between

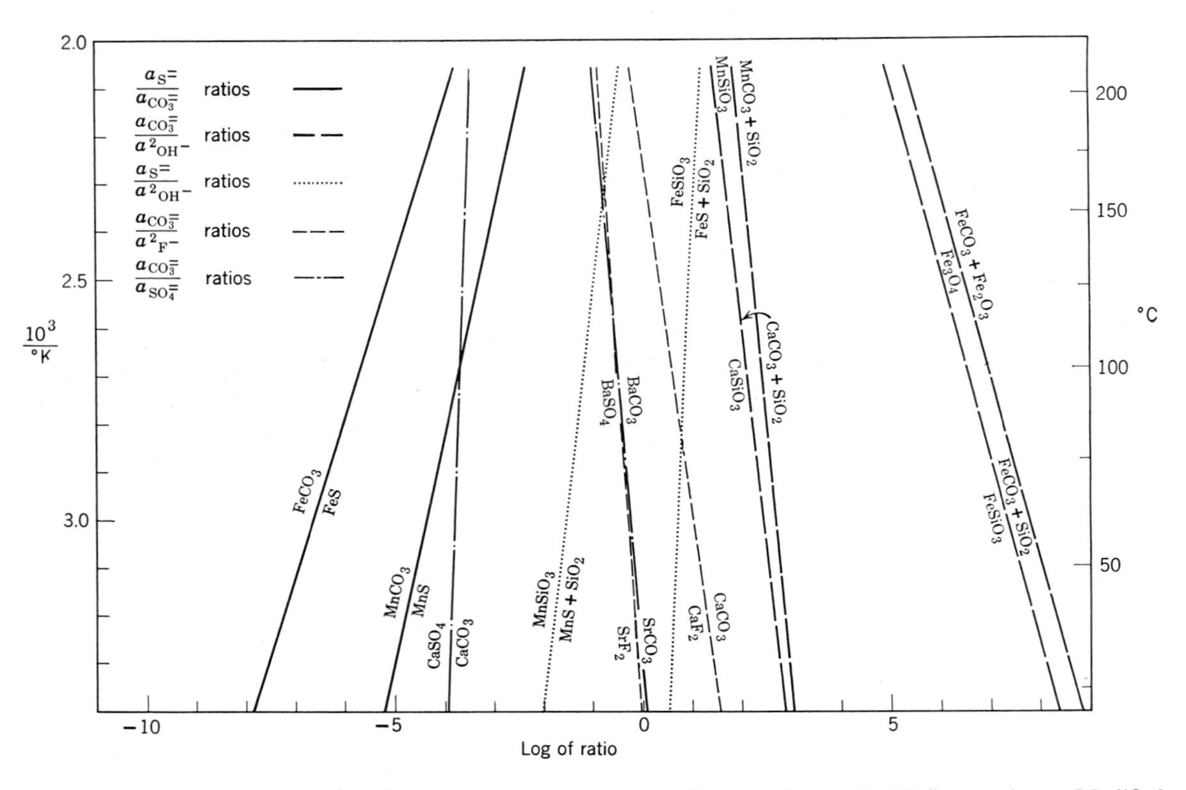

Fig. 2. Variation of anionic ratios with temperature according to the van't Hoff equation. Modified after Barton (1957), by permission.

various compounds in terms of ionic activity ratios and temperature. From the mineral assemblage it is possible to estimate the ionic ratios that prevailed during ore deposition. For example, suppose that a deposit containing calcite, barite, fluorite, galena, and sphalerite forms at 125° C and all the minerals are in equilibrium with the same solution. From figure 2 it is seen that the $a_{CO_3^=}/a_{SO_4^=}$ ratio must be greater than $10^{-3.7}$, or anhydrite would occur instead of calcite; and it must be less than $10^{-0.5}$, or witherite would form instead of barite. Other ratios can be estimated from other mineral assemblages so as to give a general idea of the relative activities of ions in the ore-forming fluid. The partial pressure of CO_2 calculated from the $a_{CO_3^=}/a^2_{OH^-}$ ratios may vary from about 10^{-8} to 10^1 atm within the 25° to 200° C temperature range with the higher pressures at the higher temperatures. The partial pressure of H_2S is lower than that for CO_2 by one to five orders of magnitude. The oxidation potential estimated from the $a_{SO_4^=}/a_{S^=}$ ratio (for 25° C) is given by the equation E_h (in volts) $= -0.059\ p\text{H} + 0.22 \pm 0.04$.

Summary of the chemical environment

Studies of fluid inclusions and thermal springs show that the low-temperature ore-forming fluid is a dominantly aqueous solution that is relatively concentrated in sodium and potassium chloride with variable, but generally minor, amounts of calcium, bicarbonate, and sulfate ions. Observations of fluid inclusions suggest that the heavy-metal content of the solution is low. Analyses of phase relations, and data from fluid inclusions and hot springs, all show that, with few exceptions, CO_2 is from one to three orders of magnitude more abundant than H_2S, and that a CO_2-rich phase is unlikely. Extremely high or low pH conditions are infrequent, and the most probable state of the solution is mildly acid to mildly alkaline. The phase relations between sulfide and sulfate minerals show that both sulfide and sulfate are present in appreciable quantities ($E_h = -0.059\ p\text{H} + 0.22 \pm 0.04$ for 25° data); thus the intermediate valency states of the sulfur are near their maximum possible concentration.

To illustrate more specifically the general aspect of the composition of an ore-forming fluid, and to facilitate later discussion of the mechanism of ore transport, the composition of the fluid for a hypothetical low-temperature mineral deposit (similar to those mentioned previously) is described in table 2. This estimate was arrived at using various lines of evidence discussed above. A temperature of 125° C is assumed. The van't Hoff equation is used to calculate the activity product constants except for water, for which empirical data are used.

TABLE 2. Partial Composition of a Hypothetical Ore Fluid, Temperature of 125° C and pH of 6.0 Assumed

From ionic ratios:	
$a_{H^+} = 10^{-6.0}$	Moles/1000 g of solution
$a_{OH^-} = 10^{-5.9}$	
$a_{H_2CO_3} = 10^{-1.9}$	
$a_{HCO_3^-} = 10^{-1.9}$	Total $CO_2 \sim 1000$ ppm
$a_{CO_3^=} = 10^{-5.6}$	
$P_{CO_2} = 10^{0.4}$ atm	
$a_{H_2S} = 10^{-3.5}$	
$a_{HS^-} = 10^{-3.5}$	Total $H_2S \sim 20$ ppm
$a_{S^=} = 10^{-9.2}$	
$P_{H_2S} = 10^{-1.6}$ atm	
$a_{SO_4^=} = 10^{-2.7}$	~ 200 ppm
$a_{F^-} = 10^{-3.0}$	~ 20 ppm
From thermal springs (before dilution) and fluid inclusions:	
[NaCl] + [KCl] = 50,000 to 300,000 ppm	

The anionic ratios required to calculate table 2 are consistent with figure 2, and the total amounts of CO_2, H_2S, and SO_4 are in agreement with the thermal-spring waters described in table 1 provided that allowance is made for 10- to 100-fold dilution by meteoric water.

The essentially neutral (at 125° C) pH of 6 was chosen as an approximation of natural environments. Reasonable compositions for hydrothermal solutions can be proposed for the pH range from about 4 to 8 (for 125°), but it is impossible to use the anionic ratios with either very high (10 or 11) or very low (1 or 2) pH values and still arrive at values for total H_2S, CO_2, and SO_4 that are consistent with the thermal-spring and fluid-inclusion data. Thus extreme pH values for the ore-forming fluid appear unlikely on the basis of indirect as well as direct evidence. An appreciable reservoir of hydrogen ion to carry on wall-rock alteration is available in H_2CO_3 and, to a much smaller extent, in HCO_3^-.

The composition of ore fluids obviously may vary from one ore deposit to another and may also change with time and place within individual ore bodies, as is evidenced by paragenesis and zoning. Thus we are faced with the problem of whether each specific type of ore deposit is derived from an entirely different type of ore solution, or whether most hydrothermal deposits merely represent different aspects of the same general environment of ore deposition. We cannot give a totally satisfactory answer at present. The apparently continuous gradation in types of hydrothermal mineralization (Noble, 1955) suggests that the second alternative is more likely, yet such authorities as Niggli (1929), Schneiderhohn (1941), and Schmitt (1950*a*, *b*) class the epithermal deposits distinctly apart from the mesothermal and hypothermal types. For the purposes of further discussion, however, we shall assume that most hydrothermal deposits represent regions within an essentially continuous, multidimensional "spectrum" of temperature, pressure, and composition variables. Only slight compositional changes are necessary to change the mineralogy of the ore being deposited; thus it is not unreasonable to assume that the compositional limits of this spectrum tend to be roughly defined by the ionic-ratio calculations and by the thermal-spring and fluid-inclusion compositions as described above. Of course, some types of mineralization, for example, that at Franklin, N. J., the redbed copper deposits, or the Colorado Plateau type uranium-vanadium ores, may fall well outside this continuous spectrum of conditions typical of most hydrothermal deposits.

Ore Transport at Low Temperature

Numerous mechanisms of ore transport have been suggested to explain the fact that mineral deposits do occur. We shall now consider some of them in terms of the chemical environment described above.

Because the ore minerals are so very insoluble in water at high as well as at low temperature, there have been several theories of nonaqueous ore-forming processes. Some geologists have favored transport by volatile halides (principally chlorides), volatile sulfides, and even volatile metals. However, Edwards (1956) has discussed the inadequacy of the volatile sulfide or metal theories to meet geologic requirements, and the physical-chemical discussions by Krauskopf (1957, and this volume) invalidate all the volatile-transport hypotheses for most low- as well as high-temperature deposits (except sublimates).

Garrels and Richter (1955) have emphasized the abundance of CO_2 in natural solutions and raised the question, "Is carbon dioxide an ore-forming fluid under shallow-earth conditions?" They show that a water-poor, CO_2-rich fluid can exist as an independent phase immiscible with water, and they suggest that such a fluid conceivably might be a solvent for some heavy metals such as occur in ores of the Colorado Plateau. Aside from the fact that there is no proof that dense CO_2 can dissolve heavy-metal sulfides there are some serious objections to this as a mechanism for most hydrothermal deposits. A dense CO_2 phase would require a high pressure of CO_2, and, as pointed out previously (Barton, 1957), the pressure of CO_2 calculated from the phase relations is too low, even at temperatures of 200° C. Also, the fluid inclusions from low-temperature deposits do not show the large amount of CO_2 required for a dense, CO_2-rich, ore-bearing phase. Smith (1954) also points out that (except for the occasional occurrence of hydrocarbons) the composition of inclusion fluids indicates that the depositing fluid was a single phase.

Ingerson (1954) has suggested that there may be two separate fluids: an early H_2S-rich fluid followed by a sulfur-poor fluid containing metals, but this mechanism fails to account for the commonly observed zoning and paragenetic relations. The same objection applies to other multiple-fluid hypotheses, and we therefore conclude that all the constituents that occur in the same paragenetic position in the ore and that are not indigenous to the local country rock were transported to the site of deposition by the same fluid.

Colloids have frequently been proposed as a medium adequate for ore transport. Colloidal transport has been championed by Lindgren (1933) and by Boydell (1928) and has some experimental support (for example, see Kania, 1936, and Frondel, 1938). Many authors cite colloidal textures as proof of colloidal ore-forming solutions, but Gruner (1933) notes that "colloform structures of sulfides do not prove colloidal transportation but show that just before deposition the particles were of colloidal dimensions." There are several sound arguments against colloidal transport. (1) Colloids have a large surface area and thus a large surface energy which crystals of appreciable size do not possess; hence colloids are metastable. At higher temperatures metastable states convert to the stable states and colloidal solutions should not persist. (2) Electrolytes in high concentration, as shown by fluid inclusions, rapidly flocculate colloids. (3) Large single crystals commonly observed in ore bodies cannot form from colloids without going through a dissolved stage. (4) Crystals of sulfide minerals are frequently observed to be etched or leached by hydrothermal solutions (for example, see Lacy and Hosmer, 1956). Although H_2S may peptize a colloidal precipitate of CuS to a comparatively stable sol, it is thermodynamically impossible for a colloidal solution to form from well crystallized, stable compounds without energy introduced from an external source. Thus the leaching cannot have been through a colloidal mechanism. If a noncolloidal hydrothermal solution is available for leaching, then it can be called upon also as the ore carrier.

Simple solubility, meaning that the concentration of an element in solution is approximately that predicted by the activity (thermody-

TABLE 3. Calculated Activity Products of Some Common Hydrothermal Minerals at 125° C

Data from Latimer (1952)

Mineral	Activity Product Constant at 125° C	Activity of Metal in Solution Described in Table 2
Calcite	$a_{Ca^{+2}} \cdot a_{CO_3^{-2}} = 10^{-8.9}$	$a_{Ca^{+2}} = 10^{-3.3}$
Barite	$a_{Ba^{+2}} \cdot a_{SO_4^{-2}} = 10^{7.9}$	$a_{Ba^{+2}} = 10^{-5.2}$
Sphalerite	$a_{Zn^{+2}} \cdot a_{S^{-2}} = 10^{-20.4}$	$a_{Zn^{+2}} = 10^{-11.2}$
Galena	$a_{Pb^{+2}} \cdot a_{S^{-2}} = 10^{-22.4}$	$a_{Pb^{+2}} = 10^{-13.2}$
Argentite	$a^2_{Ag^+} \cdot a_{S^{-2}} = 10^{-37.9}$	$a_{Ag^+} = 10^{-14.4}$
Chalcocite	$a^2_{Cu^+} \cdot a_{S^{-2}} = 10^{-39.3}$	$a_{Cu^+} = 10^{-15.1}$
Covellite	$a_{Cu^{+2}} \cdot a_{S^{-2}} = 10^{-29.6}$	$a_{Cu^{+2}} = 10^{-20.4}$
Cinnabar	$a_{Hg^{+2}} \cdot a_{S^{-2}} = 10^{-40.9}$	$a_{Hg^{+2}} = 10^{-31.7}$

namic concentration of the simple ion) of the simple aqueous ion, is completely inadequate to account for transport of most heavy metals in the ore-forming fluid. Most metal sulfides are simply too insoluble, as shown by the low-temperature data (table 3) and the experiments of Morey and Hesselgesser (1951) at elevated temperatures. Several authors (Garrels, 1944; Krauskopf, 1951; and Thompson, 1954) have shown quantitatively that the volume of solution required for ore transport by simple solubility is geologically impossible. Garrels and Dreyer (1952) and Barton (1957) have shown that geologic relations demand that the solubilities of all introduced hydrothermal minerals be equal within a few orders of magnitude and not as extremely different as the activity products (table 3) would suggest.[4] Moreover, the sequence of mineral deposition in both time and place (paragenesis and zoning) is the opposite of what would be predicted from the activity product constants. Table 4 shows that the sulfides that are least soluble in terms of their activity product constants behave as if they were the most soluble in the ore-forming fluid.[5] No values for activity

[4] For example, the ratio of the solubility products of PbS and HgS (both of which are generally considered "insoluble") is about 10^{-26} at 25° C, whereas the ratio of the solubility products for $BaSO_4$ and $MgSO_4$ (one of which is "soluble," the other "insoluble") is only about 10^{-8}.

[5] Verhoogen (1949) points out that the greater thermal coefficient of solubility of ZnS than of PbS could be used to explain the earlier paragenetic position of ZnS with respect to the less soluble PbS, but this does not provide a mechanism for the transport of adequate amounts of material.

TABLE 4. Comparison of Zoning and Paragenetic Relations among Some Heavy Metals with Relative Solubility of Sulfides and Complexing Tendency

Generalized Zoning Sequence	Generalized Paragenetic Sequence	Relative Complexibility	Relative Solubility (activity product)
Nearest surface	*Latest*	*Most stable complex*	*Most soluble sulfide*
Hg	Hg	Hg	Fe
Ag	Ag		Zn
Pb	Pb	Pb	Pb
Zn	Zn	Zn	Ag
Cu	Cu	Cu	Cu
Fe	Fe	Fe	Hg
Greatest depth	*Earliest*	*Least stable complex*	*Least soluble sulfide*

coefficients short of those related to strong complex formation can provide sufficiently high solubility. Barnes (1956) has pointed out on theoretical grounds that the stability of covalent metallic complexes follows a sequence matching in detail the commonly observed zoning and paragenetic relations. No other unrelated, geologically feasible property provides the proper sequence.

Complex ions

Complex formation can increase the solubility of some metals by many orders of magnitude, hence it is desirable to consider complexes in some detail.

The solubility of an electrolyte can be expressed most effectively in terms of a solubility product. As frequently used, K = the product of the concentrations of each ion or molecule raised to the power corresponding to its stoichiometric proportion in the reaction. For example,

$$K_{Ag_2S} = \frac{[Ag^+]^2 \cdot [S^=]}{[Ag_2S]} \quad \text{or} \quad K_{Fe_2O_3} = \frac{[Fe^{+3}]^2 \cdot [OH^-]^6}{[H_2O]^3 \cdot [Fe_2O_3]}$$

Thus, through the law of mass action, it is possible to predict quantitatively the effect of variation in concentration of any of the components of the reaction. Unfortunately, this simple picture is generally applicable only to very dilute solutions. At appreciable concentrations, various interionic and ion-solvent interactions alter the thermodynamic properties of the ions, and another function, activity, must now be introduced. The activity may be considered as a thermodynamic concentration or in other words an effective concentration. The ratio of activity to concentration is the activity coefficient, $\gamma = a_{M^{++}}/[M^{++}]$. The Debye-Hückel theory and its modifications (see Harned and Owen, 1958, or Robinson and Stokes, 1955) make it possible to calculate activity coefficients very satisfactorily in dilute solutions (provided that there is no strong complex-ion formation), but the evaluation of activity coefficients in concentrated electrolytes is mostly empirical rather than theoretical. In general, excluding the formation of complex ions, at first salts in solution increase the solubility of compounds not containing a common ion (salt effect), and then, at high concentrations of salt (on the order of 1 or 2 molal), solubility decreases (salting out). Thus the activity coefficient tends to go through a minimum. The increase in solubility due to the salt effect, however, is generally less than one order of magnitude; thus the salt effect does not provide a mechanism to get sufficient solubility for ore transport. On the other hand, complex formation can increase solubility very greatly.

The writer will here use "complex" in a broad sense to mean any combination of ions (or molecules) with a reference ion (or molecule) such that the thermodynamic properties of the reference ion (or molecule) are changed. The purely electrostatic interactions considered in the Debye-Hückel expression are not considered complexes, but the hydration of the aqueous ions is.

Hydration, the interaction of the solute with the solvent, plays an important role in determining the activity coefficient of an ion, but a completely adequate quantitative theory is still lacking. Robinson and Stokes (1955, chapter 9) have successfully used hydration to explain the behavior of many salts at concentrations several times higher than those to which the simple Debye-Hückel law applies. Bell (1958) points out the difficulty in determining the number of water molecules attached to a given ion. The changing degree of hydration with temperature, pressure, and composition of solution is a geologically important phenomenon which has had essentially no experimental study under conditions of significance to ore genesis, and this lack seriously limits the extrapolation of room-temperature data to geologic environments.

Although we write the chemical formula for an ion such as divalent copper in aqueous solution as Cu^{+2} or $CuOH^{+}$, we should realize

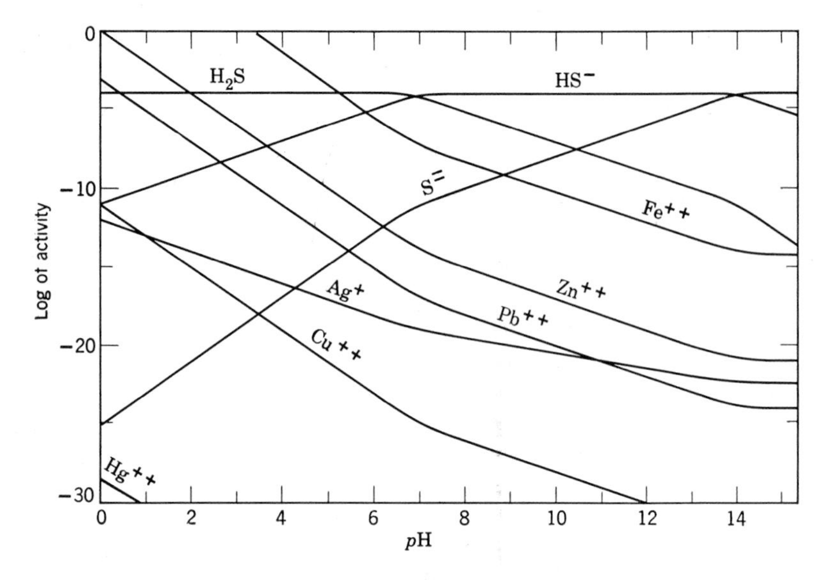

Fig. 3. Activities of metal ions in saturated solution (25° C and 1 atm).

that the copper is actually present in a form such as $Cu(H_2O)_n{}^{+2}$ or $Cu(H_2O)_{n-1}OH^+$, and that a cupric chloride complex may be $Cu(H_2O)_{n-3}Cl_3{}^-$ rather than merely $CuCl_3{}^-$. Thus, because of the role played by the solvent in aqueous solution at low temperature, it is probably incorrect to ascertain the formula of a complex on the basis of the probable coordination number of the central ion. The sulfide complex for mercury is $HgS_2{}^{-2}$ (or, more properly, perhaps something like $HgS_2(H_2O)_n{}^{-2}$), not $HgS_4{}^{-6}$ as suggested by the coordination of Hg^{+2}.[6]

Many complexes are so stable that the central ion is never thought of as a separate entity. For example, in solution S^{+6} is always tied up with 4 coordinating anions to form $SO_4{}^=$ or $S_2O_3{}^=$; C^{+4} is always in $CO_3{}^{-2}$; and O^{-2} is always in a complex like OH^- or H_2O. Other complexes, such as the various carbonate species $CO_3{}^=$, $HCO_3{}^-$, and H_2CO_3, or the sulfide species HS^- and H_2S, are stable only under certain conditions. Thus weak electrolytes, as distinct from nonelectrolytes, are

[6] In metacinnabarite, which has the ZnS structure, the mercury is tetrahedrally coordinated by 4 sulfur atoms. In cinnabar, the stable form of HgS (below 344° C), 2 of the 6 coordinating sulfur atoms are slightly closer to the mercury atom than the other 4, showing the tendency for the complex to be maintained in the crystal structure (Bethke, 1957).

classed as complexes. Complexes of even less stability form a more or less gradational series to the essentially uncomplexed solutions, just as bonding within crystals ranges from covalent to ionic.

If an alkaline solution of sulfide ion is made acid the activity of the $S^=$ ion is reduced by the ion's uniting first with one and then another H^+ to form successively HS^- and then H_2S, but at any point there is always some $S^=$, as shown in figure 3. Also plotted in figure 3 are the activities of Pb^{++}, Ag^+, Fe^{++}, Zn^{++}, Cu^{++}, and Hg^{++}, assuming that the solution is in equilibrium with the crystalline sulfides. The constants used were those calculated for 25° C.

As pH is lowered the activities of the metal ions increase. This increase in concentration of the simple ion with increasing acidity is one reason why some geologists advocate acid ore-forming solutions. As seen in figure 3, however, even very acid conditions are inadequate to bring appreciable amounts of Hg^{+2}, Ag^+, or Cu^{+2} into solution. Moreover, the sequence of solubilities is the reverse of the commonly observed paragenetic and zoning relations. Finally, the chemical environment of ore deposition does not appear to be strongly acid.

Many heavy metals form comparatively stable complex ions, a few of which will be mentioned below.[7] Figure 4 shows a great increase in the solubility of mercury and silver through the mechanism of complex sulfide and hydrosulfide ion formation. Many other metals such as Sn^{+4}, Sb^{+3}, As^{+3}, W^{+6}, Mo^{+6}, and Au^+ form sulfide and hydrosulfide complexes that are sufficiently stable (as far as is known from the data available) to explain their transport in hydrothermal fluids. The fact that high alkalinity increases the concentration of some metals as sulfide complexes has led some authors to propose highly alkaline solutions as ore-transport media. But a highly alkaline solution is not compatible with the chemical environment as described previously. Also, the low P_{H_2S} and low total dissolved sulfur calculated from the ionic ratios indicate that it is unlikely that the slightly stable complex sulfides (those of Zn or Pb, for example) occur in quantity in ore fluids (though, of course, unpredicted shifts in equilibria due to large temperature changes may invalidate this conclusion).

There are many other geologically feasible complexes, but the data are too few at present to do much more than suggest possibilities. Halide complexes of Hg^{+2}, Pb^{+2}, Ag^+, Cu^+, Cu^{+2}, and others are known. Two very stable uranyl carbonate complexes exist, and there are less stable

[7] A comprehensive compilation of stability constants for inorganic complexes will soon be published by the Chemical Society of London; Part I, *The Organic Ligands*, is now available (Bjerrum, Schwartzenbach, and Sillen, 1957).

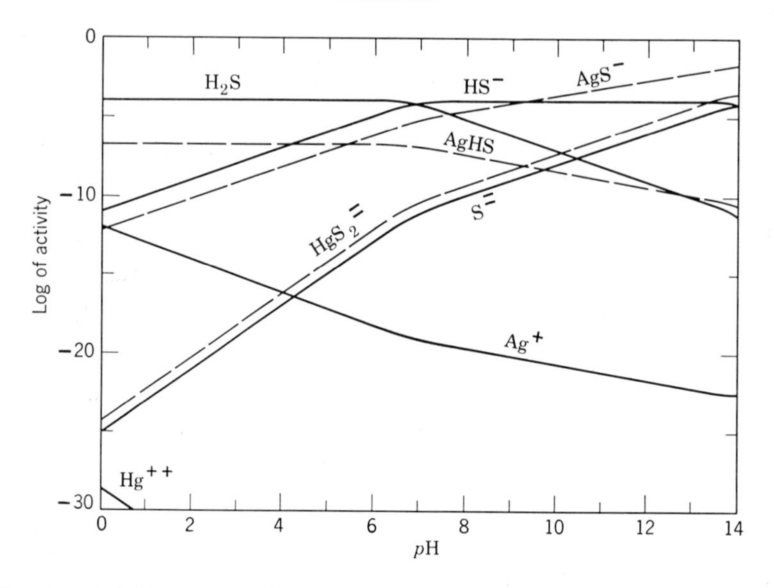

Fig. 4. Activities of complex silver and mercury ions in saturated solution (25° C and 1 atm).

carbonate complexes for U^{+4}, Th^{+2}, Cu^{+2}, the rare earths, and others. Some elements, among them W^{+6}, Mo^{+6}, V^{+5}, V^{+4}, Al^{+3}, Cr^{+3}, are sufficiently amphoteric to form complexes with OH^- or $O^=$. Sulfate complexes are known. The E_h-pH relations described earlier are such that the intermediate oxidation states of the sulfur (polysulfides, thiosulfate, sulfite, and so on) which never become quantitatively important at 25° (Garrels and Naeser, 1958) are near their maximum concentration. Paul Cloke (R. M. Garrels, written communication, 1958) has recently shown that very stable polysulfide complexes are formed with Pb^{+2}, Ag^+, and Cu^{+2}. The polysulfide mechanism has the double advantage of complexing both the sulfide and the metal ions.

There is little necessity for assigning a distinct complex for each type of mineral formed; that is, the same silver complex (probably AgHS or AgS^-) may transport the silver whether the metal occurs in argentite, a sulfosalt, native silver, or solid solution in galena. The complexes in solutions and the mineral assemblages resulting from them are determined by the bulk composition of the ore fluid (and temperature and pressure), but the nature of a complex itself has little bearing on the minerals formed from it. Thus pitchblende could precipitate by reduction from a $UO_2(CO_3)_2(H_2O)_2^{-2}$ complex, or proustite from AgS^- and

AsS_2^- complexes, or livingstonite from HgS_2^{-2} and SbS_2^- complexes, or possible hübnerite from Mn^{+2} and WS_4^{-2} complex. Polynuclear sulfide complexes may exist, but there is neither chemical evidence nor geologic necessity for them.

It is possible to offer substantial evidence that complexes are necessary for heavy-metal transport in low-temperature ore solutions. From the data presented in table 3 we note that Ca^{+2}, Ba^{+2}, Zn^{+2}, and Pb^{+2} have activities of $10^{-3.3}$, $10^{-5.2}$, $10^{-11.2}$, and $10^{-13.2}$, respectively. Variation in ionic ratios from that assumed for the compilation of table 2 can change the activities of the metals to some extent, but no reasonable assumptions for composition of solution can change the relation that the activity of Pb^{+2} is 100 times less than the activity of Zn^{+2} and that the activities of both Pb^{+2} and Zn^{+2} are many orders of magnitude less than those of Ca^{+2} or Ba^{+2}. Suppose that the ore body contains approximately equal amounts of calcite, barite, sphalerite, and galena. Then the depositing fluid must have contained roughly similar amounts of barium, lead, and zinc; in other words, the solubilities were similar. The solubility of calcium may well have been greater, because we know from fluid inclusions and thermal springs that much calcium remains in solution even though essentially all the barium, lead, and zinc is precipitated. Some mechanism is required to give extremely small activity coefficients to the lead and zinc, and the only reasonable means appears to be complexes. Some sort of complex also appears essential to account for low-temperature transport of gold, silver, copper, platinum, mercury, cadmium, zinc, lead, tin, bismuth, antimony, arsenic, vanadium, uranium, tungsten, molybdenum, and a few others. The solubilities of the alkaline-earth and manganese minerals are sufficiently high that it may be possible to explain their behavior without recourse to complexes. In comparison with other sulfide-forming metals, iron, cobalt, and nickel require much weaker complexes (or perhaps none at all?).

Transport as complex ions has the attractive feature that the solubility of heavy metals can be changed markedly through relatively small changes in composition of the solutions, thereby providing an additional mechanism for the localization of sulfides in ore shoots whereas the introduced gangue often extends far beyond ore.

Major Problems

From the chemical point of view a quantitative, theoretical model of aqueous electrolyte solutions of all concentrations at high as well as low temperatures is needed. This is a very difficult problem, and the writer has no suggestion for attacking it directly other than by extension of the standard physical-chemical techniques to higher temperatures.

We need *detailed* geologic information on the mineral relations (both from field and laboratory), fluid-inclusion compositions, and temperatures and pressures of ore deposition from many types of mineral deposits. Additional data from thermal springs and volcanic exhalations will be useful. We must examine critically the often tacitly assumed idea that all ore-forming fluids are points on a continuous spectrum of compositions, and we must study the nature of the fluids in terms of time and place as well as temperature, pressure, and composition.

Acknowledgments

The writer wishes to thank many of his colleagues, especially R. M. Garrels, E. W. Roedder, and H. L. Barnes, for critical reviews and discussions of the manuscript.

References

Barnes, H. L. 1956. Mineral zoning and ore transport; a paper presented at the 20th International Geological Congress, Mexico City.

Barton, P. B., Jr. 1956. Limitations on the possible composition of the ore-forming fluid (Abstract), *Bull. Geol. Soc. Am., 67* (pt. 2), 1669.

Barton, P. B., Jr. 1957. Some limitations on the possible composition of the ore-forming fluid, *Econ. Geol., 52,* 333–353.

Bell, R. P. 1958. The hydration of ions in solution, *Endeavour, 17,* 31–35.

Bethke, P. M. 1957. The sulfo-selenides of mercury and their occurrence at Marysvale, Utah, Ph.D. dissertation, Columbia University.

Bjerrum, J., G. Schwartzenbach, and L. G. Sillen. 1957. *Stability Constants,* Part I, *The Organic Ligands,* 105 pp., Chemical Society of London, printed by Metcalfe and Company, Ltd., London.

Bjerrum, Niels. 1929. The electrical conductivity and ionization-product of H_2O, *Intern. Critical Tables, 6,* 152.

Boydell, H. C. 1928. Operative causes in ore deposition, *Bull. Inst. Mining Met., 37,* 50–177.

Edwards, A. B. 1956. The present state of knowledge and theories of ore genesis, *Proc. Australasian Mining and Met., no. 177,* 69–116.

Ellis, A. J. 1957. Chemical equilibrium in magmatic gases, *Am. J. Sci., 255,* 416–431.

Folk, R. L. 1947. The alteration of feldspar and its products as studied in the laboratory, *Am. J. Sci., 245,* 388–394.

Frondel, Clifford. 1938. Stability of colloidal gold under hydrothermal conditions, *Econ. Geol., 33,* 1–20.

Garrels, R. M. 1944. Solubility of metallic sulfides in dilute vein forming solutions, *Econ. Geol., 39,* 472–483.

Garrels, R. M. 1957. Some free energy values from geologic relations, *Am. Mineralogist, 42,* 780–791.

Garrels, R. M., and R. M. Dreyer. 1952. Mechanism of limestone replacement at low temperature and pressure, *Bull. Geol. Soc. Am., 63,* 325–379.

Garrels, R. M., and C. R. Naeser. 1958. Equilibrium distribution of dissolved sulfur species in water at 25° C and one atmosphere total pressure, *Geochim. et Cosmochim. Acta, 15,* 113–130.

Garrels, R. M., and D. H. Richter. 1955. Is carbon dioxide an ore-forming fluid under shallow-earth conditions? *Econ. Geol., 50,* 447–458.

Gruner, J. W. 1933. The solubilities of metallic sulphides in alkali sulphide solutions, *Econ. Geol., 28,* 773–777.

Gruner, J. W. 1944. The hydrothermal alteration of feldspars in acid solutions between 200° and 400° C, *Econ. Geol., 34,* 578–589.

Harned, H. W., and B. B. Owen. 1958. *The Physical Chemistry of Electrolytic Solutions, Am. Chem. Soc. Monograph* 137, 3d ed., Reinhold, New York.

Holland, H. D. 1956. The chemical composition of vein minerals and the nature of the ore-forming fluids, *Econ. Geol., 51,* 781–797.

Holland, H. D. 1957. Thermochemical data, mineral associations, and the Lindgren classification of ore deposits (Abstract), *Bull. Geol. Soc. Am., 68* (pt. 2), 1745.

Ingerson, Earl. 1954. Nature of the ore-forming fluid at various stages—a suggested approach, *Econ. Geol., 49,* 727–733.

Ingerson, Earl. 1955*a*. Methods and problems of geologic thermometry, *Econ. Geol., 50th Anniv. Vol.,* pp. 341–410.

Ingerson, Earl. 1955*b*. Geologic Thermometry; in *Geol. Soc. Am. Spec. Paper 62,* The Crust of the Earth (Arie Poldervaart, ed.), pp. 465–488.

Kania, J. E. A. 1936. Some notes on the origin of pyritic copper deposits of the mesothermal type, *Econ. Geol., 31,* 453–471.

Kennedy, G. C. 1948. Equilibrium between volatiles and iron oxides in igneous rocks, *Am. J. Sci., 246,* 529–549.

Kordes, V. E. 1935. Die Beziehungen zwischen den Dissociationsdampfdrucken von Sulfiden und ihre Ausscheidungsfolge auf magmatogenen Erzlagerstätten, *Mineral. u. petrog. Mitt., 46,* 256–288.

Krauskopf, K. B. 1951. Physical chemistry of quicksilver transportation in vein fluids, *Econ. Geol., 46,* 498–523.

Krauskopf, K. B. 1957. The heavy metal content of magmatic vapor at 600° C, *Econ. Geol., 52,* 786–807.

Lacey, W. C., and H. L. Hosmer. 1956. Hydrothermal leaching in central Peru, *Econ. Geol., 51,* 69–79.

Latimer, W. M. 1952. *The Oxidation States of the Elements and Their Potentials in Aqueous Solutions,* Prentice-Hall, New York.

Lindgren, Waldemar. 1933. *Mineral Deposits,* McGraw-Hill Book Co., New York.

Morey, G. W., and J. M. Hesselgesser. 1951. The solubility of some minerals in superheated steam at high pressures, *Econ. Geol., 56,* 821–835.

Morey, G. W., and Earl Ingerson. 1937. The pneumatolytic and hydrothermal alteration and synthesis of silicates, *Econ. Geol., 32,* 607–761.

Niggli, Paul. 1929. *Ore Deposits of Magmatic Origin* (translation by Boydell), Thomas Munby and Co., London.

Noble, J. A. 1955. The classification of ore deposits, *Econ. Geol., 50th Anniv. Vol.,* part 1, pp. 155–169.

Owen, B. B., and S. R. Brinkley, Jr. 1941. Calculation of the effect of pressure upon ionic equilibria in pure water and salt solutions, *Chem. Revs., 29,* 461–474.

Ransome, F. L. 1907. The association of gold with alunite in the Goldfield District, Nevada, *Econ. Geol., 2,* 667–692.

Robinson, R. A., and R. H. Stokes. 1955. *Electrolyte Solutions,* Butterworths Scientific Publications, London.

Roedder, Edwin. 1958. Technique for the extraction and limited chemical analysis of fluid inclusions from minerals, *Econ. Geol., 53,* 235–269.

Roy, Rustum, and E. F. Osborn. 1952. Studies in the system alumina–silica–water, in *Problems of Clay and Laterite Genesis; A Symposium,* pp. 76–80, American Institute of Mining Engineers, New York.

Schmitt, Harrison. 1950*a*. Origin of the "epithermal" deposits, *Econ. Geol., 45,* 191–201.

Schmitt, Harrison. 1950*b*. The genetic classification of the bed rock hypogene mineral deposits, *Econ. Geol., 45,* 671–680.

Schneiderhohn, Hans. 1941. *Lehrbuch der Erzlagerstättenkunde,* vol. 1, Jena.

Smith, F. G. 1953. *Historical Development of Inclusion Thermometry,* University of Toronto Press, Toronto.

Smith, F. G. 1954. Composition of vein-forming fluids from inclusion data, *Econ. Geol., 49,* 205–210.

Thompson, G. A. 1954. Transportation and deposition of quicksilver ores in the Terlingua district, Texas, *Econ. Geol., 49,* 175–197.

Verhoogen, Jean. 1949. Thermodynamics of a magmatic gas phase, *Univ. Calif. Pubs., Bull. Dept. Geol. Sci., 28,* 91–136.

White, D. E. 1957*a*. Thermal waters of volcanic origin, *Bull. Geol. Soc. Am., 68,* 1638–1658.

White, D. E. 1957*b*. Magmatic, connate and metamorphic waters, *Bull. Geol. Soc. Am., 68,* 1659–1682.

Yoder, H. S., and H. P. Eugster. 1955. Synthetic and natural muscovites, *Geochim. et Cosmochim. Acta, 8,* 225–280.

Zies, E. G. 1929. The Valley of Ten Thousand Smokes, *Natl. Geograph. Soc. Contrib. Tech. Papers, 1* (4), 1–79.

Sulfide Systems as Geological Thermometers

GUNNAR KULLERUD

Geophysical Laboratory
Carnegie Institution of Washington

Establishment of widely applicable, reliable methods for precise geological thermometry would have profound importance to the earth sciences. The development of such methods is only beginning, but laboratory and field correlations are demonstrating the feasibility of thermometers based on physical-chemical relations as demonstrated in synthetic systems.

Extensive laboratory studies are being conducted on most of the major mineral groups, including such silicates as feldspars, micas, and amphiboles. This paper will review recent developments that have led to the application of phase-equilibrium relations among the more common sulfides, especially in ore deposits.

Systematic studies of synthetic sulfide systems have yielded information about the stability of minerals and mineral assemblages as well as of solid solutions between sulfide minerals. The application of these findings to ore bodies has produced results of great interest both to theoretical and to economic geologists. It has been possible in a number of cases to estimate temperatures as well as partial vapor pressures of sulfur during ore formation. Studies of mineral assemblages, furthermore, often provide information about the relative abundance of available metal and sulfur during deposition. Theoretical geologists are interested in all these aspects of the sulfide studies, but economic geologists find the temperature studies most rewarding.

Temperature gradients in ore deposits often indicate the direction of flow of the solutions or gases from which ores were deposited. In the future, field geologists may possibly use such gradients to solve problems in prospecting as well as in study of geological structures related to ore deposition.

In this paper we shall discuss first the stability of such minerals as pyrite and covellite, and the stability relations of some of the mineral assemblages in the copper–iron–sulfur and iron–sulfur–oxygen systems. Then we shall consider solid solutions among minerals, such as pyrrhotite–pyrite, pyrrhotite–sphalerite, and pyrite–sphalerite. Finally, examples will be given of applications of these relations to sulfides in rocks and ore bodies.

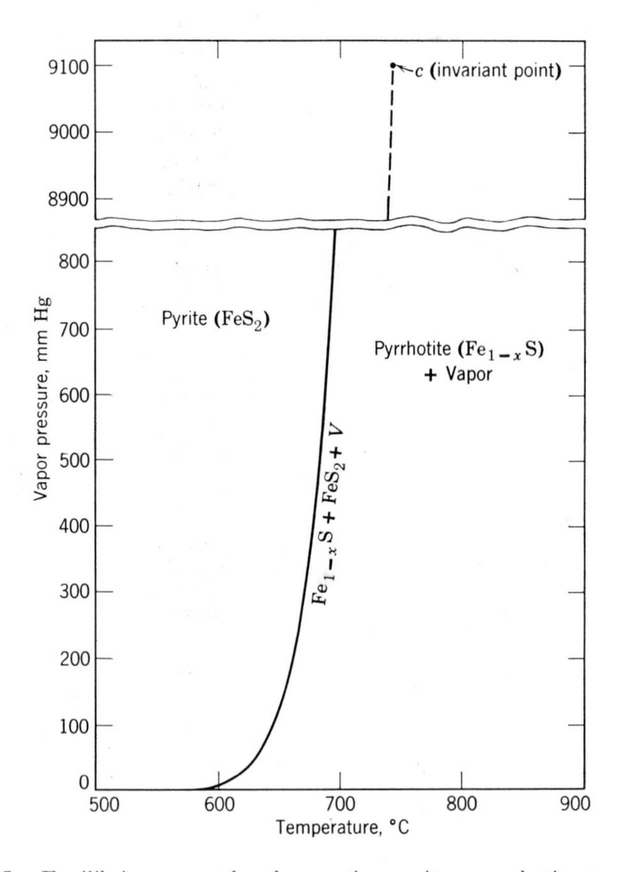

Fig. 1. Equilibrium curve for the reaction pyrite ⇌ pyrrhotite + vapor.

Stability of Minerals or Mineral Assemblages

The breakdown temperature of a mineral that decomposes by heating to a solid and a vapor is dependent upon the pressure of the vapor.[1] Unless the vapor pressure existing during the formation of the mineral can be estimated independently, the temperature of formation cannot be determined accurately. As most minerals are stable over a considerable pressure and temperature range, the occurrence of a mineral usually is not precisely diagnostic of conditions during formation.

The limits of stability of silicate-mineral assemblages have long been used by geologists as a means of estimating pressure-temperature conditions existing during the formation or metamorphism of rocks. Sulfide-mineral assemblages, or assemblages of certain common sulfides with common oxides, may likewise be used to estimate the conditions under which ore assemblages were formed.

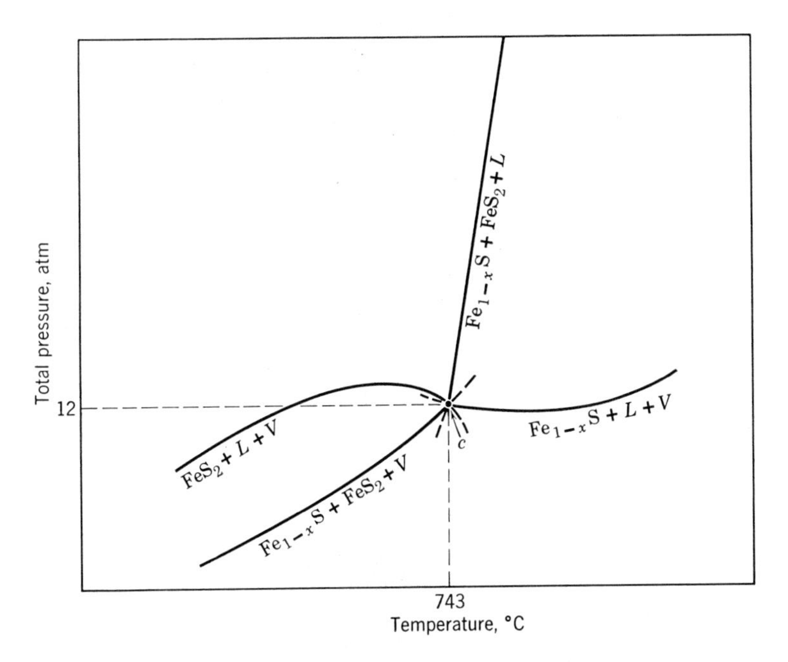

Fig. 2. Univariant point at 743° C at which the four phases pyrrhotite + pyrite + liquid + vapor coexist.

[1] The breakdown temperature depends to a lesser extent on the total pressure.

Stability of pyrite. Pyrite (FeS_2), when heated in vacuum, decomposes to pyrrhotite ($Fe_{1-x}S$) and vapor.[2] The pressure effect is such that breakdown occurs at 575° C when the vapor pressure is 2 mm Hg, and at 690° when the vapor pressure is 1 atm. The curve is shown in figure 1. On the left side of the curve pyrite is stable, and on the right side pyrrhotite and vapor are stable. The curve is univariant and represents equilibrium between pyrrhotite, pyrite, and vapor. Assuming that no other gas is present, as long as pyrite and pyrrhotite occur together the vapor pressure above the assemblage is determined by the temperature. If the temperature at which the assemblage formed is known, the vapor pressure can be determined by means of the *P*, *T* curve.

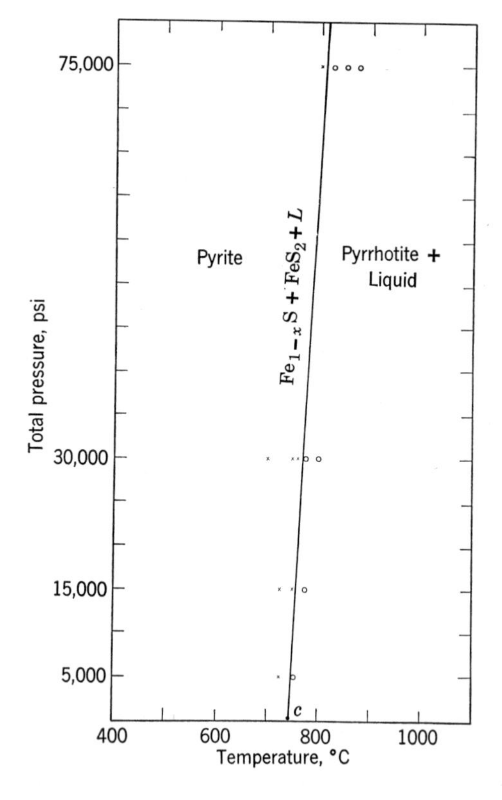

Fig. 3. The upper stability curve of pyrite. From Kullerud and Yoder (1957).

[2] It would be misleading, wherever sulfide systems are discussed, to refer to this phase as "sulfur vapor," because, although consisting mainly of sulfur, it also contains a small amount of metal.

Experiments by Kullerud and Yoder (1957) have shown that the pyrrhotite–pyrite–vapor assemblage is not stable above 743° C, where pyrite melts incongruently. The vapor pressure at this temperature is about 12 atm. The relations at this invariant point, which is the point of origin of four univariant curves, are shown in figure 2. The univariant curve $Fe_{1-x}S + FeS_2 + V$, which was in part determined by Allen and Lombard (1917), Raeder (1929), D'Or (1930*a* and *b*; 1931), Juza and Biltz (1932), and Rudder (1936), and the univariant curves $FeS_2 + L + V$ and $Fe_{1-x}S + L + V$ can all be determined by experiments in rigid silica tubes in which a vapor phase exists and in which the vapor pressure can be measured. It should be noted that pyrite cannot exist in the presence of vapor above this univariant temperature. The fourth univariant curve, $Fe_{1-x}S + FeS_2 + L$, represents the upper stability limit of pyrite. This curve, shown in figure 3, could not be determined by experiments in rigid

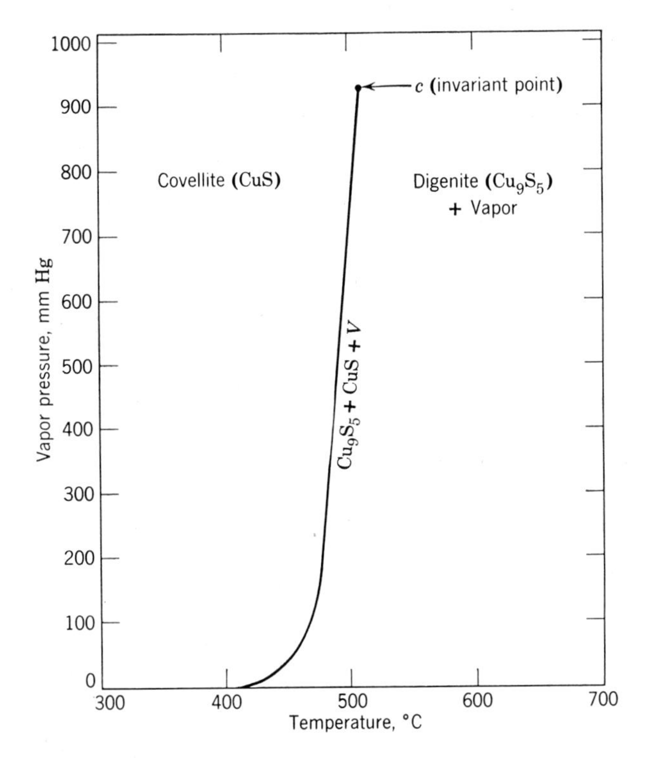

Fig. 4. Equilibrium curve for the reaction covellite ⇌ digenite + vapor.

tubes because vapor is not a phase in this univariant assemblage. It was determined by applying high pressure on welded collapsible gold tubes containing the iron and sulfur components. In all these experiments uncombined sulfur appears as a liquid (or gas).

Stability of covellite. Covellite (CuS) when heated in vacuum decomposes to digenite (Cu_9S_5) and vapor, not to chalcocite (Cu_2S) and vapor, as reported in the literature (Wasjuchnowa, 1909; Preunner and Brockmöller, 1912; and Allen and Lombard, 1917). The $CuS \rightleftharpoons Cu_9S_5 + V$ univariant curve is shown in figure 4. Breakdown occurs at 400° C when the vapor pressure is 1.5 mm Hg and at 490° C when the vapor pressure is 510 mm Hg. On the left side of this curve covellite is stable, and on the right side digenite and vapor are stable. As long as covellite and digenite occur together the vapor pressure above the assemblage is determined by the temperature. Experiments by Kullerud (1957*a*) have demonstrated that the covellite, digenite, and vapor univariant assemblage is not stable beyond a point *c* at 507° C and vapor pressure about 925 mm Hg; covellite and vapor cannot coexist above 507° C. As shown in figure 5, *c* is the point of origin of the

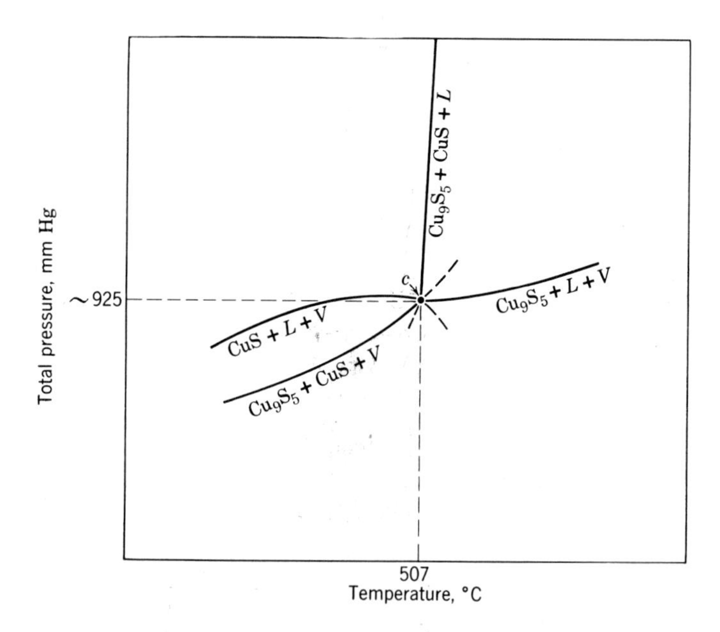

Fig. 5. Univariant at 507 ± 3° C at which the four phases digenite + covellite + liquid + vapor coexist. From Kullerud (1957).

four univariant curves: $Cu_9S_5 + CuS + V$, $CuS + L + V$, $Cu_9S_5 + L + V$, and $Cu_9S_5 + CuS + L$. The first three can be determined by experiments in rigid silica tubes in which a vapor phase exists and in which the vapor pressure can be measured; the fourth, shown in figure 6, is the $Cu_9S_5 + CuS + L$ univariant curve determined at 7500, 15,-000, and 30,000 psi.

Phase relations in the Cu–Fe–S system. This system is not only theoretically and economically very important, but probably is also the most complicated of the ternary systems containing sulfides of common occurrence in ore deposits. Merwin and Lombard (1937) studied the system at temperatures ranging from 400° to 950° C and under sulfur vapor pressures ranging from 2 to 760 mm Hg. They presented an equilibrium diagram shown in figure 7 for Cu–Fe–S under

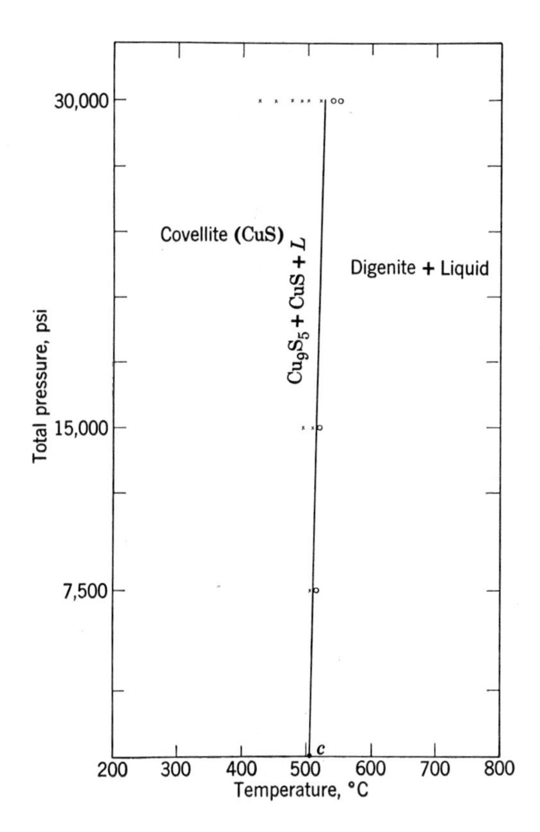

Fig. 6. The upper stability curve of covellite. From Kullerud (1957).

a "sulfur pressure" of 455 mm Hg. Schlegel and Schüller (1952) studied the Cu–Cu_2S–$CuFeS_2$–FeS–Fe part of the system at temperatures almost exclusively above 800° C. Greig, Jensen, and Merwin (1955) restudied the ternary compounds between chalcocite and pyrrhotite synthesized by Merwin and Lombard (1937) and presented a diagram showing equilibrium relations above 912° C between crystals and liquid for a part of the Cu–Fe–S system. The mineral digenite, which in polished sections strongly resembles chalcocite, was not recognized as a phase by Merwin and Lombard (1937) and was not reported by Greig, Jensen, and Merwin (1955).

The ternary phases are Cu_5FeS_4 (bornite), "Cu_5FeS_6" (sometimes referred to as "orange bornite"), $CuFeS_2$ (chalcopyrite), $Cu_3Fe_4S_6$ (unnamed), and $CuFe_2S_3$ (cubanite). Of these compounds, "Cu_5FeS_6" has not been established as a mineral, and the compound $Cu_3Fe_4S_6$ might be synonymous with the mineral valleriite. The composition of

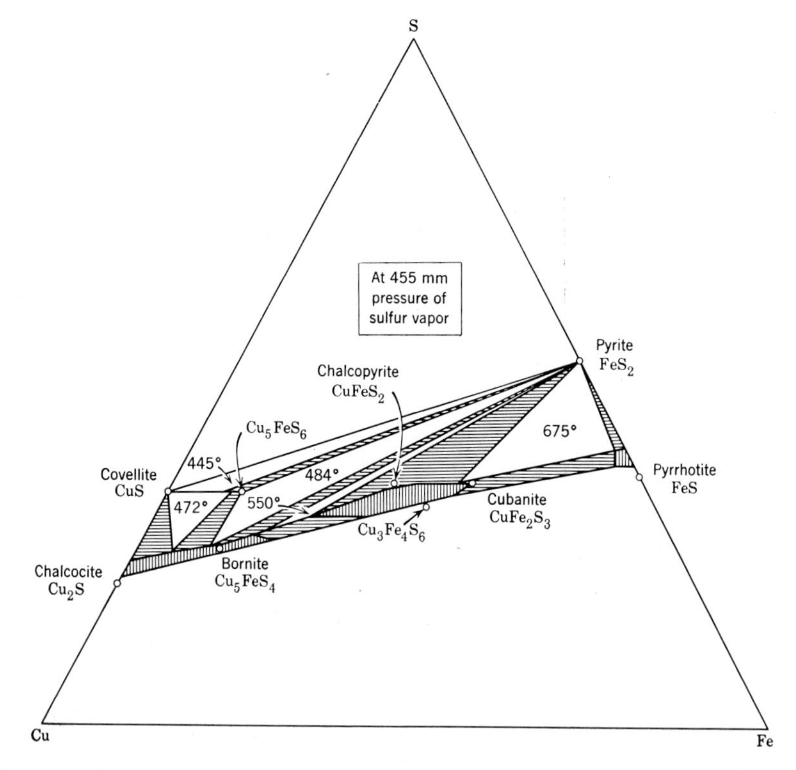

Fig. 7. Phase relations in the Cu–Fe–S system. From Merwin and Lombard (1937) (reprinted by permission).

this mineral in the literature is given as: "uncertain, perhaps $Cu_2Fe_4S_7$ or $Cu_3Fe_4S_7$." "Chalcopyrrhotite" ($CuFe_4S_6$) did not occur as a compound in the study by Merwin and Lombard (1937), and it probably should not be accepted as a mineral. The compounds of the binary systems confining the ternary Cu–Fe–S system are pyrite and pyrrhotite in the Fe–S system [3] and covellite, digenite, and chalcocite in the Cu–S system.

In figure 7 the one-phase areas in the ternary system are marked with heavy vertical lines except the "Cu_5FeS_6" area, which is marked by a horizontal line extending a short distance towards CuS from the "Cu_5FeS_6" point. At the pressure and temperatures for which the diagram is drawn, chalcocite and bornite form a complete solid solution series. Schwartz (1928) showed complete solid solution to exist at temperatures as low as 170° to 200° C. The intermediate field shows solid solution from cubanite to a point far beyond chalcopyrite.

Chalcopyrite, commonly regarded as $CuFeS_2$, is a sulfur-deficient compound (Merwin and Lombard, 1937). Its metal-to-sulfur ratio varies from about 2/1.98 to 2/1.90. For this reason $CuFeS_2$ is plotted outside the intermediate solid solution in figure 7. The third one-phase field is the pyrrhotite solid solution. Eight of the two-phase fields are marked with light horizontal lines; the remaining two, which are the covellite–"Cu_5FeS_6" and covellite–pyrite, are shown by tie lines. The eight fields are covellite–chalcocite solid solution, chalcocite solid solution–"Cu_5FeS_6," "Cu_5FeS_6"–pyrite, chalcocite solid solution–pyrite, chalcocite solid solution–intermediate solid solution, intermediate solid solution–pyrite, intermediate solid solution (cubanite)–pyrrhotite solid solution, and pyrrhotite solid solution–pyrite. The five clear areas in the diagram labeled with temperatures represent fields where three phases are stable. These are covellite–chalcocite solid solution–"Cu_5FeS_6," "Cu_5FeS_6"–covellite–pyrite, "Cu_5FeS_6"–pyrite–chalcocite solid solution, chalcocite solid solution–intermediate solid solution–pyrite, and intermediate solid solution–pyrrhotite solid solution–pyrite.

Of interest is the pyrite–intermediate solid solution relations, where the composition of the intermediate solid solution changes drastically between 550° and 675° C when in equilibrium with pyrite. The chalcopyrite–cubanite series has been studied by Schwartz (1927) and by Buerger and Buerger (1934); complete solid solution exists above

[3] Smythite (Fe_3S_4) was reported as a low-temperature mineral by Erd, Evans, and Richter (1957), and Fe_2S_3 has been reported in the literature as a precipitation product from aqueous solutions These compounds have not been synthesized in dry experiments.

about 450° C. Chalcopyrite and bornite form extensive solid solution above 475° C (Merwin and Lombard, 1937; Schwartz, 1931). Hewitt and Schwartz (1937) found that chalcopyrite and pyrrhotite form a limited solid solution.

The three phases occurring in each of the clear fields in figure 7 form univariant assemblages in equilibrium with vapor. The pressure and temperature relations for each such assemblage can conveniently be plotted in the same way as for $Fe_{1-x}S + FeS_2 + V$ or $Cu_9S_5 + CuS + V$ shown in figures 1 and 3. In figure 7 it may be noted that one point on the chalcocite solid solution + intermediate solid solution + pyrite + vapor univariant curve lies at 455 mm Hg and 550° C, and that one point on the intermediate solid solution + pyrrhotite + pyrite + vapor univariant curve at the same pressure lies at 675° C.

Phase relations in the Fe–S–O system. This system includes the common sulfides pyrite and pyrrhotite as well as the important oxides hematite (Fe_2O_3) and magnetite (Fe_3O_4). A series of experiments (Kullerud, 1957*b*) with mixtures of iron oxides and sulfur in evacuated, sealed silica tubes have produced information about some of the interesting mineral assemblages in this system. In the following discussion of the phase relationships, solid solutions in pyrrhotite, hematite, and magnetite have been neglected. The Fe_3S_4, Fe_2S_3, $FeSO_4$, and $Fe_2(SO_4)_3$ compounds have not been plotted because they are not stable at the temperatures for which the diagrams are given.

Figure 8*a* shows the relations at temperatures below about 675° C. Pyrite, pyrrhotite, and magnetite form one stable three-phase assemblage, and magnetite, pyrite, and hematite form another. It can be noted that hematite is not stable in the presence of pyrrhotite below about 675° C. These phase relations probably remain unchanged at the lower temperatures at which many ore deposits are believed to have formed.

At about 675° C the following reaction takes place: pyrite + magnetite $\rightleftharpoons$ pyrrhotite + hematite. Figure 8*b* shows that pyrite, pyrrhotite, and hematite now form a stable assemblage, as do hematite, magnetite, and pyrrhotite, while magnetite and pyrite can no longer coexist. Further changes in the phase relations occur at about 700° C, where pyrite + hematite $\rightleftharpoons$ pyrrhotite + SO_2. Figure 8*c* shows that neither hematite nor magnetite now is stable with the pyrite + pyrrhotite assemblage, whereas pyrrhotite, hematite, and magnetite still can coexist.

Figure 8*d* shows the phase relations above 743° C where pyrite no

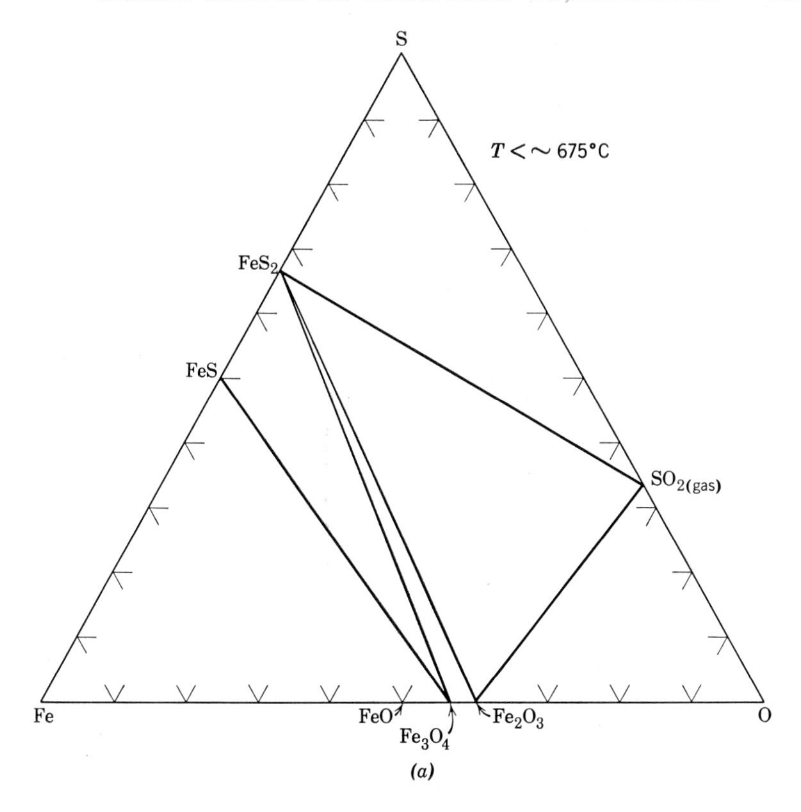

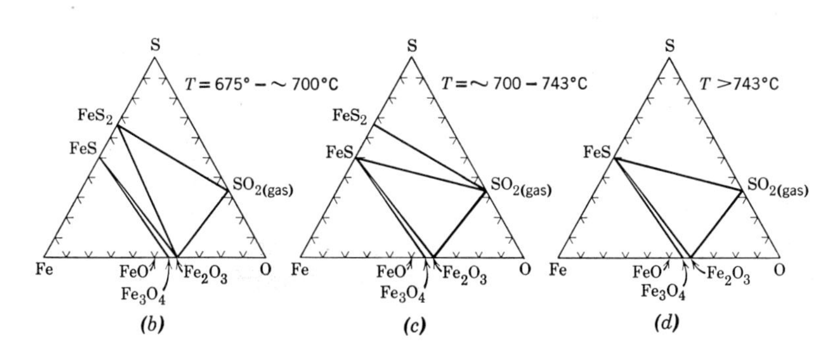

Fig. 8. Phase relations in the Fe–S–O system: (*a*) below about 675° C; (*b*) between about 675° and 700° C; (*c*) between 700° and 743° C; (*d*) above 743° C. From Kullerud (1957*b*).

longer exists. Hematite, magnetite, and pyrrhotite remain as a stable mineral assemblage.

Solid Solutions

The previously discussed methods of estimating temperatures of formation of sulfide minerals can only indicate certain wide P, T ranges within which the minerals must have formed. The concentrations of elements in solid solutions, on the other hand, vary smoothly as functions primarily of temperature and secondarily of pressure. Under certain conditions such mix-crystals may serve as reliable geological thermometers.

Thus, if a mineral A forms a solid solution with a mineral B, the equilibrium condition is that the chemical potential (partial molal free energy $\bar{F}$) for A is the same in the two phases. That is:

$$\Delta\bar{F} = \Delta\bar{H} - T\,\Delta\bar{S} = 0 \tag{1}$$

or

$$\Delta\bar{H} = T\,\Delta\bar{S} \tag{2}$$

where $\Delta\bar{F}$ is the difference in partial molal free energy of the pure A and the dissolved A, $\Delta\bar{H}$ is the difference in partial molal heat contents of pure A and dissolved A, and $\Delta\bar{S}$ is the difference in partial molal entropy of pure A and dissolved A.

For an ideal solution $\Delta\bar{S}$ is given by

$$\Delta\bar{S} = -R\cdot\ln(x) \tag{3}$$

where x is the mole fraction of A in the solid solution. Substituting equation 3 into equations 1 and 2, and rearranging terms,

$$\ln(x) = -\Delta H/RT \tag{4}$$

so that

$$x = e^{-\Delta H/RT}$$

These equations are valid only for strictly ideal solid solutions, and experience has shown that many sulfide solid solutions, at least at low temperatures, are not ideal. Hence, it is possible to use the above equations to estimate a solvus curve only when a number of points have been determined experimentally.

Provided that equilibrium was obtained, a solvus curve relates the compositions of solid solutions in pure systems to the temperatures that existed in the laboratory furnaces when the mix-crystals were formed. The accuracy with which temperatures can be determined from mix-crystal compositions depends on how accurately mix-crystal compositions can be established and on the slope of the solvus curve. Obviously, the steeper this solvus curve, the more inaccurate the temperature determinations will be.

The influence of rock pressure upon the composition of mix-crystals at any given temperature can be experimentally determined; where sufficient data are available it can also be calculated with a fair degree of accuracy. These calculations, again, are based on the assumption that the mix-crystals are ideal and that the difference in compressibility of the phases is negligible. Under such conditions the change in composition of a mix-crystal AB due to rock pressure (no gas phase is involved) may be expressed by the equation

$$x_1 = x \cdot e^{\Delta V(P-P_1)/RT} \tag{5}$$

where x and x_1 are mole fractions of A in the mix-crystals at pressures P and P_1 respectively, and where ΔV is the difference in mole volume between A and B.

The effect of pressure on composition of mix-crystals is known from experiments and calculations in only two binary sulfide systems. In both, increase in pressure causes decrease in solid solution. Experiments have shown that the influence of pressure on mix-crystal composition is greater at higher than at lower temperatures, but on an average 1000 atm of rock pressure causes exsolution from the solid solution equivalent to that caused by a decrease of about 20° C in temperature at 500° C.

Sulfide solid solutions may persist as homogeneous phases even after being cooled to normal temperatures at the slow rate found to occur in ore deposits, but usually the cooling is accompanied by exsolution phenomena. Thus, the sulfide mix-crystals found in nature commonly have changed in composition since their formation. Often the exsolved phase is found in the form of lamellae in the host mineral, and then it is at times possible to incorporate the lamellae in the composition determinations and arrive at a reliable temperature estimate. If, as frequently happens, the exsolved phase occurs as blebs and cannot be distinguished from original inclusions, minimum temperatures can be obtained by analyses of the remaining homogeneous solid solution.

All sulfide solid solutions contain impurities, sometimes as much as several per cent. Although trace element impurities usually have no measurable effect on solid solution compositions, impurities of 1 per cent or more can lead to serious errors if they are not taken into account.

Water undoubtedly was a major component of the solutions from which the ore minerals were deposited, and the application in nature of equilibrium phase relations determined by dry experiments has accordingly been subjected to criticism. In respect to hydrous mineral reactions such criticism is valid, because the presence of water is essential to the composition of the products. The situation is quite different in systems where water does not enter into the reacting phases. In sulfide systems the presence of volatiles such as water will influence the melting relations when water can form a homogeneous melt with the sulfides. On the other hand, water (or CO_2) cannot influence the subsolidus relations (mix-crystal compositions, inversion points, etc.) when it does not enter into the phases. For this reason subsolidus phase relations can be used as geothermometers where the presence of nonparticipating volatiles is immaterial. Common sulfides in ore deposits are, among others, pyrite, pyrrhotite, galena, sphalerite, and chalcopyrite. Of these minerals only FeS_2, $Fe_{1-x}S$, PbS, and ZnS are binary compounds; and, of these, pyrrhotite and pyrite, and pyrrhotite and sphalerite, form appreciable solid solutions with one another.

The FeS–FeS$_2$ system. Variation in the composition of pyrrhotite formed in equilibrium with pyrite at temperatures from 325° to 600° C has been studied by Arnold (1957). Five points on this solvus curve have been determined. Pyrrhotite formed in equilibrium with pyrite at 325° C contains about 47.2 atomic per cent Fe, and at 600° C about 46.0 atomic per cent Fe. The compositional variation over the 275° C temperature range, therefore, amounts to 1.2 atomic per cent Fe. Provided that the amount of iron in pyrrhotites can be determined within ±0.1 atomic per cent, the temperature of formation of pyrrhotites can be estimated within a limit of error of ±25° C in the 325° to 600° C temperature range. Some minor problems such as exsolution phenomena and the influence of impurities on pyrrhotite composition remain to be investigated in the synthetic FeS–FeS$_2$ system. At the conclusion of such studies the feasibility of employing the pyrrhotite–pyrite phase relations as a geological thermometer could then be explored by field tests.

The FeS–ZnS system. Detailed systematic study of the FeS–ZnS subsolidus phase relations resulted in the diagram shown in figure 9. Friedrich (1908), investigating the melting curves in this system, found a eutectic at 5 per cent ZnS and 1170° C. The rest of the diagram was determined by Kullerud (1953). All curves were established by solution as well as exsolution experiments to ensure that

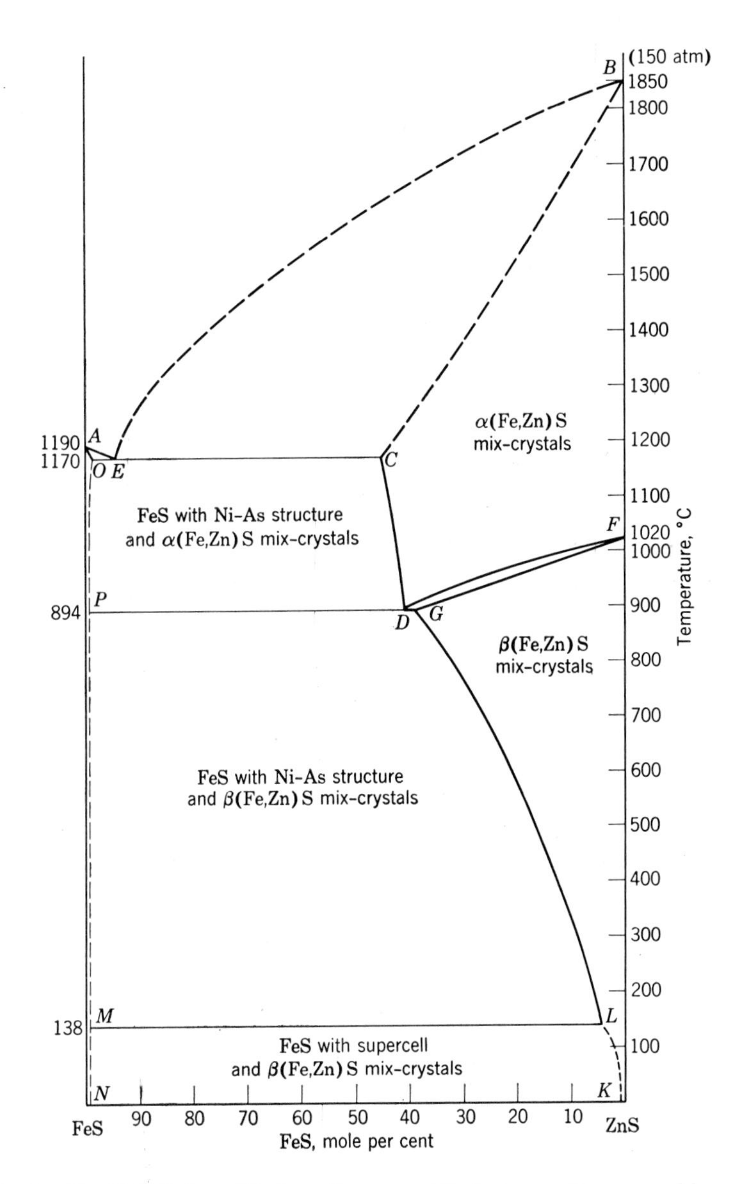

Fig. 9. The FeS–ZnS equilibrium diagram. All phases or phase assemblages are in equilibrium with vapor. From Kullerud (1953) (reprinted by permission).

equilibrium conditions had been obtained. Less than ½ weight per cent zinc goes into hexagonal FeS, even at 1170° C. Therefore, only trace amounts of zinc can replace iron in FeS at geological temperatures. Zinc sulfide occurs in two polymorphs,[4] cubic low-temperature sphalerite and hexagonal high-temperature wurtzite. The inversion temperature for pure ZnS is at 1020° C but decreases markedly when an increasing amount of iron replaces zinc in the ZnS lattice. The lowest inversion point is at 894° C, and the equilibrium sphalerite type mix-crystal formed at this temperature contains 38.9 mole per cent FeS. The wurtzite type mix-crystal field and the sphalerite type mix-crystal field are separated by a two-phase field containing both sphalerite and wurtzite type mix-crystals. The sphalerite type mix-crystal field is of importance in geological thermometry and will therefore be discussed at some length. The solvus curve *GL* represents the maximum amount of FeS that can go into stoichiometric ZnS at temperatures between 140° and 894° C. Because of extremely slow reaction rates at low temperature the portion of the curve below 400° has been calculated from thermodynamic data obtained at higher temperatures. Above 400° C the curve was experimentally determined within a limiting accuracy of ±0.3 mole per cent FeS. The low-temperature extrapolation of the curve carries this uncertainty as well as that added by assumptions made during calculations. It seems likely, however, that even the lowest part of the curve (at 140° C) is not subject to an uncertainty of more than ±0.5 mole per cent FeS (Kullerud, 1953).

The calculated maximum amount of FeS that can enter the ZnS lattice at 140° C was found to be 4.5 mole per cent. Thus between 140° and 894° C the amount of solid solution varies from 4.5 to 38.9 mole per cent, which averages a little more than 4.5 mole per cent per 100° C. The amount of FeS in sphalerite can be determined within ±0.2 mole per cent by X-ray diffraction techniques or chemical analyses. The total uncertainty in a temperature determination, therefore, is compounded by the possible error in the solvus curve and by the possible error in X-ray or chemical determination of FeS, and amounts to about 5° to 10° C, depending on the part of the solvus curve under consideration. The gentler slope at high temperatures gives more accurate temperature readings than the steeper part of the solvus. Thus it was possible to determine the temperature of formation of

[4] A third polymorph of ZnS reported by Buck and Strock (1955) was not encountered in these experiments and has not been found in ore deposits.

equilibrium type mix-crystals which consisted purely of iron, zinc, and sulfur, and which were situated on the FeS–ZnS binary join.

Almost all natural sphalerites contain some manganese and cadmium, usually less than 0.3 per cent of either, although chemical analyses have shown as much as 1.0 per cent cadmium and 2.5 per cent manganese in specimens from a few localities. Experimental study has shown that the presence of 2 per cent or less of cadmium and/or manganese has no measurable influence on the solubility of iron in sphalerite. Other metals, such as gallium, germanium, mercury, and indium, may likewise substitute for zinc in sphalerite, but the sum of these elements rarely if ever amounts to more than 0.01 per cent. Since these latter trace elements behave like the other metals by replacing zinc, but are hundreds of times less abundant, it seems logical to assume that they will have no measurable influence on the FeS–ZnS solvus curve. Elements such as selenium and tellurium may replace sulfur and therefore may influence the FeS–ZnS subsolidus relations. It has been found by a number of workers, however, that the S:Se ratio in sphalerites is normally in excess of 10,000 and that the S:Te ratio is considerably larger. For this reason both selenium and tellurium in the amounts occurring in natural sphalerites have negligible influence on the subsolidus relations.

Edwards (1955) suggested that the cadmium concentrations in sphalerites from the Broken Hill lode, Australia, are indicative of the temperature of formation of the ore lenses in this area. Fryklund and Fletcher (1956) suggested that the manganese concentrations in sphalerites from the Star Mine in the Coeur d'Alene district, Idaho, are indicative of the temperature of formation of this deposit. The presence of unusually high concentrations of cadmium or manganese in sphalerite may suggest a high temperature of formation, since the solubility of these elements in sphalerite increases with increasing temperature. Without adequate information about the distribution of these elements in other minerals of the deposit, however, their presence in sphalerite is only suggestive even in a single area. Cadmium or manganese enrichment in sphalerite could as well be occasioned by an unusual abundance of these elements as by a high temperature of formation of the sphalerite.

The binary system FeS–ZnS includes stoichiometric FeS and ZnS. Pure sphalerite as well as the various (Fe,Zn)S mix-crystals is stoichiometric, but pyrrhotite is known to be iron-deficient in all natural occurrences except in meteorites.[5] The join between ZnS or (Fe,Zn)S

[5] This meteoritic FeS is called troilite.

mix-crystals and any iron-deficient pyrrhotite is, therefore, not strictly binary. By appropriate control of the sulfur pressure over the FeS–ZnS assemblage the composition of (Fe,Zn)S mix-crystals formed in equilibrium with FeS, with $Fe_{1-x}S$, with $Fe_{1-x}S$ and FeS_2, or with FeS_2 alone may be studied. Kullerud (1953), in carrying on such studies, found no significant difference in (Fe,Zn)S mix-crystal composition (at any temperature), whether the mix-crystals were formed from

$$ZnS + FeS \rightleftharpoons (Fe,Zn)S + FeS \tag{1}$$

or

$$ZnS + Fe_{1-x}S \rightleftharpoons (Fe,Zn)S + Fe_{1-x}S + FeS_2 \tag{2}$$

or

$$ZnS + Fe_{1-x}S + FeS_2 \rightleftharpoons (Fe,Zn)S + Fe_{1-x}S + FeS_2 \tag{3}$$

as long as some pyrrhotite remained after equilibrium had been attained.[6] Since the (Fe,Zn)S mix-crystals are stoichiometric, pyrite must form when the iron content of the mix-crystals is obtained from pyrrhotite. In equations 2 and 3, therefore, pyrite is a reaction product together with (Fe,Zn)S mix-crystals.

A situation can readily be imagined in which the amount of $Fe_{1-x}S$ or the ratio between $Fe_{1-x}S$ and FeS_2 is such that at a given temperature all pyrrhotite can be disposed of partly by going into solid solution with ZnS and partly, since sulfur is produced in this way, by being converted to pyrite.

The borderline situation is that equilibrium between pyrrhotite and sphalerite is reached at the very moment the pyrrhotite disappears entirely. The reaction products are then (Fe,Zn)S mix-crystals and pyrite where the composition of the mix-crystals is identical to that obtained when an excess of $Fe_{1-x}S$ is present. If a smaller amount of $Fe_{1-x}S$ is present to start with, the reaction products are still (Fe,Zn)S mix-crystals and pyrite, but these mix-crystals contain less iron because the pyrrhotite supply is exhausted before maximum concentration can be attained. If iron were to go into the (Fe,Zn)S mix-crystals beyond the composition at which they have reached equilibrium with pyrite, vapor (consisting mainly of sulfur) would be produced and the vapor pressure over the assemblage would increase. In order to discuss the partial pressure of sulfur it may be helpful to consider the following reaction:

$$\text{Iron-rich (Fe,Zn)S} + S_{gas} \rightleftharpoons \text{Less iron-rich (Fe,Zn)S} + Fe_{1-x}S$$

[6] Equations 1, 2, and 3 are not balanced and, therefore, indicate the chemical reactions in a qualitative way only.

This reaction goes to the right as the availability of free sulfur (for instance, polysulfide in a solution or sulfur in a gas) increases. Kullerud (1953) found that the variation in composition of synthetic pyrrhotite has very little effect on the iron content of sphalerite with which it is in equilibrium. Barton and Kullerud (1957) found, however, that very iron-deficient synthetic pyrrhotite when heated above 600° C with sphalerite will produce somewhat less iron-rich (Fe,Zn)S mix-crystals than those obtained from stoichiometric FeS and ZnS at the same temperature. If the sulfur pressure over the above assemblage is further increased, the pyrrhotite converts to pyrite (at temperatures below 743° C) and the reaction written above goes strongly to the right. There is as yet very little laboratory information on the sphalerite–pyrite relationship. Since the formation of (Fe,Zn)S mix-crystals from ZnS and FeS_2 produces vapor (consisting almost entirely of sulfur) the study of such a system must be performed at controlled vapor pressures. Likewise such a system could be used for temperature estimates only if other measures of the partial vapor pressure of sulfur at the time of ore deposition were available.

The exsolution of pyrrhotite from sphalerite mix-crystals during cooling in ore deposits was studied in detail. Slight amounts of pyrrhotite have been shown to exsolve as lamellae in sphalerite in deposits formed at high temperatures (Stillwell, 1926). Such exsolution is limited to a few per cent, and has been found only in ores formed above about 600° C. In the ores of Broken Hill, Australia, which probably were deposited at temperatures near 700° C, exsolution took place during cooling but was arrested when the temperature came down to 600° C. The composition of the remaining homogeneous mix-crystals suggested a temperature of 600° C, and when the exsolved pyrrhotite was added to the FeS content a temperature of 670° C was indicated. The mechanism that arrests exsolution in ore deposits is not known with certainty. Since exsolution of FeS can be obtained from pure (Fe,Zn)S mix-crystals in about a year at 500° C in the laboratory, it was thought that the manganese and/or cadmium always present in natural sphalerites might exert an arresting influence on the exsolution. Laboratory experiments at 500° C involving sphalerite mix-crystals formed in equilibrium with pyrrhotite at 700° C as well as studies on Broken Hill ore [7] at this temperature showed that exsolution of FeS occurred from the synthetic mix-crystals but not from the ore.

[7] A sphalerite sample from this locality was ground under acetone to closely the same grain size as the synthetic mix-crystals.

Applications

The successful application of phase relations derived from synthetic systems to natural ones is dependent on coping with difficulties related to sampling and interpretation of results. It is necessary that samples collected in nature contain the mineral assemblages that have been studied synthetically. For instance, when the FeS–ZnS thermometer is applied, it is necessary that both pyrrhotite and sphalerite be present in every sample. Equilibrium diagrams produced by laboratory studies apply to mineral assemblages in nature only when these minerals actually have been formed in equilibrium with one another. Definite proof of equilibrium in natural reactions is not at present attainable, but equilibrium is generally assumed between coexisting minerals. The paragenesis of ore deposits can commonly be interpreted through field observations and by study of polished sections, and such studies should always be an integral part of any project on geological thermometry.

Geological field evidence, as well as experimental studies, has indicated that ore bodies may be deposited at temperatures varying from that existing at the surface of the earth to higher than 800° C. Variations in the mineralogy of sulfide ore assemblages, as well as deposition of ore minerals in well separated episodes, have indicated that the temperature of ore formation may vary appreciably even within single deposits. As will be seen later, temperature gradients during ore deposition are real. This means that the temperature of formation of an entire ore deposit cannot be determined from a few casually collected specimens; it is necessary to sample ore deposits systematically, both horizontally and vertically, to study temperature gradients during ore formation.

Rock pressures existing during ore formation can often be estimated from geological evidence about the amount of overburden at the time of deposition. Only very approximate estimates are required, because an uncertainty of ± 1000 bars, corresponding to an uncertainty of about $\pm 12{,}000$ feet in the estimate of the rock overburden, leads to an uncertainty of only about $\pm 20°$ C in the temperature estimates. Where temperature estimates have already been made, the partial pressure of sulfur existing during ore formation can often be estimated also by application of vapor-pressure curves determined on synthetic mineral assemblages.

Stability of pyrite. Pyrite, the most abundant of the sulfide minerals, occurs under a wide range of geological conditions. It is found in many sediments, in all grades of metamorphic rocks, and in many intrusive rocks; it is a major constituent of numerous ore bodies. When pyrite is the only sulfide present, the pressure and temperature during its formation fall on the left side of the $Fe_{1-x}S + FeS_2 + V$ and $Fe_{1-x}S + FeS_2 + L$ univariant curves shown in figures 1 and 3.

The upper stability curve of pyrite is shown in figure 9, together with the beginning-of-melting curve of a natural tholeiitic basalt and the minimum-melting curve of granite. The curve for basalt was determined by Yoder and Tilley (1956), and the melting curve of granite is taken from the work of Tuttle and Bowen (1953). It was shown by Kullerud and Yoder (1956) that at high sulfur pressures the occurrence of primary pyrite in granites and not in basalts may be accounted for by comparison of these curves. The upper stability curve of pyrite was determined under sulfur pressures equal to the total pressure; the curves for beginning of melting of tholeiitic basalt and for minimum melting of granite were determined where the water pressure was equal to the total pressure. The general relations outlined above hold for sulfur pressures much less than the total pressure, as may be seen from the small increase in the stability of pyrite with increasing pressure beyond point c (the invariant point where the phases $Fe_{1-x}S + FeS_2 + L + V$ are stable together). When the partial vapor pressure of sulfur is smaller than about 12 bars (which is the vapor pressure at the invariant point c), the stability relations of pyrite must be deduced from the $Fe_{1-x}S + FeS_2 + V$ univariant curve (see fig. 2). By keeping the partial vapor pressure of sulfur constant (by choosing any point on this univariant curve and increasing the total pressure), the stability of pyrite will depend upon the volume (ΔV_S) difference between pyrite and pyrrhotite. The change of volume caused by pyrite decomposing to pyrrhotite is ($\Delta V \sim -4$ cc/mole) negative; therefore, the stability of pyrite decreases slightly with increasing total pressure, in spite of the fact that the partial vapor pressure of sulfur is constant.[8] From any point on the $Fe_{1-x}S + FeS_2 + V$

[8] The slope of such univariant equilibrium curves may be calculated from the equation $dT/dP_t = T\,\Delta V_S/\Delta H$, where ΔV_S = volume change of solids, P_t = total pressure, ΔH = enthalpy, and T = absolute temperature (Yoder, 1955; Thompson, 1955). Since ΔH is positive, the slope will depend on the sign of ΔV, which is usually negative. The slope of this type of univariant curve will, therefore, be negative. It should be mentioned that, because the iron deficiency of pyrrhotite in equilibrium with pyrite increases with increasing temperatures, the ΔV_S for this pair is not a constant. The numerical value of ΔV_S decreases slightly with increasing iron deficiency in the pyrrhotite. In other words, the slope of these steep univariant equilibrium curves will become even steeper at increasing temperatures.

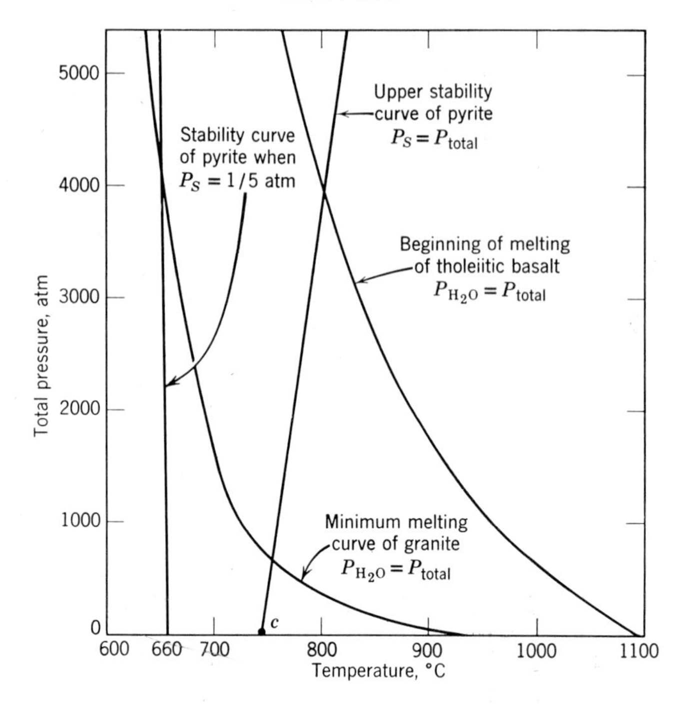

Fig. 10. Upper stability curve of pyrite ($P_S = P_{total}$) and calculated stability curve of pyrite where $P_S = 1/5$ atm shown in relation to the "beginning of melting" curve of tholeiitic basalt ($P_{H_2O} = P_{total}$) and to the "minimum melting" curve of granite ($P_{H_2O} = P_{total}$).

univariant curve a curve can be drawn which defines the stability limit of pyrite under increasing total pressure and under constant partial sulfur vapor pressure. All such curves drawn from selected points on the $Fe_{1-x}S + FeS_2 + V$ univariant curve have a very steep negative slope.

As an example assume that the total pressure on a magmatic granite was about 4000 bars when it crystallized at about 650° C (see fig. 10). On a univariant equilibrium curve drawn through 4000 bars and 650° C with the steep negative slope indicated by previous calculations, the partial vapor pressure of sulfur is 0.2 atm. If pyrite is to occur as a primary mineral in such a granite, then, the partial vapor pressure of sulfur in the granite must be at least 0.2 atm. Assuming a partial vapor pressure of sulfur of about 0.2 atm also to exist in rhyolites, it is seen that rhyolites should contain pyrrhotite and not contain pyrite as a primary mineral (see fig. 10).

The work by Kullerud and Yoder (1956) showed that pyrite does not melt congruently at any temperature. A liquid of pyrite composition will crystallize on cooling to pyrrhotite and a liquid close to pure sulfur in composition. Pyrite ore deposits of the Sulitjelma, Röros, Rio Tinto type were classified by J. H. L. Vogt (1926), Th. Vogt (1935), and others as "intrusive pyrite deposits" and were believed by these workers to have been deposited directly from a magma. The above-mentioned relations of pyrite in the iron-sulfur system exclude the formation of pyrite as a primary phase directly from a magma.

Since the $Fe_{1-x}S + FeS_2 + V$ univariant curve is relatively well known, coexistence of pyrite and pyrrhotite in many ore deposits makes it possible to estimate the partial vapor pressure of sulfur at the time of ore deposition if information is available on the temperature existing at that time. Further examples of the application of this curve for the purpose of estimating partial vapor pressures of sulfur will be given in a later section of this paper where temperatures of ore formation as deduced from solid solution relations are discussed.

Stability of covellite. Covellite occurs in nature in association with other copper minerals such as chalcopyrite, bornite, chalcocite, or digenite. It is found as a primary mineral, or in zones of secondary alteration, and has even been reported as a sublimation product.

Covellite commonly occurs in ore deposits associated with dioritic, monzonitic, or andesitic rocks. In many such localities covellite and other sulfides are also disseminated in these host rocks. The minimum melting curves of such rocks have not been investigated, but it may be inferred that they would melt at higher temperatures than granite at any given water pressure. As can be seen from figure 11, where the upper stability curve of covellite is shown in relation to the minimum melting curve of granite, covellite cannot occur as a primary mineral in granites and consequently not in dioritic, monzonitic, or andesitic rocks. It should again be pointed out that the upper stability curve of covellite was determined under sulfur pressures equal to the total pressure, whereas the curve for minimum melting of granite was determined where the water pressure was equal to the total pressure.

The general relations outlined above hold for sulfur pressures much lower than the total pressure, as is seen from the small increase in the stability of covellite with increasing pressure beyond point *c* in figure 11. *c* is the invariant point where the phases $Cu_9S_5 + CuS +$

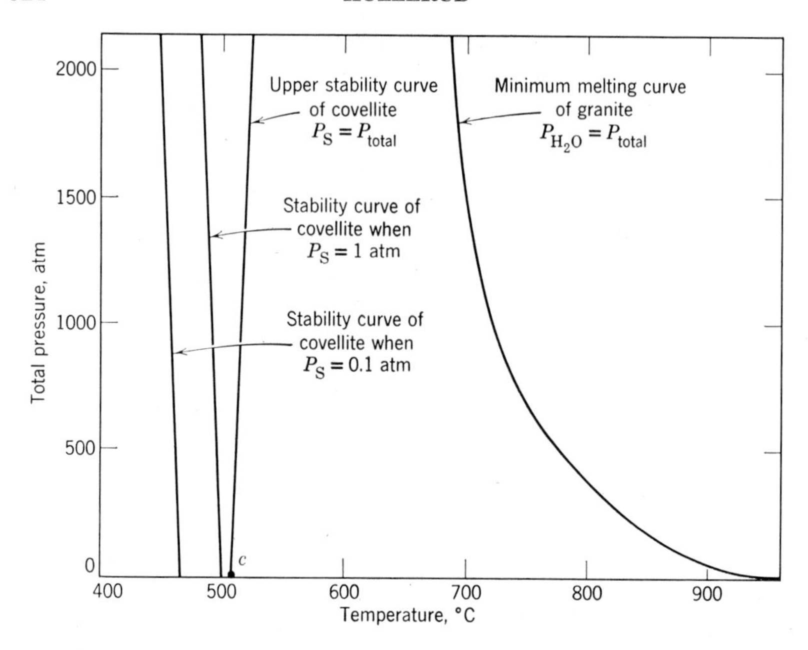

Fig. 11. Upper stability curve of covellite ($P_S = P_{total}$) and calculated stability curves of covellite when $P_S = 1.0$ atm and $P_S = 0.1$ atm shown in relation to the "minimum melting" curve of granite ($P_{H_2O} = P_{total}$).

$L + V$ are stable together. When the partial vapor pressure of sulfur is smaller than about 925 mm Hg (which is the vapor pressure at the invariant point c) the stability relations of covellite must be deduced from the $Cu_9S_5 + CuS + V$ univariant curve (see fig. 4). By keeping the partial vapor pressure of sulfur constant (by choosing any point on the $Cu_9S_5 + CuS + V$ univariant curve and increasing the total pressure), the stability of covellite depends upon the volume (ΔV_S) difference between covellite and digenite. The ΔV_S calculated from the $CuS \rightleftharpoons Cu_9S_5 + V$ relation is -6.2 cc/mole. The stability of digenite, therefore, decreases slightly with increasing total pressure, when the partial vapor pressure of sulfur is constant. From any point on the $Cu_9S_5 + CuS + V$ univariant curve a curve can be drawn which defines the stability limit of covellite under increasing total pressure and under constant partial sulfur vapor pressure. All such curves drawn from selected points on the $Cu_9S_5 + CuS + V$ univariant curve will have a steep negative slope. The univariant equilibrium curves for partial sulfur pressures of 0.1 atm and 1.0 atm are shown in figure 11.

These vapor pressures correspond to temperatures of 465° and 500° C on the $Cu_9S_5 + CuS + V$ univariant curve. It is possible that the partial vapor pressure of sulfur in many ore deposits may have been as high as 0.1 atm or even 1.0 atm; even if it were 1.0 atm, however, covellite would not be stable above 480° to 490° C at total pressures of 2000 atm.

Covellite and digenite occur together in a number of ore deposits, including, for instance, those at Butte, Montana. Whenever these minerals coexist, the partial vapor pressure above the assemblage is fixed if the temperature is known. If in such localities the temperature of formation of the assemblage can be estimated by other means, the partial vapor pressure of sulfur over the assemblage at the time of deposition can be determined.

The study of the upper stability curve of covellite (Kullerud, 1957*a*) has shown that covellite should not be deposited directly from a magma.

Phase relations in the Fe–S–O system. This system is radically different from that of copper–iron–sulfur, not only because it involves oxygen but also because it contains no geologically important ternary compounds. The phase relations commonly observed in nature are shown in figure 8*a*. Of special geological interest are the three-phase fields pyrrhotite–pyrite–magnetite and magnetite–hematite–pyrite. The three phases occurring in each field form a univariant assemblage in equilibrium with vapor.[9] The pressure and temperature relations for each of these assemblages can again be plotted in P versus T diagrams, similar to those shown in figures 1 and 3. It is clear from figure 8*a* that the vapor pressure over the pyrrhotite–pyrite–magnetite assemblage at any given temperature is smaller than that over pyrite–magnetite-hematite. Although the partial vapor pressure of oxygen is much smaller than that of sulfur, it is clear from the data by Richardson and Jeffes (1948) that a small increase in oxygen pressure leads to significant changes in mineralogy. For instance, at 600° C the partial vapor pressure of sulfur over the pyrrhotite–pyrite–magnetite assemblage is about 10^{-2} atm, while that of oxygen is about 10^{-25} atm. An increase in the partial pressure of oxygen from 10^{-25} atm to about 10^{-14} atm at this temperature results in the formation of hematite and the disappearance of pyrrhotite. In other words the pyrrhotite–pyrite–

[9] This vapor contains mainly sulfur but also some oxygen and some iron. Since the partial vapor pressure of sulfur at any temperature is many orders of magnitude greater than that of oxygen or iron, the partial vapor pressure of sulfur can for all practical purposes be regarded as equal to the total vapor pressure.

magnetite assemblage changes into the pyrite–magnetite–hematite assemblage.

The literature of ore deposits indicates that magnetite occurs in a large number of sulfide ores. Schwartz and Ronbeck (1940) tabulated 130 sulfide ore deposits all of which contain magnetite. All but 4 of them also contain pyrrhotite and/or pyrite. Six contain pyrrhotite and no pyrite, 77 contain pyrrhotite and pyrite, and 43 contain pyrite and no pyrrhotite. Hematite, which occurred in 21 of these deposits, was clearly of secondary origin in 8. On application of the Fe–S–O system (fig. 8*a*) to the 126 ore bodies which contain both iron oxides and iron sulfides, 6 lie on the pyrrhotite–magnetite join, 77 in the pyrrhotite–pyrite–magnetite field, 30 on the pyrite–hematite join, and only 13 in the pyrite–magnetite–hematite field. These findings indicate that the partial vapor pressure of oxygen during sulfide ore formation is ordinarily very low; only in 13 deposits out of 126 could it have exceeded about 10^{-25} atm, and it must always have been less than 10^{-14} atm, provided that the temperature of ore deposition did not exceed about 600° C.

As has been shown, the Fe–S–O diagram may be applied to a great number of ore deposits. Further information can be deduced if we have separate means of determining the temperature of formation of the sulfide–oxide assemblages. The Sextus mine at Röros, Norway, may serve as an example. The temperature of formation of this ore body was found by Kullerud (1953) to be about 600° C. In addition to the sphalerite and pyrrhotite used for temperature estimates, the mine also contains pyrite and magnetite. As was shown earlier, the partial vapor pressure of sulfur over the pyrrhotite–pyrite assemblage at this temperature is about 10^{-2} atm and the partial vapor pressure of oxygen over magnetite is about 10^{-25} atm.

The FeS–FeS_2 system. As was shown in the previous section the pyrrhotite–pyrite mineral assemblage is common in sulfide ore deposits. The composition of pyrrhotite deposited in equilibrium with pyrite may in the future serve as a reliable geological indicator, by means of which it may be possible to estimate not only the temperature of formation of this assemblage in nature but also the partial vapor pressure of sulfur during deposition.

Arnold (1957) applied this system as well as the FeS–ZnS system to two specimens containing pyrrhotite, pyrite, and sphalerite from Heath Steel Mine, New Brunswick, Canada. Assuming a total pressure of 2000 bars, he obtained 540° and 560° C from the two pyrrhotite–pyrite assemblages and 550° and 575° C from the two pyrrhotite–sphalerite assemblages. The temperatures of formation obtained by these two methods thus agree very closely.

The FeS–ZnS system. Natural sphalerites have been shown by analyses to contain appreciable amounts of iron and small amounts of other metals, such as manganese and cadmium. The color of this mineral in ores varies from light yellow to black, depending on the iron content. Determination of the phase relations and mix-crystal compositions in the synthetic FeS–ZnS system (Kullerud, 1953) made it possible to use the iron content of sphalerites deposited in equilibrium with pyrrhotite in geological thermometry.[10] These two minerals commonly occur together in many ore deposits and have long been known to form mix-crystals. So far this thermometer has been applied in more than 100 ore deposits.

The FeS–ZnS system was first applied to ores by Kullerud (1953), who estimated the temperatures of formation of pyrrhotite–sphalerite assemblages from specimens obtained from 54 widely scattered localities. These temperature estimates were made to demonstrate the applicability of the FeS–ZnS system to natural occurrences of pyrrhotite and sphalerite.

Edwards and Carlos (1954) determined temperatures of formation of pyrrhotite–sphalerite assemblages from numerous Australian localities. They showed there was no relation between the selenium content and the temperature of deposition of these sphalerites. This finding is in agreement with the conclusions of the discussion on trace elements in solid solutions (see p. 317).

Kullerud, Padget, and Vokes (1955) showed, by application of the FeS–ZnS thermometer to carefully selected specimens from 6 widely separated ore deposits in northern Norway, that the temperatures of formation of the analyzed pyrrhotite–sphalerite assemblages lay within a temperature range of 515° ± 40° C. These findings supported the idea of a uniform mineralization in the Caledonide schists of northern Norway as deduced from the assemblage of ore minerals and from the mode of occurrence of the ore bodies, though systematic sampling was not undertaken on any of these ore deposits.

Edwards (1956) studied the iron and manganese content in sphalerites from ore lenses in the Broken Hill lode in Australia. He concluded that the Broken Hill ore bodies were deposited at 600° C or

[10] The applicability of the phase relations of this synthetic system to natural sphalerite–pyrrhotite assemblages was discussed at length in an earlier section of this paper.

higher. This result was in agreement with findings by Kullerud (1953), who estimated by analysis of a single sphalerite a temperature of formation of 620° C without pressure correction, for a pyrrhotite–sphalerite assemblage from an unknown locality in the Broken Hill lode. By analyses of 5 sphalerites from 4 levels in the Aberfoyle tin mine, Rossarden, Tasmania, Edwards and Lyon (1957) determined that all these pyrrhotite–sphalerite assemblages were deposited at temperatures of 585° to 615° C.

The interesting work by Doe (1956) on the iron contents of sphalerites collected in a systematic fashion on two levels of the Balmat no. 2 Mine, New York, strongly indicates the existence of appreciable temperature gradients during deposition of this type of ore body. By plotting the deduced temperature for each level on a mine map, it appeared that isotherms could be drawn at 25° intervals from 350° to 500° C. Two high-temperature areas appeared when the 450° C iso-

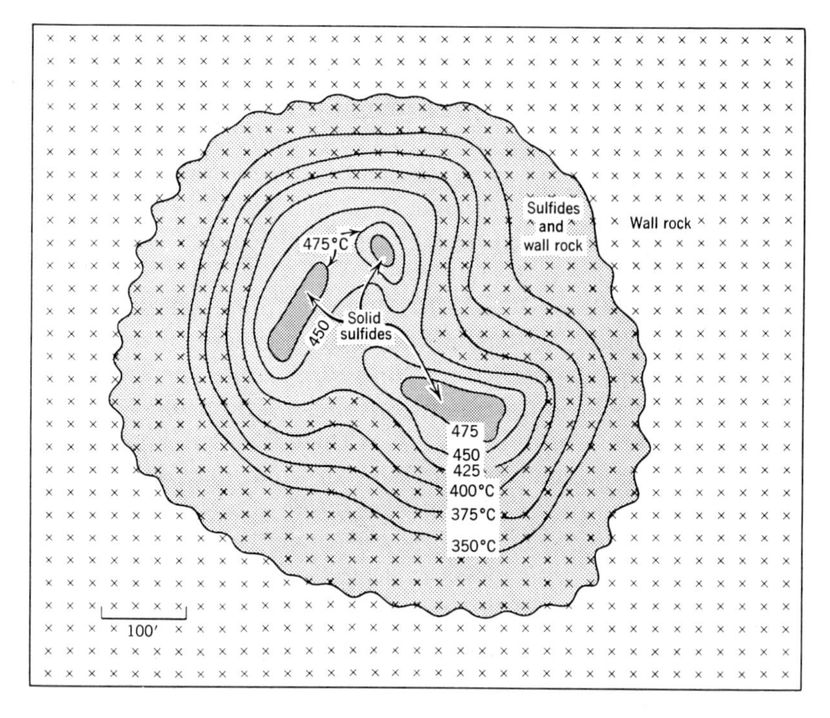

Fig. 12. Schematic plan view of the 1500-foot level of the Balmat no. 2 Mine showing isotherms based on the iron contents of sphalerites determined by Doe (1956) (reprinted by permission).

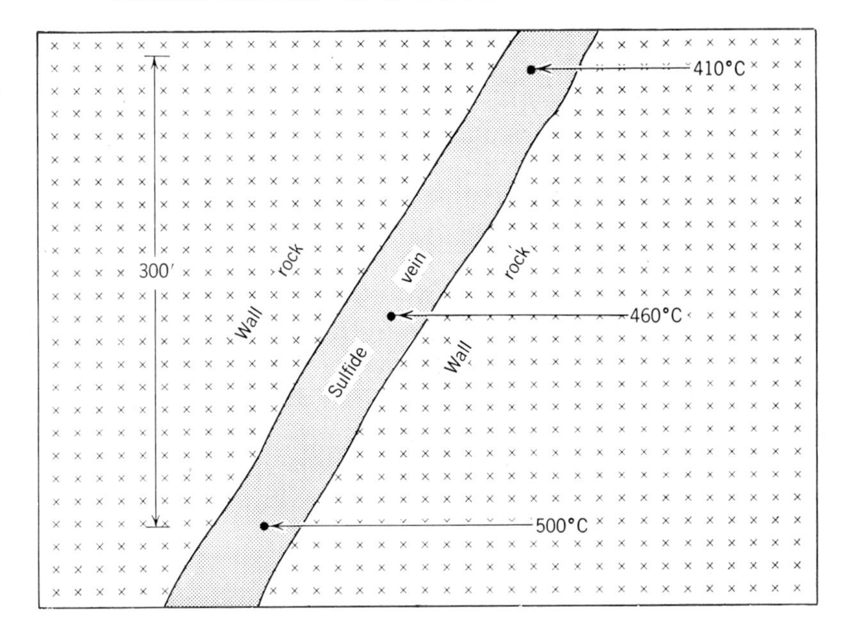

Fig. 13. The temperature variation along the dip of a sulfide vein in the Wellington Mine, Colorado.

therm was drawn, and one of them again split into two areas when the 475° C isotherm was drawn. The temperature relations as they appear from the work by Doe (1956) are shown in figure 12. Doe suggests that the three high-temperature areas may be indicative of channels or pipes through which the ore solutions were introduced. This work emphasizes the desirability of systematic sampling of ore bodies.

Coleman (1957) determined the temperature of formation of pyrrhotite–sphalerite assemblages collected from one period of mineralization in the Giant Yellowknife gold mine, N. W. T., Canada. The iron contents of these sphalerites indicated temperatures of formation ranging from 365° to 560° C.

A study of the temperatures of formation of pyrrhotite–sphalerite assemblages in several of the mines in the Breckenridge area, Colorado, was undertaken by Kullerud (1956 and 1957 unpublished). The lead and zinc fault veins in monzonitic rocks in this area carry much pyrite but only small amounts of pyrrhotite. However, pyrrhotite was present in all specimens selected for temperature studies. Figure 13 shows temperature variation in a 300-foot vertical section of the no. 4 vein in the Wellington mine. Twenty sphalerite samples were collected as close to the center of the vein as possible. The analyses showed, without exception, a remarkably uniform increase in the iron content of the sphalerites with depth. Only three of the temperatures estimated for the formation of the sphalerites are shown in figure 13. It may be noted that the temperature varies by 90° C (from 500° to 410° C) over a vertical distance of 300 feet. Similar variations were obtained from other veins in the same mine and were indicated by a few analyses of sphalerites from veins in the Minnie and Lucky mines. In the Breckenridge area these temperature studies have been used for numerous practical purposes. First, the temperature gradients indicated that the solutions which deposited the ores had moved upward along the fault fissures in the monzonite. There was, therefore, no special reason to assume that the ores would not continue at depth, as was believed by some geologists in the past. Second, sphalerite temperatures obtained from various veins on both sides of faults made it possible in two cases to correlate the veins and obtain some information about the complicated structural relations.

The excellent work by Lovering (1934) on the structural geology of the area, combined with the information obtained by sphalerite temperature studies, led to the belief that the faulted Wellington vein could be located south of the Wellington block at an estimated depth. Later drilling indicated that this assumption was correct.

Pyrite–sphalerite assemblages. It was shown in a previous section that an increase in the partial vapor pressure of sulfur above the $Fe_{1-x}S$ + (Fe,Zn)S assemblage at any given temperature would result in formation of FeS_2 and in less iron-rich (Fe,Zn)S phase. Therefore, whereas the phase relations in the FeS–ZnS system may be applied to natural occurrences of pyrrhotite and sphalerite as well as pyrrhotite–pyrite and sphalerite, the temperatures deduced from pyrite–sphalerite assemblages are almost without exception [11] lower than the real temperatures existing during the formation of the pyrite–sphalerite assemblages and should be regarded as minimum temperatures.[12]

Because of the occurrence of pyrite and sphalerite without pyrrhotite

[11] The iron content of sphalerite in a pyrite-sphalerite assemblage can only be as high as that of sphalerite in a pyrrhotite–sphalerite assemblage formed at the same temperature if at the start the former assemblage also contained the exact amount of pyrrhotite needed to saturate the sphalerite in respect to pyrrhotite at the given temperature. Therefore, at the moment saturation is reached all pyrrhotite is gone.

[12] This is contrary to an earlier statement made by Kullerud (1953), p. 109.

in many ore deposits it might be interesting to discuss what meaning minimum temperatures have. If we assume a vapor phase to exist during ore formation, the partial vapor pressure of sulfur in this vapor determines at any temperature whether pyrrhotite, pyrrhotite–pyrite, or pyrite will be deposited. We have very little information about the variation in the partial vapor pressure of sulfur throughout an ore deposit during its formation. It is certain, however, that some oxidation of the sulfur will take place when solutions are fed through channels or fractures to deposit minerals in veins or in lens-shaped ore bodies. For instance, if all the sulfur initially occurred as H_2S, oxidation would rapidly produce S_2, which again would gradually be converted into SO_2 as the distance from the point of origin increased. Therefore, if we were to plot partial pressure of sulfur (P_{S_2}) versus distance from a point of origin at a constant temperature, we would obtain a curve showing a steep increase in P_{S_2} until H_2S had been converted to S_2. This maximum would lie close to the zero point on the distance axis. From this maximum the P_{S_2} would decrease very gradually with increasing distance. Some unexpected minimum temperatures obtained from pyrite–sphalerite assemblages may be explained, if we at least tentatively accept this picture of the variations in the partial vapor pressure of sulfur.

Fryklund and Fletcher (1956), during a study of pyrite–sphalerite assemblages in the Star Mine, Coeur d'Alene district, Idaho, recorded what we might call a higher minimum temperature for the upper part of the mine than for the lower. Assuming, in accordance with the discussion above, that P_{S_2} decreased slightly as the solutions moved upward, more iron would go into the sphalerite. Thus a higher apparent temperature would be recorded at the upper levels than at the lower ones, while the true temperature of formation of the pyrite–sphalerite assemblages could readily have been just the opposite.

Along the same line of reasoning it can be seen that if, by application of pyrite–sphalerite assemblages, decreasing temperatures are recorded in the direction of the movement of the ore solutions, the true temperature gradient was actually more pronounced than that indicated by these minimum temperature readings. Temple (1956) found by using pyrite-sphalerite assemblages that the highest iron content in the sphalerites occurred in the deepest veins of the Leadhills-Wanlockhead lead and zinc deposits of the Southern Uplands of Scotland. Here not just the temperatures but also the temperature difference between the upper and lower portions of a vein are to be regarded as minimum ones; that is, the true temperature difference is larger than that indicated by the difference in the iron contents of the sphalerites coexisting with pyrite. The work by Doe (1956), see pages 328–329, indicated that pyrrhotite is a rather sparse mineral in the Balmat ore body, and pyrite is very abundant. Possibly, therefore, each single temperature reported by Doe should be regarded as a minimum one. However, if this is so, and if the conclusion of our previous discussion on partial vapor pressure of sulfur is correct, the true temperature gradients should be even more pronounced than those recorded.

Importance and Future Studies of Temperature Gradients

Temperature gradients, like those found in the vein deposits of the Breckenridge area and those that are strongly indicated in the Balmat ore body, lead to some interesting speculations about the formation of these types of ore deposits. The strong temperature gradients in the Breckenridge veins indicate that the ore solution, during deposition, cooled very rapidly as it moved upward along the fault fissures. Such cooling could be brought about if the solutions were injected into relatively cool country rocks. As the country rocks are very good insulators, they would, if exposed to a hot flowing solution for some time, prevent persistence of temperature gradients such as those recorded: as the country rocks were heated the temperature gradients would gradually become less pronounced. The present data imply that the sulfide veins in this area were deposited from hot solutions moving upward along fissures in relatively cool rocks; further, that the sulfides were deposited over short periods of time, geologically speaking, and from solutions more concentrated in metals than we customarily picture.

At present we can do little more than speculate about what the temperature relations observed in a few localities really reflect. It is essential that a number of synthetic sulfide systems be thoroughly investigated and correlated to ore deposits before final answers can be obtained. Laboratory studies are now in progress on the stabilities of minerals and mineral assemblages as well as the solid solutions among the minerals in the Cu–Fe–S, Fe–Ni–S, Fe–Zn–S, Fe–As–S, Fe–S–Se, and other sulfide type systems.

Conclusions

Information obtained from synthetic sulfide systems, when properly applied, can lead to reliable inferences about the conditions existing during the formation of sulfide ores. It is possible, by various means, to estimate not only the temperature relations in ore bodies but also the partial vapor pressures of sulfur. Where oxides as well as sulfides of iron coexist in ore deposits, we also have means of estimating limits of the possible partial vapor pressures of oxygen. Thermometers based on concentrations of metals in solid solutions provide us with uniform temperature scales over a wide range. The pyrrhotite–sphalerite thermometer when properly employed has been shown by numerous field workers to give reliable temperature estimates. Its use as a practical tool capable of solving mining problems of economic importance has been pointed out.

Temperature estimates based upon the iron content of systematically collected sphalerites deposited contemporaneously with pyrrhotite have shown that appreciable temperature gradients exist in a number of ore bodies at the time of their formation. Such gradients can be interpreted as indicative of decreasing temperatures of the ore solutions with increasing distance from their sources and hence of the direction of movement of such solutions. Studies of this kind can give valuable information in many mines about the location of ores, and in time may be refined to the point where they can serve as prospecting tools.

References

Allen, E. T., and R. H. Lombard. 1917. A method for the determination of dissociation pressures of sulphides, and its application to covellite (CuS) and pyrite (FeS_2), *Am. J. Sci., 43,* 175–195.

Arnold, R. G. 1957. Annual Report of the Director of the Geophysical Laboratory 1956–1957, *Carnegie Inst. Wash. Year Book 56,* 191–195.

Barton, P. B., Jr., and G. Kullerud. 1957. Preliminary report on the system FeS–ZnS–S and implications regarding the use of the sphalerite geothermometer, *Bull. Geol. Soc. Am., 68* (no. 12, pt. 2), 1699.

Buck, D. C., and L. W. Strock. 1955. Trimorphism in zinc sulfide, *Am. Mineralogist, 40,* 192–200.

Buerger, N. W., and M. J. Buerger. 1934. Crystallographic relations between cubanite segregation plates, chalcopyrite matrix, and secondary chalcopyrite twins, *Am. Mineralogist, 19,* 289–303.

Coleman, L. C. 1957. Mineralogy of the Giant Yellowknife gold mine, Yellowknife, N. W. T., *Econ. Geol., 52,* 400–425.

Doe, B. R. 1956. Geothermometry at the Balmat no. 2 mine, New York (unpublished thesis submitted to University of Missouri School of Mines and Metallurgy, Rolla).

D'Or, L. 1930*a*. Dissociation thermique de la pyrite, *J. chim. phys., 27,* 239–249.

D'Or, L. 1930*b*. Étude manométrique et spectrographique de la dissociation thermique de la pyrite FeS_2, *Compt. rend., 190,* 1296–1298.

D'Or, L. 1931. Dissociation thermique de la pyrite, *J. chim. phys., 28,* 377–408.

Edwards, A. B. 1955. Cadmium in the Broken Hill Lode, *Proc. Australasian Inst. Mining & Met., no. 176,* 71–96.

Edwards, A. B. 1956. Manganese and iron in Broken Hill sphalerites, *Proc. Australasian Inst. Mining & Met., no. 180,* 97–117.

Edwards, A. B., and G. C. Carlos. 1954. The selenium content of some Australian sulphide deposits, *Proc. Australasian Inst. Mining & Met., no. 172,* 31–63, 19 tables.

Edwards, A. B., and R. J. P. Lyon. 1957. Mineralization at Aberfayle Tin Mine, Rossarden, Tasmania, *Proc. Australasian Inst. Mining & Met., no. 181,* 93–145.

Erd, R. C., H. T. Evans, Jr., and D. H. Richter. 1957. Smythite, a new iron sulfide, and associated pyrrhotite from Indiana, *Am. Mineralogist, 42,* 309–333.

Friedrich, K. 1908. Die Zinkblende als Steinbildner, *Metallurgie Z. ges. Hüttenkunde, 4,* 114–128.

Fryklund, V. C., Jr., and J. D. Fletcher. 1956. Geochemistry of sphalerite from the Star Mine, Coeur d'Alene district, Idaho, *Econ. Geol., 51,* 223–247.

Greig, J. W., E. Jensen, and H. E. Merwin. 1955. Annual Report of the Director of the Geophysical Laboratory 1954–1955, *Carnegie Inst. Wash. Year Book 54,* 129–134.

Hewitt, R. L., and G. M. Schwartz. 1937. Experiments bearing on the relation of pyrrhotite to other sulfides, *Econ. Geol., 32,* 1070.

Juza, R., and W. Biltz. 1932. Das Zustandsdiagramm Pyrit, Magnetkies, Troilit und Schwefeldampf, beurteilt nach Schwefeldampfdrucken, Röntgenbildern, Dichten und magnetischen Messungen, *Z. anorg. u. allgem. Chem., 205,* 273–286.

Kullerud, G. 1953. The FeS–ZnS system: a geological thermometer, *Norsk Geol. Tidsskr., 32,* 61–147.

Kullerud, G. 1957*a*. Annual Report of the Director of the Geophysical Laboratory 1956–1957, *Carnegie Inst. Wash. Year Book 56,* 195–197.

Kullerud, G. 1957*b*. Annual Report of the Director of the Geophysical Laboratory 1956–1957, *Carnegie Inst. Wash. Year Book 56,* 198–200.

Kullerud, G., P. Padget, and F. M. Vokes. 1955. The temperature of deposition of sphalerite-bearing ores in the Caledonides of northern Norway, *Norsk Geol. Tidsskr., 35,* 121–127.

Kullerud, G., and H. S. Yoder, Jr. 1956. Upper stability curve of pyrite, *Trans. Am. Geophys. Union, 37,* 352.

Kullerud, G., and H. S. Yoder, Jr. 1957. Annual Report of the Director of the Geophysical Laboratory 1956–1957, *Carnegie Inst. Wash. Year Book 56,* 187–191.

Lovering, T. S. 1934. Geology and ore deposits of the Breckenridge mining district, Colorado, *U. S. Geol. Survey Profess. Paper 176.*

Merwin, H. E., and R. H. Lombard. 1937. The system, Cu–Fe–S, *Econ. Geol.,* supplement to *32,* no. 2, pp. 203–284.

Preunner, G., and I. Brockmöller. 1912. Gasdruckmessungen mit Spiralmanometer aus Quarzglas, *Z. physik. Chem., 81,* 129–170.

Raeder, M. G. 1929. Thermoanalytische Bestimmung der Dissoziationskurve des Pyrits, *Kgl. Norske Videnskab. Selskabs Forh., II* (no. 43), 151–154.

Richardson, F. D., and J. H. E. Jeffes. 1948. The thermodynamics of substances of interest in iron and steel making from 0° C to 2400° C, I, Oxides, *J. Iron Steel Inst. (London), 160,* 261.

Rudder, M. F. 1936. Contribution à l'étude de l'équilibre $FeS_2 \rightarrow FeS + S$, *Bull. soc. chim. France, 47*, 1225–1254.

Schlegel, H., and A. Schüller. 1952. Die Schmelz- und Kristallisationsgleichgewichte im System Kupfer–Eisen–Schwefel und ihre Bedeutung für die Kupfergewinnung, *Freiberger Forschungsh., B, Hüttenwesen-Metallurgie, 2*, 32 pp.

Schwartz, G. M. 1927. Intergrowths of chalcopyrite and cubanite: Experimental proof of the origin of intergrowths and their bearing on the geologic thermometer, *Econ. Geol., 22*, 44–61.

Schwartz, G. M. 1928. Experiments bearing on bornite-chalcocite intergrowths, *Econ. Geol., 23*, 381–397.

Schwartz, G. M. 1931. Intergrowths of bornite and chalcopyrite, *Econ. Geol., 26*, 186–201.

Schwartz, G. M., and A. C. Ronbeck. 1940. Magnetite in sulphide ores, *Econ. Geol., 35*, 585–610.

Stillwell, F. L. 1926. Observations on the mineral constitution of the Broken Hill lode, *Proc. Australasian Inst. Mining & Met., 64*, 1–76.

Temple, A. K. 1956. The Leadhills-Wanlockhead lead and zinc deposits, *Trans. Roy. Soc. Edinburgh, 63*, part I, no. 5, pp. 85–113.

Thompson, J. B., Jr. 1955. The thermodynamic basis for the mineral facies concept, *Am. J. Sci., 253*, 65–103.

Tuttle, O. F., and N. L. Bowen. 1953. Annual Report of the Director of the Geophysical Laboratory 1952–1953, *Carnegie Inst. Wash. Year Book 52*, 50.

Vogt, J. H. L. 1926. Magmas and igneous ore deposits, *Econ. Geol., 21*, 207–233, 309–332, and 469–497.

Vogt, Th. 1935. Origin of the injected pyrite deposits, *Norg. Tek. Höiskole Avhandl. til 25 års jubileet 1935*, pp. 595–607.

Wasjuchnowa. 1909. Das Gleichgewicht Cupro-Cuprisulfid, Dissertation, Berlin.

Yoder, H. S., Jr. 1955. Role of water in metamorphism, "The Crust of the Earth," *Geol. Soc. Am. Spec. Paper 62*, 505–524.

Yoder, H. S., Jr., and C. E Tilley. 1956. Annual Report of the Director of the Geophysical Laboratory 1955–1956, *Carnegie Inst. Wash. Year Book 55*, 169–171.

Some Aspects of the Geochemistry of Carbonates

JULIAN R. GOLDSMITH
University of Chicago

Carbonate minerals form in nature over an exceptionally wide temperature range, from temperatures of ground water and oceans to the highest encountered in regional metamorphism. Laboratory investigation of the carbonates has progressed rapidly in the last few years, revealing a complex phase chemistry. Experimental study of the subsolidus relations in the carbonates demonstrates the complicated behavior of mineral systems at temperatures well below the liquidus. The present paper will treat relatively recent work on heterogeneous and homogeneous equilibrium relations in the carbonates as related to composition and crystal chemistry. The fascinating problems of the nonequilibrium precipitation of carbonates and the formation of sedimentary dolomites are considered. No attempt is made to cover the problems connected with the reactions of carbonates with silicates, so important to the study of regional metamorphism.

The Anhydrous Carbonate Minerals

The pure end-member rhombohedral carbonate minerals of the calcite-structure type are: $CaCO_3$ (calcite), $MgCO_3$ (magnesite), $FeCO_3$ (siderite), $MnCO_3$ (rhodochrosite), $ZnCO_3$ (smithsonite), $CoCO_3$ (cobaltocalcite), $CdCO_3$ (otavite).

The rhombohedral carbonate minerals of the dolomite-structure type are: $CaMg(CO_3)_2$ (dolomite), $Ca(Mg,Fe,Mn)(CO_3)_2$ (ankerite), $CaMn(CO_3)_2$ (kutnahorite).

The orthorhombic carbonate minerals of the aragonite-structure type are: $CaCO_3$ (aragonite), $SrCO_3$ (strontianite), $BaCO_3$ (witherite), $PbCO_3$ (cerussite).

Anhydrous carbonates that do not fit into these three structural groups are: $CaCO_3$ (vaterite), $Mg_3Ca(CO_3)_4$ (huntite), $CaBa(CO_3)_2$ (alstonite and barytocalcite), $K_2Ca(CO_3)_2$ (fairchildite), Na_2Ca_2-$(CO_3)_2$ (shortite).

There are other multi-cation carbonates not listed here; these, plus the above six minerals, are relatively unimportant from a petrological point of view.

The Ca and Mg carbonates are by far the most abundant minerals; those containing Fe and Mn come next; those with the remaining elements are relatively uncommon. An excellent and well documented résumé of carbonate mineralogy is given in Palache, Berman, and Frondel (1951). A comprehensive review article on the properties of the calcium and magnesium carbonates has been written by Graf and Lamar (1955).

Solid solubility of the rhombohedral carbonates

The system $CaCO_3$–$MgCO_3$. A number of early workers determined the composition of Ca and Mg carbonates by a variety of methods (see Graf and Lamar, 1955, pp. 664–667), but composition-temperature relations were not considered. Moreover, most of the chemical analyses were done on materials that may have contained more than one carbonate phase. Spotts (1952) and Chave (1954) showed by X-ray methods, however, that recent calcite of organic origin may contain large amounts of Mg replacing Ca in the crystal structure, and Chave's examination of older calcites indicated that the Mg was eliminated with time. The aragonitic carbonate produced by marine organisms does not contain significant amounts of Mg.

Harker and Tuttle (1955*a* and *b*) and Graf and Goldsmith (1955) investigated the $CaCO_3$–$MgCO_3$ relations at elevated temperatures and CO_2 pressures. The solubility relations, determined at CO_2 pressures high enough to prevent decomposition of the carbonates, are shown in figure 1. The most recent data on lattice constants of the Ca–Mg carbonates, from which composition in this series can be determined, are given by Goldsmith and Graf (1958).

The solubility of $MgCO_3$ in $CaCO_3$ (calcite) is expressed by the left limb of the solvus; it is about 5 mole per cent at 500° C, and about 27 mole per cent at 900° C. All compositions to the left of the curve can exist as single-phase magnesium-containing calcites. The Mg atoms replace Ca atoms at random in the calcite structure, the solid solutions being called magnesian calcites. The general trend of the curve suggests that calcite formed under equilibrium conditions near earth-surface

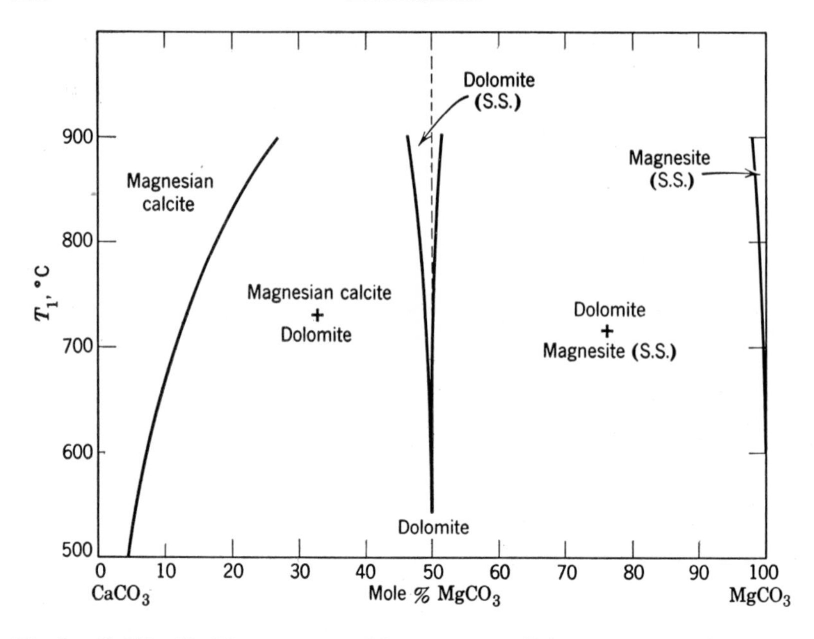

Fig. 1. $CaCO_3$–$MgCO_3$ system, at CO_2 pressures sufficient to prevent decomposition of the carbonates. S.S. = solid solution. Vertical dotted line is at the ideal dolomite composition. After data of Harker and Tuttle (1955*a* and *b*); Graf and Goldsmith (1955, 1958); Goldsmith and Graf (1958); and Goldsmith, unpublished data.

temperatures would be quite low in Mg, and this appears to be true for natural inorganically produced calcite (Goldsmith, Graf, and Joensuu, 1955). The high-magnesium calcitic parts of many marine organisms are obviously nonequilibrium structures; many of the calcareous algae contain a quantity of $MgCO_3$ in solid solution that would only be stable at approximately 800° C!

Calcium carbonate is only slightly soluble in dolomite—a matter that will be discussed more fully in connection with the structure of dolomite. Harker and Tuttle (1955*b*) did not observe dolomite to take any excess $MgCO_3$ in solid solution. The writer, however, has detected a small spacing change in X-ray patterns of runs made at 800° to 900° C on compositions between dolomite and $MgCO_3$, indicating a slight excess of $MgCO_3$ over the 1:1 ratio of ideal dolomite. The amount is very close to 1 per cent $MgCO_3$ at 900° C. At temperatures of 500° C and below, the solubility of either $CaCO_3$ or $MgCO_3$ is very low, and under equilibrium conditions the Ca:Mg ratio is essentially unity.

The system $CaCO_3$–$MnCO_3$. It has long been recognized that solid solubility is extensive in this system, for many examples of manganoan calcites and calcian rhodochrosites are known. Manganese is a common "impurity" in calcite; Palache, Berman, and Frondel (1951) state, with reference to calcite, that "A complete series extends to rhodochrosite through the substitution of Mn^{++} . . . ." However, Frondel and Bauer (1955), who studied Ca–Mn carbonates from Franklin, N. J., state that ". . . the calcite–rhodochrosite series is incomplete under the particular genetic conditions obtaining at Franklin." Their analytical data on the Franklin samples indicate a solubility gap extending from about 40 to about 75 weight per cent $MnCO_3$, but they point out that "Under some geologic conditions the series may be complete."

The solid-solution relations in this system were determined experimentally at temperatures above approximately 400° C by Goldsmith and Graf (1957*a*); the results are shown in figure 2. At temperatures above 550° C, complete solid solution exists between calcite and rhodochrosite; below that temperature a solubility gap defined by the solvus in figure 2 is present in the Mn-rich half of the system. The left limb of the solvus approaches the 1:1 Ca:Mn composition at approximately 450° C, at which temperature this composition is in equilibrium with a calcian rhodochrosite of approximately 80 mole per cent $MnCO_3$. The 1:1 Ca:Mn dolomite-type compound $CaMn(CO_3)_2$ exists, and material approaching this ideal composition has been described from three localities by Frondel and Bauer (1955). This compound, called

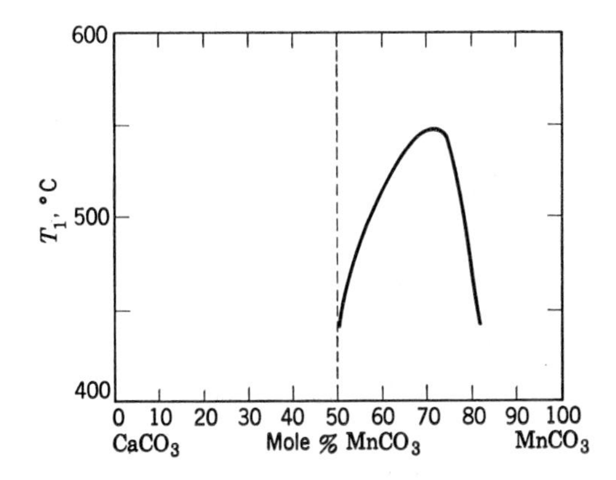

Fig. 2. $CaCO_3$-$MnCO_3$ system, at CO_2 pressures sufficient to prevent decomposition of the carbonates. After Goldsmith and Graf (1957*a*) (by permission).

kutnahorite, will be discussed in relation to figure 2 and to dolomite in a later section.

Figure 2 shows complete solid solubility between zero and 50 mole per cent $MnCO_3$ at temperatures down to approximately 400° C. Highly manganoan calcites can thus be formed at moderately low temperatures, and they are not uncommon.

The system $CaCO_3$–$FeCO_3$. A small amount (up to several per cent) of Fe replacing Ca in the calcite structure is not uncommon, and larger amounts have been noted (Palache, Berman, and Frondel, 1951). Calcian siderites have also been reported (Palache, Berman, and Frondel, 1951).[1]

Rosenberg and Harker (1956) report a solid solution of 8 mole per cent siderite in calcite and 5 mole per cent calcite in siderite at 400° C, with 14 and 5 per cent, respectively, at 500°. Using a different technique, the author (unpublished data) finds approximately 37 mole per cent $FeCO_3$ soluble in calcite at 700°. Like Rosenberg and Harker, he was unable to synthesize the compound $CaFe(CO_3)_2$. Nor has the Fe analog of dolomite been described as a natural mineral. It is likely that the pure compound $CaFe(CO_3)_2$ is not stable, at least at temperatures down to those at the earth's surface.

$FeCO_3$ is thus more soluble in calcite than $MgCO_3$, but less soluble than $MnCO_3$, as would be expected from the relative ionic radii of Ca^{++}, Mn^{++}, Fe^{++}, and Mg^{++}, which decrease in the order given. At low temperatures, however, the solubility of $FeCO_3$ in calcite is small enough so that calcites very rich in ferrous iron are rarely found. The same is not true of dolomites, in which replacement of Mg^{++} by Fe^{++} often occurs. Ankerites, or ferroan dolomites, are common, even as low-temperature minerals, but the high ferrous iron content is a consequence of the Fe^{++} for Mg^{++} replacement, and not an Fe^{++} for Ca^{++} substitution.

Other systems. If the discussion is limited to the four principal cations of the rhombohedral carbonates, only three binary combinations remain: $MgCO_3$–$FeCO_3$, $MgCO_3$–$MnCO_3$, and $FeCO_3$–$MnCO_3$. No modern experimental work has been published on these systems, but the ionic radii of Mg, Mn, and Fe are not greatly different, and on this basis significant solid solubility, even at rather low temperatures, might be expected. The results of mineral analysis appear to bear

[1] Many of the samples for which only chemical analyses are available may contain several phases. It is desirable to determine the composition by some means such as X-ray diffraction that effectively isolates the phase of interest.

this out; the series Mg–Fe and Fe–Mn are considered complete by Palache, Berman, and Frondel (1951). Of the three cations, Mg^{++} and Mn^{++} differ the most in radius, yet even here the series appears extensive (Palache, Berman, and Frondel, 1951), with an apparent tendency for $MnCO_3$ to take up more $MgCO_3$ than vice versa. As in all the known systems, the smaller ion substitutes more readily in the site of the larger ion than vice versa, and asymmetrical unmixing curves are produced.

There is no real evidence for the existence of dolomite-like compounds in these systems, although several analyses might indicate the possibility, particularly between Mg and Mn; the data are discussed by Frondel and Bauer (1955).

There are no published data on experimental work in ternary carbonate systems, although Rosenberg and Harker (1956) report that preliminary work has been done on the system $CaCO_3$–$MgCO_3$–$FeCO_3$. Graf and Goldsmith (unpublished data) have also worked on the join $CaMg(CO_3)_2$–$CaMn(CO_3)_2$ in the system $CaCO_3$–$MgCO_3$–$MnCO_3$, and these relations will be briefly discussed in a later section.

Very little quantitative work has been done on the solid-solubility relations among the orthorhombic (aragonite-type) carbonates. Data on analyses of natural materials can be found in Palache, Berman, and Frondel (1951). These carbonates contain larger cations than the rhombohedral structures, and therefore the cations so far considered are not accepted in the orthorhombic structures to a very large degree at ordinary temperatures. Ca^{++} is the only cation common to both structural types. The tendency for larger cations to go into these structures is seen in aragonite, which will accept some Sr and Pb. Calcite is not observed to contain significant amounts of these larger ions. Cork and Gerhard (1931) report complete miscibility of Sr and Ba in the orthorhombic structure. Studies of metastable precipitates of Ca–Sr and Ca–Ba carbonates have been published by Faivre (1944, 1946), and by Kallweit (1949).

The formation of metastable carbonates

The system $CaCO_3$–$MnCO_3$ shows an immiscibility gap on the Mn-rich side of the diagram (fig. 2), yet if carbonates are precipitated in the laboratory from reasonably concentrated solutions containing Ca^{++}, Mn^{++}, and $CO_3^{=}$ ions, a complete series of solid solutions is produced (Goldsmith and Graf, 1957*a*). The stable two-phase assemblage under the solvus is not observed under conditions of rapid crystallization at low temperature. In like fashion rapid precipitation in the system $CaCO_3$–$MgCO_3$ and subsequent moderate-temperature hydrothermal treatment can produce metastable magnesian calcites (Graf and Goldsmith, 1956; see also Brooks et al., 1950). In addition, dolomite is not observed to form directly under conditions of low-temperature precipitation, although it should exist in equilibrium with either calcite or magnesite over most of the compositional range of the system (fig. 1). Graf and Goldsmith (1955, p. 124) and Harker and Tuttle (1955*b*, p. 278) also note metastable Ca–Mg carbonates formed in the region under the solvus at high temperatures, by solid-state reaction.

The precipitation, by marine organisms, of metastable magnesian calcites has already been mentioned. The biochemical conditions under which these "high temperature" compositions are produced are apparently unknown, but the calcites are unquestionably metastable when the biological environment is eliminated, for example by the death of the organism. If Mg were to be incorporated in the hard parts of these forms solely under conditions of inorganic chemical equilibrium, it should appear in an assemblage of dolomite plus calcite or, if sufficient Mg were taken up, dolomite plus magnesite. No dolomite has ever been unequivocally identified in the carbonate of fresh marine organisms.

One other metastable form is very commonly produced, both organically and inorganically. Aragonite, to be discussed in more detail shortly, is now known to be the high-pressure polymorph of calcite and is always metastable at the temperatures and normally low pressures that prevail near the earth's surface.

Unmixing of rhombohedral carbonates

If crystallization takes place within a system at a bulk composition that lies in a region of immiscibility, a single homogeneous phase cannot be produced under equilibrium conditions. Similarly, if a homogeneous single phase (solid solution) is formed in a region of composition and temperature that lies above a solvus curve, equilibrium cooling will produce unmixing.

Exsolution of dolomite from a high-temperature magnesian calcite in metamorphic rocks is discussed by Goldsmith, Graf, and Joensuu (1955), and by Harker and Tuttle (1955*a* and *b*). Thin-section photographs of "perthite"-like textures are shown in both publications, those of the latter papers having been observed and described by

Coomaraswamy as early as 1902. The dolomite stringers in calcite strongly suggest origin by exsolution.

Much more common than these megascopic or microscopic features are calcites from metamorphic rocks that contain dolomite not readily observable under the microscope. This dolomite is finely disseminated in the calcitic host, and in all specimens so far examined is in the same crystallographic orientation as the host. It is almost certainly an exsolution product (Goldsmith, 1956, 1957, and in preparation). These observations were made on the typically milky calcite of numerous metamorphic carbonate rocks, both the presence and the orientation of the dolomite being observed in single-crystal X-ray photographs. The host calcite retains its identity as a single crystal, and specimens from a number of localities still contain some Mg^{++} in solid solution. Up to 5 mole per cent $MgCO_3$ in solid solution is not uncommon, particularly in carbonates from the granulite facies. The assemblage of a magnesian calcite with or without exsolved dolomite indicates that the rock was effectively quenched, and in a number of rocks the quench took place at approximately 500° C. An experimental verification of these phenomena, in which oriented exsolved dolomite was produced in single-crystal magnesian calcite hosts, has been briefly discussed in abstracts (Goldsmith, 1956, 1957).

Frondel and Bauer (1955), in discussing the Ca–Mn carbonates from Franklin, N. J., mention several samples that are mechanical mixtures of kutnahorite and a calcite-type carbonate. Professor Frondel has very kindly supplied Dr. Donald Graf and the writer with a suite of samples from Franklin, ranging from nearly pure calcite to nearly pure rhodochrosite in composition. Several samples of kutnahorite, $CaMn(CO_3)_2$, were included, and our attention was called to several that had an appearance suggestive of intergrowths. X-ray diffraction photographs showed a number of the samples to be two-carbonate assemblages, usually with one of the carbonates at or near the kutnahorite composition. Single-crystal X-ray photographs of several of the samples showed the crystallographic orientation of the two phases to be the same, as in the Ca–Mg carbonates (Goldsmith, 1957; Goldsmith and Graf, unpublished data). The kutnahorite-like phase is sometimes associated with a Ca-rich carbonate and sometimes with a Mn-rich one. Probably these textures are usually due to exsolution, thus illustrating the immiscibility gap shown on the Mn side of the diagram, figure 2.

Decomposition relations

Single-cation rhombohedral carbonates. Most of the earlier data on the decomposition reaction of the carbonates, both experimental and calculated, were obtained on calcite and magnesite; a summary of the results can be found in Graf and Lamar (1955). Aside from the early work on calcite, direct determinations of P_{CO_2}–T curves at elevated temperatures and CO_2 pressures have only recently been made.

Equilibrium curves for magnesite (Harker and Tuttle, 1955*a*), for rhodochrosite (Goldsmith and Graf, 1957*a*), and for smithsonite (Harker and Hutta, 1956), and several points on the calcite curve (Harker and Tuttle, 1955*a*) were all determined by essentially the same static technique. The carbonates or oxides (or both) were contained in pressure vessels at a known temperature and CO_2 pressure, were quenched, and examined. These reactions can usually be made to go in either direction, so there is little doubt that equilibrium is reached.

Calcite is the most refractory of the rhombohedral carbonates, and, for a fixed CO_2 pressure, the decomposition temperatures of these carbonates for which data are on hand fall in the order calcite > magnesite > rhodochrosite > smithsonite. There are no published data on siderite, but it appears to decompose at a lower temperature than rhodochrosite. Figure 3 contains the P_{CO_2}–T curves plotted as log P_{CO_2} vs. $1/T_K$ for the carbonates. Weeks (1956) has calculated several of these curves from the known thermodynamic data, and his values are in good agreement with the experimental results.

In considering the decomposition of the carbonates it must be remembered that all the curves of figure 3 represent the *highest* temperature at any CO_2 pressure at which the carbonate can exist. These are the univariant equilibrium curves for the general reaction $MCO_3 \rightleftharpoons MO + CO_2$, no other components being present. If other phases are present in the system, and can react with the carbonates, a reaction involving decomposition (loss of CO_2) can take place at significantly lower temperatures. It should also be pointed out that an extrapolation of the $ZnCO_3$ curve would indicate that smithsonite is very close to being unstable at earth-surface temperatures at the partial pressure of CO_2 that exists in the atmosphere.

Decomposition of multi-cation carbonates. In the category of multi-cation carbonates we can consider the dolomite-structure type as well as the disordered solid solutions that exist between a number of the end-member carbonates.

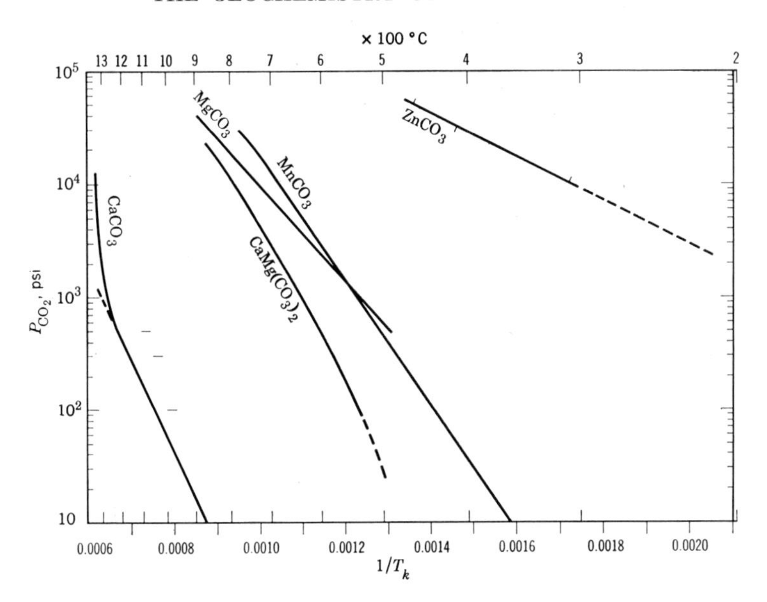

Fig. 3. The equilibrium thermal decomposition curves of carbonates, plotted as log P vs. $1/T_K$. The area to the left of each curve is the stability region of the carbonates, $CaCO_3$ (calcite), $CaMg(CO_3)_2$ (dolomite), $MgCO_3$ (magnesite), $MnCO_3$ (rhodochrosite), $ZnCO_3$ (smithsonite). The three short horizontal lines near the $CaCO_3$ curve are points recently determined for the decomposition of calcite (Harker and Tuttle, 1955*a*).

The P_{CO_2}–T curve for the decomposition of dolomite is also plotted in figure 3 (Graf and Goldsmith, 1955; Harker and Tuttle, 1955*a* and *b*). The equilibrium decomposition of dolomite does not, however, follow the straightforward two-step relation that is usually indicated by the reactions

$$\underset{\text{Dolomite}}{CaMg(CO_3)_2} \rightleftharpoons \underset{\text{Calcite}}{CaCO_3} + \underset{\text{Periclase}}{MgO} + CO_2 \quad (1)$$

followed at higher temperature by

$$CaCO_3 \rightleftharpoons CaO + CO_2 \quad (2)$$

A complication is introduced by the fact that, at high temperatures and CO_2 pressures, the calcite produced in step 1 is not pure $CaCO_3$, but, depending on the temperature and CO_2 pressure, contains more or less $MgCO_3$ in solid solution (Graf and Goldsmith, 1955). The first step of the decomposition (the equilibrium curve of dolomite in fig. 3) is more rigorously expressed by the reaction

$$\underset{\text{Dolomite}}{Ca_1Mg_1(CO_3)_2} \rightleftharpoons \underset{\text{Mg-calcite}}{Ca_1Mg_{(1-x)}(CO_3)_{(2-x)}} + \underset{\text{Periclase}}{xMgO} + xCO_2 \quad (3)$$

The composition of the magnesian calcites that are in equilibrium with dolomite (fig. 1) at sufficiently high CO_2 pressures to prevent decomposition is not strongly affected by CO_2 pressure, as only solid phases take part in the reactions (Graf and Goldsmith, 1955, p. 117). This is not true in the above decomposition reaction, however, as CO_2 appears on one side of the equation. Thus, in the field of magnesian calcite + $MgO + CO_2$ which exists to the left of the dolomite decomposition curve in figure 3, the composition of the magnesian calcites is dependent not only on temperature but also on CO_2 pressure. Any particular Mg-calcite has its own P_{CO_2}–T curve; each composition has a limiting univariant equilibrium decomposition curve beyond which that particular composition cannot exist. This is expressed by the following reaction, for any of the magnesian calcites:

$$\underset{\text{Mg-calcite I}}{Ca_1Mg_x(CO_3)_{(1+x)}} \rightleftharpoons \underset{\text{Mg-calcite II}}{Ca_1Mg_{(x-y)}(CO_3)_{(1+x-y)}} + \underset{\text{Periclase}}{yMgO} + yCO_2 \quad (4)$$

where $y \lesseqqgtr x$; i.e., magnesian calcite II is poorer in Mg than magnesian calcite I.

Thus, between the dolomite and the calcite curves of figure 3, there are an infinite number of curves for the magnesian calcites. This family of curves branches out from the P_{CO_2}–T curve of dolomite (Graf and Goldsmith, 1955). Figure 4 shows the dolomite and calcite curves as in figure 3, with several of the Mg-calcite curves, which, if extended, would join the dolomite curve at the appropriate value of P_{CO_2} and T.

It is apparent from figure 4 that in the field of magnesian calcite + periclase + CO_2 the Mg content of the calcite is dependent on both temperature and CO_2 pressure. For example, at 700° C and at 200 psi CO_2 pressure, approximately 1 mole per cent $MgCO_3$ is stable in the calcite structure, but approximately 4 mole per cent is stable at 2000 psi. In like fashion, at a fixed CO_2 pressure, *decreasing* the temperature increases the amount of Mg stable in the calcite structure. The stable Mg content increases with either increasing pressure or falling temperature until the dolomite curve is reached, at which point, of course, dolomite becomes stable. Once in the dolomite field, the effect of CO_2 pressure alone on the composition of any magnesian calcite in equilibrium with dolomite is not significant.

It should also be pointed out that if dolomite is decomposed at rather high temperatures and low CO_2 pressures (see fig. 4), as is usual in calcination processes, or in the normal differential thermal analysis

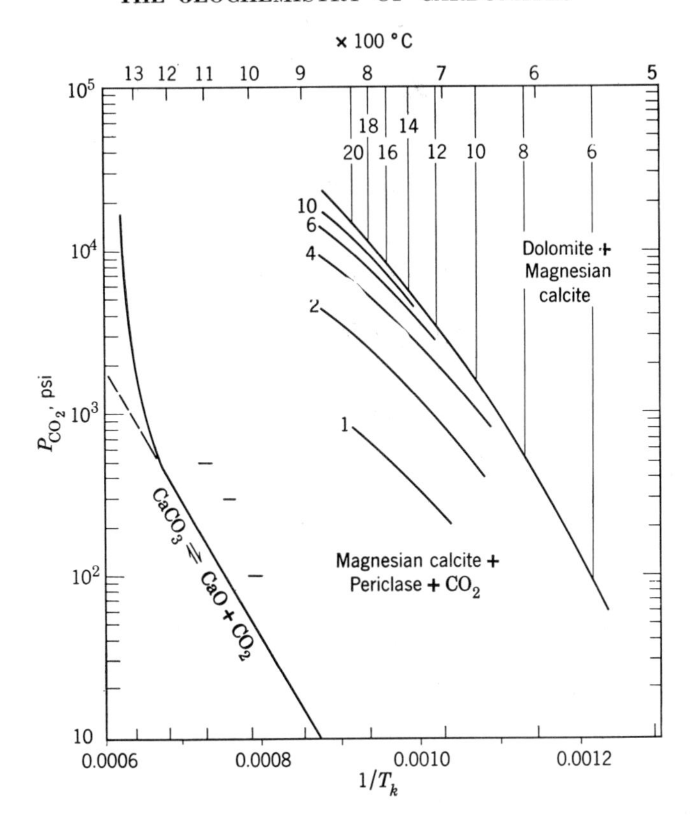

Fig. 4. The equilibrium thermal decomposition curve of dolomite (see also fig. 3), together with lines of equal Mg concentration (mole per cent) in the magnesian calcites. Mg concentrations of the calcites in equilibrium with dolomite are independent of P_{CO_2}, resulting in vertical iso-Mg lines. The numbers on the curves in the field of magnesian calcite + MgO + CO_2 are Mg concentrations (mole per cent) of these calcites. Data from Graf and Goldsmith (1955, fig. 5), modified after data of Graf and Goldsmith (1958) (by permission).

(DTA) apparatus, the calcite produced is essentially pure $CaCO_3$. This does not necessarily happen in nature, for a dense and somewhat plastic rock overburden may be capable of maintaining rather high CO_2 pressures. Thus all possibilities indicated by figure 4, on either side of the dolomite curve, may be present under different circumstances in nature. Evidence for some of these phenomena is presented by Goldsmith, Graf, and Joensuu (1955).

The behavior of the magnesian calcites in the P_{CO_2}–T region in which they are in equilibrium with MgO and CO_2 is in no way dependent upon the existence of dolomite. The effect is due to the fact that the *solid solutions* are stable over a portion of the phase diagram, and that the equilibrium vapor pressure of CO_2 varies with composition in the solid-solution series. $MgCO_3$ has a lower decomposition temperature at any CO_2 pressure than $CaCO_3$ (fig. 3), and, as might be expected, the decomposition temperature of the magnesian calcites drops with increasing Mg content.

The dependence of composition on CO_2 pressure and temperature is a general feature of carbonate solid solutions. The relations in the system CaO–MnO–CO_2 have been elucidated by Goldsmith and Graf (1957*a*). Solid solubility between rhodochrosite and calcite is complete at temperatures above 550° C (fig. 2); therefore the family of P_{CO_2}–T decomposition curves extend at elevated temperatures all the way from the curve for $MnCO_3$ to that for $CaCO_3$ in figure 3, and represent the whole composition range from pure rhodochrosite to pure calcite (Goldsmith and Graf, 1957*a*, fig. 6). The solubility gaps at lower temperatures produce an interesting complication: two phases are in equilibrium, and therefore must have the same decomposition temperature (Goldsmith and Graf, 1957*a*). A similar phenomenon is also observed in the $CaCO_3$–$MgCO_3$ system, in which the decomposition curve of the appropriate Mg-calcite joins the dolomite curve at the P_{CO_2} and T at which both are in equilibrium.

The decomposition relations of other carbonate solid solutions have not been experimentally determined. The Mg–Mn pair might present a feature of some interest as a consequence of the crossed curves of the two carbonates (fig. 3). One would expect that decomposition of a $MgCO_3$–$MnCO_3$ solid solution at lower temperatures (below 500° to 600° C) would enrich the carbonate in $MnCO_3$, but at higher temperatures would enrich it in $MgCO_3$.

Another point is illustrated by figure 3. The decomposition of $ZnCO_3$ occurs at rather low temperatures, particularly for low or moderate CO_2 pressures. Thus a solid solution of $ZnCO_3$ in calcite might be relatively unstable, even at moderate temperatures. The solubility of $ZnCO_3$ in $CaCO_3$ at moderate to elevated temperatures is quite significant (Goldsmith, unpublished data), but the limiting factor on the Zn content of the calcites of moderate- to high-temperature rocks is probably controlled by the decomposition relations. A similar situation may exist with respect to Fe. The solubility of Fe in calcite has been shown to be greater than that of Mg, yet high-temperature calcites do not appear to be enriched in Fe although they commonly are in Mg.

Polymorphic relations

Calcite and aragonite are a classic example of a polymorphic pair. Summaries of and reference to thermal and thermochemical work on the relation of these two forms are given by Graf and Lamar (1955) and by MacDonald (1956). Jamieson (1953) derived a *P-T* curve for the pair, and MacDonald (1956) experimentally determined the equilibrium curve over a temperature range from 200° to 600° C. He was the first to convert calcite to aragonite, in the stability field of aragonite. His expression for the field boundary is $P = 16T + 2400$, where P is in bars and T in degrees centigrade. This curve lies approximately 1500 bars below the curve deduced by Jamieson, but large errors are involved in both procedures. Clark (1957) has made a number of runs in a different type of apparatus, and his curve is in agreement with Jamieson's. The writer, who also has studied this equilibrium at higher temperatures and pressures in conjunction with an investigation of the general *P-T-X* relations in the system $CaCO_3$–$MgCO_3$ (unpublished data), has extended the curve to approximately 16,000 bars at 800° C,[2] in good agreement with the findings of Clark.

It is now quite clear that all the aragonite formed at or near the surface of the earth is metastable relative to calcite. It has been suggested that the presence of foreign ions such as Pb^{++} and Sr^{++} in solid solution may stabilize aragonite with respect to calcite at earth-surface conditions (see for example Johnson, Merwin, and Williamson, 1916). MacDonald (1956) has a convincing thermodynamic argument, however, indicating that the amounts of Pb^{++}, Sr^{++}, Zn^{++}, etc., found in natural aragonites are not sufficient to stabilize aragonite relative to calcite. No satisfactory explanation has yet been advanced for the common organic and inorganic crystallization of aragonite in nature.

Lander (1949) has shown that at approximately 800° C the aragonite-like form of $BaCO_3$ goes over to the calcite-type structure, and at slightly above 900° C $SrCO_3$ does the same. Lander believes that the Ba and Sr calcite structures under these conditions show rotational disorder of the CO_3 groups, as opposed to the alternating array of positioned anion groups found in true calcite. Lander further argues that an apparent high-temperature modification of $CaCO_3$ called α-calcite (first described by Boeke, 1912; see review of data in Graf and Lamar,

[2] In this connection it can also be noted that even at 800° C, and in a system in which the calcite is saturated with $MgCO_3$, aragonite takes no significant amount of Mg in solid solution.

1955) is also probably an anion-disordered form, but he was unable to work at a sufficiently high CO_2 pressure at elevated temperatures with calcite to observe this by means of X-ray diffraction.

Bridgman (1939) observed two high-pressure polymorphs of calcite that he called calcite II and calcite III. Jamieson (1957) shows that both these forms must be metastable relative to aragonite, a conclusion based on Bridgman's density data for the two polymorphs and on the *P-T* data now known on calcite–aragonite. Jamieson believes that calcite II is an anion-disordered form, much like those discussed by Lander. He states that at higher temperatures aragonite is in equilibrium with anion-disordered calcite rather than the normal form.

The Dolomite-Type Carbonates

Ordering and compound formation

The crystal structure of dolomite differs from the calcite-type carbonates in one very important respect. The Ca and Mg atoms are present in a 1:1 ratio, and are ordered or positioned in the structure in a particular array. Cation planes populated entirely by Ca^{++} alternate with those populated entirely by Mg^{++}. Between these planes lie the triangular $CO_3^{=}$ groups. Calcite is made up of alternating layers of Ca^{++} and $CO_3^{=}$ ions; thus dolomite has a lower space group symmetry than calcite, and can be looked upon as a calcite structure in which every other Ca^{++} layer is replaced by Mg^{++} (see Bragg, 1937). The additional X-ray reflections observed for dolomite, which result from the alternation of cation planes, are called order reflections. The solid solutions, such as Mg-calcites, Mn-calcites, Ca-rhodochrosites, etc., differ in that the "solute" cation is randomly positioned, or disordered in the general cation array.

A distinct compound like dolomite results only when a stable crystal structure is developed in which at least two different cation species can assume specific and different structural positions. The most important crystal-chemical difference effecting this segregation is ionic radius. Ca^{++} has an ionic radius of 1.06 Å, Mg^{++} a radius of 0.78 Å. This sizable difference is expressed by the ordered nature of dolomite and by the fact that only very limited solid solution exists between $CaCO_3$ and $MgCO_3$ except at rather high temperatures. In general, high temperatures produce expanded and more open structures, and the influence of crystal-chemical factors such as radius control is reduced. Thus many ordered compounds have a maximum temperature of existence; at higher temperatures they are observed to be disordered solid solutions, which are structurally indistinguishable from adjacent disordered compositions, and are not compounds as here defined. Numerous alloy systems illustrate this point: a low-temperature ordered structure [3] such as Cu_3Au is certainly a compound, even though some variation in composition can be tolerated. Above its disordering temperature, however, the structure is the same as the structures of all other solid solutions between Cu and Au in composition, and the property that distinguished it as a compound is lost. Moreover, if the Cu and Au atoms were more alike, the chances of an ordered structure's being stable at all would be lessened. The extreme would be the system Ag–Au, for silver and gold have essentially the same atomic radius, and no ordered structure has been observed.

On the basis of difference in radius it is possible to explain the lack of dolomite compounds in the systems $MgCO_3$–$FeCO_3$ or $FeCO_3$–$MnCO_3$,[4] where the cation-radius differences are quite small. The values for the ionic radii of the divalent elements considered are shown here (from Goldschmidt, 1954), as empirical radii, in 6-coordination.

Element (2+)	Radius, Å
Mg	0.78
Ca	1.06
Mn	0.91
Fe	0.83
Co	0.82
Zn	0.83
Cd	1.03

Combinations of the smaller cations (Mg, Fe, Co, Zn, and even Mn) might not be expected to develop ordered rhombohedral carbonates among themselves. Frondel and Bauer (1955) point out, however, that an ordered compound between Mg and Mn appears to be just as likely as that between Ca and Mn, and they cite a possible example.

More than ionic size is involved in the development of an ordered rhombohedral carbonate. The fact that a compound $CaFe(CO_3)_2$ is not observed in the system CaO–FeO–CO_2 has already been mentioned. Fe^{++} is quite similar to Mg^{++} in radius, and it is somewhat surprising that the Fe equivalent of dolomite does not appear to be stable.

[3] Usually termed "superlattice" by metallurgists.

[4] Even if a Fe–Mn ordered carbonate were formed, it might not develop observable order reflections in X-ray photographs, because of the very small difference in X-ray scattering power between Fe^{++} and Mn^{++}.

A rather large amount of Fe does replace Mg in the ankerites, yet the complete substitution has not been observed, either in nature or in the laboratory. On the basis of radius alone, the Ca–Fe compound would be more likely than the observed Ca–Mn compound, kutnahorite. In this same connection, it has been observed by the writer (unpublished data) that a solvus extends across the system $CaCO_3$–$ZnCO_3$. No ordered compound at the 1:1 composition was produced, but extensive experimentation was not carried out. Of the systems herein discussed, only $CaCO_3$–$MgCO_3$ and $CaCO_3$–$MnCO_3$ are now known to contain dolomite-type compounds.[5]

Dolomite and kutnahorite in the systems $CaCO_3$–$MgCO_3$ and $CaCO_3$–$MnCO_3$

Because of experimental difficulties only the very Ca-rich portion of the system $CaCO_3$–$MgCO_3$ has been studied above 900° C. At temperatures up to 900° C, dolomite has always appeared in the quenched product as an ordered compound. The dolomite structure seems stable at 900° C, although the possibility of at least partial disordering at this temperature with reordering during the "quench" cannot be discounted.

Even though the higher-temperature region of the phase diagram for the system $CaCO_3$–$MgCO_3$ (fig. 1) is not known, it is tempting to speculate on the behavior of the carbonates at high temperatures, on the basis of the configuration below 900° C. Graf and Goldsmith (1955) have considered a number of ways in which the known subsolidus relations can be extrapolated to higher temperatures. The melting relations of the Ca–Mg carbonates are not known, and it must be kept in mind that a solidus or melting curve may well interrupt the upward extrapolation of any of the curves of figure 1. Rough extrapolation of the two limbs of the solvus on the left-hand side of figure 1 suggests that the loop may close at approximately 1000° C.[6]

At 900° C, dolomite takes up excess $CaCO_3$ to the extent of 4 mole per cent. At the same temperature, only 1 mole per cent excess $MgCO_3$ can enter the dolomite structure. At 500° C and below, the Ca:Mg

[5] At the time of this writing the system $CdCO_3$–$MgCO_3$ has been essentially completed (unpublished data). The compound $CdMg(CO_3)_2$, or cadmium dolomite, is stable, and has a number of rather interesting properties that will be described in due course. This compound has not been described as a mineral.

[6] At which temperature the CO_2 pressure of dolomite is approximately 5000 atmospheres, and that of Mg-rich calcites somewhat less (Graf and Goldsmith, 1955).

ratio of dolomite in equilibrium with either $CaCO_3$ or $MgCO_3$ does not deviate significantly from unity. The fact that excess Ca^{++} enters the structure with greater ease than Mg^{++} is rather puzzling. The Ca^{++} in excess of the 1:1 Ca:Mg ratio obviously replaces Mg^{++} in the structure, yet this replacement of a larger for a smaller ion might be expected to be difficult, and, indeed, very little $CaCO_3$ is taken in solid solution in magnesite. On the other hand, the replacement of Mg^{++} for Ca^{++} in the structure, which would appear to be more readily accomplished as in the magnesian calcites, proves to be quite difficult, and at temperatures below approximately 700° C essentially no excess Mg^{++} is tolerated.

The system $CaCO_3$–$MnCO_3$ can perhaps be looked upon as a lower-temperature "model" of the $CaCO_3$–$MgCO_3$ system. Kutnahorite, $CaMn(CO_3)_2$, the dolomite equivalent in this system, can be disordered to the calcite-type structure; the disorder is easily quenched in and observed in single-crystal X-ray diffraction photographs (Goldsmith, 1957, and unpublished data of Goldsmith and Graf). The substitutional disorder of Ca and Mn is observed to begin in single crystals of natural kutnahorite at 450° C. The phase diagram (fig. 2) indicates that the kutnahorite limb of the solvus approaches the ideal kutnahorite composition at 450° C, a configuration that is very probably controlled by ordering at and below this temperature. The asymmetry of the system $CaCO_3$–$MgCO_3$ is also apparent in $CaCO_3$–$MnCO_3$, and in the latter system only the solvus in the Mn-rich half of the diagram has been realized experimentally. Thus the solvus that was "hypothetically closed" at about 1000° C in the Ca–Mg system is in fact closed in the Ca–Mn system, and at a temperature below 450° C. Excess $MnCO_3$ begins to be tolerated in kutnahorite only above 450° C, whereas at this temperature complete solid solution exists between calcite and the kutnahorite composition. Natural materials from Franklin, N. J.,[7] show some order present in kutnahorites with approximately 10 per cent excess $CaCO_3$ in their structure (Goldsmith, unpublished data).

It has been stated that all evidence points against the existence of a dolomite-like compound with the composition $CaFe(CO_3)_2$. The *composition* $CaFe(CO_3)_2$ can well exist in the proper P_{CO_2}–T range, even though an ordered counterpart is not stable at lower temperatures. $CaFe(CO_3)_2$ as a disordered calcite-type structure at elevated temperatures would then be analogous to $CaMn(CO_3)_2$ in the temperature range

[7] Kindly supplied by Professor Clifford Frondel.

in which it is disordered. At lower temperatures $CaFe(CO_3)_2$ would break up into two phases, one rich in calcite, the other rich in siderite, while with equilibrium cooling $CaMn(CO_3)_2$ would merely develop an ordered structure, kutnahorite.

More complex compositions

There are no published data on equilibrium syntheses of dolomite structures containing more than two cations. The solid-solubility relations of Fe relative to Mg in ankerite are unknown, but many moderate- and low-temperature natural dolomites contain large amounts of Fe in the Mg position. The sedimentary ankerites [8] present an interesting problem, and indirect methods such as calorimetry may be necessary to get information on the equilibrium relations at low temperatures.

The Mn-containing dolomites are in a structural sense analogous to the ankerites. Above approximately 750° C, a complete series extends between $CaMg(CO_3)_2$ and $CaMn(CO_3)_2$ (unpublished data of Graf and Goldsmith) and ordering reflections are observed in X-ray powder patterns of compositions containing more than approximately 50 mole per cent dolomite. At lower temperatures the relations become complex, and two or more phases replace the single phase stable at the higher temperatures. It is probable that these compositions leave the binary join, but additional work is necessary to clarify the relations. The replacement of Mg by Mn in this series is not nearly as extensive at low temperatures as the Fe for Mg replacement in ankerite.

Some Further Comments on the Crystallization of Carbonates as Related to Their Crystal Chemistry

A voluminous literature has accumulated on what is frequently referred to as "the dolomite problem." The crux of the problem has to do with the precipitation, or *failure* of precipitation, of the compound dolomite. A second problem, although not necessarily secondary in importance, is how dolomite may be later formed by means other than direct precipitation. The preponderance of evidence indicates that the dolomite in most sediments is not the primary crystalline phase.

To the best of my knowledge, dolomite has never been directly pre-

[8] The term ankerite is used throughout in an intentionally loose fashion. In general, it refers to dolomite with more than, say, 20 per cent of the Mg positions filled by Fe. The low-Fe materials can be called ankeritic dolomites or ferroan dolomites. This is a less restricted definition than that given by Palache, Berman, and Frondel (1951).

cipitated in the laboratory from solutions at room temperatures. Graf and Goldsmith (1956) describe a series of experiments in which dolomite was ultimately produced from a variety of starting materials, but hydrothermal treatment at somewhat elevated temperatures was necessary to produce ordered dolomite in reasonable laboratory times. The temperature and time necessary depend on the nature of the starting materials, but the more reactive gel-like carbonate precipitates produced a rather good dolomite, as inferred from the X-ray diffraction patterns, in several weeks at 200° C. At lower temperatures, or in shorter runs, the finely crystalline precipitates show weakened ordering reflections in powder diffraction patterns, and at still lower temperatures or shorter times they show no visible ordering reflections. In addition, the dolomite-like materials without detectable cation order tend to be enriched in $CaCO_3$, commonly up to 10 mole per cent over the ideal 50 mole per cent composition. These dolomite-like materials, produced from various starting materials with significant variations in Mg concentration, are called protodolomites (Graf and Goldsmith, 1956), defined as single-phase rhombohedral carbonates which deviate from the composition of the dolomite that is stable in a given environment, or are imperfectly ordered, or both, but which would transform to dolomite if equilibrium were established.

Goldsmith (1953) has argued that the substances most difficult to crystallize are those in which there are two or more cations occupying nonequivalent positions in the structure, particularly if the cations are crystallochemically similar and occupy positions that do not greatly differ from each other in terms of crystal energy. It is easier to produce a random than an ordered array, and, indeed, several simple phases rather than a single ordered one. This is particularly true at low temperatures, where, once "wrong" positions are attained, there is insufficient thermal energy to move atoms to the stable positions of lower energy. In short, the substances stable under any set of conditions are not necessarily the substances that crystallize. It has been suggested by Graf and Goldsmith (1956) that the "complex" nature of the dolomite structure is thus responsible for the failure of dolomite to precipitate readily as a primary phase.

In contrast to the behavior of dolomite and kutnahorite (Graf and Goldsmith, 1956, and unpublished data), the single-cation carbonates crystallize readily and well, even at low temperatures. It is important to note that at elevated temperatures dolomite is formed with no difficulty even from relatively nonreactive starting products such as well crystallized calcite and magnesite (Graf and Goldsmith, 1955, 1956;

Harker and Tuttle, 1955*a* and *b*). At temperatures above approximately 500° C, reaction proceeds reasonably fast, even in the dry state, and at significantly lower temperatures in the presence of water. Thus there is no "dolomite problem" in metamorphic and hydrothermal rocks, and there would probably be none if sedimentary phenomena took place at higher temperatures than they do.

Goldsmith and Graf (1957*b*) cite the presence, particularly in Cretaceous and younger rocks, of dolomite fractions that deviate compositionally and structurally from the ideal compound. These substances are quite common, and occur not only in young rocks from numerous localities but also in rocks at least as old as the Ordovician. The material is typically either very finely divided so that it must be examined by X-ray powder diffraction, or it forms tiny rhombs in limestone that can be examined by either powder or single-crystal diffraction methods. These finely crystalline materials that deviate from ideal dolomite all tend to have three characteristics in common:

1. Excess $CaCO_3$ in their structure. The most Ca-rich yet observed contain approximately 55 mole per cent $CaCO_3$.
2. Weakening of the Ca–Mg ordering reflections relative to the neighboring reflections, produced at least in part by the structural deviation accompanying the excess Ca.
3. The X-ray reflections from planes normal to the *c* axis or with a strong *c*-axis contribution tend to be broad and diffuse, in contrast to the reflections from planes with little or no *c*-axis contribution (see also Graf et al., 1957). This feature is a consequence of an abnormal basal-plane sequence that would not be present in the perfectly ordered dolomite structure. The diffuseness is particularly noticeable in the higher-order reflections. In general, all reflections observed on single-crystal photographs tend to be somewhat less sharp than those produced by cleavage fragments of equivalent size from larger crystals of normal dolomite.

These three features are also characteristic of the synthetic protodolomites. The natural materials range in "degree of perfection" from stoichiometric dolomite showing only sharp X-ray reflections to materials that vary only in degree but not in kind from synthetic protodolomite. It is apparent that, in the early or developmental stages, many low-temperature dolomites go through the poorly organized state observed in the laboratory syntheses. These materials are metastable with respect to normal dolomite, and are an indication of the difficulty with which this ordered compound is crystallized at sedimentary temperatures.

References

Boeke, H. E. 1912. Die Schmelzerscheinungen und die umkehrbare Umwandlung des Calciumcarbonats, *Neues Jahrb. Mineral. Geol., I,* 91–121.

Bragg, W. L. 1937. *Atomic Structure of Minerals,* Cornell University Press, Ithaca, New York.

Bridgman, P. W. 1939. The high pressure behavior of miscellaneous materials, *Am. J. Sci., 237,* 7–18.

Brooks, R., L. M. Clark, and E. F. Thurston. 1950. Calcium carbonate and its hydrates, *Phil. Trans. Roy. Soc. London, 243A,* 145–167.

Chave, K. E. 1954. Aspects of the biogeochemistry of magnesium, 1, Calcareous marine organisms, *J. Geol., 62,* 266–283.

Clark, S. P. 1957. A note on calcite–aragonite equilibrium, *Am. Mineralogist, 42,* 564–566.

Coomaraswamy, A. K. 1902. The crystalline limestones of Ceylon, *Quart. J. Geol. Soc. London, 58,* 399–424.

Cork, J. M., and S. L. Gerhard. 1931. Crystal structure of the series of barium and strontium carbonates, *Am. Mineralogist, 16,* 71–77.

Faivre, R. 1944. Étude, par diffraction des rayons X et analyse dilatométrique des carbonates mixtes de calcium et de strontium et de leurs transformation, *Compt. rend., 219,* 73.

Faivre, R. 1946. Étude par diffraction des rayons X des carbonates mixtes de calcium et de baryum, *Compt. rend., 222,* 227.

Frondel, C., and L. H. Bauer. 1955. Kutnahorite: a manganese dolomite, $CaMn(CO_3)_2$, *Am. Mineralogist, 40,* 748–760.

Goldschmidt, V. M. (edited by Alex Muir). 1954. *Geochemistry,* Clarendon Press, Oxford.

Goldsmith, J. R. 1953. A "simplexity principle" and its relation to "ease" of crystallization, *J. Geol., 61,* 439–451.

Goldsmith, J. R. 1956. Exsolution of dolomite from calcite (Abstract), *Bull. Geol. Soc. Am., 67,* 1699.

Goldsmith, J. R. 1957. Exsolution of ordered rhombohedral carbonates in the systems $CaCO_3$–$MgCO_3$ and $CaCO_3$–$MnCO_3$ (Abstract), *Acta Cryst., 10,* 762.

Goldsmith, J. R., and D. L. Graf. 1957*a*. The system CaO–MnO–CO_2: solid-solution and decomposition relations, *Geochim. et Cosmochim. Acta, 11,* 310–334.

Goldsmith, J. R., and D. L. Graf. 1957*b*. Structural and compositional variation in some natural dolomites (Abstract), *Bull. Geol. Soc. Am., 68,* 1735–1736.

Goldsmith, J. R., and D. L. Graf. 1958. Relation between lattice constants and composition of the Ca–Mg carbonates, *Am. Mineralogist, 43,* 84–101.

Goldsmith, J. R., D. L. Graf, and O. I. Joensuu. 1955. The occurrence of magnesian calcites in nature, *Geochim. et Cosmochim. Acta, 7,* 212–230.

Graf, D. L., C. R. Blyth, and R. S. Stemmler. 1957. Mixed layer effects in the rhombohedral carbonates (Abstract), *Bull. Geol. Soc. Am., 68,* 1737–1738.

Graf, D. L., and J. R. Goldsmith. 1955. Dolomite–magnesian calcite relations at elevated temperatures and CO_2 pressures, *Geochim. et Cosmochim. Acta, 7,* 109–128.

Graf, D. L., and J. R. Goldsmith. 1956. Some hydrothermal syntheses of dolomite and protodolomite, *J. Geol., 64,* 173–186.

Graf, D. L., and J. R. Goldsmith. 1958. The solid solubility of $MgCO_3$ in $CaCO_3$: a revision, *Geochim. et Cosmochim. Acta, 13,* 218–219.

Graf, D. L., and J. E. Lamar. 1955. Properties of calcium and magnesium carbonates and their bearing on some uses of carbonate rocks, *Econ. Geol., 50th Anniv. Vol.,* pp. 639–713.

Harker, R. I., and J. J. Hutta. 1956. The stability of smithsonite, *Econ. Geol., 51,* 375–381.

Harker, R. I., and O. F. Tuttle. 1955*a*. Studies in the system $CaO-MgO-CO_2$, I, The thermal dissociation of calcite, dolomite, and magnesite, *Am. J. Sci., 253,* 209–224.

Harker, R. I., and O. F. Tuttle. 1955*b*. Studies in the system $CaO-MgO-CO_2$, II, Limits of solid solution along the binary join $CaCO_3$–$MgCO_3$, *Am. J. Sci., 253,* 274–282.

Jamieson, J. C. 1953. Phase equilibrium in the system calcite–aragonite, *J. Chem. Phys., 21,* 1385–1390.

Jamieson, J. C. 1957. Introductory studies of high-pressure polymorphism to 24,000 bars by X-ray diffraction with some comments on calcite II, *J. Geol., 65,* 334–343.

Johnson, J., H. E. Merwin, and E. D. Williamson. 1916. The several forms of calcium carbonate, *Am. J. Sci.,* 4th ser., *41,* 473–513.

Kallweit, H. 1949. Mischkristalle des Systems $CaCO_3$–$SrCO_3$, mit der Emaniermethode untersucht, *Z. Naturforsch., 4A,* 140–149.

Lander, J. J. 1949. Polymorphism and anion rotational disorder in the alkaline earth carbonates, *J. Chem. Phys., 17,* 892–901.

MacDonald, G. F. 1956. Experimental determination of calcite–aragonite equilibrium relations at elevated temperatures and pressures, *Am. Mineralogist, 41,* 744–756.

Palache, C., H. Berman, and C. Frondel. 1951. *Dana's System of Mineralogy,* vol. 2, 7th ed., John Wiley & Sons, New York.

Rosenberg, P. E., and R. I. Harker. 1956. Studies in the system $CaCO_3$–$MgCO_3$–$FeCO_3$, I, Limits of solid solution along the binary join, $CaCO_3$–$FeCO_3$ (Abstract), *Bull. Geol. Soc. Am., 67* (pt. 2), 1728.

Spotts, J. H. 1952. X-ray studies and differential thermal analysis of some coastal limestones and associated carbonates of Western Australia, submitted to the University of Western Australia as M.S. thesis, 23 pp.

Weeks, W. F. 1956. A thermochemical study of equilibrium relations during metamorphism of siliceous carbonate rocks, *J. Geol., 64,* 245–270.

Diffraction Effects of Short-Range Ordering in Layered Sequences

FELIX CHAYES

Geophysical Laboratory
Carnegie Institution of Washington

The progress of experimental petrology in the past decade has placed increasing emphasis on subsolidus reactions, and in much of this work interest centers on transitions in which the initial and final forms differ slightly in certain rather minor physical properties but are evidently identical in chemical composition. Usually the differences are so subtle that they can be detected only by X-ray diffraction techniques, and it often happens that the passage from one set of properties to the other is a continuous or nearly continuous function of temperature. In solid solutions this temperature dependence is not infrequently further complicated by quite similar (or opposed) composition effects.

In numerous recent studies relations of this type either have seriously complicated the interpretation of experimental results or have themselves been among the major objects of investigation. As examples we may cite the work of MacKenzie (1954) and of Goldsmith and Laves (1954*a*, *b*) on potassium feldspar, of Tuttle and Bowen (1950), Laves and Chaisson (1950), and MacKenzie (1952, 1957) on albite and sodium-rich feldspar, of Laves and Goldsmith (1954*a*, *b*) on calcic plagioclase and anorthite, of Gay (1956) and of Gay and Bown (1956) on intermediate plagioclases, of Yoder and Eugster (1954, 1955) and Smith and Yoder (1956) on mica, of Yoder (1952) on the relation between clinochlore and aluminous serpentine, of Atlas (1952) on proto- and clino-enstatite, of Smith and Tuttle (1957) on kalsilite, of Miyashiro and Iiyama (1954) on cordierite and indialite, and of Graf and Goldsmith (1955, 1956) on dolomite. In some compounds peak separations known to vary systematically with composition were found to be temperature-sensitive as well. That the propriety of using such separations for determinative purposes hinges on satisfactory knowledge of the "thermal state" of the material in question has been pointed out by Smith and MacKenzie (1955), by Smith (1956), and by J. R. Smith and Yoder (1956).

The catalogue is by no means complete, and it now seems a fairly safe prediction that transitions of this type will be encountered in almost any reasonably detailed study of subsolidus relations in a silicate system. Their importance for petrology is too obvious to require more than passing note; aside from the fact that they are likely to turn up almost anywhere, every well understood example is a potential geothermometer.

These gradual transitions between forms which are not very different from each other are now often interpreted as ordering effects, the ordered form being regarded as stable at low and the disordered form at high temperatures. This is an inherently reasonable argument, but it is important to realize that the evidence for it is often less than impeccable. As already noted, physical differences between the forms are minor, and the experimental products are frequently of such nature that their differentiation is based entirely on powder diffraction patterns. Where single crystals can be obtained it may happen that weak or poorly resolved nodes occur in the patterns of one form and are lacking in the patterns of the other. Sometimes these diffuse maxima occur in the natural form, can be dissipated by prolonged heating of the natural crystals, and are not observed in the synthetic product, whatever the temperature at which the synthesis is conducted. Taking advantage of the usual reservation about the relative ease of formation of stable and metastable forms, the observations are readily "explained" by supposing that the naturally occurring mineral is a low-temperature and the synthetic product a high-temperature form.

Our conviction that ordered forms are in general low-temperature forms rests ultimately on energy calculations, usually made on very simple systems, for differing frequencies of "right pairs" among "nearest neighbors." From this point of view the long-range periodicity that gives rise to the superlattice of crystallography is only a special—and not energetically differentiable—case of the short-range order of theoretical metallurgy and chemical physics. If the usual crystallographic explanation of "superlattice" reflections is the only correct one, the presence of such reflections is indeed evidence of the existence of short-range ordering, for the nearest-neighbor pairings of long- and short-range order are identical. The absence of such reflections, however, is then uninformative about the level of short-range ordering, and hence of nearest-neighbor energy relations between the ordered and allegedly disordered forms.

If, on the other hand, short-range ordering as such may generate subsidiary reflections, their presence need not be informative about long-range ordering and perhaps need not, as in practice it sometimes cannot, imply the existence of a truly periodic superlattice in direct space. The intermediate plagioclases afford perhaps the best known illustration of subsidiary reflection spacings which appear to be continuous functions of composition (Gay, 1956), a phenomenon difficult or impossible to reconcile with a direct-space superlattice. The relation here is essentially linear, and may be put in the form $\delta = ax + b$, where δ is the displacement of the reflection from the nearest principal layer line and x is the composition as obtained from chemical analysis. It is customary to record x as mole per cent An (or Ab). For the c-axis projections of the subsidiary reflections, however, Chayes (in Abelson, 1957) has pointed out that if x is given as the proportion of tetrahedral sites occupied by Al ($\frac{1}{4}$ in albite, $\frac{1}{2}$ in anorthite), the slope of the regression equation does not differ significantly from unity and the intercept does not differ significantly from zero. The data are thus compatible with the notion that the underlying relation is simply $\delta_c = x$. This could be a mere coincidence, of course, but the possibility is so remote that it is natural to wonder whether there might be some more satisfying explanation.

Blandly ignoring the difficulty that makes the displacement uninterpretable by the conventional rules, we may suppose that a "separation" of δ_c in the reciprocal lattice implies the existence, in direct space, of some kind of repeat $1/\delta_c$ times as large as the unit translation along c. But, if $\delta_c = x$, then clearly $\delta_c^{-1} = x^{-1}$, and we must next wonder what physical meaning in direct space might attach to the reciprocal of the proportion of tetrahedral sites occupied by Al. The tetrahedral sites *not* occupied by Al are taken by Si, and, anticipating a little, it may be shown that x^{-1} is the average run length of Si, or the average number of successive tetrahedral sites occupied by Si, *on the assumption that the distribution of Al and Si over the tetrahedral sites is completely random.*[1]

The δ_c reflections ordinarily occur as doublets equidistant, to the error of measurement, from a point midway between the principal layer lines. As we have seen, the proportion of tetrahedral sites oc-

[1] In the symbols adopted below, let α be the proportion Al/(Al + Si). Then the expected number of unbroken runs of Si of all lengths is $N\alpha\beta$, the number of Si's is $N\beta$, and the average run length of Si is $N\beta/N\alpha\beta = \alpha^{-1}$.

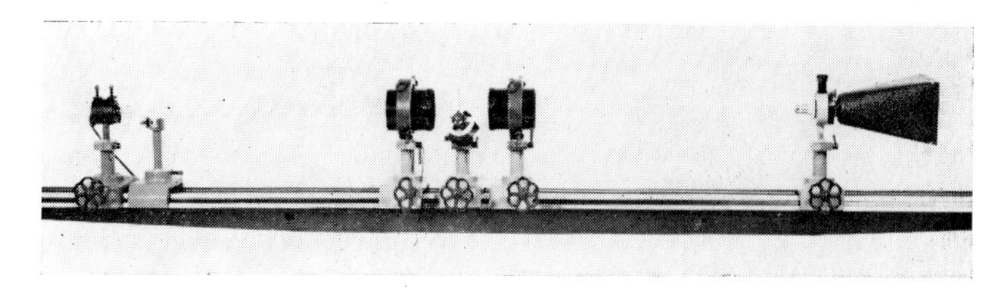

Fig. 1. Optical diffractometer. From *Carnegie Institution of Washington Year Book 57.*

cupied by Al estimates rather nicely the distance of either member of the pair from the nearer of the two layer lines between which it lies. The quantity $(1-x)$ must then estimate the distance of either member from the farther of the two layer lines, and it may also be shown that the quantity $(1-x)^{-1}$ is the average run length of Al, again on the assumption that Al and Si are randomly distributed among the tetrahedral sites.

The simplicity and strength of this relation between spacing and composition make it difficult to dismiss as accidental, yet the runs and run lengths we have been discussing have little or nothing to do with the periodicity of the superlattice of metallurgical and mineralogical crystallography. They are, however, intimately related to the pairing frequencies that form the basis of short-range ordering, as treated in theoretical metallurgy and chemical physics. The question whether specific and observable diffraction effects may be associated with disorder and varying levels of short-range order seems to have received very little attention from mineralogists.[2]

The purpose of this note is to present experimental evidence bearing on the relation between short-range ordering and diffraction in layered sequences, certainly the simplest case for experimental investigation. The experiments are performed with light of visible wavelength, and two rather distinct types of modeling are involved. The first is well known; the optical diffractometer used for the work is essentially a small version of the device described by Taylor, Hinde, and Lipson (1951). The instrument itself is shown in figure 1, and the relation between optical components and model equivalents is indicated in figure 2.

[2] It has, however, been examined in considerable detail by metallurgists; see, for instance, the excellent review by Guttman, in Seitz and Turnbull (1956), pp. 145–223.

The need for the second type of modeling arises in the design of the masks, which, together with the collecting lens, provide the optical analogues of crystals. The masks are to be arrays of layers characterized by order, disorder, or intermediate levels of ordering, where these terms connote the pairing frequencies assigned them in theoretical discussions of short-range ordering, rather than the superperiodicity of X-ray crystallography. The content of the masks is critical, and the principles upon which their design is based will no doubt be unfamiliar to many readers. The relation between pairing frequencies and run-length distributions used in the construction of the masks is therefore described in some detail.

Right Pairs, Wrong Pairs, and Runs

In the sequence

$$AAABABBAABAAAABBB$$

there are 8 runs, 4 in A, 4 in B. The sequence opens with a run of length 3 in A; this is followed by a run of length 1 in B, and so on. The nearest-neighbor pairings, upon which the theory of short-range ordering is based, are obviously governed by the number of runs. In the usual terminology, AA and BB are "wrong pairs," AB (or BA) is a "right pair." Clearly right pairs form only (and always) by the juxtaposition of the last element in one run with the first element in the next. If we are given the length of an array (N), the number of A's it contains (N_A), and the number of runs among which these are

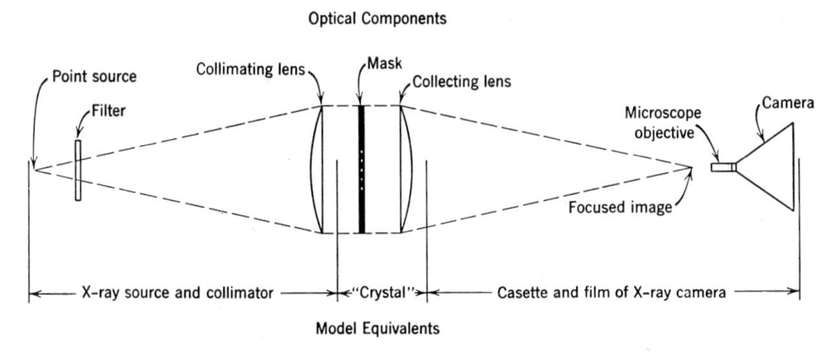

Fig. 2. Schematic diagram of optical diffractometer. *From C. I. W. Year Book 57.*

distributed (d), we can immediately count the numbers of right and wrong pairs, and so characterize the order of the array.

Alternatively, if we are given N and N_A we can vary the level of ordering by varying d in the interval $1 \leqq d \leqq N_A$, where $N_A \leqq N_B$.[3] If $d = 1$, the array is dissociated, all the A's occur in a single run at either the beginning or the end of the sequence, there are $(N_A - 1)$ wrong pairs in A, and only one right pair. If, on the other hand, $d = N_A$, all the runs of A are of length 1 and there are no wrong pairs in A; the array is then said to be at perfect short-range order.

We take as our criterion of complete disorder, a condition intermediate between dissociation and short-range order, the relative pair frequencies which would be expected if the probability that a site in the sequence is occupied by an A, the same for all sites, is simply $\alpha = N_A/N$. The probability that any site chosen at random is occupied by an A and that its nearest neighbor contains a B is then $\alpha(1 - \alpha) = \alpha\beta$. Since this probability is the same for all sites, the expected number of pairs in which the first site is an A and the second a B is simply $N\alpha\beta$. This can occur only if the first site chosen contains the last element of a run of A's, so the expected number of runs of A, $E(d)$, is also $N\alpha\beta$. Although this is strictly an expected value and subject to sampling variance, we shall regard it as an arbitrary constant defining pair frequencies at complete disorder.

Distribution of Run Lengths

If n items are randomly distributed among r cells, the probability that any cell contains exactly k items is [4]

$$q_k = \binom{n + r - k - 2}{r - 2} \div \binom{n + r - 1}{r - 1} \tag{1}$$

This probability being the same for all cells, the expected number of cells containing k items is

$$E(r_k) = rq_k \tag{2}$$

If $r = d$, the number of runs, we know that each run requires one item, so that the number of items to be randomly distributed is $n = (N_A - d)$ or $(N_B - d)$, whichever the case may be, and $k = (i - 1)$, where i is the run length. Making these substitutions in equation 1, if

[3] Throughout the discussion A designates the less abundant element.

[4] See W. Feller, *An Introduction to Probability Theory and Its Applications*, p. 59, prob. 7, John Wiley & Sons, New York, 1950.

we are given N, N_A, and d, the probabilities of runs of differing lengths in A and B become, for A,

$$q(a)_i = \binom{N_A - i - 1}{d - 2} \div \binom{N_A - 1}{d - 1} \tag{3a}$$

and for B,

$$q(b)_i = \binom{N_B - i - 1}{d - 2} \div \binom{N_B - 1}{d - 1} \tag{3b}$$

The expected numbers of runs of length i are then, from (2),

$$E(d_{Ai}) = dq(a)_i \tag{4a}$$

and

$$E(d_{Bi}) = dq(b)_i \tag{4b}$$

Writing $N_A = N\alpha$, $N_B = N\beta$, for the case of complete disorder we have

$$q(a)_i = \binom{N\alpha - i - 1}{N\alpha\beta - 2} \div \binom{N\alpha - 1}{N\alpha\beta - 1}$$

$$= \frac{N\alpha\beta - 1}{N\alpha - 1} \cdot \frac{N\alpha^2}{N\alpha - 2} \cdot \frac{N\alpha^2 - 1}{N\alpha - 3} \cdots \frac{N\alpha^2 - i + 2}{N\alpha - i} \tag{5}$$

Multiplying each term by $(1/N)/(1/N)$ and allowing N to increase indefinitely,

$$\lim_{N \to \infty} q(a)_i = \beta\alpha^{i-1} \tag{6}$$

Since $d = N\alpha\beta$, the expected number of runs of length i in A is

$$E(d_{Ai}) \cong N\beta^2\alpha^i \tag{7a}$$

a well known large-sample approximation.[5] For B, similarly,

$$E(d_{Bi}) \cong N\alpha^2\beta^i \tag{7b}$$

At complete short-range order all the A's are in right pairs, a situation which can occur only when $d = N\alpha$, so that all runs in A are of length 1 and $N\alpha$ B's are assigned, one to each intervening run. There are still $N(\beta - \alpha)$ B's to be distributed randomly among these $N\alpha$ intervening runs, so that

$$q(b)_i = \binom{N\beta - i - 1}{N\alpha - 2} \div \binom{N\beta - 1}{N\alpha - 1} \tag{8}$$

[5] See, for instance, Hald (1952), p. 344.

Expanding and taking the limit as before, we have

$$\lim_{N\to\infty} q(b)_i = \frac{\alpha}{\beta}\left(\frac{1-2\alpha}{\beta}\right)^{i-1} \tag{9}$$

and substituting (9) in (4*b*), with $d = N\alpha$,

$$E(d_{Bi}) \cong N\alpha^2\beta^{-i}(1-2\alpha)^{i-1} \tag{10}$$

Equations 7 and 10 are included here largely to permit comparison with previous work (Chayes, in Abelson, 1957), in which (7) was used without derivation. They are no more convenient to calculate than the exact solution, which must be used in any event for values of d other than those of the limiting cases. The design of an experimental mask requires first of all a calculation of run frequencies from (4), (7), or (10).

Design of a Random Sequence of Fixed Composition and Order

The use of expected numbers of runs in the design of a mask is best illustrated by a practical example. A certain amount of calculation and tabulation is unavoidable, but to keep it within reasonable limits we shall plan a short mask characterized by perfect short-range order, so that only the B runs vary in length. Suppose we are given that $N = 100$, $\alpha = 2/5$, and, since the short-range order is to be perfect, $d = N\alpha = 40$. From (4*b*) we have

$$\begin{aligned} E(d_{Bi}) &= N\alpha\left[\binom{N\beta - i - 1}{N\alpha - 2} \div \binom{N\beta - 1}{N\alpha - 1}\right] \\ &= 40\left[\binom{59-i}{38} \div \binom{59}{39}\right] \\ &= 40 \cdot \frac{39}{59} \cdot \frac{20}{58} \cdot \frac{19}{57} \cdot \frac{18}{56} \cdot \frac{17}{55} \cdot \frac{16}{54} \cdots \end{aligned} \tag{11}$$

The expected number of runs of length 1 is then $(40)\left(\frac{39}{59}\right)$, of length 2, $(40)\left(\frac{39}{59}\right)\left(\frac{20}{58}\right)$, of length 3, $(40)\left(\frac{39}{59}\right)\left(\frac{20}{58}\right)\left(\frac{19}{57}\right)$, and so on. In table 1 the calculated expectations are shown in column 2 and the resulting frequency distribution of B's in column 3. Since in any experimental mask the number of runs of each length must be integral, it is necessary to use rounded values. These and the frequency distribution of B's ob-

TABLE 1. Calculated and Rounded Run Frequencies for $N = 100, N_A = d = 40$

	Calculated		Rounded	
i	$f(i)$	$if(i)$	$f(i)$	$if(i)$
1	26.44	26.44	26	26
2	9.12	18.24	9	18
3	3.04	9.12	3	9
4	1.00	4.00	1	4
5	0.30	1.50	1 *	5
Σ	39.90	59.30	40	62

* Rounding *up* of the first $f(i) < 0.5$ usually gives optimum values for $\Sigma f(i)$ and $\Sigma if(i)$, and I have adopted it as a convention in mask design. It is not beyond reproach, and other procedures are equally defensible; in general, totals for rounded-run (and run-length) frequencies are not exact.

tained from them are given in columns 4 and 5. The calculated cumulative frequency of B's is 59.3; that from the rounded run frequencies, 62. The excess of 2 over the initial value of 60 is a measure of the discrepancy between experimental model and "parent." Its absolute value increases as the quantity $(\beta - \alpha)$ increases, and decreases rapidly with increase in N. For $N = 200$, $N_B = 120$, for instance, it happens to vanish exactly.

The numbers of runs of different lengths to be included in the sequence are shown in the next to last column of the table, and it is now necessary—or, at any rate, highly desirable—to randomize the order in which they appear. This is readily accomplished in the following fashion.

The run lengths are listed individually in any arbitrary order; to each is assigned a random number chosen in some systematic fashion from an appropriate table; these numbers are assigned ranks in order of increasing size; and the position of a run in the sequence is determined by the rank of the random number assigned to it. Table 2 illustrates the procedure.

The first B run of the sequence would have the length shown to the left of the smallest random number of the table, the second that opposite the next larger one, and so on. The sequence thus starts

$$ABABABBABBBABABABABB\cdots$$

TABLE 2. Randomizing the Run Sequence of Table 1

Run Length	Random No.	Rank	Run Length	Random No.	Rank
1	77012	35	1	81237	35
1	99688	40	1	10679	6
1	20302	11	1	58973	28
1	87101	38	1	49234	25
1	81969	36	1	36185	16
1	34807	15	1	02697	2
1	80291	34	2	55830	26
1	00849	1	2	23957	12
1	34082	14	2	06343	3
1	48144	23	2	39485	19
1	71923	30	2	48876	24
1	97766	39	2	13551	8
1	18801	10	2	74692	31
1	09013	5	2	29131	13
1	13048	7	2	38528	18
1	41789	20	3	45021	22
1	58001	27	3	06474	4
1	75657	32	3	83575	37
1	59445	29	4	17007	9
1	44889	21	5	37606	17

For anything less than perfect short-range ordering it is necessary to perform similar calculations for A as well as B. For any assigned values of N, α, and d, the run frequencies (table 1) need be calculated only once. For each random sequence exhibiting the pairing frequencies generated by these constants, however, the ranking process summarized in table 2 must be repeated.

The purpose of the calculation is to ensure that the pairing frequencies and run-length distribution in a relatively short sequence will be as close as possible to those that would be found in a very much longer sequence of the same composition and level of ordering. Since the expected run frequencies are not integral the agreement cannot be exact. For any given values of N, α, and d, however, this procedure will generate as good agreement as can be obtained; if better agreement is essential the only alternative is to enlarge N.

For the limiting cases of complete disorder and short-range order it would be possible to use a simple random sampling scheme, but this has the effect of making both composition and relative pairing frequencies into random variables, and for present purposes we have no interest in the sampling variance of either. It is in fact a very real advantage to eliminate variations of this kind from an experimental situation already sufficiently complex.

Generation of Diffraction Masks

The instrument used for this purpose, shown in figure 3, is an adaptation of one described by Willis (1957). Essentially a contact printer in which the photographic element, an 8 by 10 inch plate, may be subjected to considerable lateral dispacement between exposures, it differs from the Willis instrument chiefly in being sufficiently light-tight so that it can be loaded, used, and unloaded in full room light.

On the stage of a large dividing engine (*A*), a smaller one (*B*) is mounted, the threads of the two being normal to each other. The stage of the smaller engine carries a trough (*C*) in which the plateholder (*D*) rides. The light box (*E*) is mounted rigidly to the frame of the larger dividing engine, and from it a large light shield (*F*) is spring-loaded against the top of the track which carries the plateholder. From inside the light box a rectangular shoe containing the template is spring-loaded, through a recess in the light shield, against the plate cover.

Fig. 3. Photographic mask generator. For explanation of letter symbols see text. *From C. I. W. Year Book 57.*

Two 100-watt projection bulbs, mounted in the removable top of the light box (G), are activated by the switch of an exposure timer (H).

The loaded plateholder is slid into its track; the shoe containing the template is next lowered through the light shield and brought to rest squarely on the plate cover. The cover of the light box is put in place, making the entire assembly light-tight. Finally, the plate cover is withdrawn, and the template, which is resting on it, drops gently onto the plate.

The template now in use is simply a brass strip containing a row of 60 holes of 0.5-mm diameter, spaced 3 mm apart, parallel to the screw of the upper dividing engine. Each exposure thus generates a row of "scatterers" which serves as a two-dimensional projection, or model, of a layer in a layered structure. The distance between layers is obtained by translation of the plate with the large dividing engine; this interval, being constant in the problem now under consideration, is established by means of a detent, so that the large drum need be read only as a check. Each exposure is followed by a rotation of the large drum; the cross engine, however, is reset only when two successive layers are separated by an offset or "mistake." After a little practice, a mask of 200 layers can be completed in a little less than 1 hour of machine time.

If of suitable quality, the original pattern is reduced by a linear factor of not less than 8. If an eightfold reduction is used, the distance between rows in the finished mask is ⅛ mm, and the viewing assembly shown in figure 1 will contain two full orders of the diffraction pattern. The photographic work has so far been done exclusively on glass, 8 by 10 Kodalith plates for the original and high-contrast Eastman lantern slides for the reductions.

Some Experimental Results

The masks shown in figure 4 were constructed in the fashion just described. In each mask the number of rows (i.e., "layers") is 192, and the ratio $N_A:N_B$ is 1:2. In 4*a* the array is disordered; in 4*b* the short-range ordering is perfect. For any assigned values of N_A and N, the numbers of runs (of both elements) for these two levels of ordering differ by an amount

$$\begin{aligned}\Delta d &= 2(d_{\text{order}} - d_{\text{disorder}}) \\ &= 2\left(N_A - \frac{(N_A)(N_B)}{N}\right)\end{aligned} \tag{12}$$

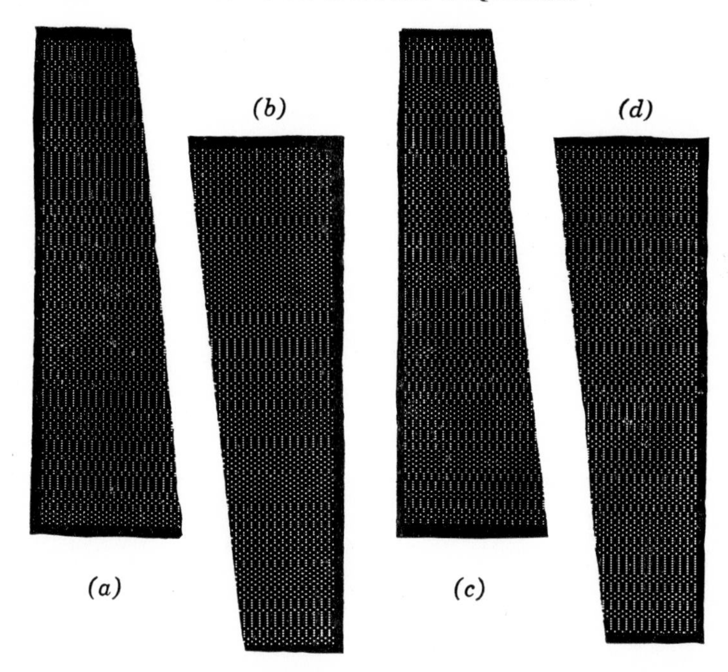

Fig. 4. Sections of masks showing varying degrees of disorder. (In the complete masks each row contains 60 holes.) In all cases $N = 192$, $N_A = 64$. (*a*) complete disorder, (*b*) complete short-range order, (*c*) ¼ short-range order, (*d*) ½ short-range order.

and for $N = 192$, $N_A = 64$, $\Delta d = 42.67$. The ordered array contains 128 runs, the disordered one 85.3, a value rounded to 86 in practice, so that there will be equal numbers of runs of each kind. Arrays constructed for $86 < d < 128$ will exhibit nearest-neighbor pairings characteristic of intermediate levels of ordering. Two such are shown in figure 4; 4*c* contains 96 and 4*d* 106 runs. The first is very nearly ¼ and the second very nearly ½ the "distance" from disorder to short-range order. Figure 5 contains the transform of each mask shown in figure 4.

There is no question that the limiting cases of complete disorder (5*a*) and complete short-range order (5*b*) differ radically. The strong doublet midway between the principal layer lines for h odd is a characteristic and readily reproducible property of short-range ordered arrays; it is lacking in disordered arrays except possibly when $N_A = N_B$.

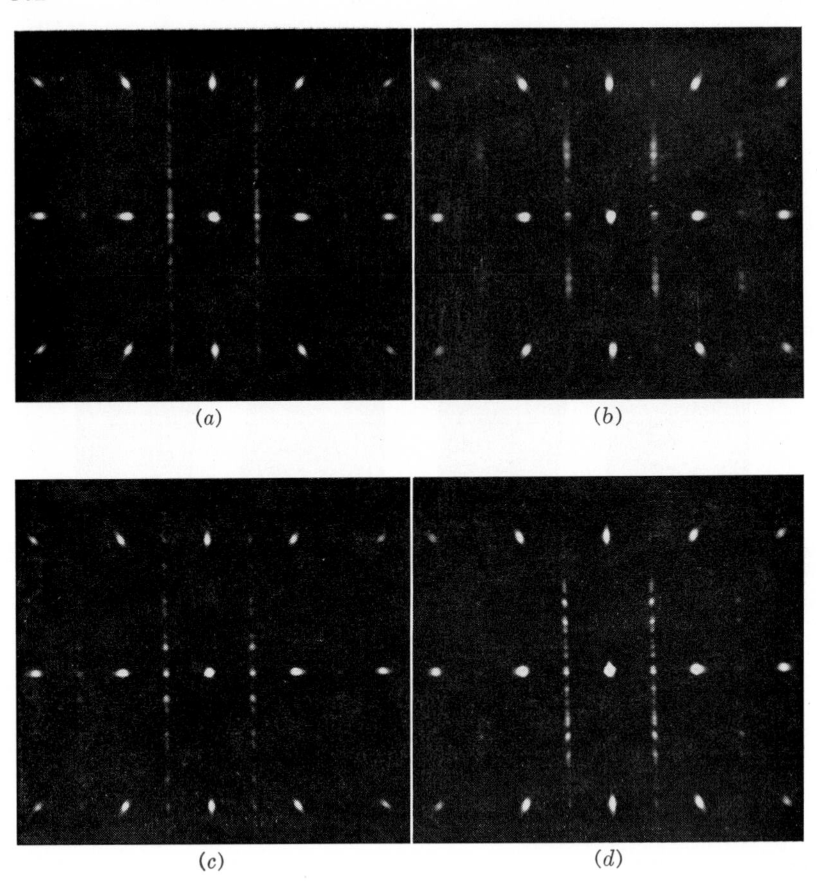

Fig. 5. Diffraction patterns of masks shown in figure 4 (letter symbols as in fig. 4).

a ratio not yet studied in detail.[6] The long-range ordered array, or superlattice, for $N_B = 2N_A$ would also contain no such doublet, Rather, it would have strong, sharp reflections at $k = N/3$, $2N/3$, in which regions the short-range ordered array yields only a very weak doublet lost at the scale of reproduction used here. Note, however, that in the transform of the *dis*ordered array, $N/3$ and $2N/3$ are the centers of fairly well defined doublets. Finally, in all four transforms there is a strong single reflection at (1, 0), on the principal layer line.

[6] Even here, according to theory (see A. J. C. Wilson, *X-Ray Optics,* pp. 45–59) one would not expect it to occur.

In the transform of a 2:1 superlattice this reflection would be much weaker than the $N/3$ and $2N/3$ nodes.

Figures 5*c* and 5*d* differ both from each other and from the limiting cases already described. The central doublet characteristic of short-range order makes its appearance in the less ordered of the two (4*c*), and its place is taken by what appears to be a single central node in the more ordered (4*d*). The "singleness" of this node is illusory, however, as is the "doubleness" of the others. The intensity spectrum along the diffuse streaks in all four transforms is exceedingly complex, and cannot be completely resolved in an instrument as small as that shown in figure 1.

At a mask length of about 200 layers the diffraction patterns so far obtained seem to be reasonably stable and reproducible. In a real crystal of any size, however, we would almost certainly be concerned with much longer sequences, and accordingly a considerable increase in the length of the experimental masks would be desirable.

Such an increase could probably be obtained by refinement and extension of the techniques already described, but the process would be time-consuming and the probability of failure, or, at any rate, of insufficient success, is high. If high-speed digital calculation can be substituted for optical experimentation, however, the only practical limitation on "mask" length is the amount of machine time that can be afforded. Such a substitution is now in process: the general form of the calculation and the more interesting of the preliminary results so far available are discussed in the next section.

Calculation of $I_{(1k)}$ for a Layered Sequence with "Stacking Faults"

From a mask, the one shown in figure 4*b*, for instance, we wish to calculate the intensity at any point along one of the diffuse streaks (h odd) in the transform (fig. 5*b*). We note that there is a true repeat along the horizontal axis (i.e., the holes are regularly spaced in each row or layer), but that normal to this direction there is no repeat. Put in another way, the unit translation is equal to the distance between holes in the direction of the rows (x) and to the length of the mask normal to this direction (y). Since the rows are of equal scattering power and differ only in registry, the relative intensity of the diffracted beam at any point in the transform is

$$\begin{aligned} I_{(hk)} &= (\Sigma e^{2\pi i(hx+ky)})^2 \\ &= (\Sigma \sin 2\pi(hx + ky))^2 + (\Sigma \cos 2\pi(hx + ky))^2 \end{aligned} \tag{13}$$

The transforms (fig. 5) indicate that visible diffuse scatter occurs only for h odd; in addition, it appears to be identical for all odd h's, except for fall-off. It is therefore necessary to sum (13) only for $h = 1$. Now the x coordinate of the first point in each row is either 0 or some fraction of the distance between points on a row, in the present case ½. The intensity of the diffracted beam of order ($1k$) is therefore

$$I_{(1k)} = (\Sigma e^{2\pi i(x_n + ky_n)})^2 \tag{14}$$

the summation extending over all x's and y's, where $x_n = 0$ or ½, and $y_n = (n - 1)/N$, n being the number of the row.

At the present writing, systematic calculation has barely begun, and only preliminary results are available. Perhaps the most interesting of these concern the relative intensities of the central doublets and (1, 0) reflections in figure 5*b*. On calculation, each half of the doublet turns out to contain no fewer than five strong maxima, separated by nearly complete extinctions. The intensity of the strongest is a little less than ½, and of the weakest a little more than ⅕, that of the (1, 0) reflection. Since the intensity of the (1, 0) reflection is ⅑ that of the undiffracted beam, the intensity contrast between the central doublet and the (0, 0) reflection is of the order 1/18 to 1/45. In a short-range ordered 2:1 sequence of $N = 999$ (instead of 192 as in fig. 4*b*), the relative intensities of (0, 0) and (1, 0) are unchanged and the ratio of the maximum intensity in the central doublet to that of the undiffracted beam, though much reduced, is certainly not less than 1/150. The spectrum is also much simplified. Now a sequence of 1000 layers would be a stack about 0.001 mm thick if the distances between layers were of the order of 10 Å, as in the micas, for instance. While further extension of the mask length will no doubt further reduce the intensity of the "non-Bragg" reflections, the range of intensities detectable in X-ray diffraction patterns of crystals is usually thought to be very much larger than 150.

There is thus at least a reasonable possibility that effects similar to those described here may indeed persist in the diffraction patterns of real crystals. This is at present no more than a possibility, but for the experimental petrologist it is a stimulating and perhaps a disturbing one, introducing new interpretive problems and perhaps assisting in the resolution of some old ones. Briefly, he may have to distinguish not only between "ordering" reflections and others, but also between at least two different kinds of ordering reflections.

References

Abelson, P. H. 1957. Annual Report of the Geophysical Laboratory, *Carnegie Inst. Wash. Year Book 56,* 151–156.

Atlas, L. 1952. The polymorphism of $MgSiO_3$ and solid-state equilibria in the system $MgSiO_3$-$CaMgSi_2O_6$, *J. Geol., 60,* 125–147.

Gay, P. 1956. The structure of the plagioclase feldspars, VI, Natural intermediate plagioclases, *Mineral. Mag., 31,* 21–40.

Gay, P., and M. S. Bown. 1956. The structure of the plagioclase feldspars, VII, The heat treatment of intermediate plagioclases, *Mineral. Mag., 31,* 306–313.

Goldsmith, J., and F. Laves. 1954*a*. The microcline-sanidine stability relations, *Geochim. et Cosmochim. Acta, 5,* 1–19.

Goldsmith, J., and F. Laves. 1954*b*. Potassium feldspars structurally intermediate between microcline and sanidine, *Geochim. et Cosmochim. Acta, 6,* 100–118.

Graf, D. L., and J. R. Goldsmith. 1955. Dolomite–magnesian calcite relations at elevated temperatures and CO_2 pressures, *Geochim. et Cosmochim. Acta, 7,* 109–128.

Graf, D. L., and J. R. Goldsmith. 1956. Some hydrothermal syntheses of dolomite and proto-dolomite, *J. Geol., 64,* 173–186.

Hald, A. 1952. *Statistical Theory with Engineering Applications,* John Wiley & Sons, New York.

Laves, F., and U. Chaisson. 1950. An X-ray investigation of the high-low albite relations, *J. Geol., 58,* 584–592.

Laves, F., and J. Goldsmith. 1954*a*. Long-range–short-range order in calcic plagioclases as a continuous and reversible function of temperature, *Acta Cryst., 7,* 465–472.

Laves, F., and J. Goldsmith. 1954*b*. On the use of calcic plagioclases in geologic thermometry, *J. Geol., 62,* 405–408.

MacKenzie, W. S. 1952. The effect of temperature on the symmetry of high-temperature soda-rich feldspars, *Am. J. Sci.,* Bowen volume, pp. 319–342.

MacKenzie, W. S. 1954. The orthoclase-microcline inversion, *Mineral. Mag., 225,* 354–366.

MacKenzie, W. S. 1957. The crystalline modifications of $NaAlSi_3O_8$, *Am. J. Sci., 255,* 481–516.

Miyashiro, A., and T. Iiyama. 1954. A preliminary note on a new mineral, indialite, polymorphic with cordierite, *Proc. Japan Acad., 30,* 746–751.

Seitz, F., and D. Turnbull. 1956. *Solid State Physics, 3,* Academic Press, New York.

Smith, J. R., and H. S. Yoder. 1956. Variations in X-ray powder diffraction patterns of plagioclase feldspars, *Am. Mineralogist, 41,* 632–647.

Smith, J. V. 1956. The powder patterns and lattice parameters of plagioclase feldspars, I, The soda-rich feldspars, *Mineral. Mag., 31,* 47–68.

Smith, J. V., and W. S. MacKenzie. 1955. The alkali feldspars, II, A simple X-ray technique for the study of the alkali feldspars, *Am. Mineralogist, 40,* 733–747.

Smith, J. V., and O. F. Tuttle. 1957. The nepheline-kalsilite system, I, X-ray data for the crystalline phases, *Am. J. Sci., 255,* 282–305.

Smith, J. V., and H. S. Yoder. 1954. Experimental and theoretical studies of the mica polymorphs, *Mineral. Mag., 31,* 209–235.

Taylor, C. A., R. M. Hinde, and H. Lipson. 1951. Optical methods in X-ray analysis, I, The study of imperfect structures, *Acta Cryst., 4,* 261–266.

Tuttle, O. F., and N. L. Bowen. 1950. High-temperature albite and contiguous feldspars, *J. Geol., 58,* 572–583.

Willis, B. G. M. 1957. An optical method of studying the diffraction from imperfect crystals, I, Modulated structures, *Proc. Roy. Soc., A, 239,* 184–191.

Yoder, H. S. 1952. The $MgO–Al_2O_3–SiO_2–H_2O$ system and the related metamorphic facies, *Am. J. Sci.,* Bowen volume, pp. 569–627.

Yoder, H. S., and H. P. Eugster. 1954. Phlogopite synthesis and stability range, *Geochim. et Cosmochim. Acta, 6,* 157–185.

Yoder, H. S., and H. P. Eugster. 1955. Synthetic and natural muscovites, *Geochim. et Cosmochim. Acta, 8,* 225–280.

Hydrothermal Investigations of Amphiboles

FRANCIS R. BOYD

Geophysical Laboratory
Carnegie Institution of Washington

Hydrothermal investigations of amphiboles have been undertaken to provide quantitative data on the upper boundary of the amphibolite facies and to increase understanding of equilibria in amphibole-bearing rocks. The stability fields of tremolite, pargasite, and magnesian riebeckite [1] have been determined, and phase diagrams for these amphiboles are presented. Data on the stability of anthophyllite and grünerite, obtained by other investigators, are also reviewed below.

Studies of chemical variation in natural amphiboles have been made by a number of authors. A summary of these studies is included to provide the reader with an over-all view of the subject and to show why particular amphiboles were selected for experimental investigation.

The chemical complexity of amphibole systems can be appreciated when it is remembered that the average igneous or metamorphic hornblende has at least ten major components: Na_2O, K_2O, CaO, MgO, FeO, Fe_2O_3, Al_2O_3, SiO_2, H_2O, and F. When simplified to an end member, a hornblende must still be treated as a part of a six-component system. In spite of the difficulties introduced by the large number of components, however, the major aspects of the phase relations can be comprehended.

Chemical Variation in Natural Amphiboles

The various monoclinic and orthorhombic amphiboles have but slight differences in crystal structure despite their wide range in chemi-

[1] Magnesian riebeckite has been studied in the author's laboratory by W. G. Ernst.

cal composition. The many formulas for amphibole end members are easily recalled if a picture of the structure is kept in mind.

The crystal structures of the monoclinic and orthorhombic amphiboles have been determined by Warren (1929, 1930) and by Warren and Modell (1930). The monoclinic amphibole structure is shown diagrammatically in figure 1. It contains double chains of SiO_4 tetrahedra running parallel to the c axis as shown in the lower diagram in

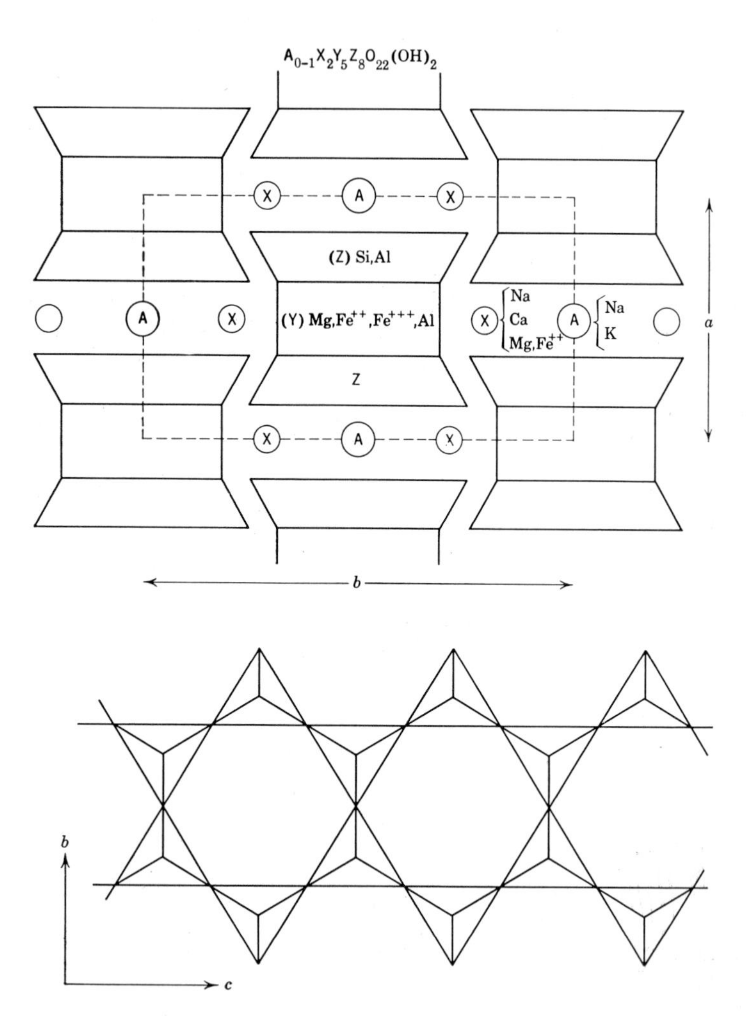

Fig. 1. Diagrammatic view of the monoclinic amphibole structure. The two diagrams are not on the same scale.

the figure. Each double chain is linked to a second double chain through shared apical oxygen ions. Six coordinated cations, surrounded by these apical oxygen ions and by hydroxyl ions, form segments whose structure is similar to that of brucite. The SiO_4 chains and "brucite" strips are represented in cross section in the upper diagram in figure 1 as units with an outline like an I beam. These units are common to both the monoclinic and orthorhombic amphiboles. The two cation positions within the I-beam units are designated by the symbols Z and Y, Z being the four coordinated position occupied by Si and Al, and Y being the six coordinated position occupied by Mg, Fe^{++}, Fe^{+++}, and Al.

In the monoclinic amphiboles there are two positions for the cations which tie the I-beam units together. One of these positions (X in fig. 1)[2] has a coordination number of 8 when occupied by Ca or Na; with a slight collapse of the structure this position can be occupied by an Mg or Fe^{++} ion. A second position (A in fig. 1) may be vacant or it may be filled by an alkali ion.

Amphiboles can be divided into three groups on the basis of the principal ion occupying the X position. In the anthophyllite–cummingtonite group the X position is occupied by Mg and Fe^{++}. In the calciferous amphiboles X is occupied by Ca, and in the alkali amphiboles by Na. The classification of amphiboles has been considered in recent years by Sundius (1946), Winchell (1945), and Miyashiro (1957). The type formulas and nomenclature given in table 1 of this paper differ from those presented by previous authors. Adding another classification of amphiboles to the literature is regrettable, but classification is never an end in itself. The present one is designed as a framework in which to carry out experimental studies of amphibole systems; it is not necessarily adapted to correlation of optical properties and composition in natural amphiboles. Oxyamphiboles are not included in this classification, inasmuch as it is not certain that they have true stability fields; i.e., it is possible that they are metastable phases formed by oxidation of pre-existing amphiboles.

There is no evidence of immiscibility within any of the three groups in the geologic temperature range. However, amphiboles of one group have probably only a limited miscibility with members of the other two groups. A miscibility gap certainly exists between members of the anthophyllite–cummingtonite group and the calciferous amphiboles.

[2] The symbol X is generally used to cover all Ca, Na, K ions in the structure. Nevertheless, two structural positions are involved, and it is useful to designate them separately.

TABLE 1

Calciferous Amphiboles	
Tremolite–ferrotremolite	$\circ Ca_2(Mg,Fe^{++})_5Si_8O_{22}(OH)_2$
Tschermakite–ferrotschermakite	$\circ Ca_2(Mg,Fe^{++})_3Al_2{}^{VI}Al_2{}^{IV}Si_6O_{22}(OH)_2$
Edenite–ferroedenite	$NaCa_2(Mg,Fe^{++})_5Al^{IV}Si_7O_{22}(OH)_2$
Pargasite–ferropargasite	$NaCa_2(Mg,Fe^{++})_4Al^{VI}Al_2{}^{IV}Si_6O_{22}(OH)_2$
Alkali Amphiboles	
Richterite–ferrorichterite	$NaNaCa(Mg,Fe^{++})_5Si_8O_{22}(OH)_2$
Glaucophane–ferroglaucophane	$\circ Na_2(Mg,Fe^{++})_3Al_2{}^{VI}Si_8O_{22}(OH)_2$
Magnesian riebeckite–ferroriebeckite	$\circ Na_2(Mg,Fe^{++})_3Fe_2{}^{+++}Si_8O_{22}(OH)_2$
Eckermannite–ferroeckermannite	$NaNa_2(Mg,Fe^{++})_4Al^{VI}Si_8O_{22}(OH)_2$
Magnesian arfvedsonite–ferroarfvedsonite	$NaNa_2(Mg,Fe^{++})_4Fe^{+++}Si_8O_{22}(OH)_2$
Anthophyllite–Cummingtonite Group	
Anthophyllite–cummingtonite–grünerite	$(Mg,Fe^{++})_7Si_8O_{22}(OH)_2$
Gedrite–ferrogedrite	$(Mg,Fe^{++})_5Al_2{}^{VI}Al_2{}^{IV}Si_6O_{22}(OH)_2$

Symbol ○ refers to vacant alkali position.
Roman numeral superscripts designate coordination of Al.

Associations of a hornblende or tremolite with anthophyllite or cummingtonite are well known. Good analyses of such pairs (e.g., Tilley, 1957) show an amount of Ca in the anthophyllite or cummingtonite and an amount of Mg and Fe^{++} in a coexisting hornblende corresponding to about 15 per cent solid solution.

Members intermediate between the calciferous amphiboles and alkali amphiboles, such as richterite and kataphorite, exist, but they are rare. Sundius (1946, p. 35) concluded that an unmixing zone probably exists between the alkaline and lime alkaline hornblendes. Miyashiro and Banno (1958, p. 107) have reported the association of glaucophane and actinolite in the same rock. The evidence is inconclusive but suggests limited miscibility between at least some members of these two groups.

A miscibility gap probably exists between the alkali amphiboles and members of the anthophyllite–cummingtonite group. The author knows of no analyses of amphiboles intermediate in composition between these groups. Nevertheless, the association of an alkali amphibole with a cummingtonite or anthophyllite has not been reported. It is likely that if such an association is discovered it will be riebeckite + grünerite, since both occur in iron formations and in alkalic pegmatites.

Calciferous Amphiboles

An informative study of chemical variation in the calciferous amphibole group has been made by Hallimond (1943). Figure 2 is a diagram similar to that developed by him, on which have been plotted selected analyses. The coordinates in the figure are two of the principal substitutions in the calciferous amphibole group. The filling of the vacant position (A) in the structure with alkalies, with a compensating substitution of Al for Si, is plotted as the ordinate. The coupled substitution (Al^{VI},Fe^{+++})–Al^{IV} for (Mg,Fe^{++})–Si is plotted as the abscissa. The analyses selected have close to 2.0 Ca ions per formula unit and a minimum of extraneous components such as Ti, and they show a reasonable degree of electrostatic balance. About 40 of the analyses plotted in figure 2 were taken from Hallimond's study, and the numbers correspond to those in his table 1. The remaining dozen, identified by letters, were collected from more recent literature.

The analyses fall in a broad band trending from $\circ Ca_2Fm_5Si_8O_{22}(OH,F)_2$ to $(Na,K)Ca_2Fm_4(Al^{VI},Fe^{+++})Al_2{}^{IV}Si_6O_{22}(OH,F)_2$. They show a tendency to group by geologic environment. The points clustering near $\circ Ca_2Fm_5Si_8O_{22}(OH,F)_2$ are the common tremolites and actinolites of metamorphosed, siliceous dolomites and impure limestones. The analyses that fall between $(Na,K)Ca_2Fm_4(Al^{VI},Fe^{+++})Al_2{}^{IV}Si_6O_{22}(OH,F)_2$ and $(Na,K)Ca_2Fm_5Al^{IV}Si_7O_{22}(OH,F)_2$ are, for the most part, from skarn deposits formed by reaction of carbonate and feldspathic rocks. Igneous hornblendes lie approximately midway between $\circ Ca_2Fm_5Si_8O_{22}$-$(OH,F)_2$ and $(Na,K)Ca_2Fm_4(Al^{VI},Fe^{+++})Al_2{}^{IV}Si_6O_{22}(OH,F)_2$. Examples are *a*, a hornblende from a diorite, and *l*, a hornblende from a rapakivi granite.

Many regional metamorphic hornblendes cannot be plotted on this diagram because 15 to 25 per cent of the lime is commonly replaced by alkalies. Metamorphic hornblendes that can be included fall approximately along a line joining $\circ Ca_2Fm_5Si_8O_{22}(OH,F)_2$ and point *f*. Amphiboles from the green schist facies, such as *b*, lie close to $\circ Ca_2Fm_5Si_8O_{22}$-$(OH,F)_2$. Points *k* and *j* are hornblendes from the epidote amphibolite facies, and points *f* and *g* are from high-grade Adirondack rocks.

It is apparent from the distribution of analyses in figure 2 that $\circ Ca_2Fm_5Si_8O_{22}(OH,F)_2$ and $(Na,K)Ca_2Fm_4(Al^{VI},Fe^{+++})Al_2{}^{IV}Si_6O_{22}$-$(OH,F)_2$ are the most important end-member series of the calciferous amphiboles. The composition of most calciferous amphiboles can be roughly approximated by points along the join between these end members. Both pargasite and ferropargasite (see table 1) are represented

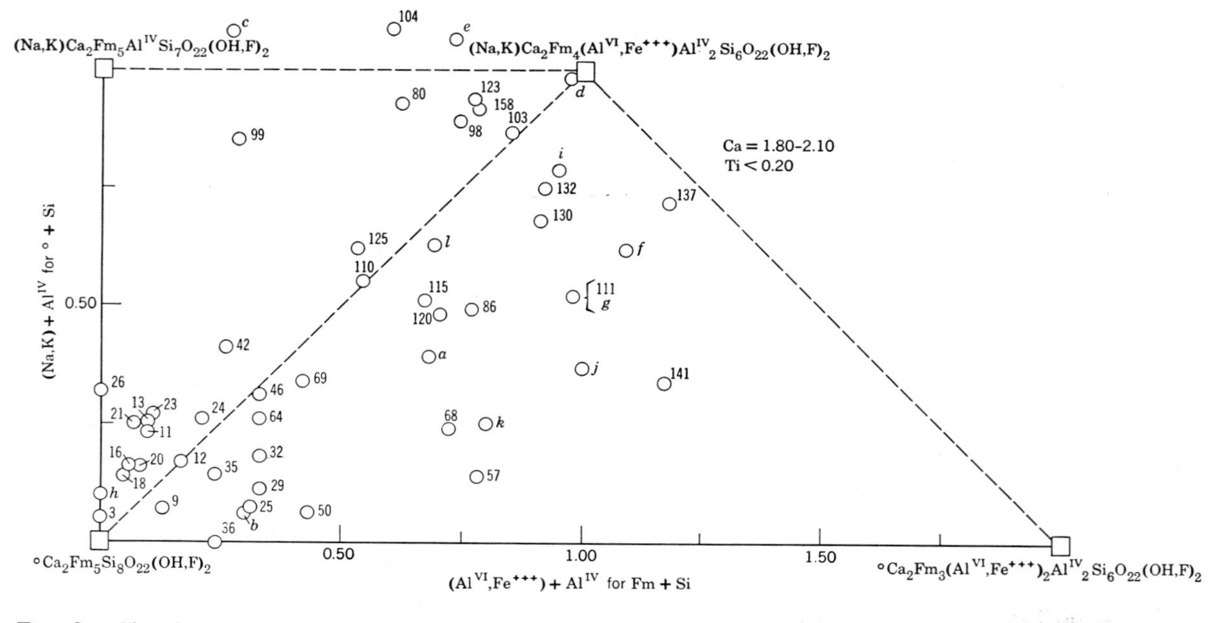

Fig. 2. Chemical variation in natural calciferous amphiboles. Numbered analyses are from Hallimond (1943, table 1). The symbol Fm represents $Fe^{++} + Mg$.

(*a*) Hornblende, Allen and Kramer, 1955, p. 528.
(*b*) Actinolite, Eskola, 1925, p. 43.
(*c*) Edenite, Palache, 1935, p. 73.
(*d*) Pargasite, Larsen, 1941, p. 49, no. 9.
(*e*) Pargasite, Larsen, 1941, p. 49, no. 8.
(*f*) Hornblende, Buddington, 1952, p. 42, no. 4.
(*g*) Hornblende, Buddington, 1952, p. 42, no. 3.
(*h*) Tremolite, Engel, personal communication, spec. no. A-14-10, Gouverneur, N. Y.
(*i*) Pargasite, Mackenzie, unpublished manuscript, spec. no. VT250a, Tinaquillo, Venezuela.
(*j*) Hornblende, Seitsaari, 1953, p. 89, table 4.
(*k*) Hornblende, Seitsaari, 1953, p. 89, table 5.
(*l*) Hornblende, Sahama, 1947, p. 160.

among the points falling near $(Na,K)Ca_2Fm_4(Al^{VI},Fe^{+++})Al_2{}^{IV}Si_6O_{22}$-$(OH,F)_2$. Pargasite occurs in skarns, ferropargasite in granitic rocks. Tremolite is much more abundant than ferrotremolite, although the latter has been found in nature. K is sometimes an important constituent of hornblendes, but the K/Na ratio is always less than 1. High-grade amphiboles tend to be rich in F: in high-grade rocks amphibole is often the only hydrous phase, and the F is concentrated in it; in low-grade rocks the F is distributed through a number of hydrous phases.

Experimental Data for Tremolite

The field of stability of tremolite is shown in figure 3. Above the curve, tremolite breaks down to diopside + orthorhombic enstatite + quartz + vapor. In this temperature range there is about 5 per cent $MgSiO_3$ in solution in the diopside and 5 per cent $CaMgSi_2O_6$ in the enstatite (Boyd and Schairer, unpublished data on the system $MgSiO_3$–$CaMgSi_2O_6$).

The optical properties of synthetic tremolite are shown in table 2 along with projected values for natural tremolite given by Winchell (1951, p. 435). The agreement is good. Figure 4 shows an X-ray pattern of synthetic tremolite and the pattern of a particularly pure, natural tremolite from Gouverneur, N. Y.

Tremolite was the first calciferous amphibole investigated, because of its chemical simplicity and its importance as a metamorphic mineral. The investigation turned out to be particularly difficult, how-

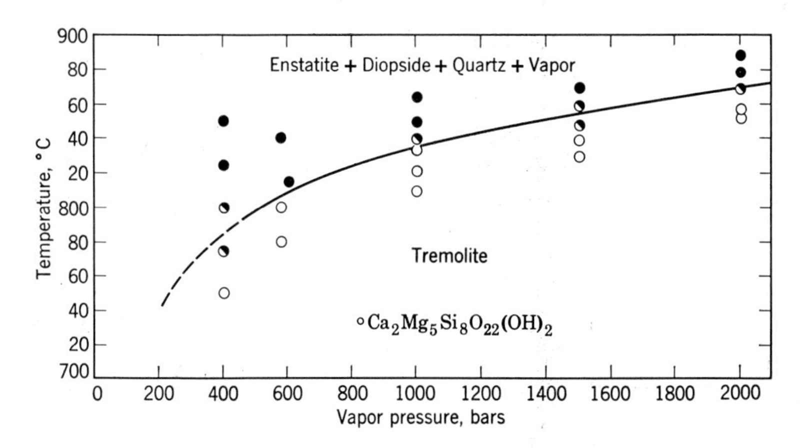

Fig. 3. The breakdown curve of tremolite.

TABLE 2. Optical Properties of Synthetic Tremolite and Pargasite *

	γ	$\gamma - \alpha$	$2V$	$\gamma \wedge C$
Synthetic tremolite	1.625	0.024	−73°	17°
Tremolite (Winchell)	1.628	0.030	−88°	18°
Synthetic pargasite	1.645	0.021	+74°	26°
Pargasite (Winchell)	1.64	0.02	+85°	28°

* The author is indebted to J. R. Smith for measurement of the optic angles of synthetic pargasite and tremolite.

Table is from *C. I. W. Year Book 54*, corrections added.

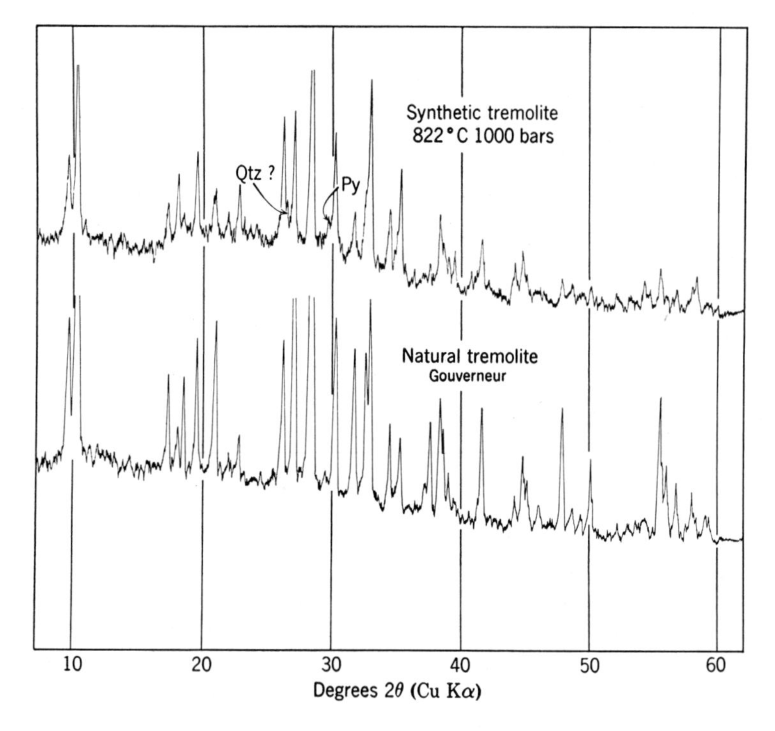

Fig. 4. X-ray diffractometer patterns of synthetic tremolite and a natural tremolite from Gouverneur, N. Y. Small amounts of quartz and pyroxene are present in the synthetic tremolite.

ever, because of the reluctance of tremolite to nucleate and the tendency of pyroxene and quartz to persist metastably even in the presence of tremolite nuclei.

It is usual in hydrothermal investigations to start with an oxide mix or a glass, since these materials are generally more reactive than the stable phases. Once a curve has been obtained with an oxide mix or a glass as a starting material, attempts can be made to reverse the reaction and demonstrate equilibrium.

This technique proved impractical for tremolite. If a run is made with an oxide mix or glass in the interval between the breakdown curve and about 50° below the curve, the chance of obtaining a perceptible amount of tremolite is roughly 1 in 3. Any tremolite formed is usually sparse, coarse grains making up about 0.1 per cent of the run, the remainder being pyroxene and quartz.

The procedure for locating the curve that eventually proved successful was to start with a mixture of 50 per cent submicroscopic tremolite and 50 per cent pyroxene and quartz. This material was prepared by heating an oxide mix or glass seeded with synthetic tremolite for a week at 500° to 600° C and 1000 to 2000 bars H_2O. This procedure commonly gave 50 per cent tremolite and occasionally much larger yields.

The fine-grained tremolite produced under these conditions is highly reactive. Held above its stability curve it readily breaks down to pyroxene and quartz; held within its stability field it recrystallizes and gradually grows at the expense of the pyroxene and quartz. In a zone of indifference about 20° wide along most of the investigated length of the curve the relative proportions of tremolite and of pyroxene and quartz will not change sufficiently to permit location of the curve.

The breakdown curve of tremolite is in a surprisingly high-temperature range. Tremolite usually forms in nature by reaction of dolomite and quartz. Since the Ca/Mg ratio in dolomite is 1:1 and in tremolite 2:5, the reaction of these minerals produces tremolite + calcite. Tremolite will react with calcite at higher temperature to yield diopside and quartz; this reaction liberates CO_2 as well as H_2O, and the temperature of the reaction is a function of the CO_2 pressure as well as of the H_2O pressure. Data on the tremolite–calcite reaction have not been obtained, but the reaction must take place at a lower temperature, for a given H_2O pressure, than the breakdown of pure tremolite. For this reason, tremolite usually disappears in pro-grade metamorphism at considerably lower grade than is implied by the curve of figure 3.

Tremolite is occasionally found in calcite-free skarns. In such an environment it persists into the sillimanite zone. The assemblage diopside + enstatite + quartz, on the other hand, is found only in magmatic rocks, pyroxene granulites, and hornfelses. Examples are the charnockites of Uganda (Groves, 1935, p. 164) and the diorites of Electric Peak in Yellowstone Park (Iddings, 1899, p. 99).

Experimental Data for Pargasite

Pargasite lies in a six-component system, and the phase relations for this composition are correspondingly complex. Nevertheless, pargasite is easily synthesized. The principal problems encountered in working out the diagram in figure 6 were due to the large number of breakdown products rather than to any difficulty in defining the boundaries of the pargasite stability field.

The optical properties of synthetic pargasite are given in table 2, and an X-ray pattern is shown in figure 5. The patterns of tremolite

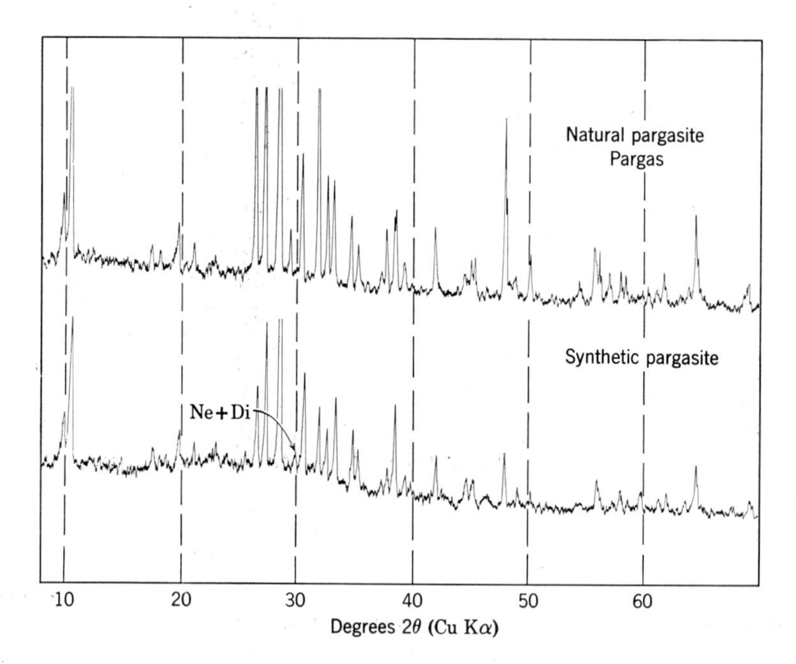

Fig. 5. X-ray diffractometer patterns of synthetic pargasite and a natural pargasite from Pargas, Finland. Small amounts of nepheline (Ne) and diopside (Di) are present in the synthetic pargasite. From *C. I. W. Year Book 54*.

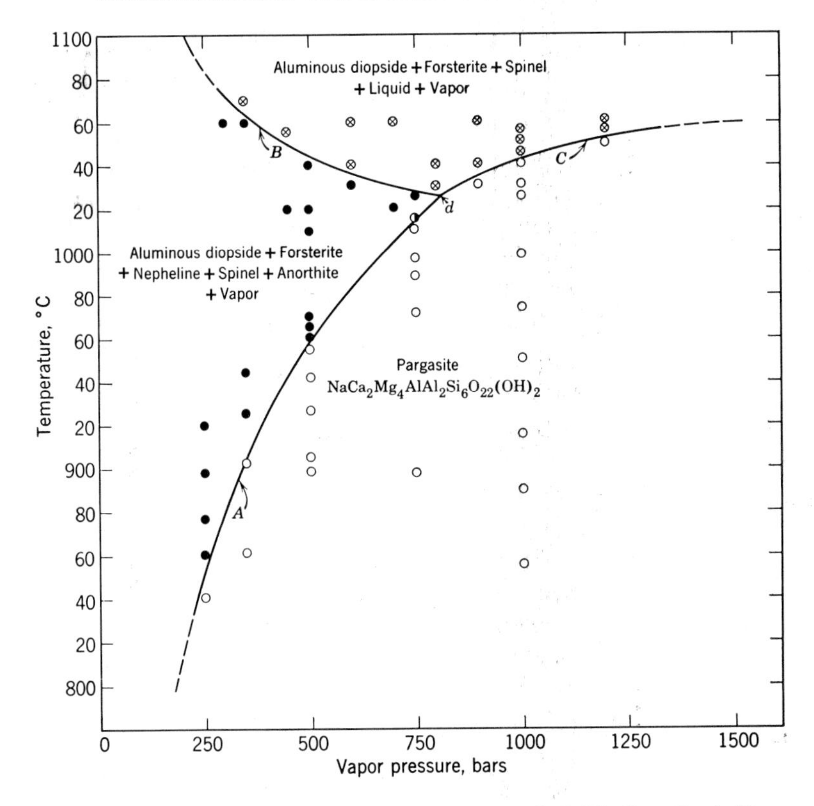

Fig. 6. The stability field of pargasite. From *C. I. W. Year Book 55.*

and pargasite are most easily distinguished by the position of a peak (probably 151) at about 33° 2θ (Cu Kα). In a tremolite pattern this peak is at 33.05° 2θ; in a pargasite pattern, at 33.38° 2θ.

It has been possible to obtain enough synthetic pargasite to determine its water content—a matter of particular interest because a number of natural amphiboles are suspected of having more than their theoretical amount of water. The water content of synthetic pargasite was found to be 1.95 $\pm$0.3 per cent, in excellent agreement with the theoretical value of 1.92 per cent.

A temperature-vapor pressure diagram for pargasite is presented in figure 6. This diagram consists of three curves (*A*, *B*, and *C*) which intersect at an invariant point (*d*). These curves are located with an accuracy of about $\pm$3° C. Boundary *A* is the curve for the breakdown of pargasite to anhydrous crystalline phases + vapor. Boundary *B* represents the beginning of melting of these anhydrous phases in the presence of vapor. The stable assemblage in the region bounded by curves *A* and *B* consists of aluminous diopside + forsterite + nepheline + minor spinel and anorthite + vapor. If this crystalline assemblage is placed in the region above curve *B*, it undergoes partial melting and the stable phases become aluminous diopside + forsterite + spinel + liquid + vapor. Both anorthite and nepheline are replaced by melt as the temperature is raised above curve *B*. This reaction probably proceeds in two steps, the two curves being so close together that they cannot be separately determined. Curves *A* and *B* intersect at invariant point *d* at 1025° and 800 bars. At vapor pressures greater than 800 bars, pargasite melts incongruently along curve *C* to aluminous diopside + forsterite + spinel + liquid + vapor.

Comparison of figures 3 and 6 shows that substitution of soda and alumina in the structure greatly extends the temperature range over which a calciferous amphibole can stably exist. Tremolite breaks down at a temperature of 835° at a vapor pressure of 1000 bars. At that same pressure, pargasite is stable up to a temperature of 1040°. This is in accord with the common observation that hornblendes are found in nature at metamorphic grades above the breakdown of tremolite. The assemblage hornblende + augite + hypersthene + quartz is often found in granulites and quartz diorites.

The phase diagram of pargasite can be used to model the relations between the amphibolite facies, the magmatic region, and the pyroxene hornfels or pyroxene granulite facies. In many igneous rocks hornblendes are found to have grown in equilibrium with a melt. Under some conditions of temperature and vapor pressure, therefore, the amphibolite facies and magmatic region must adjoin one another. But, in the pyroxene hornfels and pyroxene granulite facies, mineral assemblages are found that must have formed at lower temperatures than those required for a melt but higher than those possible for an amphibole. In figure 6 the stability field of pargasite can be taken to represent the amphibolite facies in this system. The magmatic region is represented by the area above curves *B* and *C*. Along curve *C* the magmatic region and amphibolite facies adjoin, permitting the stable association of an amphibole and a melt. In the area bounded by curves *A* and *B*, neither an amphibole nor a melt is stable, and this area is, therefore, a pyroxene facies. Thus the pyroxene facies represent a condition of low vapor pressure. *In this particular system* the vapor pressure must be less than 800 bars for a subsolidus pyroxene assemblage to be stable.

Eight hundred bars is probably of the right order of magnitude for the limiting vapor pressure in a pyroxene facies in most rock systems. Yoder and Tilley (1956, p. 170) have investigated the melting of tholeiite under H_2O pressure; they found that hornblende forms at high pressure. The intersection of the curve for the reaction of hornblende to form pyroxene and the curve for the beginning of melting of the basalt was found to be approximately 925° and 1400 bars. A subsolidus pyroxene assemblage cannot, therefore, exist in a rock of basaltic composition at an H_2O pressure greater than about 1400 bars. In granites, the hornblendes are more iron-rich than the hornblendes of gabbroic rocks. The iron-rich hornblendes can be expected to have breakdown curves that lie at least several hundred degrees below their magnesian counterparts. However, the curve for the beginning of melting of granite lies about 200° below the solidus curve of basalt (Tuttle and Bowen, 1953, p. 50; Yoder and Tilley, 1956, p. 170), and it is probable that the intersection of the minimum melting curve of granite and an iron-rich hornblende $\rightarrow$ pyroxene reaction curve would be in the vicinity of 1000 bars.

Thus an estimated upper limit for the H_2O pressure in a pyroxene hornfels or pyroxene granulite can be set at a value of the order of 1000 bars. This same value gives the minimum H_2O pressure necessary for the crystallization of a calciferous hornblende in equilibrium with a rock melt.

Pargasite–Quartz

The join pargasite–quartz was investigated in the hope of obtaining a curve for the reaction pargasite + quartz $\rightleftharpoons$ labradorite + diopside + enstatite. Reconnaissance runs on this join, however, revealed that pargasite is not stable in the presence of quartz and, hence, that an equilibrium curve for the reaction does not exist. The stable assemblages encountered with quartz are labradorite + diopside + enstatite and tremolite + plagioclase + minor enstatite.

These data are in accord with natural occurrences of magnesian pargasites. All the analyzed magnesian pargasites known to the author come from undersaturated environments. At the type locality at Pargas, quartz and pargasite have been noted to be incompatible (Laitakari, 1921, p. 102). Nevertheless, ferropargasite is found to occur typically in pegmatites and granites, in association with quartz. Pargasite and ferropargasite appear to behave toward quartz in a manner analogous to forsterite and fayalite.

Anthophyllite–Cummingtonite

Most amphiboles in the series anthophyllite–cummingtonite–grünerite can be considered as phases in the system $MgO–FeO–SiO_2–H_2O$. Anthophyllite can take alumina into its structure through the substitution of $Al^{VI}–Al^{IV}$ for (Mg,Fe)–Si. Aluminous orthoamphiboles (gedrite) have not yet been studied in the laboratory. Portions of the system $MgO–FeO–SiO_2–H_2O$ have attracted the attention of a number of workers, but despite intensive investigation the phase relations within the system have not yet been worked out. In many ways the anthophyllite–cummingtonite amphiboles and associated phases present one of the most challenging problems in experimental petrology.

In figure 7 the principal phases of interest in the system $MgO–FeO–SiO_2–H_2O$ are shown on a temperature-composition diagram. The partial pressure of H_2O is not specified but is assumed constant. P_{O_2} is assumed low enough to prohibit the coexistence of magnetite and quartz. The diagram has been constructed partly from field evidence and partly from laboratory data. It is intended solely as an aid in visualizing the problems in this system; there are many points that are not now understood.

A field for talc is present at temperatures lower than those at which amphiboles make their appearance. It is presumed that a complete solid solution exists between talc and its iron analogue, minnesotaite. At higher temperatures members of the talc series break down to amphiboles + quartz. Amphiboles intermediate in the composition range $Fe_7Si_8O_{22}(OH)_2–Mg_7Si_8O_{22}(OH)_2$ can be either orthorhombic or monoclinic. In natural specimens neither symmetry form extends across the whole composition range. Anthophyllites are restricted to the range between the pure Mg end member and a composition of about $Mg_{40}Fe_{60}$.[3] Natural cummingtonites extend from the pure Fe end member to about $Fe_{25}Mg_{75}$. A cummingtonite has been synthesized by the author with a composition of $Fe_{16}Mg_{84}$. A possible interpretation of these data is that the inversion curves between orthorhombic and monoclinic forms are cut off on the low-temperature end by the field for talc and on the high-temperature end by the breakdown of the amphiboles. The breakdown products of the amphiboles will be

[3] Various "ferroanthophyllites" have been described (Peacock, 1928, pp. 260–263; Shannon, 1924, pp. 323–324). They are asbestiform, and optical determination of orthorhombic symmetry is open to question. Several of them have chemical compositions indicating that they are actually ferrotremolites.

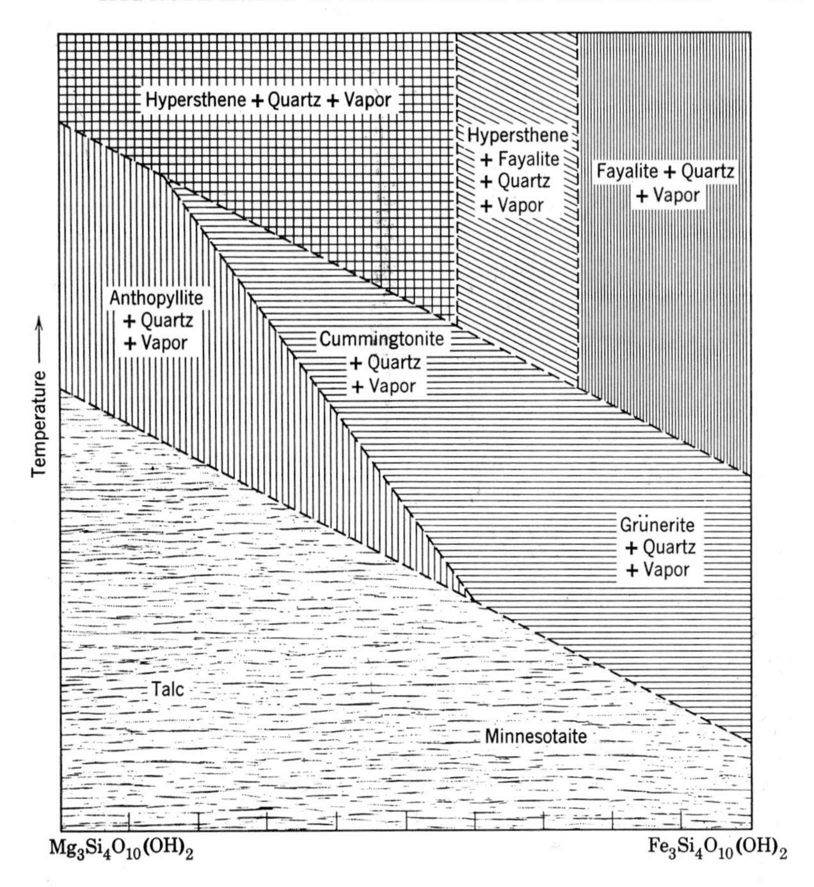

Fig. 7. Hypothetical temperature-composition diagram for the join $Mg_3Si_4O_{10}$-$(OH)_2$–$Fe_3Si_4O_{10}(OH)_2$.

hypersthene + quartz, fayalite + quartz, or hypersthene + fayalite + quartz. The curves bounding the fields of hypersthene and fayalite in figure 7 are drawn according to hydrothermal data obtained by the author. These data are not in agreement with dry data presented by Bowen and Schairer (1935, p. 164). The reasons for the disagreement are not known.

Anthophyllite was first synthesized by Bowen and Tuttle (1949, p. 444) in their study of the system MgO–SiO_2–H_2O, but no field of stability was found. The amphibole formed as a metastable product of the breakdown of talc, and broke down to enstatite and quartz on continued heating. Yoder (1952, p. 587) also synthesized anthophyllite as a metastable phase in his investigation of the system MgO–Al_2O_3–SiO_2–H_2O.

Synthesis of grünerite has been reported by Flaschen and Osborn (1957, p. 927). These authors state that they obtained it as an intermediate product in the breakdown of minnesotaite to fayalite + quartz. They thus found the behavior of grünerite to be apparently similar to that of anthophyllite. J. R. Smith (1957, p. 230) made a careful and detailed investigation of the system FeO–F_2O_3–SiO_2–H_2O under a variety of partial pressures of oxygen, but obtained only fayalite, quartz, and iron oxides.

The author (Boyd, 1955, p. 117) has investigated the join $Mg_7Si_8O_{22}(OH)_2$–$Fe_7Si_8O_{22}(OH)_2$ and has synthesized a number of orthoamphiboles, clinoamphiboles, and hypersthenes. The relations found for anthophyllite by Bowen and Tuttle and by Yoder were confirmed. Amphiboles lying between $Mg_7Si_8O_{22}(OH)_2$ and $Fe_7Si_8O_{22}(OH)_2$ in composition do not, however, behave like anthophyllite; that is, they do not break down when held for long periods at the temperatures and pressures at which they were formed. Nevertheless, it proved impossible to grow orthoamphibole or clinoamphibole from hypersthene and quartz. Since the breakdown of these amphiboles could not be reversed, the possibility remains that they formed metastably. No amphiboles richer in iron than about $Mg_{40}Fe_{60}$ could be synthesized; grünerite was not obtained. In runs with a bulk composition richer in iron than $Mg_{40}Fe_{60}$, fayalite always appeared.

It is apparent that the conditions for the stability of anthophyllite, cummingtonite, and grünerite have not been found. Yoder (1952, p. 610) has suggested that anthophyllite might be stable in a water-deficient system, but other explanations are possible. For example, it is possible that a field for anthophyllite will appear at a higher temperature than talc at vapor pressures higher than those under which this system has thus far been studied (2000 bars). Or, anthophyllite may turn out to be stable only under a combination of high lithostatic pressure and relatively low vapor pressure (Thompson, 1955, p. 98). In view of the widespread occurrence of anthophyllite, cummingtonite, and grünerite, the problem is critical.

Alkali Amphiboles

The alkali amphiboles are currently being investigated at the Geophysical Laboratory by W. G. Ernst (1957, p. 228). He has completed a preliminary diagram for magnesian riebeckite. He has also synthesized ferroriebeckite and glaucophane, which are the most important of the alkali amphiboles; data on them will be presented by him in the near future. Magnesian riebeckite has been found in a number of low-grade schists and metasediments (e.g., Miyashiro and Iwasaki, 1957).

Magnesian riebeckite contains iron, and its stability field depends on the partial pressure of oxygen. Variation of P_{O_2} in a system that contains iron can influence not only the positions of the univariant curves but also the phases that appear. In figure 8 the upper diagram represents the most oxidizing conditions investigated; these were obtained with a hematite–magnetite buffer (Eugster, 1957, p. 1760). In the middle diagram the buffer was magnetite + fayalite + silica, and in the lower one magnetite + wüstite. Variation of P_{O_2} affects the position of the incongruent melting curve of riebeckite; the change produced is about 35° at 2000 bars vapor pressure. The effect of P_{O_2} on the nature of the breakdown products is pronounced. For example, acmite occurs as a breakdown product of riebeckite only under the most oxidizing conditions.

The low range of vapor pressure in which incongruent melting of riebeckite takes place is noteworthy. In this system, unlike calciferous amphibole systems, anhydrous assemblages unaccompanied by melt are limited to vapor pressures less than about 250 bars. However, the incongruent melting curve of magnesian riebeckite is in the same high range of temperatures as the breakdown curves of tremolite and pargasite. These data, and preliminary data on other alkali amphiboles, indicate that there will be no great difference in the stability ranges of the alkali and calciferous amphiboles. This fact is in accord with the natural occurrences of members of both groups. Under sufficiently high vapor pressures, both alkali and calciferous hornblendes are stable in the magmatic temperature range.

Acknowledgments

S. P. Clark, Jr., H. P. Eugster, and W. G. Ernst have read this paper and offered numerous suggestions, which have led to its improvement. The author is indebted to J. B. Thompson for the method of representing the amphibole structure utilized in figure 1.

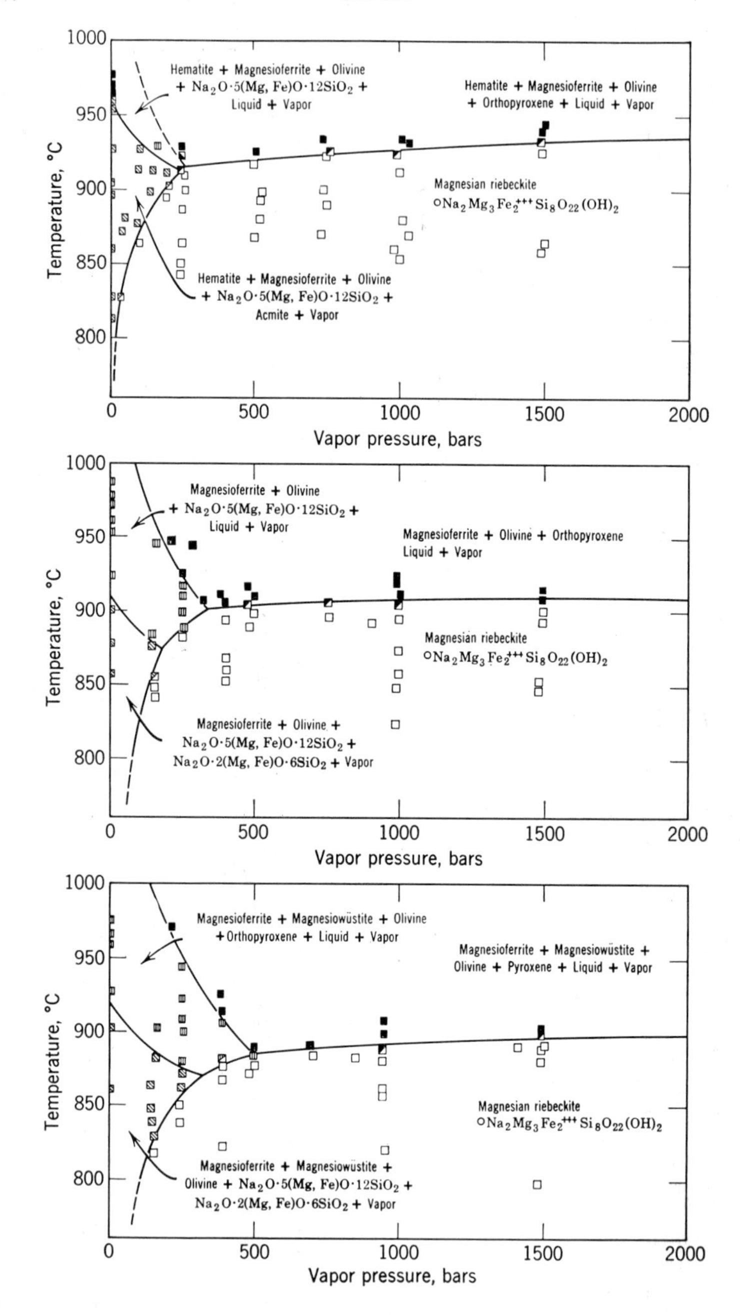

Fig. 8. Preliminary diagrams for the stability field of magnesian riebeckite; after W. G. Ernst (1957, p. 229).

References

Allen, R. D., and H. Kramer. 1955. Hornblende in diorite pegmatite, San Bernardino County, Calif., *Am. Mineralogist, 40,* 527–530.

Bowen, N. L., and J. F. Schairer. 1935. The system MgO–FeO–SiO_2, *Am. J. Sci.,* 5th series, *29,* 151–217.

Bowen, N. L., and O. F. Tuttle. 1949. The system MgO–SiO_2–H_2O, *Bull. Geol. Soc. Am., 60,* 439–460.

Boyd, F. R. 1955. The anthopyllite-cummingtonite group, Annual Report of the Director of the Geophysical Laboratory for 1954–1955, *Carnegie Inst. Wash. Year Book 54,* 117–118.

Buddington, A. F. 1952. Chemical petrology of some metamorphosed Adirondack gabbroic, syenitic, and quartz syenitic rocks, *Am. J. Sci., Bowen Volume,* pp. 37–132.

Ernst, W. G. 1957. Alkali amphiboles, Annual Report of the Director of the Geophysical Laboratory for 1956–1957, *Carnegie Inst. Wash. Year Book 56,* 228–230.

Eskola, P. 1925. Basic rocks in the Karelian formations, *Fennia, 45* (no. 19), 1–93.

Eugster, H. P. 1957. Heterogeneous reactions involving oxidation and reduction at high pressures and temperatures, *J. Chem. Phys., 26,* 1760–1761.

Flaschen, S. S., and E. F. Osborn. 1957. Studies of the system iron oxide–silica–water at low oxygen partial pressures, *Econ. Geol., 52,* 923–943.

Groves, A. W. 1935. The charnockite series of Uganda, British East Africa, *Quart. J. Geol. Soc. London, 91* (pt. 2), 150–207.

Hallimond, A. F. 1943. On the graphical representation of the calciferous amphiboles, *Am. Mineralogist, 28,* 65–89.

Iddings, J. P. 1899. The igneous rocks of Electric Peak and Sepulchre Mountain, Geology of Yellowstone National Park, *Monographs of the U. S. Geol. Survey, 32* (pt. 2), 89–148.

Laitakari, A. 1921. Petrographie und Mineralogie der Kalksteinlagerstätten von Parainen (Pargas), *Bull. comm. géol. Finlande, 54,* 1–113.

Larsen, E. S. 1941. Alkalic rocks of Iron Hill, Gunnison County, Colorado, *U. S. Geol. Survey Profess. Paper 197-A,* 1–64.

Mackenzie, D. B. An unusual high-temperature Alpine type peridotite from Venezuela. Unpublished manuscript.

Miyashiro, A. 1957. The chemistry, optics, and genesis of the alkali-amphiboles, *J. Fac. Sci. Univ. Tokyo, Sect. II, 11* (pt. 1), 57–83.

Miyashiro, A., and S. Banno. 1958. Nature of glaucophanitic metamorphism, *Am. J. Sci., 256,* 97–110.

Miyashiro, A., and M. Iwasaki. 1957. Magnesioriebeckite in crystalline schists of Bizan and Sikoku, Japan, *J. Geol. Soc. Japan, 63,* 698–703.

Palache, C. 1935. The minerals of Franklin and Sterling Hill, Sussex County, N. J., *U. S. Geol. Survey Profess. Paper 180,* 1–133.

Peacock, M. A. 1928. The nature and origin of the amphibole-asbestos of South Africa, *Am. Mineralogist, 13,* 241–286.

Sahama, Th. G. 1947. Rapakivi amphibole from Uuksunjoki, Salmi area, *Bull. comm. géol. Finlande, 140,* 159–162.

Seitsaari, J. 1953. A blue-green hornblende and its genesis from the Tampere schist belt, Finland, *Bull. comm. géol. Finlande, 159,* 83–98.

Shannon, E. V. 1924. Iron amphibole from Idaho, *Am. J. Sci.,* 5th series, *8,* 323–324.

Smith, J. R. 1957. Reconnaissance in the system $FeO–Fe_2O_3–SiO_2–H_2O$, Annual Report of the Director of the Geophysical Laboratory for 1956–1957, *Carnegie Inst. Wash. Year Book 56,* 230–231.

Sundius, N. 1946. The classification of the hornblendes and the solid solution relations in the amphibole group, *Sveriges Geol. Undersökn. Årsbok 40* (no. 4), 1–36.

Thompson, J. B. 1955. The thermodynamic basis for the mineral facies concept, *Am. J. Sci., 253,* 65–103.

Tilley, C. E. 1957. Paragenesis of anthophyllite and hornblende from the Bancroft area, Ontario, *Am. Mineralogist, 42,* 412–416.

Tuttle, O. F., and N. L. Bowen. 1953. Beginning of melting of some natural granites, Annual Report of the Director of the Geophysical Laboratory for 1952–1953, *Carnegie Inst. Wash. Year Book 52,* 50.

Warren, B. E. 1929. The structure of tremolite, *Z. Krist., 72,* 42–57.

Warren, B. E. 1930. The crystal structure and chemical composition of the monoclinic amphiboles, *Z. Krist., 72,* 493–517.

Warren, B. E., and D. I. Modell. 1930. The structure of anthophyllite, *Z. Krist., 75,* 161–178.

Winchell, A. N. 1945. Variations in composition and properties of the calciferous amphiboles, *Am. Mineralogist, 30,* 27–50.

Winchell, A. N. 1951. *Elements of Optical Mineralogy, Part II, Descriptions of Minerals,* 4th ed., New York.

Yoder, H. S. 1952. The $MgO–Al_2O_3–SiO_2–H_2O$ system and related metamorphic facies, *Am. J. Sci., Bowen Volume,* pp. 569–627.

Yoder, H. S., and C. E. Tilley. 1956. Natural tholeiite basalt-water system, Annual Report of the Director of the Geophysical Laboratory for 1955–1956, *Carnegie Inst. Wash. Year Book 55,* 169–171.

Reduction and Oxidation in Metamorphism

HANS P. EUGSTER

Geophysical Laboratory
Carnegie Institution of Washington
and The Johns Hopkins University

Reduction and oxidation reactions proceeding in geologic environments have long been accepted as factors influencing the formation of rocks and mineral assemblages. Whereas their importance within the earth's crust is illustrated by differences in the states of oxidation, their mechanism and effect cannot be evaluated directly, but must be inferred from the mineral assemblages with the aid of reconstructive experiments. Redox reactions as an integral part of metamorphism have not yet been considered quantitatively. It is the purpose of this paper to show that with data available as well as with some new experimental information such a treatment can be rewarding. Redox reactions during the formation of igneous rocks are not less important. They follow the principles outlined here but will not be discussed specifically.

In considering the quantitative aspects of redox reactions in metamorphism we must first clarify the relationship between the state of oxidation of a mineral or mineral assemblage and P_{O_2} of the gas phase in equilibrium with it. We can then discuss the effects of changes of P_{O_2} on this mineral or mineral assemblage.

An alternative and less direct approach would be to compare the Fe^{+2}/Fe^{+3} ratios of a large number of metamorphic rocks and look for systematic changes. A decrease of this ratio has been found for the change of shale to slate (Nanz, 1953). Higher degrees of metamorphism do not seem to produce any trends in the state of oxidation of mineral assemblages. Both hematite and magnetite are known to be stable at even the highest degrees of metamorphism (see, e.g., James, 1955). Progressive metamorphism clearly leads to more anhydrous assemblages, but not necessarily to more reduced or more oxidized ones. Changes in the Fe^{+2}/Fe^{+3} ratios of course do occur during progressive metamorphism. Such changes must depend upon individual environments.

The System Fe–O

The relationship between P_{O_2} of the gas phase and the state of oxidation of the solids must be clarified first. Relevant data for most metal–oxide systems are available, either from direct measurements or by calculation from Gibbs free energy changes (see Richardson and Jeffes, 1948; Kubaschewski and Evans, 1951). By far the most important element undergoing changes in the state of oxidation under geologic conditions is iron. An analysis of the systems Fe–O and Fe–Si–O can be used to demonstrate many of the relationships for more complex phase assemblages and it provides a key to the understanding of redox reactions in metamorphism.

Available data on the system Fe–O have been assembled most recently by Darken and Gurry (1945, 1946, 1953). All phase boundaries were determined at a total pressure of 1 atm. Free oxygen in the gas phase was controlled by using appropriate mixtures of ($CO + CO_2$) or of ($H_2 + H_2O$). For the present purpose all data are recalculated to partial pressures of oxygen,[1] using the equilibrium constants given by Wagman et al. (1945). The locations of the phase boundaries determined at 1 atm are not measurably different from those at the vapor pressures of the system itself. The relationships can be built up most readily from isobaric sections. Figure 1 gives such a section at a pressure of 10^{-18} atm.[2] The compositions of the vapor phases are drawn schematically since they are not known. The heavy line in this section is the locus of all solids that can coexist with a vapor. Above 830° C all bulk compositions between pure iron and almost pure oxygen at this pressure are represented by metallic iron + vapor. Wüstite can coexist with vapor only between 775° and 830° C, magnetite only between 500° and 775° C, and hematite only below 500° C. A range of vapors can coexist with one solid of a

[1] Arbitrarily, all diagrams and discussions of diagrams are in terms of P_{O_2}, since experimental determinations are more closely related to P_{O_2}. But it must be remembered that the small pressures involved have no physical reality and must be considered in a statistical sense. Therefore, some general discussions are in terms of the chemical potential of oxygen (μ_{O_2}), which as a variable is equivalent to P_{O_2} (and to the activity of oxygen, a_{O_2}).

[2] Strictly speaking, $P_{gas} = P_{Fe} + P_{O_2}$. For all except the most iron-rich composition we can safely simplify $P_{gas} = P_{O_2}$. Nevertheless, it should be remembered that for most temperatures the vapor pressure of metallic iron is greater than the oxygen pressure of its oxides.

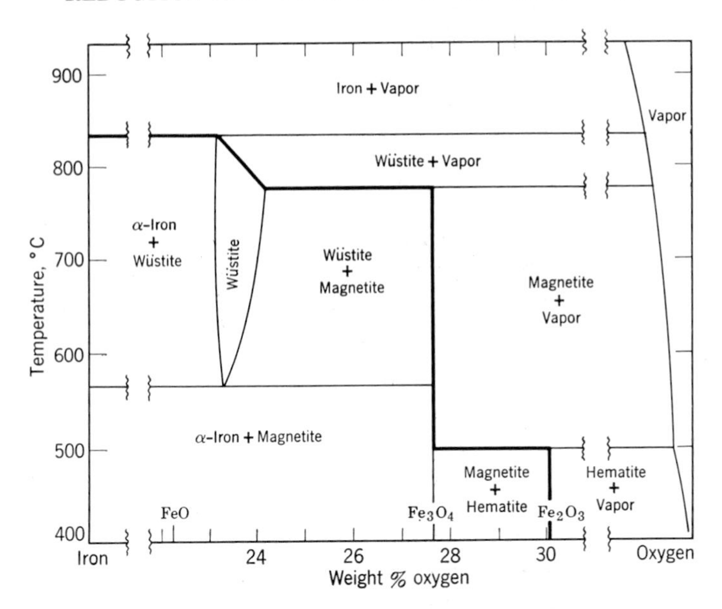

Fig. 1. Isobaric section through a portion of the system Fe–O at a pressure of 10^{-18} bar. The iron contents of the vapors are not known and have been represented schematically. The heavy line appears again in figure 2 as an "isobar."

fixed composition, but the composition of the vapor is defined when it coexists simultaneously with two solids. Changes in the relative masses of the two solids affect the bulk composition but have no influence on the vapor composition. On the other hand, for an isobarically invariant equilibrium the bulk composition of the system does not determine the relative masses of the three coexisting phases unless some other property, such as the internal energy of the system, is also known. Members of solid solutions (such as wüstite) coexist with a range of vapors over a range of temperature, but a specific member is in equilibrium with a vapor only at one temperature (for a given pressure), and the composition of this vapor is fixed.

The heavy line in figure 1 may be called an isobar. A series of such isobars have been superimposed in figure 2, omitting the vapor compositions.

The data used in constructing these isobars are essentially those assembled by Darken and Gurry (1945, 1946). Richardson and Jeffes (1948, 1949) give linear approximations for the four reactions at 1 atm total pressure: [3]

[3] Reaction 2 represents curve (*b*) in figure 7, 3 represents (*c*), and 4 represents (*e*).

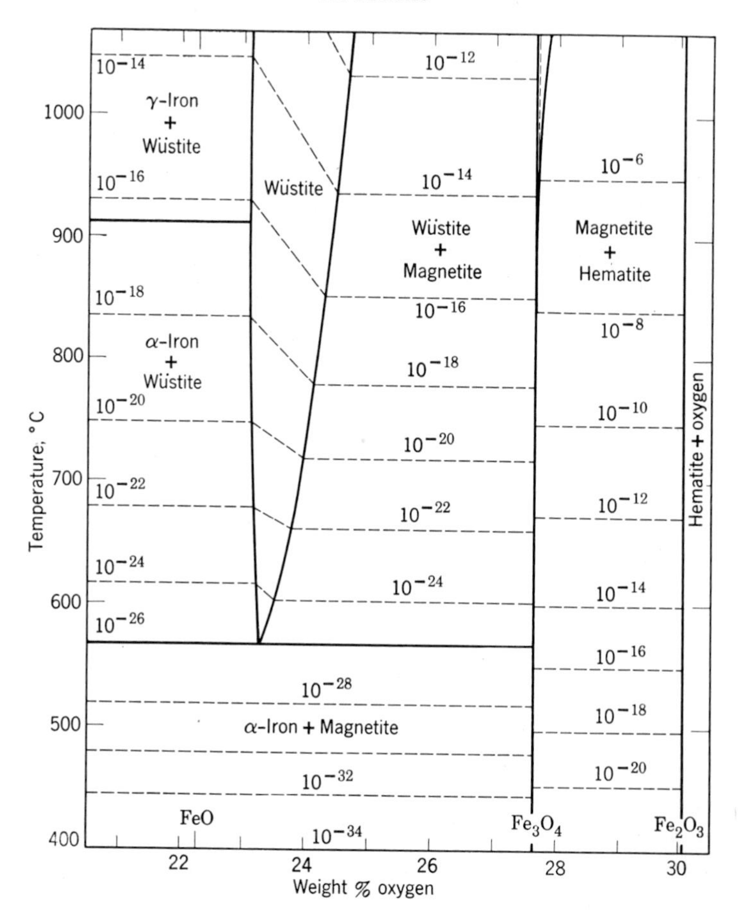

Fig. 2. *T-X* diagram of a portion of the system Fe–O. Phase boundaries as determined by Darken and Gurry (1945, 1946) at a total pressure of 1 atm. Isobars are dashed, and their positions are based on data discussed below.

(1)
$$\tfrac{3}{2}\mathrm{Fe} + \mathrm{O}_2 \rightleftharpoons \tfrac{1}{2}\mathrm{Fe}_3\mathrm{O}_4$$
$$\Delta G = -133{,}900 + 41.1T \qquad (298°\text{–}833°\ \mathrm{K})$$
$$\log P_{\mathrm{O}_2}(\mathrm{atm}) = -(29{,}260/T) + 8.980$$

(2)
$$2\mathrm{Fe} + \mathrm{O}_2 \rightleftharpoons 2\mathrm{FeO}$$
$$\Delta G = -124{,}100 + 29.90T \qquad (298°\text{–}1642°\ \mathrm{K})$$
$$\log P_{\mathrm{O}_2}(\mathrm{atm}) = -(27{,}120/T) + 6.534$$

$$6FeO + O_2 \rightleftharpoons 2Fe_3O_4$$

$$\Delta G = -149{,}250 + 59.80T \qquad (298°\text{–}1642° \text{ K}) \tag{3}$$

$$\log P_{O_2}(\text{atm}) = -(32{,}616/T) + 13.068$$

Measurements for the equilibrium $4Fe_3O_4 + O_2 \rightleftharpoons 6Fe_2O_3$ were extended by Norton (1955) to temperatures as low as 800° C. Taking these values into account, and ΔG^{298} as given by the National Bureau of Standards (1952), Norton arrives at the following approximation:

$$4Fe_3O_4 + O_2 \rightleftharpoons 6Fe_2O_3$$

$$\Delta G = -114{,}000 + 65.9T \qquad (298°\text{–}1730° \text{ K}) \tag{4}$$

$$\log P_{O_2}(\text{atm}) = -(24{,}912/T) + 14.400$$

Isobars must cross fields where two solids coexist isothermally, since in a two-component system three-phase equilibria (two solids + vapor) are isobarically invariant. Fields for a single solid solution such as wüstite are traversed by the isobars in lines descending from left to right. These lines will in general be curved, but have been drawn straight for lack of more accurate data. Whether a solid or a group of solids coexists with a vapor at a particular temperature and pressure must always be decided from a completed isobaric section such as figure 1. A single invariant equilibrium is present within the range of figure 2: iron + wüstite + magnetite + vapor. The temperature of this invariant point is given by Darken and Gurry (1945) as 560° C, by Foster and Welch (1956) as 570° C, and the pressure as 10^{-26} atm. It is therefore not encountered in figure 1.

A series of isobaric sections such as figure 1 can be used to construct a *P-T-X* model of the system Fe–O. An attempt at drawing such a model between 500° and 1000° C is shown in figure 3. Only the surfaces representing solids in equilibrium with vapors and vapors in equilibrium with solids are indicated. The former surfaces are ruled parallel to the compositional axis or are inclined (wüstite) or nearly vertical (magnetite, hematite). The latter surfaces lie close to the oxygen end of the diagram and consist of four curved surfaces, intersecting along the following three boundaries: vapor coexisting with (iron + wüstite), vapor coexisting with (wüstite + magnetite), and vapor coexisting with (magnetite + hematite). The exact location of these latter surfaces has not been determined. The front and back faces of figure 3 show isothermal sections at 500° and 1000° C. The base is a *T-X* projection corresponding to figure 2, and the left side is a *P-T* projection showing the projections of the (solid 1 + solid 2 + vapor) surfaces.

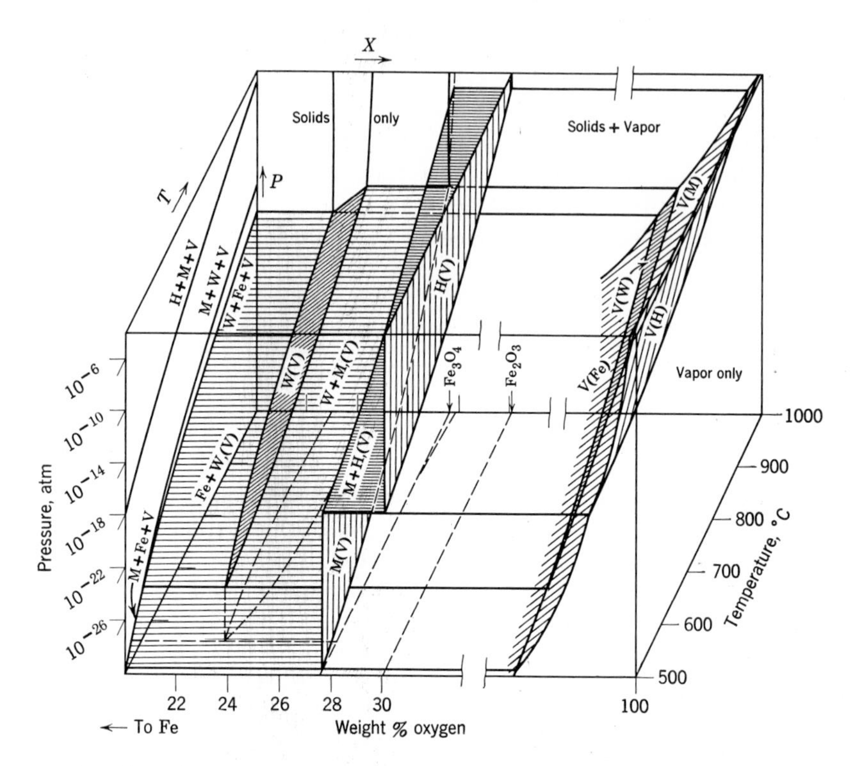

Fig. 3. *P-T-X* model of the system Fe–O between 500° and 1000° C. Surfaces lying within the (solids only) and (solids + vapor) spaces have been omitted and can be located by their intersections with the surfaces of the *P-T-X* model. On the front and back faces of the model, isothermal sections are indicated. The projection onto the base corresponds to figure 2, and that onto the left panel to the central portion of figure 4.

H = hematite; M = magnetite; W = wüstite; Fe = iron; *V* = vapor; H(*V*) = hematite in equilibrium with vapor; M(*V*) = magnetite in equilibrium with vapor; W(*V*) = wüstite in equilibrium with vapor; *V*(H) = vapor in equilibrium with hematite; *V*(M) = vapor in equilibrium with magnetite; *V*(W) = vapor in equilibrium with wüstite; *V*(Fe) = vapor in equilibrium with iron; Fe + W, (*V*) = iron + wüstite in equilibrium with vapor; W + M,(*V*) = wüstite + magnetite in equilibrium with vapor; M + H,(*V*) = magnetite + hematite in equilibrium with vapor. Notation suggested by J. W. Greig.

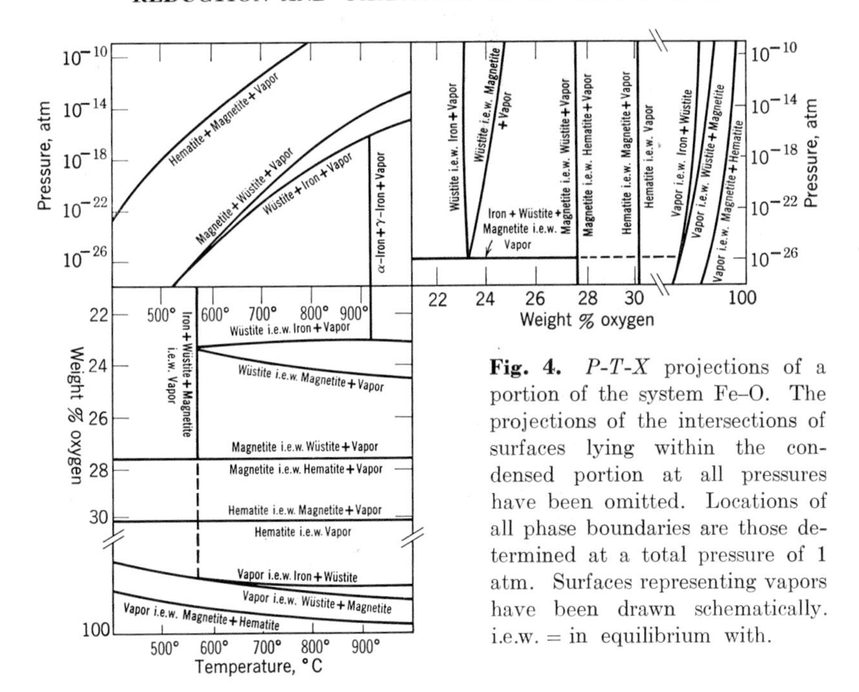

Fig. 4. *P-T-X* projections of a portion of the system Fe–O. The projections of the intersections of surfaces lying within the condensed portion at all pressures have been omitted. Locations of all phase boundaries are those determined at a total pressure of 1 atm. Surfaces representing vapors have been drawn schematically. i.e.w. = in equilibrium with.

A conventional *P-T*, *T-X*, and *P-X* projection of this portion of the Fe–O system is given in figure 4. Since surfaces themselves cannot be projected, figure 4 contains only the projections of the intersections of two or more surfaces. Only the intersections of surfaces present in figure 3 have been projected. The *P-T* projection of figure 4 will be used extensively in the following discussions and must always be understood in the context of the complete *P-T-X* model.

Portions of the System Fe–Si–O

The addition of Si to the Fe–O system introduces two more geologically important phases: quartz (tridymite at higher temperature) and fayalite. Figure 5 shows an isobaric section at a pressure of about 10^{-20} atm. Only surfaces representing solids that can coexist with vapors have been indicated.[4] The composition of the vapor is defined at a given tempera-

[4] The conjugate surfaces representing the composition and temperature of vapors that can coexist with solids lie close to the oxygen corner and have been omitted in figure 5.

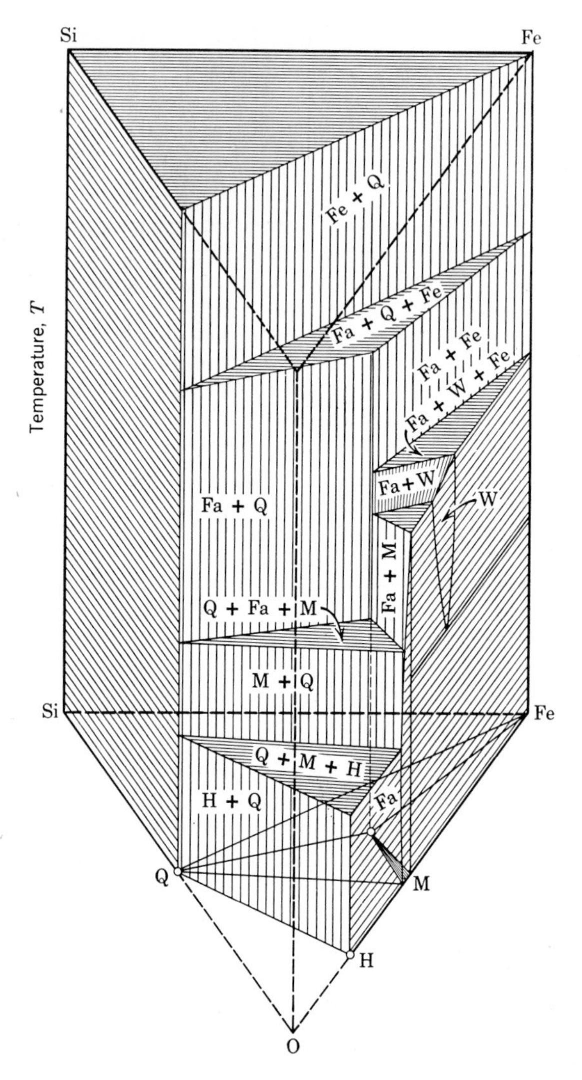

Fig. 5. Isobaric section through a portion of the system Fe–Si–O at a pressure of 10^{-20} bar. Only surfaces representing solids in equilibrium with vapors have been drawn, omitting vapors. Fa, fayalite; Q, quartz; W, wüstite; M, magnetite; H, hematite; *V*, vapor.

ture if it coexists with three solids. Five such cases are present in figure 5: quartz + magnetite + hematite coexisting with vapor; quartz + fayalite + magnetite coexisting with vapor; fayalite + magnetite + wüstite coexisting with vapor; fayalite + wüstite + iron coexisting with vapor; and fayalite + quartz + iron coexisting with vapor. The surfaces representing these five univariant four-phase equilibria appear as curves in the *P-T* projection of figure 6.[5] The location of curve (*a*) for the reaction iron + quartz + oxygen $\rightleftharpoons$ fayalite was extrapolated from high-temperature measurements by Darken (1948), and by Schenck, Franz, and Laymann (1932), assuming that ΔG varies linearly with temperature. The location of curve (*d*) for the reaction fayalite + oxygen $\rightleftharpoons$ magnetite + quartz is less certain. Darken's extrapolation (1948) using his high-temperature measurements and the 900° C point of Schenck et al. (1932) conflicts with an inferred position of this equilibrium at lower temperatures derived from work on annite. In view of the large uncertainty attached to the 900° C point, the inferred value at 650° C and Darken's value at 1118° C have been used to locate curve (*d*).

Figure 6 contains important information relevant to geology and a partial answer to the question: What is the relationship between the states of oxidation of the solids and the partial pressure of oxygen of the vapor phase in equilibrium with them? According to figure 6 magnetite can exist only between curves (*c*) and (*e*). Hematite exists only at and above (to the upper left of) curve (*e*). Most environments in the earth's crust lie above curve (*c*), within the magnetite and hematite fields. On rare occasions the region below curve (*b*) is reached, since metallic iron is known to occur within the earth's crust. Most famous are the occurrences in basalts cross-cutting coal beds, as on the Island of Disco (Greenland). The highest oxygen pressures are found in environments equilibrated with the earth's atmosphere. Although this range of pressures covers several tens of orders of magnitude, for metamorphic processes we can consider a much narrower region. Magnetite extends over only about eight orders of magnitude of oxygen pressures. The pressures are strongly dependent upon temperature. For certain mineral assemblages, such as hematite + magnetite, fayalite + quartz + magnetite, P_{O_2} is defined by the assemblage of solids and the temperature. Other assemblages of solids, such as magnetite + quartz, are insensitive to changes in the oxygen pressures if such changes do not exceed specified upper and

[5] It is evident that in a *P-T* projection three of these univariant curves, (*b*), (*c*), and (*e*), coincide with univariant curves in the system Fe–O. The addition of quartz does not alter the location of curve (*e*) in figure 6.

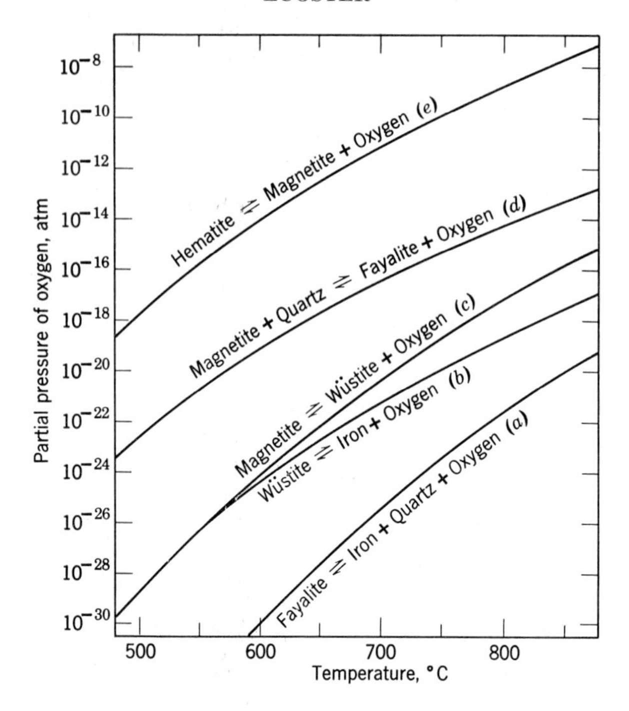

Fig. 6. P_{O_2}–T diagram at a total pressure of 1 atm of part of the system Fe–Si–O. Curves (*a*), (*b*), (*c*), (*d*), and (*e*) correspond to the phase assemblages of the five planes parallel to the temperature axis of figure 5, representing three solids in equilibrium with vapor.

lower limits. All iron-bearing silicates occupy an area in a P_{O_2}–T section such as figure 6, some with an upper boundary beyond which the silicate oxidizes (often to hematite + iron-free silicates) and all with a lower boundary below which the silicate is reduced. It is important to note that there is no direct relation between the P_{O_2}–T curves for oxides and silicates of the same state of oxidation. Fayalite is stable within the magnetite field and within that of metallic iron.

Recently P_{O_2}–T curves for several hydrous silicates have been determined experimentally (see p. 412). These curves form a geologic P_{O_2}–T grid and contain implications for many important mineral assemblages.

Effects of the Presence of Water

The effects of addition of water to these simple systems must be considered next. At supercritical conditions, the chief species present in the fluid are H_2O, O_2, and H_2. Their concentrations are determined by the thermal dissociation of water

$$H_2O \rightleftharpoons H_2 + \tfrac{1}{2}O_2$$

with the following constant

$$(Kp)_T = \frac{P_{H_2} \times (P_{O_2})^{1/2}}{P_{H_2O}}$$

Wagman et al. (1945) have tabulated *Kp*'s at 1 atm total pressure for a series of temperatures (table 1). Interpolations for even-hundred degrees centigrade lead to the values in table 2. Knowledge of *Kp* makes

Equilibrium Constants for the Dissociation of Water

TABLE 1		TABLE 2	
T, °K	log *Kp*	*T*, °C	log *Kp*
500	−22.8855	300	−19.647
600	−18.6323	400	−16.305
700	−15.5832	500	−13.827
800	−13.2285	600	−11.903
900	−11.4978	700	−10.395
1000	−10.0610	800	−9.175
1100	−8.8830	900	−8.142
1200	−7.8936		

it possible to calculate the partial pressure of hydrogen (P_{H_2}) that is equivalent to a specific P_{O_2} at a given temperature and water pressure. These hydrogen pressures are very much larger than the equivalent oxygen pressures under geologic conditions, and are physically significant.

Water affects dry iron-rich mineral assemblages particularly through the formation of hydrous silicates and through drastic changes in diffusion rates. We shall first discuss the consequences in a region where no hydrates form and where transport of material is not of importance.

No hydrous phases are present

If we add water to the system Fe–O in the range of temperatures and pressures considered here, the vapor in equilibrium with solids consists essentially of H_2O, of a mixture of $H_2O + H_2$, or of a mixture of $H_2O + O_2$. The composition of this vapor cannot be calculated accurately for a given temperature and pressure, since the dissociation constants

TABLE 3. Composition of an Aqueous Vapor in Equilibrium with Pairs of Iron Oxides at 1 Atm in Mole Per Cent

Temperature, °C	Hematite + Magnetite	Magnetite + Wüstite	Magnetite + Iron	Wüstite + Iron
400	0.001% H_2 99.999% H_2O	. . . . . .	89.75% H_2 10.25% H_2O	. . . . . .
500	0.001% H_2 99.999% H_2O	. . . . . .	80.25% H_2 19.75% H_2O	. . . . . .
600	0.001% H_2 99.999% H_2O	63.6% H_2 36.4% H_2O	. . . . . .	69.7% H_2 30.3% H_2O
700	0.001% H_2 99.999% H_2O	40.3% H_2 59.7% H_2O	. . . . . .	65.2% H_2 34.8% H_2O
800	0.001% H_2 99.999% H_2O	23.5% H_2 76.5% H_2O	. . . . . .	61.0% H_2 39.0% H_2O
900	0.001% H_2 99.999% H_2O	14.3% H_2 85.7% H_2O	. . . . . .	58.5% H_2 41.5% H_2O

for water at high pressures are not known. The significant points nevertheless become clear if we use 1 atm data as a first approximation.

Table 3 gives the composition of an aqueous vapor phase (in mole per cent) equilibrated with hematite + magnetite, magnetite + wüstite, and magnetite + iron for a series of temperatures and for a water pressure of 1 atm ($P_{H_2O} = 1$ atm). Compositions in the last two columns can be considered to represent the most hydrogen-rich vapors that would be encountered in geologic environments. Figure 7 shows isothermal sections through the system Fe–O–H (no hydrates), indicating the vapor compositions given in table 3. For a hematite–magnetite assemblage the aqueous vapor is essentially pure H_2O over the whole temperature range considered. For assemblages of solids with a lower oxygen pressure it is a mixture of $H_2O + H_2$ (neglecting small amounts of oxygen), and for assemblages with a higher oxygen pressure it may be considered a mixture of $H_2O + O_2$ (neglecting small amounts of hydrogen).

The particular case where hydrogen and oxygen are present in the ratio 2:1 (bulk composition of the vapor is H_2O, neglecting small amounts of iron) is governed by the following two conditions:

$$P_{O_2} = \left[\frac{(Kp)_T \times P_{H_2O}}{P_{H_2}}\right]^2 \quad \text{and} \quad \frac{P_{H_2}}{P_{O_2}} = \frac{2}{1}$$

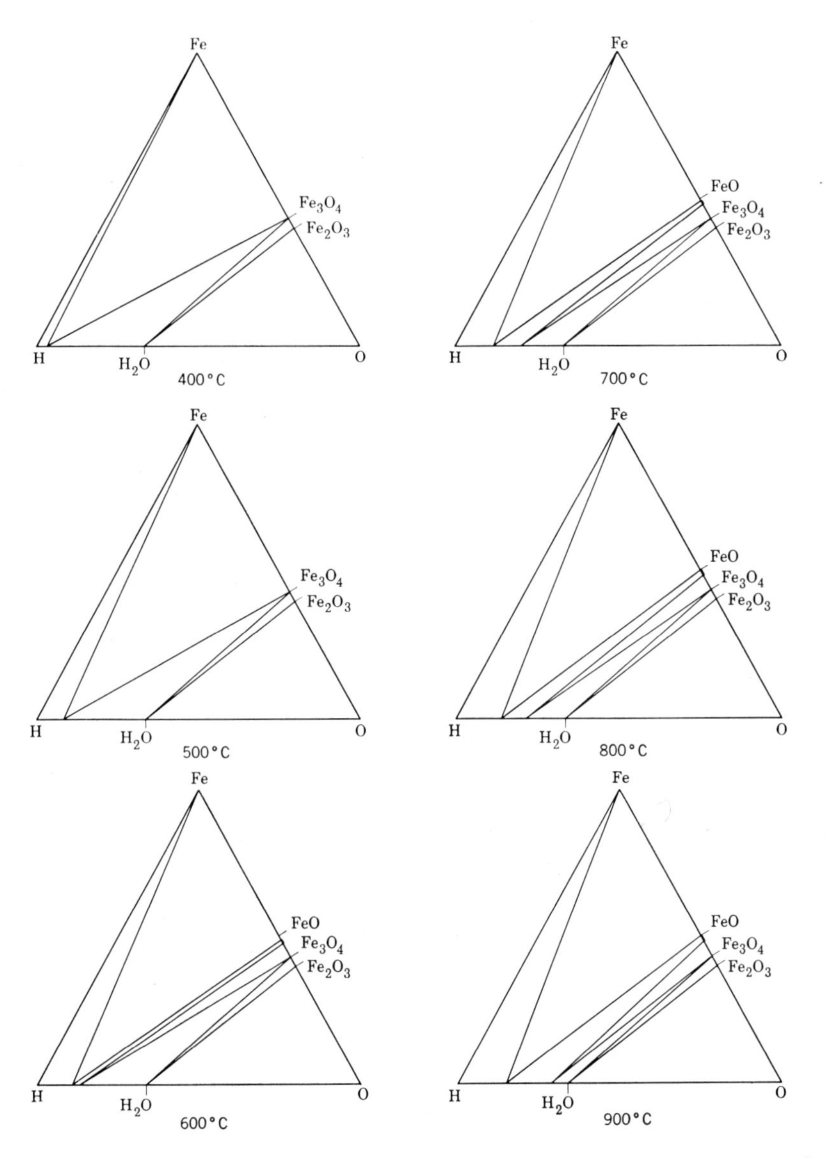

Fig. 7. Isothermal sections through the system Fe–O–H at a water pressure of 1 atm. Compositions in mole per cent.

P_{H_2} and P_{O_2} can be calculated for any temperature and 1 atm water pressure.

$$P_{O_2} = \left[\frac{(Kp)_T \times P_{H_2O}}{2}\right]^{2/3} \quad \text{and} \quad P_{H_2} = 2\left[\frac{(Kp)_T \times P_{H_2O}}{2}\right]^{2/3}$$

Table 4 gives the partial hydrogen pressures satisfying these conditions for a series of temperatures. These data have been plotted in the P_{H_2}–T

TABLE 4. Logarithms of the Hydrogen Pressures for an Aqueous Vapor of the Bulk Composition (H_2O)

T, °C	log P_{H_2}
300	−12.998
400	−10.770
500	−9.118
600	−7.835
700	−6.830
800	−6.016
900	−5.328

diagram of figure 8, and the curve has been labeled "pure water." The hydrogen pressures in the aqueous phase in equilibrium with hematite + magnetite, magnetite + wüstite, and wüstite + iron at 1 atm water pressure are also presented. Below 1050° C an aqueous vapor of the bulk composition H_2O coexists with hematite, and above this temperature with magnetite. Fayalite, for instance, cannot coexist with H_2O, but only a mixture of ($H_2O + H_2$). At a given temperature fayalite can be in equilibrium with a range of such mixtures, the range being indicated by the width of the P_{O_2}–T field of fayalite in figure 6.

Let us consider now the effects on the chemical potential of oxygen of adding an aqueous vapor at constant T to a previously dry mineral assemblage, say magnetite + hematite. At a given temperature and pressure magnetite + hematite define μ_{O_2} of the system. If the aqueous vapor added is different in composition from H_2O, μ_{O_2} of either the solids or the vapor will have to be adjusted. The relative masses of solids to vapor added will decide whether μ_{O_2} of the resulting system (solids + aqueous vapor) will be determined by μ_{O_2} of the dry solids or μ_{O_2} of the vapor. If the individual masses of the solids are large, the system is buffered in relation to additions or subtractions of oxygen or hydrogen, since μ_{O_2} of the system will remain constant as long as some hematite and magnetite are present simultaneously. An aqueous vapor never

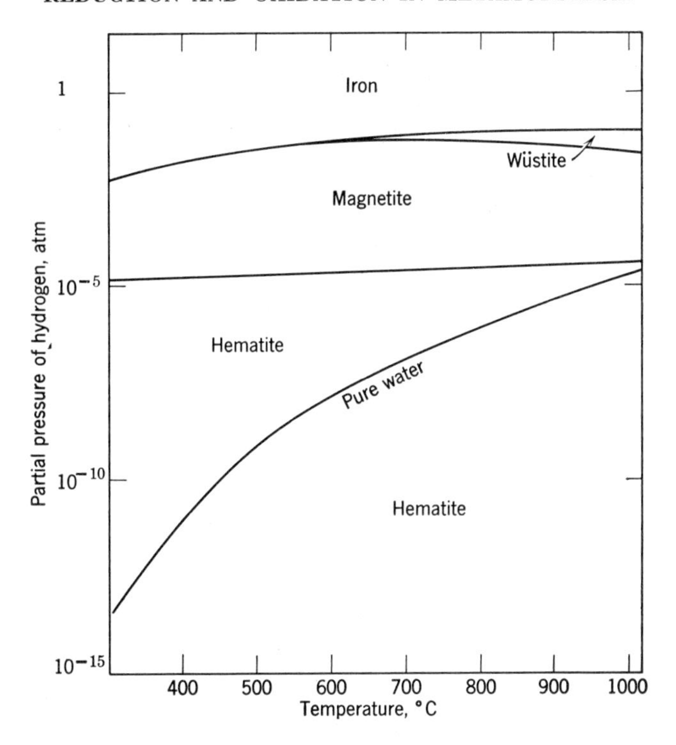

Fig. 8. P_{H_2}–T diagram of a portion of the system Fe–O–H at a water pressure of 1 atm. No hydrates have been assumed to form. For the meaning of the curve labeled "pure water" see text.

will be buffered, since changes in oxygen or hydrogen contents will immediately be reflected in changes of μ_{O_2}. The chemical potential of oxygen of a magnetite–hematite rock therefore will remain unchanged during metamorphism unless large amounts of hydrogen or oxygen are added, whereas the relative masses magnetite to hematite (total oxygen content of the solids) will vary frequently and readily. Some specific examples will be discussed later (p. 421).

The presence of water in iron-rich rocks affects transport processes drastically. The diffusion of hydrogen in one direction has the same net effect on redox reactions as the diffusion of oxygen in the opposite direction. Diffusion rates of hydrogen are much greater than those of either water or oxygen. Therefore, if water is present during metamorphism, much greater areas will be equilibrated in relation to μ_{O_2} gradients.

Hydrous silicates are present

P_{O_2}–T curves for iron oxides and fayalite have been presented in figure 6. Fayalite is the only silicate for which the effects of P_{O_2} on stability have been published (Darken, 1948). Unfortunately, no quantitative data on the stability of the hydrous silicates in the system Fe–Si–O–H are available (Smith, 1957). Greenalite, minnesotaite, and grünerite have reportedly been synthesized (Flaschen and Osborn, 1957), but reactions proceed so slowly that it was not feasible to determine phase boundaries. The most complete experimental information available in this connection is the work on a ferrous biotite, annite (Eugster, 1957*a* and *b*). This work was made possible by controlling P_{O_2} of the charge during the experiments at high total pressures (Eugster, 1957*a*). An osmotic double-tube system is employed, the charge being contained in the inner sealed platinum tube. This inner tube is surrounded by an oxygen buffer (such as magnetite + hematite + water), which in turn is protected by an outer sealed gold tube. Hydrogen diffuses through the platinum tube and imposes μ_{O_2} and μ_{H_2} of the buffer upon the charge. Attainment of equilibrium can be demonstrated by standard procedures. This experimental technique is now used extensively in investigating the phase relations of iron-rich amphiboles, micas, chlorites, and spinels.

The P_{H_2O}–P_{O_2}–T Stability Volume of Hydrous Iron Silicates as Illustrated by Annite

An understanding of the stability relations of hydrous iron-bearing silicates is of great importance for the interpretation of both igneous and metamorphic processes; some of the reactions involving such silicates are hydration-dehydration reactions, some are redox reactions, and others are a combination of the two. It is imperative that the effects of changes in P_{O_2} be separated from those of changes in P_{H_2O}.

The type of analysis necessary will be demonstrated by using annite, $KFe_3^{+2}AlSi_3O_{10}(OH)_2$, the ferrous analogue of phlogopite, as an example. Annite is stable within a P_{tot}–P_{O_2}–T volume, which will be explained by first using P_{O_2}–T sections.

P_{O_2}–T sections at a constant total pressure

The P_{O_2}–T section at a constant total pressure ($P_{tot} = P_{gas} = 2000$ bars $\approx P_{H_2O} + P_{H_2}$) and a constant bulk composition (except for hydrogen content) is given in figure 9. The locations of the curves (*a*), (*b*), (*c*), (*d*), and (*e*) are the same as those of the corresponding curves in figure 6. They represent the P_{O_2}–T curves of the buffers used for the

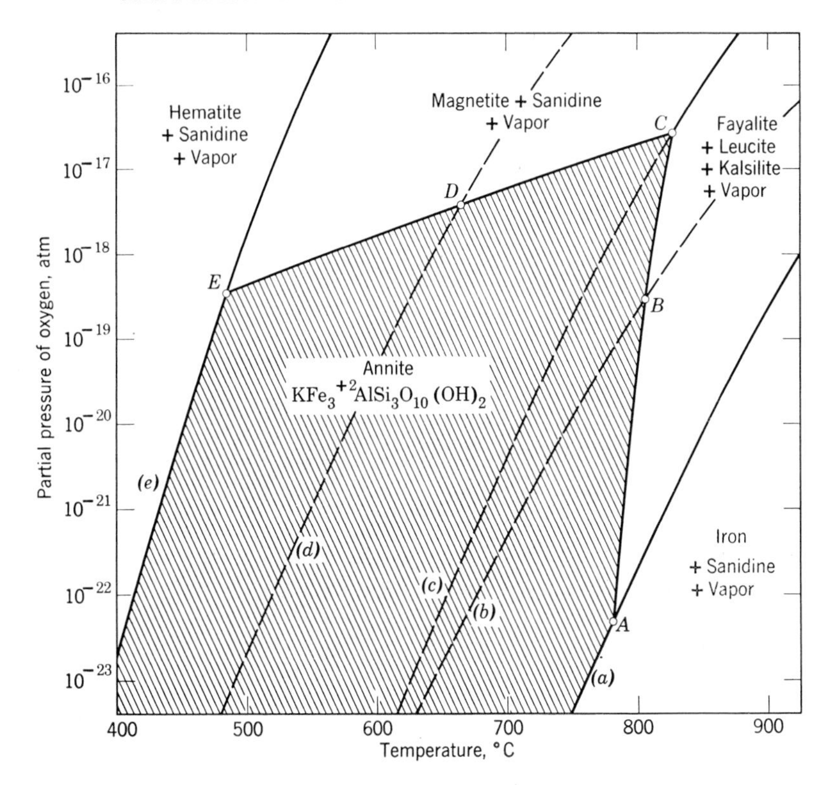

Fig. 9. Isobaric P_{O_2}–T section [$P_{tot} = (P_{H_2O} + P_{H_2}) = 2000$ bars] of the phase relations of annite. Curves (*a*), (*b*), (*c*), (*d*), and (*e*) are those of figure 6. Phase boundaries are in solid lines; P_{O_2}–T curves for buffers employed, which are not simultaneously phase boundaries, are dashed.

control of P_{O_2} and P_{H_2} during the runs.[6] Experiments at constant and known P_{O_2} can be performed only along these five curves. The location of points A, B, C, D, and E has been determined by reversing the corresponding reactions (within $\pm 5°$ C). Some of the phase boundaries for annite coincide with parts of the buffer curves. Portions of curves for buffers which are not phase boundaries for annite are dashed. The field of stability of annite is defined by four univariant curves (univariant

[6] Curves (*a*) to (*e*) of figure 6 are based on 1 atm data. A total pressure of 2000 bars will affect the locations of these curves. Corrections cannot be calculated accurately because of the lack of the necessary data for gas mixtures, but preliminary calculations indicate that they will be small. Therefore, the P_{O_2} scales of all diagrams are based on the 1 atm data of the buffers.

at a constant total pressure only): curve (*a*) below point *A*, curve *ABC*, curve *CDE*, and curve (*e*) below point *E*. The four assemblages that can coexist with annite are: (1) iron + sanidine + vapor, (2) fayalite + leucite + kalsilite + vapor, (3) magnetite + sanidine + vapor, and (4) hematite + sanidine + vapor. The following reactions are represented by the univariant curves:

$$(1)\quad 2KFe_3AlSi_3O_{10}(OH)_2 \rightleftharpoons 2KAlSi_3O_8 + 6Fe + 2H_2O + 3O_2$$

$$(2)\quad 2KFe_3AlSi_3O_{10}(OH)_2 \rightleftharpoons KAlSi_2O_6 + KAlSiO_4 + 3Fe_2SiO_4 + 2H_2O$$

$$(3)\quad 2KAlSi_3O_8 + 2Fe_3O_4 + 2H_2O \rightleftharpoons 2KFe_3AlSi_3O_{10}(OH)_2 + O_2$$

$$(4)\quad 4KAlSi_3O_8 + 6Fe_2O_3 + 4H_2O \rightleftharpoons 4KFe_3AlSi_3O_{10}(OH)_2 + 3O_2$$

The more reduced assemblages are on the right, and the more oxidized ones on the left. All curves have a slope with

$$\left(\frac{\partial P_{O_2}}{\partial T}\right)_{P_{tot}} > 0$$

The formulations in reactions 1 and 2 are somewhat schematic since the (OH) groups released from annite will not combine to H_2O, but to a mixture of (H_2O + H_2), and the actual amount of oxygen released on the right-hand side will therefore be slightly higher.

A, *C*, and *E* are points where three of the five assemblages meet. They are intersections of curves which are univariant in the P_{tot}–P_{O_2}–T space [7] with the plane of figure 9. A detailed analysis shows that *A* and *C* each actually are double points (*A′*, *A″*, and *C′*, *C″*), which cannot be separated experimentally. *B* and *D* are not points of special significance on the respective phase boundaries and do not belong to such univariant curves but are points that can be determined experimentally, since they also lie on the buffer curves (*b*) and (*d*), respectively.

Without analyzing figure 10 in greater detail,[8] we can draw the geologically significant conclusions:

1. Annite cannot coexist with hematite at an oxygen pressure higher than that of a hematite–magnetite assemblage. For a given temperature the P_{O_2} of a hematite–magnetite assemblage is the highest P_{O_2} at which annite is still stable.

[7] Curves (α), (γ), and (ε) of figure 10.

[8] Detailed documentations and discussions will be published elsewhere.

2. Annite is stable to the lowest geologically possible oxygen pressures, since it extends even below the wüstite field. The lower boundary for fayalite, curve (*a*), coincides with that for annite below point *A*.

3. Annite can exist within the field of stability of magnetite up to temperatures represented by the curve *CE*. The temperatures at which annite coexists with sanidine and magnetite depend very strongly on the magnitude of the oxygen pressure. Point *E* lies at 485° C, and point *C* at 827° C. The location of the equilibrium for one and the same reaction is shifted more than 300° C for an equivalent change in P_{O_2} of about two orders of magnitude.[9]

It is obvious that this pronounced effect will be very significant in assigning variables to reactions observed in natural mineral assemblages.

4. Point *C* at 827° C is the highest temperature, and simultaneously also the highest P_{O_2}, at which annite can exist at 2000 bars ($P_{H_2O} + P_{H_2}$). A drop in temperature at constant P_{O_2} will result in the formation of magnetite + sanidine; a rise in temperature at the same P_{O_2} will lead to fayalite + leucite + kalsilite. Geologically speaking, sanidine + magnetite can be considered the high-temperature and annite the low-temperature assemblage, because in nature an increase in temperature is usually accompanied by an increase in P_{O_2}. This relationship is well illustrated by point *D*. Below 665° C on curve (*d*) annite is stable. An increase in temperature will often approximately follow curves for buffered assemblages such as curve (*d*), and will therefore lead to magnetite + sanidine.

5. Below curve (*c*) magnetite is not stable. Between curves (*c*) and (*a*) annite reacts to form fayalite + leucite + kalsilite + vapor at high temperatures. A possible assemblage would be wüstite + sanidine + vapor. In all ranges investigated it was found to be less stable than fayalite + leucite + kalsilite + vapor. This latter assemblage is equivalent to the high-temperature assemblage of the phlogopite composition: forsterite + leucite + kalsilite + vapor (Yoder and Eugster, 1954).

6. Annite coexists with fayalite + leucite + kalsilite along curve *ABC*. This equilibrium does not depend strongly on the magnitude of P_{O_2}. The slight positive slope of the curve signifies that some oxygen is participating in the reaction either because annite contains some ferric iron, because fayalite is deficient in oxygen, or because the stoichiometric water given off by the hydrate is converted to a vapor of the composition ($H_2O + H_2$).

[9] It must be remembered that the corresponding change in P_{H_2} is more impressive. The vapor in equilibrium with annite at point *C* is much richer in hydrogen than that in equilibrium with annite at point *E*. Hydrogen pressures were not calculated, for lack of data on the dissociation constant of water at high pressures.

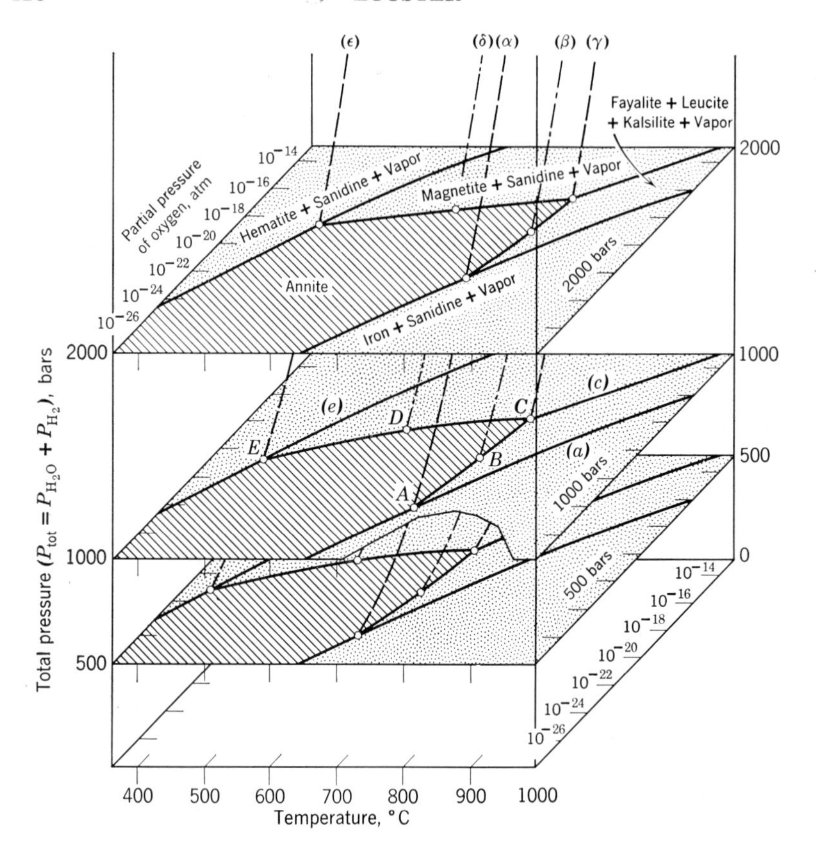

Fig. 10. P_{tot}-P_{O_2}-T model of the phase relations of annite, $KFe_3{}^{+2}AlSi_3O_{10}$-$(OH)_2$, presented in isobaric sections. For explanation of curves (α), (β), (γ), (δ), and (ε) see text.

The P_{tot}–P_{O_2}–T stability volume

From a series of isobaric sections like that in figure 9 it is possible to construct a three-dimensional diagram with P_{tot} ($= P_{H_2O} + P_{H_2}$), P_{O_2}, and T as independent variables. Figure 10 shows such a diagram. Isobaric sections have been indicated at 500, 1000, and 2000 bars. The points A, B, C, D, and E are the same as in figure 9. A, C, and E lie on univariant lines representing the reactions

(ε) annite ⇌ sanidine + magnetite + hematite + vapor (at point E)

(γ) annite ⇌ sanidine + magnetite + fayalite + leucite + vapor (at point C)

(α) annite $\rightleftharpoons$ fayalite + iron + sanidine + leucite + vapor
(at point A)

Reaction (ε) can be described in a four-component system, whereas five components are necessary to express all phases present in reactions (γ) and (α). It should be kept in mind that along these three curves P_{O_2} does not remain constant, since points A, C, and E move along curves (a), (c), and (e) with changes in the total pressure.

Curves (α), (γ), and (ε) are the intersections of three bivariant surfaces each, while curves (β) and (δ) each lie within bivariant surfaces. Seven such bivariant surfaces are present in figure 10 and have been drawn explicitly in figure 11. They are defined by the following curves: S_1: (e) below point E and (ε); S_2: (e) above point E and (ε); S_3: (ε) and (γ); S_4: (c) above point C; S_5: (γ) and (α); S_6: (a) below point A and (α);

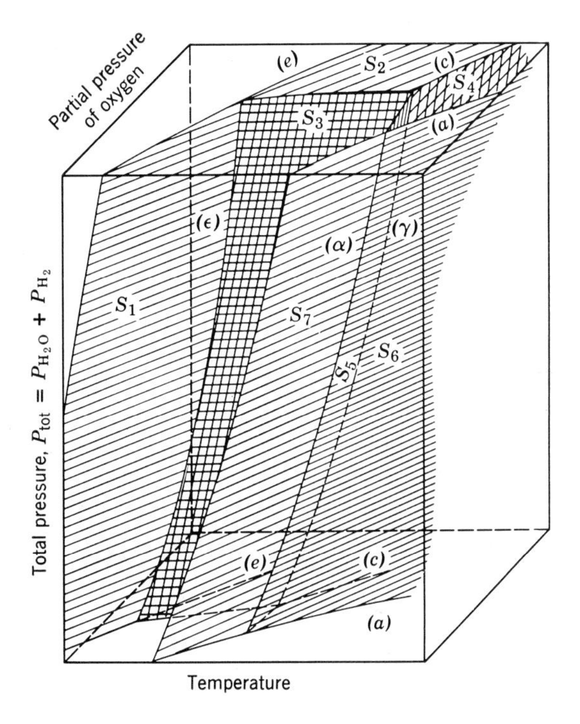

Fig. 11. P_{tot}-P_{O_2}-T model as in figure 10, but bivariant surfaces S_1, S_2, S_3, S_4, S_5, S_6, and S_7 and univariant curves (α), (γ), and (ϵ) are emphasized. Annite is stable in the space bound by surfaces S_1, S_3, S_5, and S_7. Phase assemblages existing in the remaining spaces can be determined by comparison with figure 10.

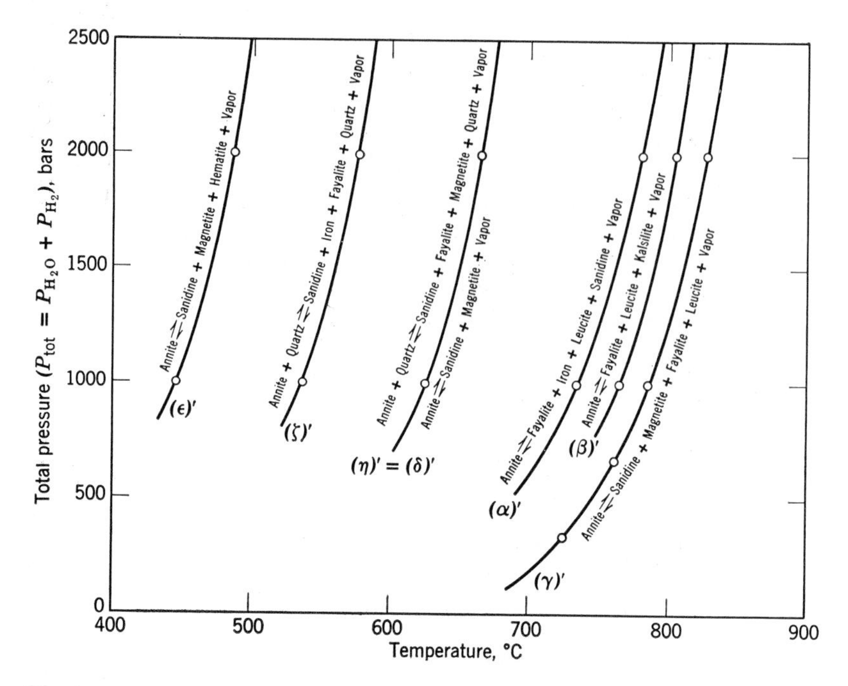

Fig. 12. P_{tot}–T diagram ($P_{tot} = P_{H_2O} + P_{H_2}$) showing phase relations of annite and annite + quartz. Curves $(\alpha)'$, $(\beta)'$, $(\gamma)'$, $(\delta)'$, and $(\epsilon)'$ are projections of the curves (α), (β), (γ), (δ), and (ϵ) of figure 10, projected along the P_{O_2} axis.

S_7: (a) above point A and (α). They separate five volumes in the P_{tot}–P_{O_2}–T space, representing the assemblages annite + vapor, hematite + sanidine + vapor, magnetite + sanidine + vapor, fayalite + leucite + kalsilite + vapor, and iron + sanidine + vapor.

The data contained in figures 9 and 10 can also be presented in a projection along the P_{O_2} axis onto the P_{tot}–T plane. Figure 12 shows the five curves (α), (β), (γ), (δ), and (ε) in such a projection. The projected curves are labeled $(\alpha)'$, $(\beta)'$, $(\gamma)'$, $(\delta)'$, and $(\varepsilon)'$. It is understood that along each of the curves the oxygen pressure does not remain constant but changes in accordance with the buffers used.

For iron-free silicates, P_{H_2O}–T curves drawn at a fixed bulk composition ("upper stability limits") represent univariant reactions; that is, for a given water pressure the reaction proceeds at a fixed temperature. For iron-rich silicates like annite not all such curves represent univariant reactions, but some are arbitrary curves on bivariant surfaces, as for example curves $(\beta)'$ and $(\delta)'$.

Figure 12 contains some information on the stability of annite in the presence of an excess of quartz not shown in figures 9 and 10. For a bulk composition annite + quartz, the high-temperature assemblage fayalite + sanidine occupies the whole space between curves (*a*) and (*d*) of figure 9 and the field where annite appears is much smaller, point *D* representing the highest temperature. The location of curve *ED* is not changed measurably by the addition of quartz.[10] Curve $(\zeta)'$ of figure 12 was determined with a (fayalite + iron + quartz) buffer, and the 2000-bar point lies on curve (*a*) of figure 9.

The implications of the work on annite on the interpretation of other hydrous iron silicates are evident. Many of the general relationships will be analogous in that all such silicates will occupy a volume in the P_{tot}–P_{O_2}–T space. Portions of curves (*a*) to (*e*) may often be phase boundaries in even much more complex systems. Some significant points can be formulated as follows:

1. All iron-bearing silicates occupy a region within a P_{O_2}–T section such as figure 9. The fields of stability of ferric silicates will in general extend to higher oxygen pressures than those of ferrous silicates, with the oxygen pressure of the atmosphere as a limit.
2. No direct correlations exist between the state of oxidation of iron in the solids and their P_{O_2}–T curves. Ferrous silicates may be oxidized within the magnetite field (e.g., fayalite), on the magnetite–hematite boundary (annite), or within the hematite field. Each silicate must be investigated separately.
3. All phase boundaries representing redox reactions are affected by changes in P_{O_2} and are therefore inclined to the P_{O_2} axis.
4. Phase boundaries representing equilibria which do not involve a transfer of oxygen lie parallel to the P_{O_2} axis. It must be remembered, nevertheless, that a release of H_2O from solids on dehydration represents a transfer of oxygen if the aqueous vapor with which the solids are in equilibrium does not have the composition H_2O.

Laboratory Data on Other Iron Silicates

The discussion of the stability of annite has clearly shown that for the interpretation of mineral assemblages containing iron silicates it is paramount that the stability of the participating iron silicates be known in terms of the first-order variables T, P_{tot}, P_{H_2O}, and P_{O_2}. The simplifying assumptions $P_{tot} \approx P_{H_2O}$ or $P_{tot} \approx (P_{H_2O} + P_{H_2})$ are sometimes

[10] Curve (δ) therefore has become a univariant curve in the P_{tot}–P_{O_2}–T space for annite + quartz, since it now is the intersection of two bivariant surfaces [labeled $(\delta)' = (\eta)'$ in fig. 11]. (ζ) also is a univariant curve in this space.

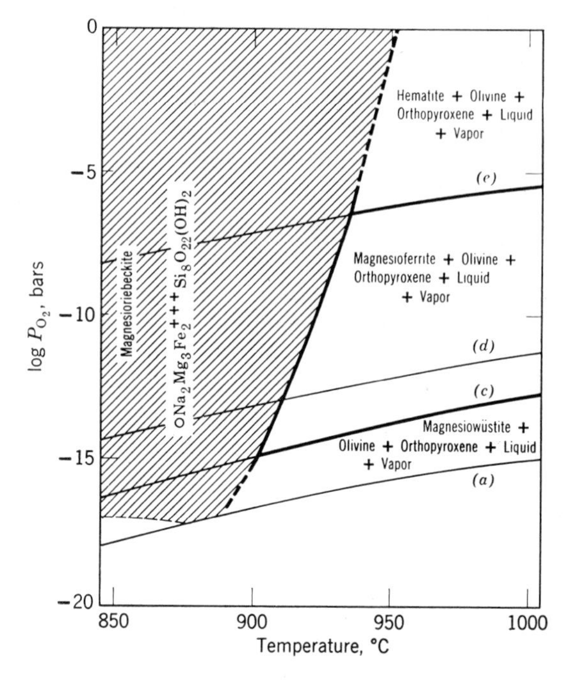

Fig. 13. P_{O_2}–T section of the phase relations of magnesioriebeckite at a total pressure of 2000 bars [$P_{tot} = (P_{H_2O} + P_{H_2}) = 2000$ bars]. Curves (c), (d), and (e) are those of figure 6. Phase boundaries in heavy lines; curves for P_{O_2} buffers in light dashed lines. From Ernst (1958).

permissible. Muan (1958) has recently summarized high-temperature data available on the crystallization of "dry" silicates and oxides containing iron. Iron oxides, fayalite, and annite are the only compounds for which subsolidus data with P_{O_2} as a variable have been discussed so far. Data on the stability of magnesioriebeckites obtained by Ernst (1957) are presented in another section (see p. 394). Ernst (1958) has published a P_{O_2}–T section at $P_{tot} = (P_{H_2O} + P_{H_2}) = 2000$ bars, which is reproduced in figure 13.

Magnesioriebeckite, $Na_2Mg_3Fe_2{}^{+3}Si_8O_{22}(OH)_2$, is a good example of a silicate containing predominantly ferric iron. Its field of stability must extend to oxygen pressures greater than those of curve (e), and it is likely to be stable at oxygen pressures of the atmosphere. The lowest oxygen pressures at which it was encountered are those of a wüstite–iron assemblage. Ernst found a direct correlation between the refractive indices of the magnesioriebeckites and the oxygen pressures at which they were synthesized. These indices can be changed reversibly if a magnesioriebeckite synthesized at a low P_{O_2} is held in an environment with a higher P_{O_2}, and vice versa.

Stability of Hydrous Silicates with Intermediate Mg/Fe Ratios

Pure iron end members such as annite are very rare in nature. Most natural minerals are members of solid solutions, frequently with a magnesian end member. The join phlogopite–annite is a good example. Eugster and Wones (1958) have analyzed the phase relations on such a join. Wones (1958) has determined some of the phase boundaries of intermediate biotites. Employing a Cu-CuO buffer, which has a slightly higher oxygen pressure than a magnetite–hematite assemblage below 650° C, he has found that phlogopites containing as little as 20 per cent annite exsolve hematite + almost pure phlogopite within the hematite field close to the hematite–magnetite boundary [curve (*e*), fig. 6]. It appears as if intermediate biotites behave similarly to annite. Nevertheless, extrapolations from end members must be treated with caution.

The data reviewed so far bear on a great number of geologic problems. We shall concentrate on three questions of general interest.

Metamorphism of Precambrian Iron Formations

The compositions of parts of the Precambrian iron formations of Michigan and Minnesota lie almost wholly within the system Fe–Si–O–H and are therefore good examples to demonstrate some of the relationships discussed in previous sections. Remarks in this section are restricted to the "oxide-facies" (James, 1955). This facies consists of rhythmically banded iron oxide–chert rocks, with the individual bands up to ½ inch thick.[11] In many cases the iron oxide bands contain either magnetite or hematite, but not both. Most interesting in this context are cases where magnetite–chert units are interbedded with hematite–chert units. Such beds are often not more than a few feet thick and persist laterally over considerable distances.[12] Boundaries between hematite–chert units and magnetite–chert units are sharp and straight, suggesting that the differences in the oxygen contents are linked to original sedimentary differences. The effects of metamorphism on such units have been discussed by James (1955). Yoder (1957) also has considered possible se-

[11] See for instance plates in Van Hise and Bayley (1897).

[12] Good examples are exposed in the stratigraphic lower portions of the Republic node (James, 1955).

quences of dehydration reactions during progressive metamorphism.

Three inferred conditions can be distinguished: (1) the complex remained dry during metamorphism; (2) some water was probably present, but P_{H_2O} was not high enough for hydrates to form; (3) P_{H_2O} was high and hydrous silicates are present.

1. No mineralogical changes are visible. Intensity of metamorphism is indicated by the grain size in the chert bands. Both hematite and magnetite are stable to the highest degrees of metamorphism. Boundaries between magnetite–chert and hematite–chert units remain sharp. It is not known directly whether differences in μ_{O_2} exist between these units, since it is conceivable that μ_{O_2} has a fixed value throughout such an interbedded magnetite–hematite complex at a fixed temperature. Observations of example 3 indicate that marked differences exist between the magnetite units and the hematite units. Nevertheless, no exchange of oxygen is traceable through mineral assemblages even at highest grades of metamorphism.

2. In this example mineralogical changes in the oxide bands are clearly discernible, but no new minerals appear. Boundaries between hematite–chert and magnetite–chert units remain sharp and can still be traced by the color of the chert (red and gray, respectively). But close to this boundary large hematite plates ("specularite") appear within the magnetite bands and magnetite can be found within the hematite bands. Hence across such boundaries no gradients in the chemical potential exist for a certain distance. This region, which can be inches or feet wide, indicates exchange of oxygen between the two units during metamorphism, probably sparked by the presence of water (diffusion of hydrogen).

3. Hydrous silicates are very abundant in the oxide facies, particularly greenalite, minnesotaite, and grünerite. They are consistently found only in the magnetite–chert units separating the individual magnetite bands from the chert bands. The absence of silicates in hematite–chert units can best be explained by assuming that μ_{O_2} was too high for these essentially ferrous silicates to form.

Minnesotaite and especially grünerite do not grow solely at the expense of greenalite during progressive metamorphism, but also form at the expense of magnetite and chert, since the width of the silicate bands often increases with higher degrees of metamorphism.

A particularly interesting problem is raised by the virtual absence of fayalite. It has only been found in special locations in the Mesabi, Vermilion, and Gunflint ranges, usually related to contact effects of gabbros associated with the Duluth gabbro. Fayalite should form from quartz

+ magnetite whenever P_{O_2} lies below that of curve (*d*) (see fig. 6), even at low temperatures, provided that P_{H_2O} is low enough to prevent the formation of hydrates. It did not form in most of the banded magnetite–chert layers, probably because P_{O_2} was too high.[13] This would mean that fayalite-bearing rocks, which are usually considered to be the highest-grade equivalents of the metamorphosed iron formations, must have formed in a more reducing environment and not necessarily at the highest temperatures, although in many cases both conditions may have been fulfilled simultaneously.

Redox Reactions and Mineral Facies

A few remarks on the relation between redox reactions and the mineral facies principle may be useful. A particular mineral facies is characterized by specific ranges of a set of physical variables. A mineral facies whose critical assemblage is sensitive to changes in P_{H_2} (and therefore also P_{O_2}, since in natural environments water is always present where hydrogen is present) [14] must hence be defined by giving not only the ranges of pressures and temperatures over which it is stable but also the permissible limits of P_{H_2} or P_{O_2}.

Thompson (1955) has discussed a system containing mobile components, such as volatiles, and he states, "The field of stability of a mineral facies . . . is . . . dependent on pressure, temperature, *and* the chemical potential of the mobile components." Hydrogen is clearly the most mobile of all volatile components of rocks. Since redox reactions are often coupled with hydration-dehydration in nature, we may be forced to treat such systems as open simultaneously to at least two mobile components: hydrogen and water.

Reduction and Oxidation during Metamorphism

In the previous sections it has been demonstrated that the temperatures at which redox reactions proceed depend strongly upon the magnitude of P_{O_2} (or μ_{O_2}) of the system to which the participating phases belong. The question therefore arises as to what defines P_{O_2} of a complex mineral assemblage and when and where changes of P_{O_2} are likely to occur during metamorphism.

Rocks containing both the reduced and oxidized members of a redox

[13] Reaction rates are not likely to be responsible for the absence of fayalite, since fayalite forms rapidly even at low water pressures and temperatures.

[14] A good example is the relation between the epidote–amphibolite and the amphibolite facies, which in general involves differences in the states of oxidation.

reaction, such as magnetite + hematite, magnetite + fayalite + quartz, annite (or biotite) + magnetite + K-feldspar, have a fixed P_{O_2} at any given temperature. Furthermore, this P_{O_2} is unaffected by additions or subtractions of hydrogen as long as the masses of the solids prevail (buffered system).

Rocks with assemblages unbuffered in relation to P_{O_2} often contain ferrous–ferric silicates whose composition defines P_{O_2} of the assemblage. Small additions or subtractions of hydrogen will change both P_{O_2} and the Fe^{+2}/Fe^{+3} ratio of the iron silicate (see magnesioriebeckite, p. 420). In such unbuffered assemblages P_{O_2} will often have been defined and imposed by a larger external system. Changes in P_{O_2} of this external system will be reflected in changes of temperatures at which particular redox reactions proceed.[15]

Changes in P_{O_2} of a mineral assemblage are produced by addition of either hydrogen, or a mixture of hydrogen + water, or an oxygen-rich aqueous phase. Therefore, reduction and oxidation most readily occur during metamorphism where water is present. Whether a mineral assemblage is being oxidized or reduced depends on the composition of the aqueous phase added. If the oxygen and hydrogen contents of this aqueous phase are such that it has the same P_{O_2} as the mineral assemblage, no changes in oxidation state occur, however much water is added.

Geologists often suspect that water itself can be oxidizing, the oxygen being derived from thermal dissociation. Whether this inference is correct or not can be decided for specific cases only. The answer will be determined by the relative magnitudes of P_{O_2} of the mineral assemblage and of P_{O_2} (or the H:O ratio) of the aqueous phase, which is being added to the rocks concerned. In unbuffered mineral assemblages both P_{O_2} and the Fe:O ratio of the solids change readily, whereas in buffered assemblages P_{O_2} remains constant while the Fe:O ratio of the solids changes, until the buffering capacity is exhausted.

Extensive oxidation in nature is usually connected with large volumes of waters, which are derived from an environment near the surface. Only waters directly or indirectly in contact with the atmosphere are capable of carrying enough oxygen to produce secondary ore bodies of the extent of those in the Precambrian iron formation.

[15] It is interesting to note that Thompson (1957) has observed that metamorphic assemblages of pelitic rocks can be treated more successfully if P_{O_2} is assumed to be determined by the mineral assemblage itself and not by an external system.

Acknowledgments

It is a great pleasure to acknowledge the help and advice of P. H. Abelson, F. R. Boyd, J. W. Greig, H. L. James, G. J. F. MacDonald, E. H. Roseboom, J. B. Thompson, and D. R. Wones.

References

Darken, L. S. 1948. Melting points of iron oxides on silica; phase equilibria in the system Fe–Si–O as a function of gas composition and temperature, *J. Am. Chem. Soc., 70,* 2046.

Darken, L. S., and R. W. Gurry. 1945. The system iron–oxygen, I, The wüstite field and related equilibria, *J. Am. Chem. Soc., 67,* 1398.

Darken, L. S., and R. W. Gurry. 1946. The system iron–oxygen, II, Equilibrium and thermodynamics of liquid oxide and other phases, *J. Am. Chem. Soc., 68,* 798.

Darken, L. S., and R. W. Gurry. 1953. *Physical Chemistry of Metals,* McGraw-Hill Book Company, New York, 535 pp.

Ernst, W. G. 1957. Annual Report of the Director of the Geophysical Laboratory, 1956–1957, *Carnegie Inst. Wash. Year Book 56,* 228.

Ernst, W. G. 1958. Annual Report of the Director of the Geophysical Laboratory, 1957–1958, *Carnegie Inst. Wash. Year Book 57,* 201.

Eugster, H. P. 1957*a*. Heterogeneous reactions involving oxidation and reduction at high pressures and temperatures, *J. Chem. Phys., 26,* 1760.

Eugster, H. P. 1957*b*. Annual Report of the Director of the Geophysical Laboratory, 1956–1957, *Carnegie Inst. Wash. Year Book 56,* 161.

Eugster, H. P., and D. R. Wones. 1958. Annual Report of the Director of the Geophysical Laboratory, 1957–1958, *Carnegie Inst. Wash. Year Book 57,* 194–195.

Flaschen, S. S., and E. F. Osborn. 1957. Studies in the system iron oxide–silica–water at low oxygen partial pressures, *Econ. Geol., 52,* 923.

Foster, P. K., and A. J. E. Welch. 1956. Metal-oxide solid solutions, 2, Activity relationships in solid solutions of ferrous oxide and manganous oxide, *Trans. Faraday Soc., 52,* 1636.

James, H. L. 1955. Zones of regional metamorphism in the Precambrian of northern Michigan, *Bull. Geol. Soc. Am., 66,* 1455.

Kubaschewski, D., and E. Ll. Evans. 1951. *Metallurgical Thermochemistry,* Butterworth-Springer, London.

Muan, A. 1958. Phase equilibria at high temperatures in oxide systems involving changes in oxidation states, *Am. J. Sci., 256,* 171.

Nanz, R. H. 1953. Chemical composition of Precambrian slates with notes on the geochemical evolution of lutites, *J. Geol., 61,* 51.

National Bureau of Standards. 1952. Selected values of chemical thermodynamic properties, *Natl. Bur. Standards Circ. 500.*

Norton, F. J. 1955. Dissociation pressures of iron and copper oxides, *General Electric Report 55-RL-1248.*

Richardson, F. D., and J. H. E. Jeffes. 1948. The thermodynamics of substances of interest in iron and steel making from 0° C to 2400° C, I, Oxides, *J. Iron Steel Inst. (London), 160,* 261.

Richardson, F. D., and J. H. E. Jeffes. 1949. Discussion of "The thermodynamics of substances of interest in iron and steel making from 0° C to 2400° C, I, Oxides," *J. Iron Steel Inst. (London)*, *161,* 229; *163,* 147, 379.

Schenck, R., H. Franz, and A. Laymann. 1932. Gleichgewichtsuntersuchungen über die Reduktions-, Oxidations- und Kohlungsvorgänge beim Eisen XI, *Z. anorg. allgem. Chem.*, *206,* 129.

Smith, J. R. 1957. Annual Report of the Director of the Geophysical Laboratory, 1956–1957, *Carnegie Inst. Wash. Year Book 56,* 230.

Thompson, J. B. 1955. The thermodynamic basis for the mineral facies concept, *Am. J. Sci.*, *253,* 65.

Thompson, J. B. 1957. The graphical analysis of mineral assemblages in pelitic schists, *Am. Mineralogist, 42,* 842.

Van Hise, C. K., and W. S. Bayley. 1897. The Marquette iron-bearing district of Michigan, *U. S. Geol. Survey Monograph 28,* 608 pp.

Wagman, D. D., J. E. Kilpatrick, W. J. Taylor, K. S. Pitzer, and F. D. Rossini. 1945. Heats, free energies, and equilibrium constants of some reactions involving O_2, H_2, H_2O, C, CO, CO_2, and CH_4, *J. Research Natl. Bur. Standards, 34,* 143.

Wones, D. R. 1958. Annual Report of the Director of the Geophysical Laboratory, 1957–1958, *Carnegie Inst. Wash. Year Book 57,* 195.

Yoder, H. S., Jr. 1957. Annual Report of the Director of the Geophysical Laboratory, 1956–1957, *Carnegie Inst. Wash. Year Book 56,* 232.

Yoder, H. S., Jr., and H. P. Eugster. 1954. Phlogopite synthesis and stability range, *Geochim. et Cosmochim. Acta, 6,* 157.

Local Equilibrium in Metasomatic Processes

JAMES B. THOMPSON, JR.

Department of Mineralogy and Petrography
Harvard University

Although metasomatic processes have commonly been thought beyond the sphere of applicability of the phase rule and other thermodynamic relationships pertaining to phase equilibrium, a considerable amount of progress has been made in recent years in understanding them. The theoretical basis lies in the assumption that equilibrium will tend to be maintained *locally* even though the system as a whole may be distinctly out of equilibrium. The work of the Russian petrologist D. S. Korzhinsky [1] has been pre-eminent in the application of this approach to petrologic and mineralogic problems. Unfortunately much of Korzhinsky's work has appeared neither in English nor in English translation, and its full significance has not been generally appreciated. Several writers in this country, mainly physical chemists and others dealing with metallurgical problems, have followed similar reasoning. Notable in this respect are papers by F. N. Rhines (1940) and L. S. Darken (1942). The writer will attempt to present some of the main features of the above approach to metasomatism with certain necessary revisions and reinterpretations. An essentially graphical argument based on consideration of some simple compositional systems will be presented first, mainly as an aid to the intuitive reasoning of readers familiar with the principles of phase equilibrium, and will be followed by a detailed consideration of the phase rule and its thermodynamic basis with reference to metasomatic problems.

Though not treated specifically in what follows, the relatively new field known as the thermodynamics of irreversible processes has con-

[1] See list of references at end of this paper.

siderable bearing on the understanding of metasomatic phenomena and touches on the discussion at several points. Recent summaries of the state of knowledge in this field have been presented by Prigogine (1955) and Denbigh (1951). The concept of local equilibrium (Darken, 1942, p. 158) which will be employed extensively below has, furthermore, some resemblance to the principle of "microscopic reversibility" which is fundamental to the thermodynamics of irreversible processes.

This paper will not be concerned with the detailed nature of the processes of diffusion with respect to either the nature of the diffusing particles or the quantitative aspects of diffusion rates, but rather with the essentially qualitative behavior of phase assemblages in which changes of bulk composition take place through transfer of material.

Metasomatic Processes

We shall, for the purposes of this paper, define a metasomatic process as any process involving a change in the bulk composition of the mineral assemblage. The terms "metasomatism" and "metasomatic" as used in geologic literature are by their nature interpretative rather than descriptive, inasmuch as only the final products can be observed. In some instances the interpretation is, at least by general agreement, on safe grounds, but in others it is admittedly highly speculative. About the only geologic process of a metasomatic nature that can actually be observed while it is taking place is weathering. Other processes, however, such as metasomatism at igneous contacts, in the wall rocks adjacent to veins, and in the reactions between siliceous schists and ultramafic or carbonate rocks in metamorphic terranes, can almost certainly be accepted as fact. Metasomatism on a regional scale, though commonly convenient in "explaining" certain rock types, can rarely be proved unequivocally except with respect to such "fugitive" components as H_2O or CO_2.

There are many alternative ways of describing inferred metasomatic processes. If, for example, we had reason to believe that a forsterite rock had been converted into an enstatite rock, we could express the occurrence equally well in any of the ways below, depending on how we define our system. Metasomatism, for example, is commonly regarded as involving the "introduction" or "removal" of material, but statements to that effect are meaningless unless the reference state has been clearly specified. The reference state, in this context, may be regarded as arbitrarily established when the limits of the thermodynamic system [2] have been defined. Thus, in the above example, any of the following statements is equally correct:

1. Defining the thermodynamic system as that which contains N grams of rock, we may say: "Relative to N grams of rock, 0.17 N grams of SiO_2 have been added and 0.17 N grams of MgO removed."

2. Defining the thermodynamic system as that which contains N atoms of oxygen, we may say: "Relative to N atoms of oxygen, $1/12$ N atoms of silicon have been added and $1/6$ N atoms of magnesium removed."

3. Defining the thermodynamic system as that which contains N grams of SiO_2, we may say: "Relative to N grams of SiO_2, 40 N grams of MgO have been removed."

4. Defining the thermodynamic system as that which contains N grams of MgO, we may say: "Relative to N grams of MgO, 60 N grams of SiO_2 have been added."

5. Defining the thermodynamic system as that which has a volume of 1 liter we may say: "Relative to a volume of 1 liter, 549 grams of MgO have been removed and 549 grams of SiO_2 added."

The number of alternative statements of this sort is virtually limitless. Each is correct and may be derived from any of the others provided that we have the necessary physical and chemical data pertaining to the initial and final states of the rock, and quite independently of the details of the process involved whereby the one became the other. Distinctions as to which components "moved" are thus as meaningless and unnecessary as the distinction in structural geology between "overthrusts" and "underthrusts," and for the same reason. The way of defining the thermodynamic system, however, may determine whether or not a thermodynamic system is regarded as open or closed, hence as metasomatic at all. Thus, using convention 5 above, the thermal expansion of quartzite would be metasomatic owing to "removal" of SiO_2. In this paper we shall define as "metasomatic" any process in which the ratio of any two components, whether expressed in weight or gram-formula units, is varied.

Problems related to the choice of a reference state have also been emphasized by the experimental work of Hartley (1946) and of Smigelskas and Kirkendall (1947) making use of inert markers. The phenomena observed were somewhat startling and have become known as the *Kirkendall effect.* The relation between the choice of reference

[2] To avoid confusion the term "thermodynamic system" has been used for a system in the sense of Gibbs (1928), and the term "compositional system" for a system in the sense used in experimental studies of phase equilibria.

and such effects has been made clear in papers by Darken (1948*a*, 1951) and by Hartley and Crank (1949).

The Principle of Local Equilibrium

Though a large volume of rock commonly contains mutually incompatible phases and is thus not in internal equilibrium, it is generally possible to regard any part of such a thermodynamic system as substantially in internal equilibrium if that part is made sufficiently small. With respect to thermal equilibrium this is possible, in principle, in the presence of thermal gradients, as long as no actual discontinuities in temperature exist within the volume selected. With respect to phase equilibrium the requirement would be met if no mutually incompatible phases were in actual contact and if phases of variable composition were to show only continuous variation from point to point.

The following arguments will be based mainly on the assumption that spontaneous internal changes in rocks will be such as to establish local equilibrium, if departures therefrom exist, and that local equilibrium [3] is characteristic of virtually all rocks that have undergone recrystallization, whether or not complete internal equilibrium has ever been attained. The validity of this assumption can be tested by theoretical consideration of its consequences and comparison of the predicted phenomena with those observed in natural mineral assemblages.

Before proceeding with a purely theoretical discussion, it will probably help to consider first the consequences of local equilibrium in the presence of compositional gradients. The arguments may perhaps be presented most easily if we start with some simple binary compositional systems: first, systems in which all phases are of fixed composition, and, second, systems in which phases of variable composition appear, before attempting an understanding of ternary and higher compositional systems.

Binary Compositional Systems

The compositional system MgO–SiO_2

Let us suppose that there exists a region in a volume of rock which is pure MgO (as periclase) and another region which is pure SiO_2

[3] Whether the local equilibrium state is stable or metastable does not affect the argument.

(as quartz), and that between these two regions there is a *continuous variation in bulk composition* from one region to the other. A thermodynamic system so defined is thus one in which the sequence of phases and phase assemblages is precisely that encountered in passing from one extreme to the other in the compositional system. If the entire thermodynamic system is at pressures and temperatures such that enstatite is the stable form of $MgSiO_3$ and no liquids are present, the sequence of phases in passing from the periclase region to the quartz region would be (as shown in fig. 1):

1. A region with mixed periclase and forsterite, the proportion of periclase decreasing outward from the pure periclase rock until a surface (F) is reached where the proportion of periclase has dropped to zero. This surface would in turn mark the beginning of:
2. A region with mixed forsterite and enstatite, the proportion of forsterite decreasing toward the quartz rock until a surface (E) is reached beyond which lies:
3. A region with mixed enstatite and quartz, the proportion of enstatite dropping steadily until a pure quartz rock is attained.

Within each of the three above regions local equilibrium prevails, since only phases known to be mutually compatible are present; hence there should be no tendency for any reactions to take place despite the gradient in bulk composition. At the bounding surfaces, F and E, however, this is emphatically not the case, and local equilibrium does not prevail. This is because, along surface F, small amounts of periclase on the one side are but infinitesimally separated from the

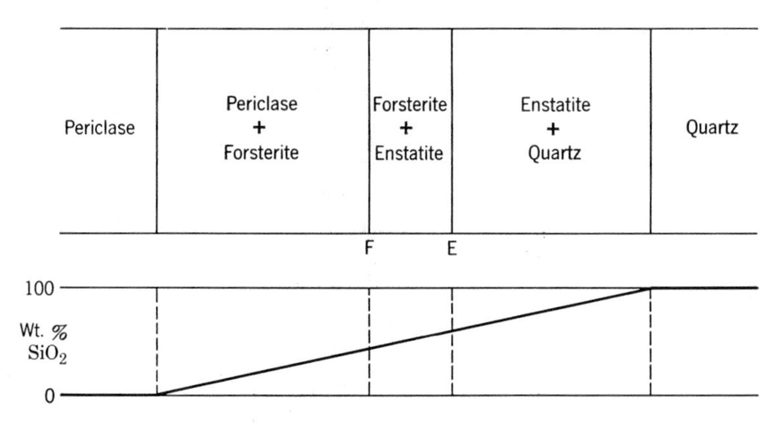

Fig. 1. Sequence of phase assemblages such that there may be a smooth gradient in bulk chemical composition from pure MgO to pure SiO_2.

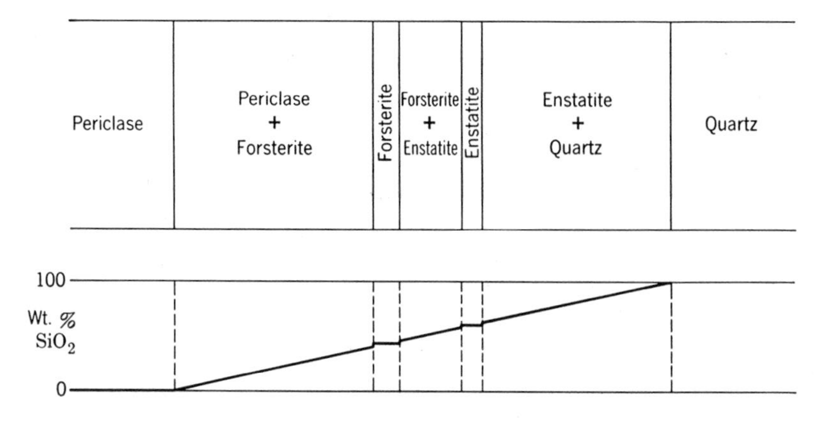

Fig. 2. The sequence of phase assemblages of figure 1 modified by reactions establishing local equilibrium.

small amounts of enstatite on the other. Both from experiment (Bowen and Anderson, 1914) and from observation of natural assemblages we know that periclase and enstatite will react to form forsterite. If diffusion permits (whether through the crystals, along their interfaces, or through some interstitial solvent is immaterial), the periclase and enstatite should react to form a widening layer of forsterite. Whether the widening would occur principally at the expense of one or the other of the initial two-phase volumes would depend on the relative diffusion rates in forsterite of the species involved and would be indeterminate in the final product unless the initial state were known. This last aspect, however, is not pertinent in the subsequent discussion.

Similarly, a widening layer of pure enstatite should form at surface E. Assertion of local equilibrium should thus lead, in time, to a configuration like that in figure 2. How wide the monomineralic zones could become would depend on the diffusion rates and the time available. It is possible, if a temperature gradient were present, that owing to the effect of thermal diffusion (*Soret effect*) a "steady state" might be attained (Denbigh, 1951) such that there would be no further transfer of mass relative to markers in the monomineralic layer. In such an event, however, there would still be a possibility that the monomineralic layers would continue to widen owing to the establishment of similar gradients in each of the individual grains making up the two-phase zones and the consequent tendency toward "thermal sorting" of the phases.

As the monomineralic layers thicken, the incompatible phases become farther removed from each other, and the reaction, at least in the absence of a thermal gradient, should proceed at a decreasing rate. If both the pure quartz rock and the pure periclase rock were to prove inexhaustible, the configuration of the mineral assemblages should, if time, distances, and diffusion rates permit, approach that of figure 3, where all bimineralic or two-phase zones have been eliminated. In the absence of a thermal gradient the forsterite and enstatite layers should thicken with time, further separating the incompatible phases but without altering the qualitative features of the configuration as long as the limiting "source" rocks are not exhausted. With a thermal gradient the zones might actually narrow (though not disappear) or, in a "steady state" (Denbigh, 1951), not change with time. We shall, for convenience, refer to a configuration such as that of figure 3 as a "steady state" configuration, since, in appropriate circumstances, it might persist indefinitely without macroscopic change.

Should the periclase be used up but the quartz prove inexhaustible a possible true equilibrium configuration, with no incompatible phases remaining in the entire thermodynamic system, would be as in figure 4*a*, and if *vice versa* as in figure 4*b*. Figure 4*c* shows the true equilibrium configuration if both were used up. It is also possible that either the periclase, or the quartz, or both, might be exhausted before the elimination of all two-phase regions, yielding the possible true equilibrium configurations shown in figure 5. The only other possibilities with true

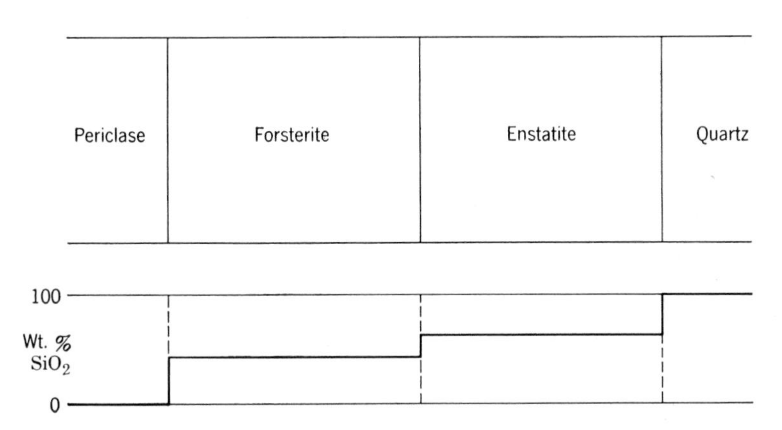

Fig. 3. Sequence of phase assemblages that should ultimately form if the periclase and quartz rocks were to prove inexhaustible.

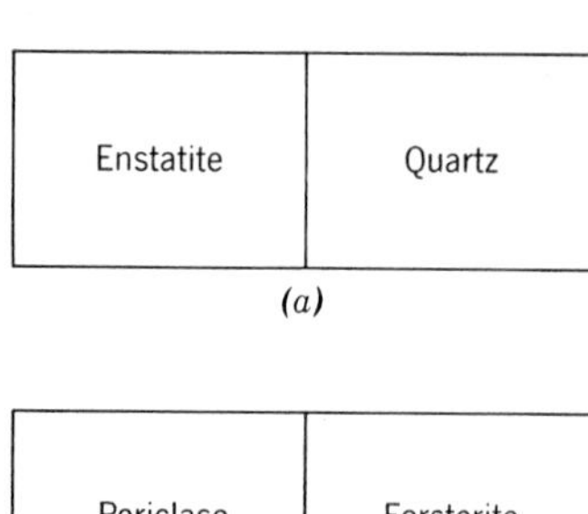

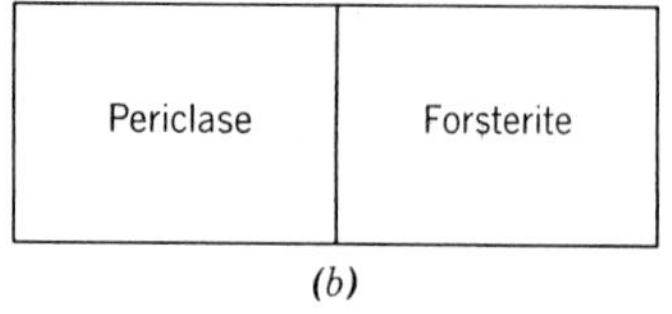

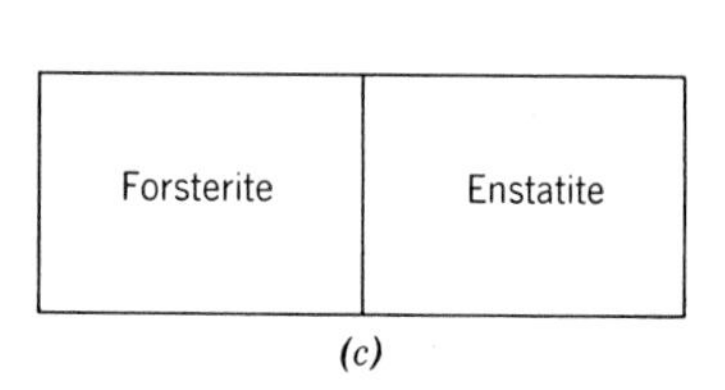

Fig. 4. Possible distributions of phases that might follow that of figure 3: (*a*) if the quartz rock persisted but the periclase rock were consumed; (*b*) if the periclase rock persisted but the quartz rock were consumed; and (*c*) if both the quartz rock and periclase rock were consumed.

equilibrium throughout would be either pure enstatite or pure forsterite, but these would require a unique total composition for the entire system. We shall, for convenience, refer to the true, nonlocal, equilibrium configurations as "final" configurations.

At least two points of interest may be noted, assuming that the arguments hold: first, that a diffusional process can actually produce discontinuities in bulk composition where none existed before; second, that there appears to be a tendency for metasomatic reactions to reduce the number of phases in an assemblage. Figure 6 suggests that there is indeed some validity to the above arguments inasmuch as the compositional system Al_2O_3–SiO_2 is closely analogous to MgO–SiO_2.

The compositional system Fe–O

The compositional system Fe–O (for experimental data see Darken and Gurry, 1946) has some similarities to the preceding compositional system with the added complication, at high temperatures (560° and above), of crystalline phases of variable composition in the system. To parallel the discussion of the system MgO–SiO_2 we might specify, as initial configuration of the system, an iron bar separated from pure oxygen gas by a zone with a continuous variation in bulk composition from pure iron metal to pure oxygen gas. If the temperature through-

Enstatite	Enstatite + Quartz	Quartz

(a)

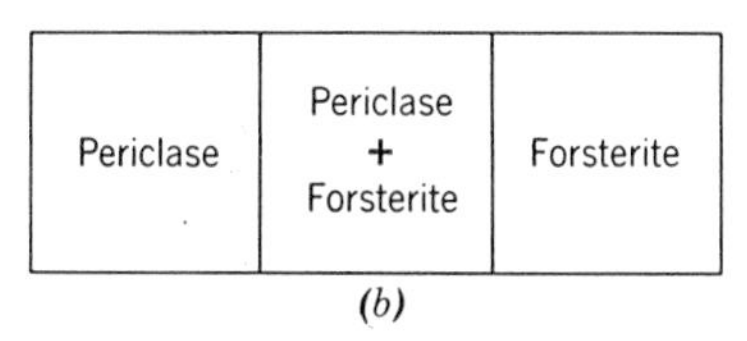

Forsterite	Forsterite + Enstatite	Enstatite

(c)

Fig. 5. Possible sequences of phase assemblages that might follow that of figure 2 if either [(*a*) or (*b*)] or both [(*c*)] of the limiting materials were exhausted before elimination of all two-phase zones.

Fig. 6. Synthetic corundum (*a*), separated from siliceous crucible by layer of mullite (*b*). Partially fused crucible wall shows sharply defined layering. Specimen in Mineralogical Museum, Harvard University. Though not distinct in the photograph, the boundary between the corundum and mullite is sharp and there is no zone where the two phases are mixed.

out were in the vicinity of 1100° C the sequence of phases outward from the pure metal should be:

1. Taenite (γ-iron) with an increasing proportion of wüstite (Fe-rich).

2. A layer of finite thickness containing wüstite only, the composition of the wüstite showing a continuous change from iron-rich on the side toward the metal to iron-poor at the boundary with zone 3.

3. A layer of magnetite and wüstite with the proportion of magnetite increasing outward.

4. A layer of finite thickness containing magnetite only with the magnetite changing outward in composition in the same manner as the wüstite.

5. A layer of magnetite and hematite, hematite increasing outward.

6. Hematite, becoming more porous outward toward the pure gas, perhaps terminating in fine needles to avoid mechanical difficulties.

The boundary between zones 5 and 6 is analogous to the initial zone boundaries in the discussion of the compositional system $MgO–SiO_2$, and we should expect a layer of pure hematite to form there. The more iron-rich regions, however, would look more like the somewhat advanced state shown in figure 2, except that the one-phase layers, magnetite and wüstite, are not of constant composition. Within these layers, however, there is a departure from local equilibrium owing to the compositional gradient. At complete internal equilibrium the wüstite or magnetite would have to be of constant composition throughout. In the monomineralic layer the effects of diffusion would be to lessen the compositional gradients unless opposed by the Soret effect. Since the compositions at the borders of the layers must, if the system is isothermal, remain constant (in the wüstite layer the wüstite on the iron side must be the wüstite compatible with iron, and on the magnetite side the wüstite compatible with magnetite), the gradient can be lessened only by thickening the monomineralic layer. As in the preceding discussion a thickening of the layer also has the effect of separating other incompatible phases (iron and magnetite in the case of the wüstite layer) by a greater distance. Possible steady-state or final configurations would be of the same sort as those encountered in the discussion of the compositional system $MgO–SiO_2$.

Actual examples of oxidation of iron at high temperature are, in fact, in accord with the above discussion (Pfeil, 1929; Scheil and Kiwit, 1936), though complicated in certain instances by exsolution phenomena on cooling (Scheil and Kiwit, 1936, p. 405).

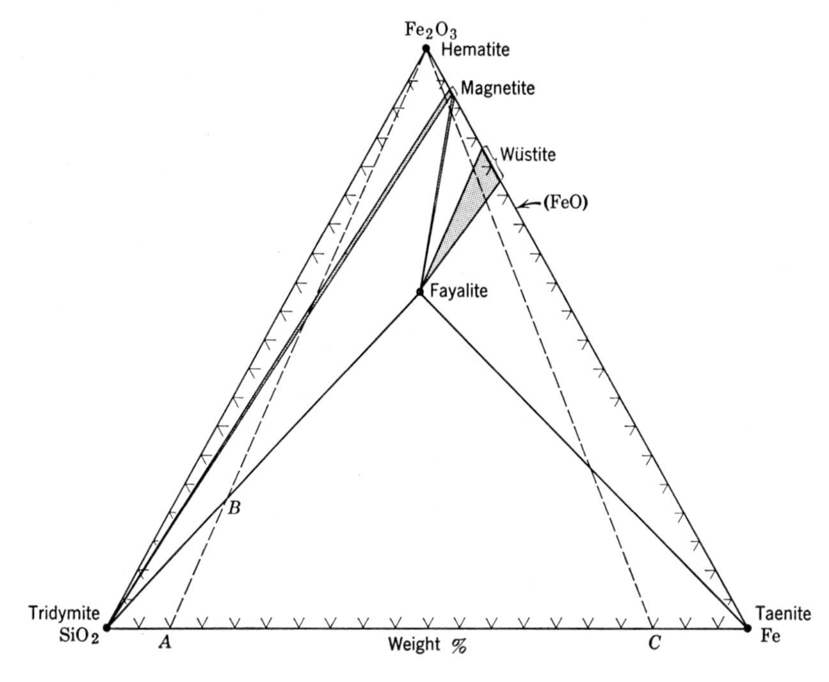

Fig. 7. The compositional system Fe–Fe_2O_3–SiO_2 at 1100° C and 1 atm. After Muan (1955) and Darken and Gurry (1946).

Ternary Compositional Systems

As an example of the behavior of a ternary compositional system we may add silicon to the preceding system and consider the portion Fe_2O_3–SiO_2–Fe of the system Fe–Si–O. Figure 7 is based mainly on data of Darken (1948*b*) and Muan (1955). If, as in the simpler compositional systems, we were to suppose a continuous compositional gradient from a region of pure hematite to a region of tridymite and taenite in the ratio indicated by point *A*, the sequence of mineral assemblages for such a continuous variation in composition may be deduced from figure 7. Adjacent to the rock of composition *A* there would be a zone containing the three-phase assemblage tridymite–taenite–fayalite. This zone would terminate, with the proportion of taenite dropping to zero, at a surface representing the composition *B*. Along this surface the three-phase assemblage would be in contact with the three-phase assemblage tridymite–fayalite–magnetite. As in the previous examples a departure from local equilibrium is involved owing

Tridymite + Taenite	Tridymite + Fayalite	Tridymite + Magnetite	Hematite

Fig. 8. Sequence of assemblages that might form by reaction between hematite and an assemblage of composition *A* in figure 7.

to the presence of the incompatible phases magnetite and taenite in close proximity. These would react in the presence of tridymite to form fayalite. We should thus expect a two-phase region of tridymite and fayalite to form and widen at the expense of the three-phase regions on either side of it. The two-phase region magnetite–tridymite would also tend to widen, and if the hematite rock and rock *A* were not exhausted before elimination of the three-phase fields a stage such as that in figure 8 might be attained in time.

As pointed out by Rhines (1940), the bulk composition at any point in a two-phase assemblage formed in this way need not lie on the original compositional axis. In general it seems likely that it would not, inasmuch as the particles or species capable of independent motion relative to the phase boundaries will probably not have compositions that can be correlated directly with a compositional axis selected at random. Experiments with inert markers like those employed by Hartley (1946) and Smigelskas and Kirkendall (1947) might, in simple instances of this sort, make it possible to identify the actual species involved and their relative movements.

If the initial compositional variation were from hematite rock to rock *C*, we might expect, under similar circumstances, that a sequence of zones like that in figure 9 should develop. Were either the hematite rock or rock *A* or *C* to become exhausted, final configurations analogous

Tridymite + Taenite	Fayalite + Taenite	Fayalite + Wüstite	Fayalite + Magnetite	Tridymite + Magnetite	Hematite

Fig. 9. Sequence of assemblages that might form by reaction between hematite and an assemblage of composition *C* in figure 7.

to those encountered in discussion of the binary compositional systems might be attained with the elimination of all incompatibilities. Depending on the circumstances such a final configuration might or might not have a surviving three-phase region analogous to the surviving two-phase regions in our discussion of the compositional system $MgO–SiO_2$. As in the binary compositional systems, we note here, again, the tendency of the metasomatic process to decrease the number of phases in an assemblage and to create discontinuities in bulk composition. The illustrations in the paper by Rhines (1940) show that the above arguments are consistent with the sequences of assemblages actually observed in the oxidation of binary alloys.

So far, even though the last examples were drawn from a ternary compositional system, we have considered initial compositional gradients with respect to only *one* compositional variable. In a ternary system, however, we may have gradients with respect to as many as *two* independent compositional variables. By way of illustration let us suppose that there are three parallel prisms of rock, one all hematite, one all tridymite, and the other all taenite, and that the region between them has the form of a triangular prism and shows complete and continuous variation in bulk composition between the three extremes. A section through this prism would then be analogous to the triangular

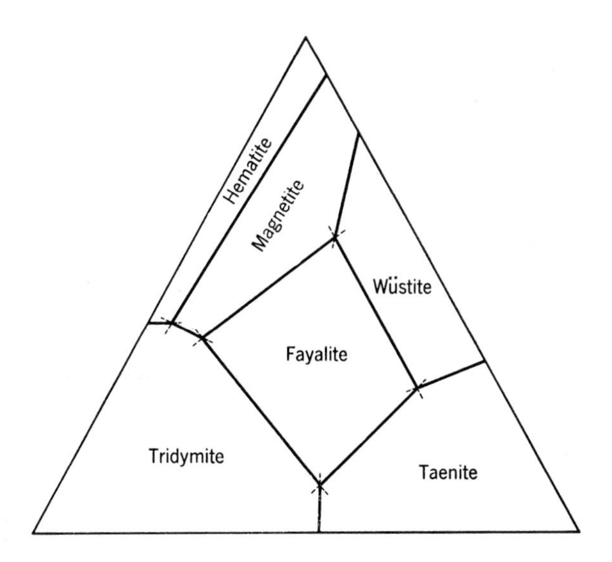

Fig. 10. Distribution of phases that might form by prolonged reaction at the junction of inexhaustible masses of hematite, tridymite, and taenite.

diagram of figure 7, inasmuch as all possible bulk compositions between the three extremes are therein represented in continuous variation. As above, two-phase zones would tend to replace three-phase zones, but the main matters of interest may be brought out by focusing our attention on the point in the triangle corresponding to the composition of fayalite. This would correspond, in the triangular prism itself, to a line of fayalite composition. In the immediate vicinity of such a line local equilibrium fails owing to the presence in close proximity of the phases tridymite, magnetite, wüstite, and taenite. Tridymite is incompatible with wüstite, and magnetite is incompatible with taenite. Reaction between these phases so as to relieve local incompatibilities would result in a *one-phase* zone of fayalite which would tend to replace the adjacent two-phase and three-phase zones. Were the three limiting rocks to prove inexhaustible, the configuration, in cross section, would, in time, approach that of figure 10 with only one-phase zones remaining. The form of the one-phase zones should, in this example, be prismatic, and only those phases that are mutually compatible should appear in juxtaposition.

It is of interest to note that, in a steady-state configuration such as that of figure 10, the compositional changes in passing through the system along a suitably chosen path may show culminations and depressions, in the sense of the front petrologists, with respect to certain components. Thus, in passing from taenite rock to wüstite rock by way of fayalite rock, SiO_2 would pass through an abrupt culmination and Fe through a depression, though the content of Fe_2O_3 would increase, stepwise, at each boundary.[4]

Should any two or all three of the limiting source rocks become exhausted in the above example, possible final states might be attained, in time, analogous to those in two-component compositional systems. In no final state of complete equilibrium at a randomly chosen pressure and temperature could more than three phases survive, nor could there be more than one three-phase region or three two-phase regions. The possible final states for exhaustion of all three source rocks would be those of figure 11 (assuming that the bulk composition of the entire thermodynamic system is such that it cannot occur as an assemblage of less than three phases). That in figure 11(*b*) would occur only if the three source rocks were to become exhausted before elimination of the polyphase zones.

[4] See Darken (1948*b*) on the formation of siliceous scale in the oxidation of iron, and Scheil and Kiwit (1936), Rhines (1940), and Darken (1942) for discussion of this and related phenomena.

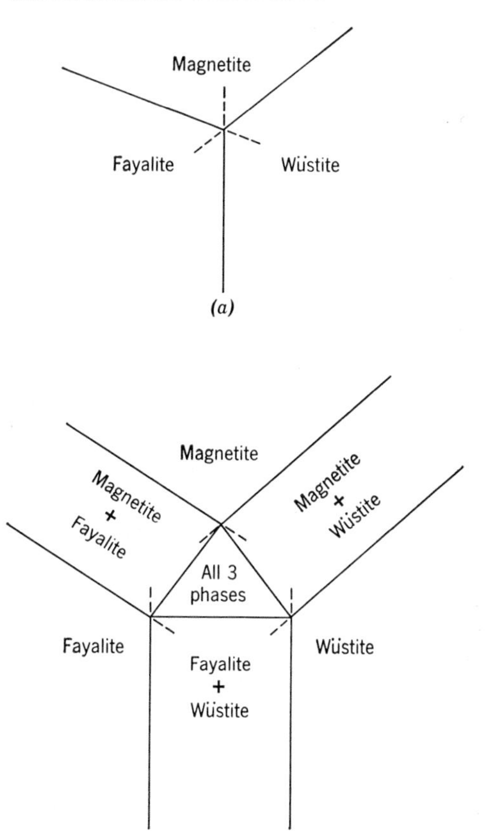

Fig. 11. Distribution of phases that might form: (*a*) following a distribution such as that in figure 10 if all three limiting materials became exhausted; and (*b*) following a distribution such as that in figure 7 if the three limiting types became exhausted before elimination of the three-phase zone magnetite–fayalite–wüstite.

Multicomponent Compositional Systems

Arguments like those above can be applied to four-component or quaternary compositional systems (Rhines, 1940), but for quinary and higher compositional systems a more generalized approach is needed, owing to the limitations of graphical representation in two dimensions. The results thus far, however, appear to be consistent with the generalization that in a steady-state configuration the maximum number of phases in any local thermodynamic system is equal to the number of components necessary to define all phases in the entire complex less the number of independent compositional gradients in the initial state. This appears, furthermore, to be consistent with the equation

$$\phi \leqq n - n_m \tag{1}$$

(Korzhinsky, 1936; see also Thompson, 1955), where n is identified as the number of components, ϕ as the number of phases in the assemblage, and n_m as the number of mobile components.

Korzhinsky's equation may be arrived at rather quickly by consideration of the Gibbs phase rule (Gibbs, 1928, pp. 96–97)

$$\text{Variance} = n + 2 - \phi \equiv W \tag{2}$$

if we assume, in each mineral assemblage considered, that the externally controlled variables are pressure, temperature, and a variable such as the chemical potential or activity of each mobile component. If these $n_m + 2$ variables are to be arbitrarily set by conditions external to the assemblage, then the assemblage, if in equilibrium within its environment, must, in general, have a variance equal to or greater than $n_m + 2$. Hence, if

$$W \geqq n_m + 2 \tag{3}$$

we have, from equation 2,

$$n + 2 - \phi \geqq n_m + 2 \tag{4}$$

or, by rearranging,

$$\phi \leqq n - n_m \tag{1}$$

There are, however, several pitfalls in this derivation. The phase rule was arrived at by Gibbs through consideration of the conditions for complete internal equilibrium in an assemblage of phases, whereas in the examples discussed above only the *local* assemblages were regarded as being necessarily in internal equilibrium. The significance of n, moreover, the number of components of the assemblage, is that this be the number of *independently variable* components in the assemblage. In several of the examples discussed the local assemblage consisted of a substance of fixed composition such as pure forsterite, pure enstatite, or pure fayalite. Each of these is, by Gibbs' definition, a *one-component* assemblage, making it rather difficult to reconcile equation 1 with the phase rule of Gibbs, equation 2, in such occurrences. Owing to difficulties of this sort the writer will, in the latter part of this paper, discuss, in more detail, the phase rule and its bearing on metasomatic phenomena.

A second difficulty in the interpretation of equation 1 arises in the concept of a "mobile" component, inasmuch as motion is, after all, relative. Thus we may describe compositional changes in a thermodynamic system in terms of "motions" of different sets of components, depending on what we choose to regard arbitrarily as "stationary." As a further example of possible confusion of this sort, let us consider an assemblage at a randomly chosen pressure and temperature in which changes take place with respect to *all* compositional variables. Inasmuch as the number of independent compositional variables in an n-component compositional system is $n - 1$, such an assemblage can have no more than one phase. Were we to express this idea by stating that "all components of the assemblage are mobile" we would arrive at the erroneous conclusion that such an assemblage would have no more than zero phases. The statement that "all components are mobile" is thus meaningless unless one wishes to imply that the thermodynamic system as a whole has moved relative to some arbitrary coordinate system, a change that is not necessarily "metasomatic" in the sense of this paper.

That the arguments leading to equation 1 have an element of truth, however, is suggested by figure 12, representing natural occurrences in multicomponent compositional systems. Figure 12*A* is a photograph of a specimen showing monomineralic zones developed at the contact between a bed of marble and a bed of mica schist. That original sedimentation could have produced materials that would yield such pure, monomineralic layers on metamorphism is highly unlikely, owing to the restricted compositional ranges of the phases involved. In similar occurrences seen by the writer the zones embay the adjacent rocks along joints or follow faults or other discordant features, hence are not original features. In figure 12*B* a calc–silicate rock from the same general locality shows a layer of hornblende developed along the edge of a dike of granite that cuts across the bedding.

Conspicuous reaction zones at the contact between ultramafic bodies and siliceous country rocks have been described by Read (1934) and by Phillips and Hess (1936). Though many components are involved the individual zones are commonly monomineralic or bimineralic. The work of Dennen (1951) shows abrupt changes in composition near igneous contacts, some components exhibiting culminations and others depressions. The results, in general, are consistent with theoretical predictions. It might be emphasized, however, that most standard methods of sampling tend to round off any true discontinuities that might be present (see Hicks, 1934, p. 170). To understand completely the contact zones studied by Dennen we would, furthermore, have to know in detail the distribution of the actual mineral assemblages involved.

Further examples of abrupt compositional changes occur in the

A

B

Fig. 12. *A*. Specimen from Vermont showing reaction skarn developed between mica schist (top) and marble (bottom). Monomineralic layers are hornblende (*a*), diopside (*b*), and garnet (*c*). Garnet layer invades marble at right. *B*. Calc-silicate granulite from same locality showing layer of dark hornblende developed along contact with granitic dike (left).

sharp boundaries developed in the weathering of impure limestone. Simplified mineral assemblages are also characteristic of such clearly metasomatic processes as weathering and wall-rock alteration adjacent to veins.

The Phase Rule

Components of a single phase

An *actual* component (Gibbs, 1928, p. 64) of a phase may be defined as any material of specified composition but unspecified physical state that may, independently of other components, be both added to and subtracted from the phase, in finite amounts, without destroying the homogeneity of the phase. It is immaterial in this connection whether either the initial or the compositionally varied phase is stable or metastable relative to any other phase or assemblage of phases. A phase is said to have n actual components if n, and no fewer than n, actual components suffice to define (or to write formulas for) the compositions of all other actual components of the phase. Any set of n actual components of the phase such that none of the n have compositions that can be expressed in terms of any of the others is a set of *independent* actual components. Any such set will thus suffice to define the composition of the phase in question as well as that of any other phase that may be connected with the first by continuous compositional variation without loss of homogeneity.

Inasmuch as the physical state of a component is unspecified it is not necessary that it correspond in composition to a phase that may be connected with the initial phase in the above manner, or even that it have the composition of any one homogeneous phase stable under the conditions encountered. Thus we may speak of $FeSiO_3$ as an actual component of pyroxene even though material of that composition at the temperature and pressure considered would not be pyroxene at all, but a mixture of olivine and quartz or of olivine and tridymite. It is commonly convenient, but not necessary, that a set of n actual components be chosen such that each has a simple chemical formula, and commonly convenient, but again not necessary, that the set be chosen so that the components of the phase in question may be expressed in terms of a positive quantity of each actual component. Although it is convenient in certain contexts to choose components that correspond in composition with atomic, molecular, or ionic species, such a procedure is not necessary and may, in fact, be impossible as far as any actual components of complex crystalline phases are concerned. Thus the actual components of an Na–Ca plagioclase may be taken as $NaAlSi_3O_8$ and $CaAl_2Si_2O_8$ or as any pair of components that may be expressed in terms of these. There are, however, no known molecular species having compositions that can be so expressed, and if such do exist they are almost certainly not present as real entities in the crystalline phase itself.

For any set of n independent actual components of a given phase, 1, there is an equation of the sort [5] (Gibbs, 1928, p. 88, eq. 97)

$$\sum_{i1} M_{i1}\, d\mu_{i1} = V_1\, dP - S_1\, dT \tag{5}$$

One of the actual components, that having the composition of the phase itself, is unique in that if it is one of the set its mass fraction must be unity. Hence, for this component, k, we have

$$d\mu_{k1} = V_1\, dP - S_1\, dT \tag{6}$$

showing that the chemical potential of this component (hence its activity) cannot be varied, in a phase of composition k, independently of temperature and pressure. We shall accordingly refer to such a component as the *inactive* actual component, or, more simply, as the *inactive* component of the phase, it being understood that it is also an actual component. The inactive component, however, unlike other actual components, may be varied in content in a phase, at a given pressure, temperature, and content of other components, without altering in any way the intensive properties of the phase.

A phase having but one actual component is what is commonly called a *pure substance* and may be characterized further as *compound* or *elemental* depending on whether or not it can be split into other substances. A *solution* is thus a phase with more than one actual component. It must be admitted that it may, in practice, be difficult or impossible to distinguish between a pure compound substance and a solution in which the compositional variation is restricted to a very

[5] General notation:

$i, j, k, \cdots \doteq$ components.
$1, 2, 3, \cdots \doteq$ phases.
P = pressure.
T = temperature.
V_1 = volume per unit mass of phase 1.
S_1 = entropy per unit mass of phase 1.
μ = chemical potential.
μ_{i1} = chemical potential of component i in phase 1.
M_{i1} = mass fraction of component i in phase 1.

small but finite range, and consequently that it is impossible to prove whether pure compound substances in the strictest sense actually exist or do not exist. Nevertheless, many phases exist, some of them natural minerals, that may be regarded, within the limits of measurement currently available, as pure compound substances. Thus quartz as encountered in the compositional system Si–O is within the limits of our knowledge a pure substance having the fixed composition (its only actual component) SiO_2. Even though the ratio of silicon to oxygen may, in fact, be varied in quartz this variation cannot now be measured. From this it must follow that partial molar quantities relating to variations in composition with respect to such components cannot be measured. To avoid the appearance of nonmeasurable quantities in our equations we will consider only such actual components as have been proved to exist though admitting that others may ultimately be shown to exist.[6]

We shall designate as *nonvariable* components of a phase any substances of defined composition but undefined physical state that may be *extracted from* the phase in question but not without destroying the homogeneity of that phase. Si and O are thus nonvariable components of quartz, and MgO and SiO_2, or Mg, Si, and O, are nonvariable components of forsterite. There is always the possibility that with refinement of measurement a nonvariable component may be shown to be, in fact, an actual component of a given phase.

As a further class of components we may consider those that may be added to the phase in question or subtracted from it, *but not both,* without destroying the homogeneity of the phase. Gibbs (1928, p. 64) used the term *possible* components for those that may be so added. Examples would be Fe_2SiO_4 with respect to a pure magnesian forsterite, Fe_2O_3 with respect to a magnetite of composition Fe_3O_4, and FeS_2 with respect to a pyrrhotite of composition FeS. Gibbs did not consider the possibility of subtraction alone without addition as is observed in the case of Fe with respect to a pyrrhotite of composition FeS, or of Fe or FeO with respect to a magnetite of composition Fe_3O_4. The problems relating to these two types of components are sufficiently similar, however, to merit extending the term *possible* components to

[6] All phases believed, within current limits of measurement, to have but one actual component have chemical formulas consistent (again within our limits of measurement) with the law of multiple proportions. Alleged exceptions (Hückel, 1950, p. 26) to the law involve erroneous application thereof to phases such as a wüstite or a sulfur-rich pyrrhotite that clearly contain more than one actual component, hence are crystalline solutions, not pure substances.

cover both, referring when necessary to those that can be subtracted but not added without loss of the homogeneity of the phase in question as possible components in the *negative* sense.

Suppose that i is a possible component of phase 1, and that k is the composition of phase 1. There are then possible phases, 2, in which *both* i and k are actual components. If we choose both i and k as independent components and consider only variations of phases, 2, such that $M_{i2} + M_{k2} = 1$, then we may write for any of these phases

$$M_{i2}\, d\mu_{i2} + M_{k2}\, d\mu_{k2} = V_2\, dP - S_2\, dT \tag{7}$$

Owing to the choice of components, $M_{i1} = 0$, and the sign of M_{i2} is positive if i is a possible component of phase 1 in the positive sense, and negative if i is a possible component of phase 1 in the negative sense.

There is abundant evidence that in the limit $M_{i2} \to 0$, in such instances, the chemical potentials of i and k obey limiting laws of the type

$$M_{i2}\left(\frac{\partial \mu_{i2}}{\partial M_{i2}}\right)_{P,T} = AT \tag{8}$$

and

$$M_{k2}\left(\frac{\partial \mu_{k2}}{\partial M_{k2}}\right)_{P,T} = AT \tag{9}$$

where A is a constant that may be regarded as fixed, for a given phase, by the choice of component, i. If i is a possible component in the positive sense A must be positive, approaching zero if the composition of i be taken sufficiently close to that of k, and if i is a possible component in the negative sense A must be negative, again approaching zero if the composition of i be taken sufficiently close to that of k. Equations 8 and 9 are in essence the same as those employed by Gibbs (1928, pp. 135–138, 419–424) in discussing phenomena related to extreme dilution, the main difference in the present discussion being the generalization to include the occurence of possible components in the negative sense. Equations 8 and 9 might also be regarded as generalized forms of the laws of Henry and Raoult, respectively, such that terms relating to the structural constitution of the phase are omitted.[7]

[7] In a molecular solution, where M_s is the mass fraction of a given molecular species, and Henry's law in standard form is obeyed, $A = R/W_s$, where W_s is the molecular weight of species s. For a generalized component, i, expressable in terms of s and the component of the phase, j, $A = R/W_sB$, where B is the mass fraction of i in the species s if its composition be expressed in terms of i and j. B is thus positive if i is a possible component in the positive sense and negative if i is a possible component in the negative sense.

Owing to the abundant evidence that equation 8 is obeyed by any actual component in the limit where it becomes a possible component, and the absence of evidence to the contrary, we shall suppose, until it is disproved, that it expresses a generally valid natural law. With this assumption, then, we will consider the chemical potential of a component possible in the positive sense to be $-\infty$, and that of a component possible in the negative sense to be ∞. As pointed out by Gibbs (1928, p. 138, footnote), theoretical discussions of polyphase equilibria may be greatly simplified if this is so. In the years since the work of Gibbs the laws of ideally dilute solution have received abundant confirmation, and their theoretical basis in statistical mechanics appears sound.

Equilibrium in a polyphase assemblage

According to Gibbs (1928, p. 65), a requirement for internal equilibrium in a polyphase assemblage is that the chemical potential of any component must be the same in all phases in which it is an *actual* component, or

$$\mu_{i1} = \mu_{i2} = \mu_{i3} \cdots \tag{10}$$

Where an actual component, i, of a phase has a composition that can be expressed in terms of a set of actual components, j, of other phases, this relationship may be expressed by an equation of the sort

$$m_i^* = \sum_j \nu_{ji} m_j^* \tag{11}$$

where m_i^* indicates a unit mass of i, j, etc., and the terms ν_{ji} indicate the mass fraction of j in matter having the composition i. At complete internal equilibrium, with no restrictions placed on reactions between the phases, there exists, for each equation of type 11, an equilibrium condition of the sort (Gibbs, 1928, p. 72)

$$\mu_i = \sum_j \nu_{ji} \mu_j \tag{12}$$

Where a component, i, is a possible component in the positive sense of phase 1, and an actual component of another phase, 2, Gibbs (1928, p. 66) gives the condition of equilibrium as

$$\mu_{i1} \geqq \mu_{i2} \tag{13}$$

Where i is a possible component in the negative sense of phase 1 and an actual component of phase 2, the analogous condition, though not specifically considered by Gibbs, would be

$$\mu_{i1} \leqq \mu_{i2} \tag{14}$$

If i were a possible component (in either sense) in phase 1, and its composition were expressable in the manner of equation 11, there would be, if i were a possible component in the positive sense, a condition of the sort

$$\mu_{i1} \geqq \sum_j \nu_{ji}\mu_j \tag{15}$$

and if i were a possible component in the negative sense, a condition of the sort

$$\mu_{i1} \leqq \sum_j \nu_{ji}\mu_j \tag{16}$$

However, we shall accept the general validity of the generalized law of dilution of equation 8. With this acceptance, as pointed out by Gibbs (1928, p. 138, footnote), the inequalities in relations 13, 14, 15, and 16 become impossible. We are then led to the conclusion that a component with a composition expressable in any way in terms of actual components of other phases in the assemblage cannot be a possible component of any phase in the assemblage, at complete internal equilibrium, even though its presence as an actual component may be too small to detect analytically in certain instances. With this provision, the relations 13 and 14, divested of the inequalities, become indistinguishable from equation 10, and equations 15 and 16 similarly indistinguishable from 12.

Chemical potentials of components other than actual components of the phases

If for component i there exists a relationship such as equation 11, let us temporarily redefine the limits of our assemblage (thermodynamic system) so as to exclude all phases in which i is an actual component. If, then, phases remain in which all components j are actual components we may regard equation 12 as defining μ_i even though i is not an actual component of any phase in the system as redefined. No practical difficulties can arise through such a definition inasmuch as wherever phases containing i as an actual component are present equation 12 must hold.

Similarly, let us suppose that there is a phase in an assemblage such that i is an actual component of that phase but components j are not; and let us redefine the thermodynamic system so as to exclude all other phases. We may then regard equation 12 as expressing relations that must hold with respect to the chemical potentials of components that may be related to i by an equation such as 11, whether or not these are actual components of the phase in question (see Gibbs, 1928, p. 79). Again no difficulties can arise inasmuch as wherever phases containing components j as actual components are also present equation 12 must hold.

Components of a polyphase assemblage

The components of an assemblage of coexisting phases may be defined analogously to those for a single phase. Thus, an *actual* component is one that may both be added to and subtracted from the assemblage, in finite amounts, without adding an extra phase to the assemblage; a *possible* component is one that may be added without adding an extra phase, or similarly subtracted, but not both; and a *nonvariable* component is one that may be neither added nor subtracted without adding an extra phase.

Any actual component of a phase in an assemblage is also an actual component of the assemblage, but an actual component of an assemblage is not necessarily an actual component of any of the phases in it. Thus SiO_2 is an actual component in an assemblage containing an orthopyroxene and a common olivine in equilibrium, but it is not an actual component of either phase taken separately. An assemblage may be said to have n actual components if n, and no fewer than n, actual components suffice to define (or to write formulas for) all other actual components of all phases in the assemblage.

Certain of the actual components of an assemblage, however, have unique properties in that their content in the assemblage may be varied by simply altering the proportions of the phases, leaving their intensive properties unchanged. The compositions (inactive components) of the phases themselves have this property, as do other components that may be related to them as the component i is related to components j in equation 11. The number n' of (independent) inactive components in an assemblage is thus a number such that n', and no fewer than n', components suffice to define, or write formulas for, all other inactive components of the assemblage. If ϕ is the number of phases in the assemblage,

$$n' = \phi - r \tag{17}$$

where r is the number of independent equations 11 relating the compositions of the phases. Inasmuch as any inactive component is an actual component but the reverse is not necessarily true, we have also

$$n' \leqq n \tag{18}$$

Dependence of the chemical potentials

Owing to the ϕ equations 6 and the r equations 12 relating the chemical potentials in equations 6, the number of independent variables, W', in equations 6 is given by the equation

$$W' = n' + 2 - \phi \tag{19}$$

which may be regarded as a phase rule with respect to the inactive components of the assemblage. The variance, W', cannot be less than zero, n' cannot be less than 1, and ϕ cannot be less than n'. We have, therefore, for assemblages in complete internal equilibrium, the following inequalities:

$$1 \leqq n' \leqq \phi \leqq n' + 2 \tag{20}$$

It is interesting that there are only three possible relationships between ϕ and n'. If ϕ exceeds n' by 2 the system is invariant, must have at least three phases, and can exist, as an equilibrium assemblage, only at a unique pressure and temperature. If ϕ exceeds n' by 1 the system is an azeotropic state, univariant with respect to pressure and temperature, and must have at least two phases. If ϕ equals n', however, the pressure and temperature may be chosen independently; hence a natural equilibrium assemblage occurring over a finite volume should be of this type in any but exceptional circumstances.

Similarly, in the set of ϕ equations 5 in an assemblage of ϕ phases, the number of independent variables, W, in equations 5 and the pertinent equations 12 is given by the familiar Gibbs phase rule:

$$W = n + 2 - \phi \tag{2}$$

where n is the number of actual components in the assemblage. If the pressure and temperature are chosen arbitrarily, the variance, W, must in general be at least 2; hence ϕ will not be greater than n, though it may be less. Hence we have the relationship

$$\phi \leqq n \tag{21}$$

known as the mineralogical phase rule of Goldschmidt (1911), and generally true in rocks.

Inasmuch as the chemical potentials of the nonvariable components of the assemblage may be related to those of the actual components of the assemblage by equations like 12, it is convenient, in dealing with metasomatic phenomena, to define a number, n'', such that n'', and no fewer than n'', components suffice to define, or write formulas for, all actual components of all phases in a given *sequence* of metasomatic assemblages. We will refer to these as the n'' *ultimate* components of the metasomatic sequence. The variance, W'', with respect to the ultimate components of the sequence is thus, owing to equations 5 and the appropriate equations 12,

$$W'' = n'' + 2 - \phi \tag{22}$$

in any ϕ-phase local assemblage of the sequence. Since

$$n \leqq n'' \tag{23}$$

we may expand the inequalities (20):

$$1 \leqq n' \leqq \phi \leqq n' + 2 \leqq n + 2 \leqq n'' + 2 \tag{24}$$

In the general case, where the pressure and temperature are chosen independently and arbitrarily, these reduce to

$$1 \leqq n' = \phi \leqq n \leqq n'' \tag{25}$$

Metasomatism and the Phase Rule

In a metasomatic assemblage the content with respect to certain components is related to environmental conditions rather than to an initial bulk composition. We may conclude, then, that the chemical potentials (or activities) of these components will be fixed by environmental conditions. In an assemblage occupying a finite volume, we should expect that these chemical potentials would, in general, vary from point to point independently of pressure and temperature. The number of components of a given kind for which the potentials may be set arbitrarily at an arbitrary pressure and temperature, however, is limited by equations 2, 19, and 22.

Let a' be this number with respect to the inactive components of the assemblage; let a be the corresponding number with respect to the actual components of the assemblage; and let a'' be the corresponding number with respect to the ultimate components of the sequence of assemblages. We have, then, from equations 2, 19, and 22,

$$2 + a' = n' + 2 - \phi \tag{26}$$

or, because n' cannot be greater than ϕ,

$$a' = 0 \tag{27}$$

Similarly,

$$\phi = n - a \tag{28}$$

and

$$\phi = n'' - a'' \tag{29}$$

Also, because ϕ cannot be less than 1,

$$a'' \leqq n'' - 1 \tag{30}$$

Let us suppose that certain of the chemical potentials of the ultimate components of a metasomatic sequence were environmentally controlled, with respect to the local assemblage, in a given process. Then, if n''' is the number of independent components of this sort, we have

$$0 \leqq n''' \leqq a'' \tag{31}$$

and, from equation 30,

$$\phi \leqq n'' - n''' \tag{32}$$

which may be regarded as a form of Korzhinsky's phase rule for metasomatic systems, modified so as to avoid the difficulties arising in connection with equation 1. The n''' externally controlled chemical potentials or activities cannot, at an arbitrary pressure and temperature, include any activities of inactive components, or more than $n - \phi$ activities of actual components of the local assemblage.

The identification of the inactive components of an assemblage is extremely useful in the analysis of metasomatic assemblages. Addition or subtraction of an inactive component leaves all chemical potentials in the assemblage unaltered in much the same way that an inflow or outflow of heat does not alter the temperature of a mixture of ice and pure water.

In the graphical examples in the first part of this paper the steady-state configurations are consistent with continuous variation, throughout the rock, of the activities of those components whose proportions have been altered in the local assemblages. In the steady-state configuration, moreover, all three-dimensional regions are eliminated in which components of this sort are inactive. The topological properties of figures 3, 8, 9, and 10 are thus those of diagrams in which chemical potentials or activities have been chosen as variables rather than mass fractions or mole fractions. Their topologic relation to composition diagrams is the same as that of pressure-temperature diagrams to volume-entropy diagrams in one-component systems (see Gibbs, 1928, pp. 33–54). Darken (1948*b*) has made effective use of activity-activity diagrams in his analysis of siliceous scale in the oxidation of iron.

Metasomatism must, in detail, take place through the relative movements of various species of particle. Though the above discussion has not been concerned with the identification of such species it appears probable that a molecular or atomic species having a composition that is an *inactive* component of a local assemblage is *not* a species that was actively involved in the formation of that assemblage from some other assemblage by a metasomatic process.

Acknowledgments

The writer is indebted to D. J. Milton for making available his translation into English of one of Korzhinsky's papers, and to A. L. Albee, S. P. Clark, Jr., H. P. Eugster, D. S. Korzhinsky, D. J. Milton, J. L. Rosenfeld, and E-an Zen, for their comments on the manuscript at various stages.

References

Bowen, N. L., and O. Anderson. 1914. The binary system $MgO–SiO_2$, *Am. J. Sci.* (ser. 4), *37,* 487–500.

Darken, L. S. 1942. Diffusion in metal accompanied by phase change, *Trans. Am. Inst. Mining Met. Engrs., 150,* 157–171.

Darken, L. S. 1948*a*. Diffusion, mobility and their interrelation through free energy in binary metallic systems, *Trans. Am. Inst. Mining Met. Engrs., 175,* 184–201.

Darken, L. S. 1948*b*. Melting points of iron oxides on silica; phase equilibria in the system Fe–Si–O as a function of gas composition and temperature, *J. Am. Chem. Soc., 70,* 2046–2053.

Darken, L. S. 1951. Formal basis of diffusion theory, in *Atom Movements,* American Society for Metals, Cleveland, Ohio.

Darken, L. S., and R. W. Gurry. 1946. The system iron–oxygen, II, Equilibrium and thermodynamics of liquid oxide and other phases, *J. Am. Chem. Soc., 68,* 798–816.

Denbigh, K. G. 1951. *The Thermodynamics of the Steady State,* Methuen and Company, London.

Dennen, W. H. 1951. Variations in chemical composition across igneous contacts, *Bull. Geol. Soc. Am., 62,* 547–558.

Gibbs, J. W. 1928. *The Collected Works of J. Willard Gibbs,* vol. I, Yale University Press, New Haven, Conn.

Goldschmidt, V. M. 1911. Die Kontaktmetamorphose im Kristianiagebiet, *Videnskapsselskapets-Skrifter I, Mat.-Naturv. Kl.,* no. 11.

Hartley, G. S. 1946. The swelling and solution of a high polymer solid considered as a diffusion process, *Trans. Faraday Soc., 42B,* 6–11.

Hartley, G. S., and J. Crank. 1949. Some fundamental definitions and concepts in diffusion processes, *Trans. Faraday Soc., 45,* 801–818.

Hicks, L. C. 1934. An x-ray study of the diffusion of chromium into iron, *Trans. Am. Inst. Mining Met. Engrs., 113,* 163–178.

Hückel, W. 1950. *Structural Chemistry of Inorganic Compounds,* vol. I, Elsevier Publishing Company, New York.

Korzhinsky, D. S. 1936. Mobility and inertness of components in metasomatosis, *Izvest. Akad. Nauk S. S. S. R., Ser. Geol.*, no. 1, pp. 58–60.

Muan, A. 1955. Phase equilibria in the system FeO–Fe_2O_3–SiO_2, *J. Metals*, *7*, 1–12.

Pfeil, L. B. 1929. The oxidation of iron and steel at high temperature, *J. Iron Steel Inst. (London)*, *119*, 501–560.

Phillips, A. H., and H. H. Hess. 1936. Metamorphic differentiation at contacts between serpentine and siliceous country rock, *Am. Mineralogist*, *21*, 333–362.

Prigogine, I. 1955. *Introduction to Thermodynamics of Irreversible Processes*, Charles C Thomas, Springfield, Ill.

Read, H. H. 1934. On zoned associations of antigorite, talc, actinolite, chlorite, and biotite in Unst, Shetland Islands, *Mining Mag.*, *23*, 519–540.

Rhines, F. N. 1940. A metallographic study of internal oxidation in the alpha solid solutions of copper, *Trans. Am. Inst. Mining Met. Engrs.*, *137*, 246–290.

Scheil, E., and K. Kiwit. 1936. Einfluss von Legierungszusätzen auf das Zundern des Eisens, *Arch. Eisenhüttenw.*, *9*, 405–417.

Smigelskas, A. D., and E. O. Kirkendall. 1947. Zinc diffusion in alpha brass, *Trans. Am. Inst. Mining Met. Engrs.*, *171*, 130–142

Thompson, James B., Jr. 1955. The thermodynamic basis for the mineral facies concept, *Am. J. Sci.*, *253*, 65–103.

List of additional papers by D. S. Korzhinsky dealing with metasomatic processes

Korzhinsky, D. S. 1941. Deposits of metasomatic contact reaction, *Doklady Akad. Nauk S. S. S. R.*, *33* (no. 2), 133–135.

Korzhinsky, D. S. 1942. Concept of geochemical mobility of the elements, *Zapiski Min. Soc. S. S. S. R.*, *71* (nos. 3–4), 160–168.

Korzhinsky, D. S. 1944. Relationship between the mineralogical composition and the chemical potential value of the components, *Zapiski Min. Soc. S. S. S. R.*, *73* (no. 1), 62–73.

Korzhinsky, D. S. 1946. Metasomatic zoning in wall rock alteration and veins, *Zapiski Min. Soc. S. S. S. R.*, *75* (no. 4), 321–332.

Korzhinsky, D. S. 1947. "Filtration effect" in solutions and its role in geology, *Izvest. Akad. Nauk S. S. S. R., Ser. Geol.*, no. 2, pp. 35–48.

Korzhinsky, D. S. 1949. The phase rule and systems with completely mobile components, *Doklady Akad. Nauk S. S. S. R.*, *64* (no. 3), 361–364.

Korzhinsky, D. S. 1950*a*. Phase Rule and Geochemical Mobility of Elements, International Geological Congress, Report of 18th Session, Great Britain, part II, pp. 50–65.

Korzhinsky, D. S. 1950*b*. Differential Mobility of Components and Metasomatic Zoning in Metamorphism, International Geological Congress, Report of 18th Session, Great Britain, part III, pp. 65–80.

Korzhinsky, D. S. 1950*c*. Equilibrium factors in metasomatism, *Izvest. Akad. Nauk S. S. S. R., Ser. Geol.*, no. 3, pp. 21–49.

Korzhinsky, D. S. 1951*a*. Derivation of equations for metasomatic infiltration zoning, *Doklady Akad. Nauk S. S. S. R.*, *77* (no. 2), 305–308.

Korzhinsky, D. S. 1951*b*. General marks of infiltration metasomatosis zones, *Doklady Akad. Nauk S. S. S. R.*, *78* (no. 1), 95–98.

Korzhinsky, D. S. 1951*c*. Infiltration metasomatic zoning and the formation of veins, *Izvest. Akad. Nauk S. S. S. R., Ser. Geol.*, no. 6, pp. 64–86.

Korzhinsky, D. S. 1952*a*. Granitization as magmatic replacement, *Izvest. Akad. Nauk S. S. S. R., Ser. Geol.*, no. 2, pp. 56–69.

Korzhinsky, D. S. 1952*b*. Derivation of an equation for the metasomatic zonality by simple diffusion, *Doklady Akad. Nauk S. S. S. R., 84* (no. 4), 761–764.

Korzhinsky, D. S. 1952*c*. The distinction between the infiltration and diffusion metasomatic columns in relation to the minerals of variable composition, *Doklady Akad. Nauk S. S. S. R., 86* (no. 3), 596–600.

Korzhinsky, D. S. 1953*a*. On the problem of the equation development of infiltration and diffusion metasomatic zoning, *Doklady Akad. Nauk S. S. S. R., 88* (no. 3), 523–526.

Korzhinsky, D. S. 1953*b*. Theory of infiltration metasomatism with development of reaction minerals, *Izvest. Akad. Nauk S. S. S. R., Ser. Geol.*, no. 4, pp. 13–35.

Korzhinsky, D. S. 1953*c*. Infiltration metasomatism in the presence of temperature gradient and contact metasomatic leaching, *Zapiski Min. Soc. S. S. S. R., 82* (no. 3), 161–172.

Korzhinsky, D. S. 1953*d*. The outline of metasomatic processes, *Publ. Akad. Nauk S. S. S. R. (Smirnoff volume)*, pp. 332–452.

Korzhinsky, D. S. 1954. Theory of the infiltration metasomatic zoning, *Publ. Akad. Nauk S. S. S. R.*, 32 pp.

Korzhinsky, D. S. 1956. Derivation of thermodynamic potentials of a system with variable components, *Doklady Akad. Nauk S. S. S. R., 106* (no. 2), 295–298.

Activation Analysis Applied to Geochemical Problems[1]

GEORGE W. REED

Argonne National Laboratory, Lemont, Illinois

Radiochemical analytical techniques are proving to be extremely useful and sensitive tools in geochemical studies. Activation analysis, in particular, has found widespread application in the determination of minor and trace elements in materials of geological interest. Other applications of radiochemical techniques involve, for instance, the measurement of naturally occurring radioactivities and the use of radioactive tracers for the study of geochemically interesting systems.

The following discussion will be concerned, first, with a general review of activation analysis as an analytical technique, and, second, with the application of these techniques to the study of the uranium content of meteorites.

Activation analysis, as generally applied, involves the production of a radioactive isotope by neutron absorption and the subsequent measurement of its amount by counting techniques. All isotopes are able to capture neutrons to give nuclides, many of which are radioactive. The invention of the nuclear reactor or pile, which provides a copious supply of neutrons, has given great impetus to this type of analysis.

In a historical sense nature carried out activation processes long before the era of reactors, ion accelerators, or (α, n) sources. Among the natural nuclides of present interest are C^{14}, H^3, Be^7, S^{35}, and Cl^{39}. Some of the reactions involved are shown in table 1; they all result from cosmic-ray interactions. These reactions, of course, do not exhaust the type of reactions occurring; for example, radioactive decay by α-particle emission from uranium may lead to the production

[1] Based on work performed under the auspices of the U. S. Atomic Energy Commission.

TABLE 1. Radionuclides in Nature

Nuclide	Half-Life	Reaction
C^{14}	5568 yr	$N^{14}(n, p)C^{14}$
H^3	12.4 yr	Spallation
Be^7	53 days	Spallation
S^{35}	87 days	Spallation
P^{32}	14 days	Spallation
Cl^{39}	55 min	$A^{40}(\mu^-, n)Cl^{39}$

of neutrons by (α, n) reactions. These neutrons when captured by U^{238} produce finally Pu^{239}; they may also lead to fission and thus fission products.

The relatively low activities and frequently weak radiations made recognition of these processes difficult until recently. More than a decade ago, however, Libby (1946) had begun searching for C^{14} and H^3, and the success of this search is well known.

Since meteorites, especially chondrites, are often considered typical in composition of cosmic matter in general (Urey, 1952), we shall restrict our discussion for the most part to meteorites. Neutron activation is ideally suited to the study of meteorites, for its sensitivity permits small amounts to be used, thus conserving these already rare objects.

One of the earliest applications of neutron activation for this purpose was made by Brown and Goldberg (1949*a*). Some of the elements measured in meteorites by this technique are listed in table 2. It is evident that the periodic chart has been spanned.

One of the major difficulties with other methods of analysis at the parts-per-million level is contamination from reagents, containers, and air. Such contamination can be minimized in neutron activation inasmuch as no chemical processing is necessary before irradiation. Radioactivation usually permits the simultaneous determination of several elements, in the same sample. Moreover, in some instances not only the elemental content but also the isotopic composition can be determined, since two or more isotopes of an element may yield radioactive products.

Three factors play major roles in establishing the applicability of activation analysis: (1) the intensity of the neutron source or the neutron flux, which in several reactors is in the range of 10^{12} to 10^{13} neutrons/cm^2 sec; (2) the probability that the isotope will capture a neutron to form a radioactive nuclide—a probability referred to as the

TABLE 2. **Activation Analyses of Meteorites**

Nuclide	Content, g/g		Investigator
	Stone *	Iron	
He^3	$(0.13–9) \times 10^{-6}$ (cc/g)		Fireman and Schwarzer (1957)
Li^6	$(1.1–6.2) \times 10^{-7}$	$<10^{-9}$	Fireman and Schwarzer (1957)
Co	$(3–1000) \times 10^{-6}$		Smales, Mapper, and Wood (1957)
Ni	$10^{-4}–10^{-2}$		Smales, Mapper, and Wood (1957)
Cu	$10^{-5}–10^{-4}$		Smales, Mapper, and Wood (1957)
Ga		$(1–9) \times 10^{-5}$	Brown and Goldberg (1949)
Rb	$(1–3) \times 10^{-6}$		Cabell and Smales (1957)
Pd		$(2–7) \times 10^{-6}$	Brown and Goldberg (1949)
Cs	$(0.01–0.1) \times 10^{-6}$		Cabell and Smales (1957)
Ba	4×10^{-6}	$\lesssim 10^{-9}$	Hamaguchi, Reed, and Turkevich (1957) Reed, Hamaguchi, and Turkevich (1958)
Re		0.6×10^{-6}	Brown and Goldberg (1949*b*)
Au		$(0.1–10) \times 10^{-6}$	Goldberg, Uchiyama, and Brown (1951)
Th	4×10^{-8}	3×10^{-11}	Bate, Huizenga, and Potratz (1957)
U	10^{-8}	$10^{-12}–10^{-10}$	Hamaguchi, Reed, and Turkevich (1957) Reed, Hamaguchi, and Turkevich (1958)

* Chondrites.

activation cross section and measured in units of 10^{-24} cm^2, a barn; (3) the "detectability" of the radiations from the radioactive product.

The first two factors, flux and cross section, need no further discussion at this point. We will, however, elaborate on the last. Detectability of the radiations from the radioactive product depends on the type of radiation, usually β^- but frequently γ, its energy (very low-energy β's are difficult to measure), and the half-life of the radioactive nuclide formed (very short-lived nuclides disappear too rapidly, and very long-lived ones may require long irradiation periods before sufficient amounts of the desired radioactivity are accumulated). The total amount of activity (saturation disintegration rate) made in an infinitely long irradiation is

$$D^{\infty} = N \times nv \times \sigma$$

where N is the number of atoms of the parent nuclide and nv and σ are the flux and cross section. The amount of radioactivity available for measurement will be only a fraction of this, for the following reasons. Saturation activities usually are not achieved or desired; there is a period between the end of the irradiation and the time of measurement during which the sample decays; chemical processing of the sample causes losses; and, finally, the detection efficiency of the counting arrangement is limited. The measured activity can be expressed as

$$A = D^{\infty}(1 - e^{-\lambda\tau})e^{-\lambda t} \times G \times E \times Y$$

where the second and third factors are the fraction of saturation and decay during processing; the fourth is the geometry or the fraction of the primary radiations from the sample "seen" by the counter; the fifth factor, E, includes the effects due to absorption by the sample, counter window, and air and to scattering by the sample and backing on which the sample is mounted. The last factor, Y, is the chemical yield.

Normally, to avoid absolute calibration of the measuring technique, a comparison procedure making use of a monitor is adopted. The monitor should be almost identical to the sample, having as nearly as possible the same elemental constitution and total neutron cross section. It also contains a known amount of the element to be determined. Use of the monitor eliminates the necessity of knowing the flux, the cross section, the fraction of saturation, and the over-all efficiency of detection. The requirements are that the sample and monitor be of comparable size and composition; that they be placed adjacent to each other so that the neutron flux will be the same; and that the activities isolated be measured as samples having approximately the same weight and mounted identically.

Standard instruments such as end-window Geiger-Müller or proportional counters and scintillation counters are used to measure the radioactivity.

In order to indicate the sensitivity of the technique, the periodic chart of sensitivities as given by Meinke (1955) is reproduced in figure 1. These are not limiting values since they are based on the isolation and measurement of considerable amounts of radioactivity. In general, much smaller amounts can be accurately measured. Table 3, also from Meinke, shows the relative sensitivities of various methods for some of the elements of current interest to us. Gross normalizations were necessary for such a comparison in order to adjust the various methods to a common sensitivity basis of micrograms per milliliter for a 25- to 50-ml solution and a 10 per cent error. For the radioactivation

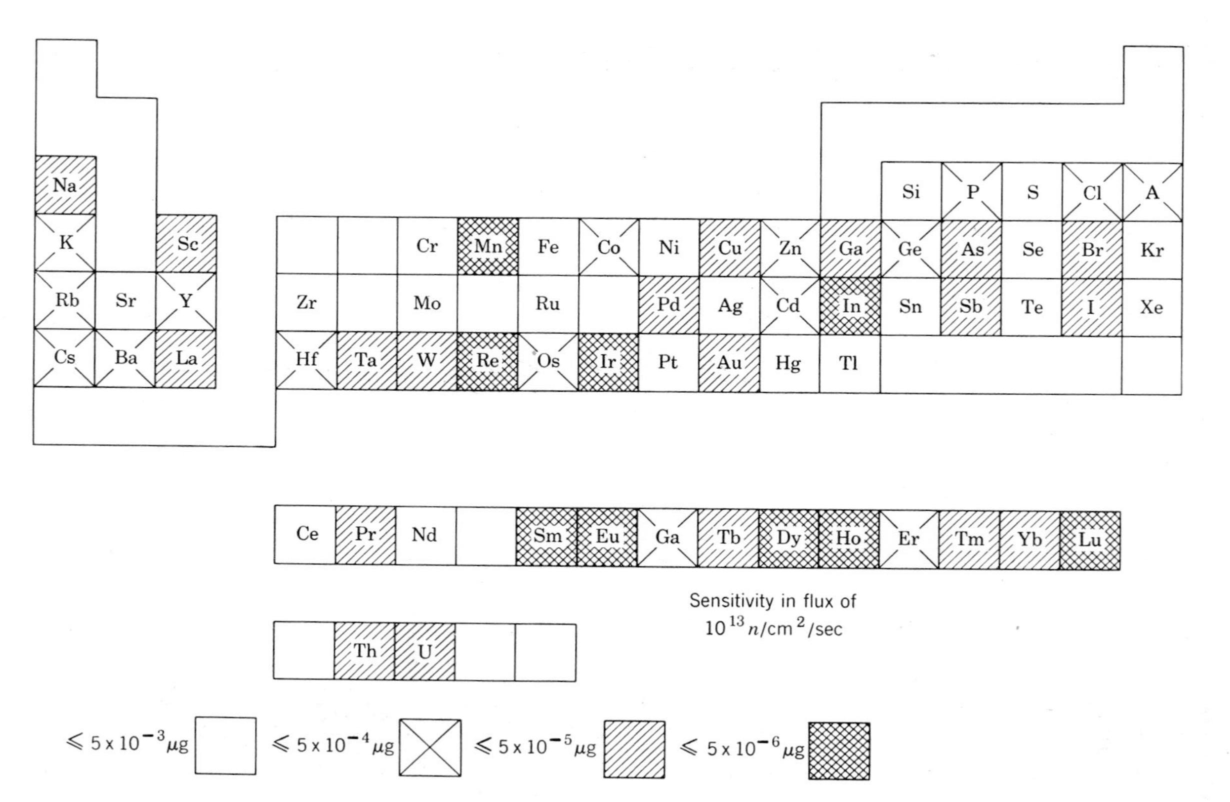

Fig. 1. Activation analysis sensitivities. Adapted from Meinke (1955), by permission.

Table 3. Sensitivity Comparisons, μg/ml

From W. W. Meinke (1955), by permission

Z	Element	Oak Ridge LITR Reactor	Copper Spark	Graphite Direct-Current Arc	Flame Spectrophotometer	Sensitive Color Reaction	Amperometric Titration
56	Ba	0.0025	0.1		3.0		25.0
62	Sm	0.0003	0.2		100.0		
78	Pt	0.005	0.2		200.0	0.1	
80	Hg	0.0065	5.0	2.0	100.0	0.08	
81	Tl	0.03		0.2	1.0		
82	Pb	0.1	0.05	0.2	20.0	0.03	3.0
83	Bi	~0.02	0.2	0.2	300.0	1.0	300.0
90	Th	(0.0001)	0.2				
92	U	0.0005	1.0		10.0	0.7	

technique this corresponds to several hundreds of counts per minute. The LITR reactor referred to in the table has a flux of about 10^{13} n/sec cm^2. The value in parentheses for thorium is from an estimate by Bate (1957). Except perhaps for lead the greater sensitivity of the activation technique is quite apparent.

So far we have discussed only that activation process which accompanies neutron capture to form an isotope of one mass number greater. The neutrons usually involved are of thermal energies, that is, have velocities governed by the thermal vibrations in the moderator of the pile, but this is not always the case. Even with thermal neutrons, processes other than simple capture may occur, such as fission at the heavy end of the periodic table and (n, p) and (n, α) reactions at the light end. In irradiating samples close to or inside of fuel elements to obtain the maximum neutron flux, fairly high-energy neutrons are encountered. These will lead to (n, p), $(n, 2n)$, (n, α), and (n, f) reactions in many nuclides. Examples of some of these reactions that have been or are being used in meteoritic studies are listed herewith.

(a) Radiative capture.

$$Z^A(n, \gamma)Z^{A+1} \xrightarrow{\beta^-} (Z+1)^{A+1}$$

$$_{83}\mathrm{Bi}^{209}(n, \gamma)\,_{83}\mathrm{Bi}^{210} \xrightarrow[5\ \mathrm{d}]{\beta^-} {}_{84}\mathrm{Po}^{210} \xrightarrow[138.4\ \mathrm{d}]{\alpha} \mathrm{Pb}^{206}$$

(*b*) Fission.

$$Z^A(n, f)[(Z')^{A'} + (Z - Z')^{A-A'-n's}]$$

$$U^{235}(n, f)Ba^{140} + \text{Complementary fragment}$$

$$\xrightarrow[12.8\ d]{\beta^-} La^{140} \xrightarrow[40\ hr]{\beta^-} Ce^{140}$$

(*c*) Others (n, p), (n, α), $(n, 2n)$.

$$He^3(n, p)\ H^3 \xrightarrow[12\ yr]{\beta^-} He^3$$

$$Li^6(n, \alpha)\ H^3 \xrightarrow[12\ yr]{\beta^-} He^3$$

$$Pb^{204}(n, 2n)\ Pb^{203} \xrightarrow[52\ hr]{e.\,c.} Tl^{203}$$

As already stated, factors that may limit application of the activation method are the possibility of production of the radioactive nuclide and its detection. The above reactions leading to the production of He^3 indicate a factor that may have the opposite effect, that is, the production of the sought-after activity by other types of reactions. In the study of meteorites and geological problems a number of these reactions may become important.

Analysis of Meteorites

Cosmic abundances in the heavy-mass region are in general small and frequently can be determined only by studying the earth and meteoritic material. This section of the cosmic abundance curve is not well defined, for many of the reported abundances were measured by less sensitive techniques and without full appreciation of contamination problems. We are currently engaged in redetermining abundances in the region from mercury through uranium.

Our original interest in applying radioactivation techniques to such a study arose from the concern Urey (1952) has often expressed about the consequences of the heat generated in the earth and the moon if the reported cosmic abundances of uranium and thorium are correct. Anthony Turkevich, of the University of Chicago, and H. Hamaguchi, who has returned to the Tokyo University of Education, have collaborated in the redetermination of the uranium contents of stone and iron meteorites (Hamaguchi, Reed, and Turkevich, 1957; Reed, Hamaguchi, and Turkevich, 1958). We shall present the results of this work and indicate some of the implications. Thorium is currently being measured by the activation technique by Bate, et al. (1957, 1958) at the Argonne National Laboratory and St. Louis University.

Accurately known uranium contents of meteoritic material would shed light on (1) the cosmic abundance of uranium; (2) the relation between uranium, helium, and lead contents, hence age measurements; (3) radioactive heat generation in planets; (4) the distribution of uranium in planetary objects. Therefore uranium has been one of the most extensively studied of the heavy elements. Table 4 lists many of the investigations of uranium in meteoritic material, with the techniques used and the quantities found.

In the radiochemical technique about 1 g of iron or a few tenths of a gram of stone meteorite is irradiated in sealed quartz vials in a high flux reactor. In the case of the iron meteorites the surface of the sample

TABLE 4. Previous Investigations of Uranium in Meteorites

Investigators	Type Sample	Method	Quantity Measured	Quantity in Reagents, Background, etc
Chackett et al. (1950)	Stone meteorites, ~20g	Rn and Tn counting and/or fluorimetric	U $\sim 10^{-7}$ g/g	...
Davis (1950)	Iron and stone meteorites, pallasites, 5–10 g	Count α's from Rn and Tn	U $\sim 2 \times 10^{-8}$–10^{-7} g	Bkg $\sim 5\alpha$ c/m, $\sim 9 \times 10^{-8}$ g U
Dalton et al. (1953)	Iron meteorite, ~100 g	Count α's from Rn and Tn	Tn ~ 6.5 d/hr Rn ~ 14 d/hr	Reagents? Bkg, 30 d/hr
Dalton et al. (1953)	Iron meteorite, 10–15 g	Fluorimetric	U $\sim 5 \times 10^{-8}$ g	Reagents 10–20% of sample
Dalton et al. (1953)	Iron meteorite, 40 g	Fluorimetric	U $\sim 2 \times 10^{-7}$ g	Reagents ~20–50% of sample
Dalton et al. (1953)	Iron meteorite, 40 g	Fluorimetric	U $\sim 2 \times 10^{-7}$ g	Reagents and U^{233} tracer $\sim 10^{-7}$ g U
Van Dijk et al. (1954)	Stone meteorites	Photographic emulsion	3–6 $\times 10^{-8}$ g U/g	Bkg$\gtrsim$ 50% of total (139) single tracks
Reasbeck and Mayne (1955)	Stone meteorites	Rn and Tn counting and/ or fluorimetric	0.8 $\times 10^{-8}$ g U/g	...
Tilton (1952, 1956)	Stone meteorites, 5–15 g	Mass spectrometer, isotope dilution	U $\sim 10^{-7}$–5 $\times 10^{-8}$ g	10^{-8}–5 $\times 10^{-9}$ g U
Hurley (1957)	Stone meteorites	Low level α counting of crushed stones	U $\sim 10^{-8}$ g	...
Deutsch et al. (1956)	Iron meteorites	Photographic emulsion	<6 $\times 10^{-9}$ g U/g	Bkg > 85% of total (2000) α tracks
Starik and Shats (1956)	Iron and stone meteorites, 8–18 g	Fission counting of U and fluorimetric	~2 $\times 10^{-8}$ g U/g in irons 2.4 $\times 10^{-7}$ g U/g in stones	10–20% of U content of meteorites

is dissolved after the irradiation and discarded in order to remove any activities arising from surface contamination. The sample is then dissolved in the presence of suitable carriers and tracers, and the desired nuclides are separated by fairly standard radiochemical procedures. The stone meteorites may be irradiated as powders or as small chunks. The chunks, involving less handling and presenting the smaller surface, are less likely to become contaminated. The same results were obtained with both forms of sample.

The nuclides selected for determination were Np^{239} and the fission chain Ba^{140}-La^{140}. The reactions leading to each are as follows:

$$U^{238}(n, \gamma)U^{239} \xrightarrow[\beta^-]{23.5\text{ m}} Np^{239} \xrightarrow[\beta^-]{2.33\text{ d}} Pu^{239} \rightarrow U^{235}\text{ series}$$

$$U^{235}(n, f)Ba^{140} + \text{Complementary fission fragment chain}$$

$$\xrightarrow[\beta^-]{12.8\text{ d}} La^{140} \xrightarrow[\beta^-]{40\text{ hr}} Ce^{140}$$

Barium carrier and Np^{237} tracer (a 2.2×10^6 yr α emitter) were added to measure the amount of the desired activities recovered from the purification procedure. The isolated activities were identified by means of decay and absorption curves. Monitor samples of meteorite or a synthetic mixture of meteoritic composition spiked with a known amount of uranium were irradiated simultaneously with the samples and were subjected to the same separation and counting procedure. The β activity of the samples was measured with flow-type proportional end window counters. A cosmic-ray-shielded counter having a background of about 1.1 c/m (about 8 to 10 per cent of that of a standard counting arrangement) was used in many measurements. The α activity from the Np^{237} tracer was measured in the proportional counter and also in a parallel-plate ionization chamber.

Measurement of Np^{239} and fission Ba^{140}-La^{140} not only gives two independent determinations of the uranium content but also permits an estimate of the isotopic composition of meteoritic uranium since one nuclide comes from U^{238} and the other from U^{235}. The barium contents of the meteorites were also measured. The barium isolated contained radioactivities arising from the capture of neutrons by the several naturally occurring isotopes. The nuclide usually measured was Ba^{131}, an 11.6-day electron capture activity arising from neutron capture by Ba^{130}. The barium sample was measured until the Ba^{140}-La^{140} equilibrium was established. Then the lanthanum was separated and measured, and from a master Ba^{140}-La^{140} growth and decay curve the

TABLE 5. U and Th Contents of Stone Meteorites

From Hamaguchi, Reed, and Turkevich (1957), by permission

Meteorite	U Content, 10^{-8} g/g			Th Content, 10^{-8} g/g *
	Via Np^{239}	Via Ba^{140}-La^{140}	Literature	
Forest City	0.99	1.06	6 †	4.4
Modoc	1.08	1.08	1, 2, 2, 6; ‡ 10; † 1.1 ± 0.2 §	4.5
Richardton	1.30	1.13		. . .
Holbrook	1.40	1.12		(4.0)
Beardsley	. . .	. . .		4.3
Nuevo Laredo	12.6	12.6	20 †	54
Johnstown, Colo.	. . .	. . .		0.55
Minerals:				
Hualali basalt	46.3	45.2	49.8 ‖	
Twin Sisters dunite	0.10	0.12	1.6 ‖ 2.4 ¶	

* Bate, Huizenga, and Potratz (1957).
† Patterson (1955).
‡ Patterson (1957).
§ Tilton (1952).
‖ Tilton (1956).
¶ Davis (1950).

amount of Ba^{140}-La^{140} equilibrium activity could be determined. The difference between this and the total activity measured at the same time gave the Ba^{131}. Four chondrites gave an average barium content of 3.6 μg/g of meteorite. Nuevo Laredo gave a value about 10 times higher.

The results obtained thus far on the uranium contents of stone meteorites are shown in table 5. Four samples, all chondrites, show an average uranium content of 1.1×10^{-8} U/g meteorite. The scatter, about 10 per cent, is consistent with the error of the method. From the neptunium and fission barium results it follows that the isotopic composition of the uranium is the same as that of terrestrial uranium within 10 per cent. The isotope dilution value of 1.1×10^{-8} g/g for Modoc by Tilton (1952) and also Patterson (1957) as well as values of 0.8

and 1.0×10^{-8} g/g for two other chondrites measured by Reasbeck and Mayne (1955) and by Davis (1950) are consistent with the average given above. Some contradictory data have been given by Chackett et al. (1950) and by Starik and Shats (1956). Their results on chondrites are an order of magnitude higher. The uranium contents given by Patterson (1955) (table 5) were obtained indirectly from the Pb^{206} and Pb^{207} contents and hence cannot be compared uncritically with the results given here.

That the chondritic average does not necessarily apply to all meteorites is seen in the Nuevo Laredo specimen, sometimes identified as an achondrite, which has ten times as much uranium. Furthermore, different achondrites yield different uranium contents. The Norton County achondrite measured by Tilton (1952) was found to contain 0.01 ppm U. If the thorium-uranium ratio is about 4 and constant, the uranium in the Johnstown, Colorado, achondrite should be about 10^{-9} on the basis of thorium measurements by Bate et al. (1957). The basalt and dunite were comparison samples previously measured by Tilton (1956) and by Davis and Hess (1949) using isotope dilution and radon counting, respectively. The results for the basalt, which contains much more uranium, agree, whereas the dunite shows much less uranium via activation and suggests that at this level (10^{-9} g/g) the likelihood of contamination has become serious. It is even greater for the iron meteorites. Here the uranium content is extremely low. The data are given in table 6. They were treated in two ways, depending on how well the radioactivity attributed to a given nuclide could be characterized. Any sample having less than 1 c/m or an uncertain decay was classified as giving only a limit (columns 3 and 4). Samples that had greater than 1 c/m and reasonable decay and absorption behavior, when measured, led to the values reported in columns 5 and 6. The counting rates were usually less than 5 c/m. Since two measurements were obtained from each sample of meteorite, the total number of determinations was about twice the number of irradiations (column 2). Occasionally a sample was lost.

No isotopic ratios could be reliably established. It can be seen that most of the values for the uranium content of iron meteorites fall in the range 10^{-12} to 10^{-10} g/g. The distribution of the data is indicated in figure 2. All previous workers have reported uranium contents 10 to 1000 times greater than those given here.

Thorium in meteorites has been measured by Bate, Huizenga, and Potratz (1957, 1958) by the activation technique. They measured the 27.4-day Pa^{233} daughter of Th^{233} formed when a neutron is cap-

TABLE 6. Uranium Content of Iron Meteorites

From Reed, Hamaguchi, and Turkevich (1958), by permission

Units of 10^{-11} g/g

Meteorite	Number of Samples Irradiated	Number of Determinations Leading Only to Limit	Range of Limits	Number of Determinations Leading to Values	Range of Values
Tamarugal	5	4 *	8–60	5	0.3–3.5
Carbo	6	7	1.6–50	5	0.3–7.0
Thunda	5	7	5–20	3	0.5–32
Canyon Diablo	2	2	2–5	2	0.5–1.4
Arispe	1	2	4–20		
Coahuila	1	2	16–20		
Henbury	1	2	0.7–6		
Brenham (Fe phase)	4	5	1.2–28	3	0.5–12

* One sample of Ba^{140} for Tamarugal had an apparent uranium content of 200×10^{-11}. We consider this to have been accidental contamination. The corresponding neptunium result was 3.3×10^{-11}.

tured by Th^{232}. There have been few previous measurements of the thorium content of stone meteorites and a rather large number of measurements on iron meteorites. Again, the activation technique gives results which are lower by orders of magnitude. The thorium content of stone meteorites is about 4×10^{-8} g/g (table 5) and hence is consistent with what would be predicted using a terrestrial Th/U ratio of around 4. The value for two iron meteorites is about 10^{-11}, which is lower than many of the uranium values.

The significance of these results can best be illustrated in the following summary.

Cosmic abundance. Accepting Suess and Urey's (1956) hypothesis that the chondrites represent average cosmic matter except for the volatile elements, the cosmic abundance of uranium is 7.8×10^{-3} atom of uranium to 10^6 atoms of silicon. This is close to the estimate of Patterson, Brown, Tilton, and Inghram (1953) based on their measurements of the uranium content in Canyon Diablo troilite, the chondrite Modoc, and the achondrite Norton County. The average cosmic abundance was arrived at by assuming the relative proportions of stone, iron, and troilite phases in meteoritic matter as given by H.

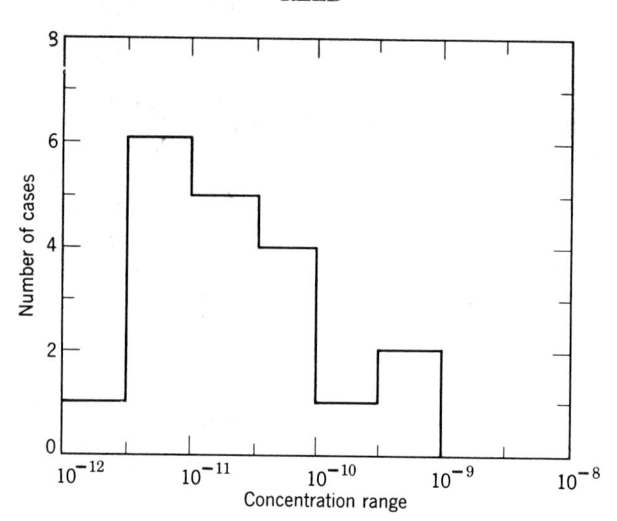

Fig. 2. Frequency distribution: uranium content of iron meteorites, from Reed, Hamaguchi, and Turkevich (1958), by permission.

Brown (1949). The iron results of Davis (1950) and Arrol, Jacobi, and Paneth (1942) were used.

Thus uranium is the least abundant of all the elements for which reliable data are available.

U, Pb, He contents and age measurements. Since lead and helium are the end products of uranium and thorium decay much effort has been expended in attempting to correlate the amount of lead and helium with the amount of uranium and thorium, in particular in relation to age determination. In terrestrial rocks ages based on U-Pb, Th-Pb, Pb^{206}-Pb^{207}, K-A, and Rb-Sr techniques have frequently been found to be concordant. In age measurements of meteorites, Pb-Pb and K-A have been most generally used. Since argon is volatile, heating and crystallization processes may lead to its loss and thus cause a scatter in ages by the K-A method. The oldest ages by this method are about 4.3 billion years. Extremely careful work has been done by Patterson (1955) using the Pb-Pb method, which is not subject to the difficulty of loss like the K-A technique. The results now, however, are somewhat in doubt since the uranium required to account for the lead he observed (see table 5) is not in agreement with that found in our measurements, at least in the Forest City and Modoc meteorites. There can be little doubt about Nuevo Laredo, which gave an age of

4.55 billion years. Here the absolute amount of uranium is in fair agreement and the lead isotopic ratios are so abnormal that a correction for any reasonable amount of contamination will not affect this age.

Paneth's (Arrol, Jacobi, and Paneth, 1942) classical approach to age measurements was via U-He. This method gave ages varying over a wide range and not in agreement with more recent measurements. Sufficient new information has been accumulated to re-evaluate the method. We assume that the uranium contained in chondrites is constant at about 1.1×10^{-8} g/g and of normal isotopic composition, and that the Th-U ratio is 3.6. The possibility that a portion of the helium observed in meteorites arises from cosmic-ray spallation reactions was originally suggested by Bauer (1947). Since both He^3 and He^4 are formed by this process an attempt can be made to estimate the amount of cosmic-ray-produced He^4 and thus deduce the amount of radiogenic He^4. The cosmic-ray-produced He^4/He^3 ratio can be taken as about 4 on the basis of the ratio measured in iron meteorites having large ratios of cosmogenic to radiogenic helium, on the basis of the results from high-energy nuclear reactions, and on other evidence.

With these assumptions, radiogenic helium ages have been estimated for a number of meteorites by Reed and Turkevich (1957). It is interesting that some of these ages fall in the 4×10^9 yr range and all the others are less than 10^9 yr. The data are given in table 7. This grouping is quite distinct. There appear to be fewer A-K ages in the young group and a much greater scatter. The few Rb-Sr and Pb-Pb ages measured all fall in the 4.5×10^9 yr range. It appears, therefore, that after the accumulation of meteoritic matter about 4.5×10^9 yr ago some of the material lost its radiogenic helium about 10^9 yr ago. Some argon was also lost. Apparently, at about this time many meteorites underwent heating or some alteration.

Distribution. The uranium distribution ratio between the silicate and metal phases of planetary bodies is greater than 100 on the basis of the 10^{-8} g/g in chondrites and $<10^{-10}$ g/g in iron meteorites. This may actually be a lower limit to the theoretical value of approximately 10^{12} calculated by Urey (1955*a*).

Heat generation. Urey (1952, 1955*a* and *b*) has raised the question about the excess heat generated in the earth, moon, and Mars by radioactivity if the older uranium and thorium measurements were accepted. He assumes that the moon and Mars have the same mean concentration of uranium, thorium, and potassium as the chondrites. Using the chondritic uranium values (1.1×10^{-8} g/g), assuming a

TABLE 7. Age Data on Stone Meteorites

From Reed and Turkevich (1957), by permission

Meteorite	Weight, kg	Radiogenic He Age, billion years	Other Ages, billion years	Via	Reference
Khovtneyi Khutov	195	4.3	3.00	K-A	Gerling and Levskii (1956) *
Bjurbole	330	4.0	3.60	K-A	Gerling and Levskii (1956) *
			4.32	K-A	Geiss and Hess (1957) *
Elenovka	70	4.0	4.00	K-A	Gerling and Levskii (1956)
Ochansk	500	4.0	4.50	K-A	Gerling and Levskii (1956)
Saratov	328	3.8	3.80	K-A	Gerling and Levskii (1956)
Akaba	3	3.7	3.6	K-A	Thomson and Mayne (1955)
Holbrook			4.17	K-A	Wasserburg, Hayden, and Jensen (1956) *
	240	0.90	4.40	K-A	Geiss and Hess (1957)
Pervomaiskii Poselok					
Black	49	0.94	1.8	K-A	Gerling and Levskii (1956)
Gray		0.63	0.64		
Alfianella	228	0.84			
Kunashak	200	0.55	0.70	K-A	Gerling and Levskii (1956)
Nuevo Laredo	0.5	0.45	4.52	Pb-Pb	Patterson (1955) *
			3.1–3.6	K-A	Reynolds and Lipson (1956)
Norton County	1000	...	4.40	K-A	Geiss and Hess (1957)

* Based on He^4/He^3 ratio = 4/1.

Th-U ratio of 3.6 which is now indicated by the work of Bate et al. (1957), and using Edwards' (1955; Edwards and Urey, 1955) potassium value (8.23×10^{-4} g/g), Urey (1956) concludes that no serious problem exists any longer as far as the heat loss and generation in the earth are concerned.

Thus the radioactivation technique, because of its great sensitivity and freedom from contamination, can be very useful in measuring trace-element contents of materials. A much broader sampling of meteorites is, of course, desirable; however, the results already obtained have contributed significantly to the solution of many perplexing problems.

Finally we may mention briefly investigations currently under way in our laboratories. We are determining the elemental abundances of mercury, thallium, bismuth, and lead in meteoritic material. All three major phases—stone, iron, and troilite—are being measured. The results should shed light on such problems as (1) the abundances, (2) the distribution relationships in different phases, (3) the possibility of loss of mercury by heating during or subsequent to formation of the meteorites, (4) U-Pb balance, (5) possible course or courses of nucleogenesis, taking into account that especially lead and bismuth can be produced by neutron capture, by lighter elements, and also by decay of uranium, thorium, and neptunium, whereas mercury and thallium are not made by the last process.

References

Arrol, W. J., R. B. Jacobi, and F. A. Paneth. 1942. Meteorites and the age of the solar system, *Nature, 149,* 235.

Bate, G. L. 1957. Private communication.

Bate, G. L., J. R. Huizenga, and H. A. Potratz. 1957. Thorium content of stone meteorites, *Science, 126,* 612.

Bate, G. L., H. A. Potratz, and J. R. Huizenga. 1958. Thorium in iron meteorites: a preliminary investigation, *Geochim. et Cosmochim. Acta.* In press.

Bauer, C. A. 1947. Production of He in meteorites by cosmic radiation, *Phys. Rev., 72,* 354.

Brown, H. 1949. Relative abundances of nuclear species, *Revs. Modern Phys., 21,* 625.

Brown, H., and E. Goldberg. 1949*a*. The neutron pile as a tool in quantitative analysis; the Ga and Pd content of iron meteorites, *Science, 109,* 347.

Brown, H., and E. Goldberg. 1949*b*. *Phys. Rev., 76,* 1260.

Cabell, M. J., and A. A. Smales. 1957. *Analyst, 82,* 390.

Chackett, K. F., J. Golden, E. R. Mercer, F. A. Paneth, and P. Reasbeck. 1950. The Beddgelert meteorite, *Geochim. et Cosmochim. Acta, 1,* 3.

Dalton, Golden, Martin, Mercer, and Thomson. 1953. *Geochim. et Cosmochim. Acta, 3,* 272.

Davis, G. L. 1950. Radium content of ultramafic igneous rocks, III, Meteorites, *Am. J. Sci., 248,* 107.

Davis, G. L., and H. H. Hess. 1949. Radium content of ultramafic igneous rocks, II, Geological and chemical implications, *Am. J. Sci., 247,* 856.

Deutsch, Houtermans, and Picciotto. 1956. *Geochim. et Cosmochim. Acta, 10,* 166.

Edwards, G. 1955. Na and K in meteorites, *Geochim. et Cosmochim. Acta, 8,* 285.

Edwards, G., and H. C. Urey. 1955. Determination of alkali metals in meteorites by a distillation process, *Geochim. et Cosmochim. Acta, 7,* 154.

Fireman, E. L., and D. Schwarzer. 1957. *Geochim. et Cosmochim. Acta, 11,* 252.

Geiss, J., and D. C. Hess. 1957. *Phys. Rev., 107,* 540.

Gerling, E. K., and L. K. Levskii. 1956. *Doklady Akad. Nauk S. S. S. R., 110,* 750.

Goldberg, Uchiyama, and Brown. 1951. *Geochim. et Cosmochim. Acta, 2,* 1.

Hamaguchi, H., G. W. Reed, and A. Turkevich. 1957. Uranium and barium in stone meteorites, *Geochim. et Cosmochim. Acta, 12,* 337.

Hurley, P. M. 1957. *Bull. Geol. Soc. Am., 68,* 379.

Libby, W. F. 1946. Atmospheric H^3 and radiocarbon from cosmic radiation, *Phys. Rev., 69,* 671.

Meinke, W. W. 1955. Trace element sensitivity: comparison of activation analysis with other methods, *Science, 121,* 177.

Patterson, C. C. 1955. The Pb^{207}/Pb^{206} ages of some stone meteorites, *Geochim. et Cosmochim. Acta, 7,* 151.

Patterson, C. C. 1957. Private communication.

Patterson, C., H. Brown, G. R. Tilton, and M. Inghram. 1953. Concentration of U and Pb and the isotopic composition of Pb in meteoritic material, *Phys. Rev., 92,* 1234.

Reasbeck, P., and K. Mayne. 1955. Ages and origin of meteorites, *Nature, 176,* 186.

Reed, G. W., H. Hamaguchi, and A. Turkevich. 1958. Uranium contents of iron meteorites, *Geochim. et Cosmochim. Acta, 13,* 248.

Reed, G. W., and A. Turkevich. 1957. Uranium, helium and the ages of meteorites, *Nature, 180,* 594.

Reynolds, J., and J. I. Lipson. 1957. *Geochim. et Cosmochim. Acta, 12,* 330.

Smales, Mapper, and Wood. 1957. *Analyst, 82,* 75.

Starik, I. E., and M. M. Shats. 1956. Determination of uranium in stone and iron meteorites, *Geokhimiya, 2,* 2.

Suess, H. E., and H. C. Urey. 1956. Abundances of the elements, *Revs. Modern Phys., 28,* 53.

Thomson, S. J., and K. I. Mayne. 1955. *Geochim. et Cosmochim. Acta, 1,* 169.

Tilton, G. R. 1952. Distribution of trace quantities of uranium nature, Ph. D. thesis, University of Chicago.

Tilton, G. R. 1956. Private communication.

Urey, H. C. 1952. The abundances of the elements, *Phys. Rev., 88,* 248.

Urey, H. C. 1955*a*. Origin and age of meteorites. *Nature, 175,* 321.

Urey, H. C. 1955*b*. The cosmic abundances of K, Cu, Th and the heat balances of the earth, the moon, and Mars, *Proc. Natl. Acad. Sci. U. S., 41,* 127.
Urey, H. C. 1956. The cosmic abundances of K, Cu, and Th and the heat balances of the earth, the moon, and Mars, *Proc. Natl. Acad. Sci. U. S., 42,* 889.
Van Dijk, Th., C. de Jager, and J. de Metter. 1954. The uranium content of a stone meteorite, *Mem. soc. roy. sci. Liège, 14,* 495.
Wasserburg, G. J., R. J. Hayden, and K. J. Jensen. 1956. *Geochim. et Cosmochim. Acta, 10,* 153.

Chondrites and the Chemical Composition of the Earth

GORDON J. F. MAC DONALD[1]
Massachusetts Institute of Technology

The chemical composition of the earth poses a problem both tantalizing and frustrating. Materials available at the surface can be sampled and analyzed in great detail, but the main mass of the earth cannot, and we must depend upon indirect approaches. Despite the speculative aspects of any discussion of the earth's interior, recent developments in astrophysics and in studies of meteorites call for a review of the data relating to the chemical composition of the earth. The new evidence supports the idea that the earth may have a composition similar to that of chondritic meteorites. Some of the consequences of such a hypothesis are examined in this chapter.

Observations on the Earth

The major effort in classical geochemistry has been the accumulation of detailed chemical analyses of rocks found at or near the earth's surface (Clarke and Washington, 1924; Rankama and Sahama, 1950; Goldschmidt, 1954). From these analyses, the composition of the crust, defined as the solid matter lying above the Mohorovičić discontinuity, can be estimated. Table 1 lists the distribution of mass in the earth, taking into account the variation in thickness of the crust between continental and oceanic regions (Ewing and Press, 1956; Byerly, 1956). Table 2 gives the composition of nonvolatile elements of the crust based on Clarke and Washington's compilation in continental areas and on Vinogradov's (1956) review of analyses of oceanic basalts. The composition is listed in terms of the number of atoms

[1] Present address: Institute of Geophysics, University of California, Los Angeles.

TABLE 1. Distribution of Mass

	Mass in Grams	Fraction of Earth
Earth	5.977×10^{27}	1.000
Core	1.9×10^{27}	0.315
Mantle	4.1×10^{27}	0.681
Crust	2.38×10^{25}	0.004
Oceanic > 2400 m	0.62×10^{25}	
Continental	1.76×10^{25}	
Oceans	1.42×10^{24}	
Atmosphere	5.1×10^{21}	

of an element per 10^6 atoms of silicon. Table 3 gives the mass of the elements contained in the crust.

Determining the composition of the remainder of the earth is extraordinarily difficult. We cannot make a direct chemical analysis of the material, but must depend on chance samples brought up from below. The interpretation of a given specimen—whether it is representative of deep material or is merely a differentiate—is not at all straightforward. Thus, Ross, Foster, and Myers (1954) interpret the close mineralogical and chemical similarity of dunites and olivine bombs as indicating that these materials are the principal constituents of the upper mantle. In the present paper we present reasons for believing that the upper mantle is not predominantly olivine but that the uniformity in composition and mineralogy of dunites and olivine

TABLE 2. Crustal Abundances

	Oceanic Crust 0.26	Continental Crust 0.74	Total Crust
Na	1.08×10^5	1.26×10^5	1.21×10^5
Mg	2.36×10^5	8.80×10^4	1.26×10^5
Al	4.15×10^5	3.06×10^5	3.34×10^5
Si	1.00×10^6	1.00×10^6	1.00×10^6
P	5.76×10^3	4.30×10^3	4.68×10^3
K	2.71×10^4	6.75×10^4	5.70×10^4
Ca	2.14×10^5	9.21×10^4	1.24×10^5
Ti	2.40×10^4	1.33×10^4	1.11×10^4
Mn	5.11×10^3	1.72×10^3	2.60×10^3
Fe	1.95×10^5	9.30×10^4	1.19×10^5

bombs indicates that these materials are the end product or residue of a process of differentiation or partial fusion.

Eclogite inclusions in kimberlite pipes are associated with inclusions of peridotite and dunite. They contain occasional diamonds and are enclosed within the diamond-bearing kimberlite. The stability of field of diamond, as outlined by thermochemical data and experimental work (Buddy, Hall, Strong, and Wentorf, 1955), strongly suggests that the eclogite inclusions crystallized at a depth of at least 80 to 100 km. The kimberlite inclusions represent unaltered material that crystallized at a depth of 100 km or more.

Table 4 lists the atomic abundances of the major elements in eclogites, ultrabasic rock, peridotites, and dunites. The eclogite abundances are based on the average of analyses of 11 nonkyanite-bearing eclogites reported by Williams (1932). The ultrabasic abundances are Vinogradov's (1956) average of 99 dunites, peridotites, and pyroxenites. The dunite and peridotite averages are Daly's (1933).

Fortunately, geophysical data place additional limits on speculations regarding the chemical make-up of the earth. The elastic properties of the material below the Mohorovičić discontinuity are similar to the elastic properties of dunites, peridotites, and eclogites as measured in the laboratory (Birch, 1952). Presumably, any rock containing predominantly olivine, pyroxene, and garnet would have the appropriate elastic properties for upper-mantle material, provided that the iron content is not too high (iron lowers the elastic wave velocity) (Birch, 1952).

TABLE 3. Crustal Abundances

	Mass in Grams		
	Oceanic Crust	Continental Crust	Total Crust
Na	1.26×10^{23}	5.00×10^{23}	6.26×10^{23}
Mg	2.94×10^{23}	3.69×10^{23}	6.63×10^{23}
Al	5.41×10^{23}	1.43×10^{24}	1.97×10^{24}
Si	1.43×10^{24}	4.85×10^{24}	6.28×10^{24}
P	8.85×10^{21}	2.28×10^{22}	3.16×10^{22}
K	5.44×10^{22}	4.57×10^{23}	5.11×10^{23}
Ca	4.38×10^{23}	6.37×10^{23}	1.07×10^{24}
Ti	5.09×10^{22}	1.11×10^{23}	1.62×10^{23}
Mn	1.39×10^{22}	1.63×10^{22}	3.02×10^{22}
Fe	5.61×10^{23}	8.86×10^{23}	1.45×10^{24}

TABLE 4. Possible Samples of Upper Mantle

	Eclogite	Ultrabasic Rocks (Vinogradov)	Peridotite	Dunite
Na	5.82×10^4	3.05×10^4	2.78×10^4	2.39×10^3
Mg	4.44×10^5	7.09×10^5	1.25×10^6	1.70×10^6
Al	2.54×10^5	1.32×10^5	1.29×10^5	2.50×10^4
Si	1.00×10^6	1.00×10^6	1.00×10^6	1.00×10^6
P	1.46×10^3	4.80×10^3	1.92×10^3	5.22×10^2
K	1.49×10^4	1.58×10^4	7.10×10^3	6.29×10^2
Ca	2.21×10^5	2.36×10^5	8.70×10^4	1.85×10^4
Ti	1.36×10^4	7.76×10^3	1.71×10^3	3.71×10^2
Cr	1.36×10^3	4.68×10^3	...	...
Mn	3.29×10^3	2.96×10^3	3.66×10^3	3.34×10^3
Fe	2.41×10^5	2.17×10^5	1.58×10^5	1.67×10^5
Ni	6.94×10^2	3.35×10^3	...	...

Seismology establishes that the mantle of the earth is a solid in the sense that it can transmit shear waves. The core cannot, and so must be essentially liquid. Studies of magnetic phenomena reveal that the material near the surface must be a good electrical insulator, and that the conductivity increases with depth. Studies of the change of temperature with depth, coupled with the determination of the thermal conductivity, provide most important limits on the distribution of heat-producing radioactive elements within the earth. The mean density of the earth requires that there be material of density greater than 3 somewhere within the earth. The moment of inertia of the earth, derived from astronomical observations, is such that the heavier material must be concentrated toward the center. Seismology provides further data in that the detailed distribution of mass within the earth is fixed by the elastic constants, derivable from seismic studies, and by the mean density and moment of inertia.

Observations on Solar Abundances

Measurements of the intensities of absorption lines in the solar spectrum, coupled with calculations of the effects of pressure, relative motion, and magnetic fields on the shape and strength of the lines, give information about the relative abundance of the elements in the solar atmosphere. These spectroscopic results do not approach the precision of classical chemical analysis, but the sampling problem that hampers the interpretation of meteoritic and crustal abundances is less troublesome. Aller, Goldberg, and co-workers at Michigan have recently carried out an extensive program of measurement of the solar spectra leading to improved values of the solar abundances.

A major difficulty in comparing the composition of the sun's outer surface with that of terrestrial or meteoritic material is the fact that major metallic elements like magnesium, silicon, and iron are present only to the extent of a few parts in ten thousand in the solar atmosphere; hydrogen and, to a lesser extent, helium predominate. Furthermore, the use of solar abundances in discussions of the gross chemical features of the earth is necessarily based on two assumptions: (1) the sun and the earth are genetically related, both having been derived from the same parent material; (2) the composition of the solar atmosphere is representative of the total mass of the sun.

The degree to which the composition of the outer layers of the sun represents the whole depends on the amount of mixing of the material in the sun. The structure of the surface of the sun is indicative of violent motion, and mixing very likely penetrates to considerable depth. Greenstein and Richardson (1951) argue from considerations of nuclear physics about the abundance of lithium that the sun may be chemically homogeneous to a depth equal to half its radius. Similar conclusions were derived from the beryllium-lithium ratio (Greenstein and Tandberg-Hanssen, 1954).

The sun's atmosphere may thus be representative of about 4 to 5 per cent of the total mass of the sun. In the model of the sun constructed by Schwarzschild, Howard, and Harm (1957), the convective zone extends only to 18 per cent of the radius so that a smaller percentage of the sun's mass is represented in the sun's atmosphere.

We shall return later to the question of the abundance of elements in the sun in comparison with chondritic meteorites.

Meteorites

Meteorites, particularly the chondrites, are thought by many to represent the best chemical model of the earth. It may seem strange that the interplanetary debris that happens to land on the earth should be accorded such importance in discussions of its over-all chemical nature, but four features of meteorites indicate a close genetic relationship with the solar system. Meteorites appear to be members of the solar system rather than stray bits of extraneous matter. As far as they have been investigated, nonradiogenic isotopes found in them are in the same ratio as in terrestrial elements. Meteoritic iron, oxygen, silicon, and sulfur isotopes have all shown ratios similar to those found on the earth, if the natural variation of the ratios and instrumental errors are taken into account. Indeed, the meteoritic ratios of isotopes are now commonly used as the reference points in discussions of terrestrial isotopic fractionation. The age of meteorites determined by A^{40}-K^{40} measurements (Geiss and Hess, 1958; Wasserburg and Hayden, 1955*a*, 1955*b*), by the Rb^{87}-Sr^{87} method (Schumaker, 1956*a*, 1956*b*), and by the lead method (Patterson, 1955; Patterson, Tilton, and Inghram, 1955) are in agreement with the age of the earth estimated from the abundances of the lead isotopes (Masuda, 1958). Finally, the work of Reed and others on the content of heat-producing elements in meteorites, combined with present-day heat-flow measurements, shows that the present rate of heat production in the earth is consistent with the hypothesis that the earth as a whole, or perhaps a major portion of the earth, is made up of chondritic material.

Urey and Craig (1953) reviewed the analytical data relating to stony meteorites. Since then, Wiik (1956) has published additional analyses. Table 5 gives the average atomic composition of the 94 chondrites reviewed by Urey and Craig plus the additional 11 analyses of Wiik. Urey and Craig separate the meteorites into a high-iron and a low-iron group. The difference between the two groups is not great, and the average composition of all chondrites will be used in the present paper.

TABLE 5. Chondritic Meteorites

	High Group 47	Low Group 58	Average 105
Na	4.87×10^4	5.00×10^4	4.94×10^4
Mg	9.46×10^5	9.25×10^5	9.34×10^5
Al	7.90×10^4	7.92×10^4	7.91×10^4
Si	1.00×10^6	1.00×10^6	1.00×10^6
P	4.39×10^3	4.67×10^3	4.55×10^3
S	1.10×10^5	1.00×10^5	1.04×10^5
K	5.95×10^3	5.94×10^3	5.94×10^3
Ca	5.84×10^4	5.26×10^4	5.52×10^4
Ti	2.35×10^3	2.20×10^3	2.27×10^3
Cr	6.61×10^3	8.59×10^3	7.70×10^3
Mn	5.63×10^3	5.66×10^3	5.64×10^3
Fe	8.42×10^5	6.06×10^5	7.12×10^5
Co	2.84×10^3	1.70×10^3	2.21×10^3
Ni	4.76×10^4	2.74×10^4	3.64×10^4

The stone meteorites include a group characterized by textures similar to those of terrestrial basalts (the basaltic achondrites), and an intermediate group called the chondritic achondrites. The average composition of these two groups is listed in table 6 (Urey and Craig,

TABLE 6. Achondritic Meteorites

	Chondritic Achondrites 12	Basaltic Achondrites 25
Na	1.33×10^4	3.31×10^4
Mg	8.64×10^5	3.02×10^5
Al	2.44×10^4	2.84×10^5
Si	1.00×10^6	1.00×10^6
P	1.61×10^3	1.74×10^3
S	1.25×10^4	8.09×10^3
K	2.67×10^3	7.08×10^3
Ca	2.45×10^4	2.29×10^5
Ti	1.72×10^3	7.73×10^3
Cr	1.25×10^4	6.50×10^3
Mn	6.28×10^3	6.96×10^3
Fe	2.50×10^5	2.93×10^5
Ni	3.31×10^3	...

1953; Wiik, 1956). Although the distinction between the stony meteorites is based primarily on macroscopic structure, the classification is also a chemical one. The chondrites have a remarkably uniform composition, the range being indicated by the difference between the low- and high-iron groups of Urey and Craig. The achondrites show a wider range of composition; many of them approximate basalts.

Iron meteorites contain about 90 per cent by weight of iron, 8.5 per cent of nickel, and smaller amounts of other elements. The relative proportion of iron and stone meteorites is a matter of some controversy. Among "finds," iron meteorites are more abundant; in observed falls the stones predominate. Most current estimates (Watson, 1956, p. 125; Urey, 1952, pp. 192 ff.) place the ratio of stones to irons at about 10 to 1.

Table 7 compares chondritic and solar abundances of metallic elements. The three most abundant metallic elements are silicon, magnesium, and iron, both in the sun and in chondritic meteorites. Sulfur is notably abundant in the sun, but the reliability of solar-sulfur data is low. The principal difference between meteoritic solar abundances lies in the low abundance of the iron-group elements (with the ex-

TABLE 7. Solar Abundances

	Aller (1957)	Greenstein (1956)	Ratio of Solar Abundance (Aller) to Chondritic Abundance
Na	5.03×10^4	7.75×10^4	1.01
Mg	4.80×10^5	1.44×10^6	0.51
Al	4.07×10^4	5.88×10^4	0.51
Si	1.00×10^6	1.00×10^6	1.00
P	6.9×10^4	1.7×10^4	1.51
S	3.7×10^5	4.2×10^5	3.56
K	2.29×10^3	4.25×10^3	0.39
Ca	6.03×10^4	7.95×10^4	1.09
Ti	2.29×10^3	3.55×10^3	1.01
Cr	2.51×10^4	9.35×10^3	3.26
Mn	5.30×10^3	6.91×10^3	0.94
Fe	1.45×10^5	5.75×10^5	0.20
Co	7.5×10^2	5.25×10^3	0.34
Ni	1.59×10^4	5.25×10^4	0.44

ception of chromium and manganese) in the sun. Allowing for a factor of uncertainty of 2 in the solar data, we can say that the composition of meteorites and that of the sun's atmosphere do not differ in major ways except for potassium and iron. Unfortunately, both these elements are critical to any discussion of the composition of the earth, since potassium is a heat-producing element and iron undoubtedly is one of the principal elements determining the earth's density. The abundances of the metallic elements in the solar atmosphere and in chondrites are nevertheless remarkably similar. This agreement supports the hypothesis of Urey (1952) and his co-workers (Urey and Craig, 1953; Suess and Urey, 1956) that the chondritic meteorites provide a good sample of the nonvolatile-element composition of the solar system.

Radioactivity in Chondrites and the Earth's Heat Budget

The heat escaping from the interior of the earth is derived largely from the decay of the uranium and thorium families and the unstable isotope of potassium, K^{40}. It is interesting to compare the amount of heat produced in a hypothetical earth of chondritic composition with the amount actually escaping from the earth. This comparison is made especially valuable by recent redeterminations of the radioactivity of chondrites, using the powerful technique of neutron activation analysis.

The values obtained for the uranium content of chondrites average 1.1×10^{-8} g/g (Hamaguchi, Reed, and Turkevich, 1957), and the mean content of potassium is about 8.0×10^{-4} g/g (Edwards, 1955). The abundance of thorium is less well known. In many natural materials the Th/U ratio ranges from 3 to 4, and Bate, Huizenga, and Potratz' (1957) neutron activation studies on five samples of four chondrites give thorium contents ranging from 4 to 9×10^{-8} g/g with all but one value between 4.0 and 4.7×10^{-8} g/g. It seems likely that the Th/U ratio in chondrites is equal or very nearly equal to that of terrestrial materials. If the whole earth is made up of chondritic material, the heat production is about 2.2×10^{20} calories per year. Since the abundance of radioactive elements in iron meteorites is very much less than in chondrites (Reed and Turkevich, 1955; Reed, Hamaguchi, and Turkevich, 1958), a model of the earth having an iron core and chondritic mantle would have a heat production of about 1.5×10^{20} cal/yr. Heat-flow measurements on continents and oceans indicate a rate of loss of heat from the earth's interior of $1.9\ (\pm 1) \times 10^{20}$ cal/yr (Bullard, 1954; Bullard, Maxwell, and Revelle, 1956). The rate of loss of heat from the earth thus does not differ significantly from the rate of heat production in an earth entirely or largely composed of chondritic material.

Arguments based on the rate of production of heat within the earth do not allow a distinction between an earth model containing an iron core and chondritic mantle and a model assuming a chondritic composition for the whole earth. The low ratio of iron meteorites to chondrites, together with the low iron content of the solar atmosphere, however, points toward a chondritic composition for the whole earth. This hypothesis is consistent with the present rate of loss of heat from the earth but not with what we know about the distribution of density within the earth, if the presently accepted view that the mantle is largely olivine and the core iron-nickel is correct. The three principal density-determining metals are silicon, iron, and magnesium. If we assume a mantle made up largely of $(Mg,Fe)_2SiO_4$, either as olivine or as some high-pressure polymorph with $Mg/Fe = 9$, and a core of iron-nickel, the ratio of the sum of iron, magnesium, and nickel to silicon is 3.3 as compared with the chondritic ratio 1.65 (table 8). A similar contradiction arises if we assume that the mantle has a peridotitic composition. Using Daly's (1933) average peridotite

TABLE 8. Relative Abundances of Iron, Magnesium, and Silicon in Various Earth Models

Composition of Mantle		Composition of Core		$\frac{Fe + Mg + Ni}{Si}$ for Whole Earth	$\frac{Fe}{Mg}$ for Whole Earth
$(Mg,Fe)_2SiO_4$	Mg/Fe = 9	(Fe,Ni)	Fe/Ni = 15	3.3	0.78
$(Mg,Fe)SiO_3$	Mg/Fe = 9	(Fe,Ni)	Fe/Ni = 15	1.8	1.04
Peridotite		(Fe,Ni)	Fe/Ni = 15	2.9	1.3
Chondritic meteorite				1.65	0.71
Solar atmosphere				0.71	0.30

(table 3), the ratio (Fe + Ni + Mg)/Si for the earth as a whole is 2.9. Maintaining the hypothesis that chondrites are representative chemical samples of the solar system leaves us with various possibilities. Either the assumed composition of the mantle, core, or both is incorrect, or some process of differentiation may have concentrated iron and magnesium relative to silicon during the early stages of the earth's history. Urey (1954) discusses the possibility of differentiation by volatilization; it is difficult to imagine a volatilization process in which silicon was lost relative to iron-magnesium yet in which potassium was not lost.

An iron core is consistent with a chondritic composition for the earth, provided that the mantle has an (Fe + Mg)/Si ratio 1, as is illustrated in table 8. This implies a mantle made up dominantly of magnesium-iron pyroxene. Birch (1952) shows that the elastic properties of enstatite-hypersthene differ significantly from the elastic properties of the upper mantle. It is possible that pyroxenes undergo a phase transition to a phase with the appropriate elastic properties in the upper 200 km of the earth, but such a transition has not been observed experimentally (MacDonald, 1956). The upper mantle might have a higher (Fe + Mg)/Si ratio than the lower mantle, but this seems unlikely.

In the following section it is argued on the basis of seismic and heat-flow data that the upper mantle approximates eclogite (table 4) in composition and phase. The lower mantle is then taken to be largely $(Mg,Fe)_2SiO_4$. For such a mantle a chondritic model for the earth requires a core composition of $(Fe,Ni)_{1.6}Si$. The Fe/Mg ratio in such an earth is 0.71, in agreement with the chondritic ratio. The composition of the core is not uniquely determined by abundance arguments because of the uncertain composition of the mantle. It does appear likely that the core contains major amounts of silicon, if the chondritic hypothesis is maintained. Further arguments for the presence of silicon in the core have been proposed by Ringwood (unpublished).

MacDonald and Knopoff (1958) argue that a composition for the outer core of $(Fe,Ni)_{1.6}Si$ is consistent with the density of the outer core. The representative atomic number of the material of the core, on the basis of the Thomas-Fermi-Dirac equation of state and Bullen's density distribution, is 22. The representative atomic number of $Fe_{1.6}Si$ is 22.8, and iron has a representative atomic number of 26. Furthermore, the extrapolated electrical properties of $Fe_{1.6}Si$ are consistent with the requirements of the dynamo theory of the magnetic field. Though these arguments demonstrate the consistency of an iron-silicon core with presently available data, they do not uniquely determine the core composition. Other elements, hydrogen, helium, and sulfur, could reduce the representative atomic number.

Homogeneity of the Mantle

It is evident that the crust represents strongly differentiated material. Further, the data of seismology, coupled with equation-of-state arguments, suggest that the mantle and core differ markedly in chemical composition. Of importance to petrology and geophysics is the question of the chemical homogeneity of the mantle itself. Thanks to advances in measurement of heat flow, in analytical chemical techniques, and in the understanding of the transfer of heat in solids at high temperatures, certain fairly definite statements can be made about the chemical homogeneity of the mantle. They depend on the present rate of heat loss from the earth and on an assumption about the total radioactive heat sources.

Birch (1958), using the chondritic model for the earth, showed that the present rate of heat loss requires that the radioactive material be concentrated near the surface. Essentially all the heat generated by radioactivity must be escaping, and the radioactive sources must be concentrated in the upper few hundred kilometers. It is well known that uranium, thorium, and potassium are markedly more abundant at the surface in continental than in oceanic areas (Birch, 1954, 1958; Bullard, 1954). Assuming for a continental crust a potassium content of 2.6 per cent, a uranium content of 2.3×10^{-6} g/g, and a thorium content of 8×10^{-6} g/g (Birch, 1954), the heat production in the continental crust corresponds to a heat flow of 0.8×10^{-6} cal/cm^2 sec, or two-thirds of the total. The oceanic crust is thin, and since the radioactive heat production in basalts is low, virtually all the measured heat flow must be coming from below the crust. We can readily estimate the depth through which radioactive elements that give rise to the oceanic heat flow are distributed. The mean distance Δx through which heat will diffuse in a time Δt is approximately $(d\ \Delta t)^{1/2}$, where d is the thermal diffusivity. The radiative contribution to thermal conductivity being taken into account, the maximum diffusivity expected in the upper mantle is of the order of 3×10^{-2} cm^2 sec (Clark, 1957*a*, 1957*b*; MacDonald, unpublished). If the age of the earth is 4.5×10^9 yr, the heat sources giving rise to the present rate of heat flow must be concentrated in the upper 600 to 700 km, provided that all the heat is transferred by radiation and thermal conduction. An even shallower depth for radioactive sources would be indicated by a lower and perhaps more probable value of the thermal diffusivity. The chondritic model thus requires that a major portion of the uranium, thorium, and potassium of the earth be concentrated within the upper 600 km. It would be expected that elements such as sodium and aluminum, and to a lesser extent calcium, which are closely associated with potassium in silicate materials, would also be concentrated in the upper few hundred kilometers of the mantle.

On the chondritic model, the material above 600 to 700 km must have a uranium content of about 5×10^{-8} g/g. Basalts have a uranium content 10 times greater, and dunites appear to have a uranium content 50 times less (Hamaguchi, Reed, and Turkevich, 1957). So far only the Twin Sister dunite has been analyzed by neutron activation techniques, but if the low value reported by Hamaguchi et al. is representative, dunite is ruled out as the dominant constituent of the upper mantle. Even the higher uranium contents of dunites obtained by wet chemical techniques (Tilton, 1956) are still a factor of 5 lower than that required by the chondritic model. If the radioactivity is concentrated over a shallower depth, the discrepancy between the required radioactivity and that found in dunites widens. On chemical grounds a material having radioactivity intermediate between basalt and dunite is qualitatively reasonable. Partial fusion of such material would tend to concentrate the radioactive elements in the lower-melting fraction, presumably basalt, depleting the radioactive content of the residue, dunite.

On the basis of a chondritic model for the earth, the upper mantle would be composed of material in which the radioactive elements are present in amounts from a third to a tenth of their abundance in basalts, though with greater abundance than in dunites. A rock intermediate in composition between eclogite and dunite (table 4) would meet this requirement and would also satisfy seismic requirements. A mixture of eclogite, dunite, and peridotite would also account for the heterogeneous assemblage of inclusions found in the diamond-bearing kimberlite pipes.

Temperatures in a Chondritic Earth

An alternative line of argument also leads to the conclusion that the mantle of the earth is highly differentiated. If the heat sources are distributed uniformly through the mantle, the temperature probably exceeds the melting point. A definite statement cannot be made because of the uncertainties in the thermal properties of the mantle. Bullard (1954) calculates that the temperature at depth exceeds the melting-point temperature unless the radioactivity is concentrated within the upper 150 km. Since Bullard's work, Clark (1956, 1957*a* and *b*) has demonstrated the importance of radiative transfer of heat. Radiation increases the thermal conductivity, thus decreasing the temperature gradient required to remove the heat from the earth's interior. Calculations assuming spherical symmetry and steady-state conditions illustrate the relative importance of the distribution of heat sources and the various thermal parameters, but, because of these restrictive assumptions, the calculations cannot be considered as giving the actual temperature distribution.

The steady-state distribution of temperature in a solid is determined by

$$-A(x_i, t) = \frac{\partial}{\partial x_i}\left(k\frac{\partial T}{\partial x_i} + R_i\right)$$

where A is the rate of heat generation per unit volume, k is the ordinary thermal conductivity, and R_i is the net flux of radiant energy. For earth problems the flux of radiant energy can be written as (Clark, 1957*a*)

$$R_i = \frac{16n^2s}{\epsilon} T^3 \frac{\partial T}{\partial x_i}$$

where ϵ is the opacity, n is the index of refraction, and s is the Stefan-

Boltzmann constant. The effective radiative conductivity thus varies as the cube of the temperature and inversely with the opacity. The opacity will increase with temperature principally because of an increase in electrical conductivity. A possible form for the variation of opacity with temperature is

$$\epsilon = \epsilon_0 + [(120\pi\sigma_0 e^{-E/2kT})/n]$$

where ϵ_0 is the opacity at low temperature, E is the width of the energy gap for electronic conduction, and k is Boltzmann's constant. Calculation of temperatures thus requires estimates of six quantities: A, k, ϵ_0, n, σ_0, and E, and their variation with depth. The ordinary thermal conductivity k and the index of refraction n are known for rock-forming minerals; as their variation with temperature and pressure may be small it will be neglected. The quantities σ_0 and E control the temperature dependence of the radiative conductivity and can be estimated for the earth from studies of the electrical conductivity, if the mechanism for this conductivity is assumed.

The temperature is most sensitively dependent on the distribution of radioactivity and on the opacity. Clark's (1957*b*) measurements on minerals indicate an opacity at room temperature of 10 to 30 cm^{-1}. The increase of opacity with temperature depends critically on whether the mechanism of electrical conduction within the earth is ionic or electronic. Runcorn and Tozer (1955) suppose that the conductivity in olivine is electronic, in which case the parameters in opacity equations should have the values $E = 3$ ev, $\sigma_0 = 10\ ohm^{-1}\ cm^{-1}$. If the major mechanism is ionic, as suggested by Hughes (unpublished), then the electronic contribution to the opacity is reduced, and the appropriate constants are $E = 3$ ev, $\sigma_0 = 1\ ohm^{-1}\ cm^{-1}$. In the calculations reviewed below, the index of refraction is taken as a constant equal to 1.7, and the ordinary conductivity as 6×10^{-3} cal/cm sec °C.

In table 9 are listed the steady-state temperatures for an undifferentiated mantle of chondritic composition as a function of the thermal parameters. The temperatures were determined by numerical computations, carried out on the Massachusetts Institute of Technology I. B. M. 704 digital computer, using a space interval of 1 km.

The rate of heat production in chondrites is about 1.18×10^{-15} cal/sec g. The steady-state surface heat flow resulting from a mantle having this rate of heat production is 0.95×10^{-6} cal/cm² sec. The temperatures in the upper mantle depend on the choice of the initial opacity ϵ_0; the deep temperatures are also a function of the mechanism of electrical conductivity. For comparison, the melting temperatures calculated using Simon's (1953) formula for diopside (Yoder, 1952) are listed. Taking into account that the present heat flow in the oceans is 30 per cent greater than that used in table 9, it is almost certain that the temperature in an undifferentiated mantle exceeds the melting-point gradient even for the most favorable choice of thermal constants. Such a calculation neglects the possibility of any phase transitions within the mantle. The estimate of melting-point gradients within the mantle is most uncertain. However, the fusion temperatures listed in table 9 are higher than most published estimates (Verhoogen, 1956). Any lower melting-temperature gradient strengthens the argument for a differentiated mantle.

Table 10 lists five steady-state temperature distributions in a differentiated mantle. In all, the surface heat flow is 1.3×10^{-6} cal/cm^2 sec. In cases 1, 3, and 5 the heat flow from below 400 km is 0.27×10^{-6} cal/cm^2 sec. As for an undifferentiated mantle, the steady-state temperature most closely approaches the probable melting temperature in the region 100 to 600 km. A closer investigation of these and other distributions of heat sources indicates that the steady-state temperature will exceed the melting temperature if the heat flow from below 400 km is greater than 0.1 to 0.4×10^{-6} cal/cm^2 sec. The wide range is due to the uncertainty in melting-point gradient coupled with the probable range of values for the opacity.

The calculations reviewed above refer to conditions under the oceanic crust. In continental areas the high concentration of radio-

TABLE 9. Steady-State Temperatures in an Undifferentiated Mantle of Chrondritic Composition

Depth, km	Melting T, °C	1	2	3
120	1750	1520	1300	1300
230	2150	2280	1820	1810
430	2800	3120	2400	2350
630	3300	3750	2840	2690
1030	4350	4750	3600	3150
2890	7800	7000	5640	4070

1. $\epsilon_0 = 30$ cm^{-1}. Electrical conductivity in the earth due to electronic conduction.

2. $\epsilon_0 = 10$ cm^{-1}. Electrical conductivity in the earth due to electronic conduction.

3. $\epsilon_0 = 10$ cm^{-1}. Electrical conductivity in the earth due primarily to ionic conduction.

TABLE 10. Steady-State Temperatures in a Differentiated Mantle

Depth, km	1	2	3	4	5
120	1730	1715	1440	1430	1730
220	2380	2320	1880	1840	2360
320	2730	2610	2100	2030	2690
420	2920	2710	2220	2100	2860
1020	3490	. . .	2890	. . .	3320
2890	4310	. . .	4270	. . .	3910

1. Radioactive heat production above 400 km, 8.3×10^{-15} cal/g sec; from 400 to 2890 km, 3.515×10^{-16} cal/g sec. $\epsilon_0 = 30\ cm^{-1}$. Electrical conductivity in earth due to electronic conduction.

2. Radioactive heat production above 400 km, 9.91×10^{-15} cal/g sec; no radioactivity below 400 km. $\epsilon_0 = 30\ cm^{-1}$. Electrical conductivity in earth due to electronic conduction.

3. Radioactivity distributed as in column 1. 0 to 400 km, $\epsilon_0 = 10\ cm^{-1}$; 400 to 1000 km, $\epsilon_0 = 30\ cm^{-1}$; 1000 to 2890 km, $\epsilon_0 = 100\ cm^{-1}$. Electrical conductivity in earth due to electronic conduction.

4. Radioactivity distributed as in column 2. ϵ_0 distributed as in column 3.

5. Same as column 1 but with electrical conductivity primarily ionic.

active heat sources in the crustal materials significantly reduces the temperature.

Arguments based on the temperature distribution in the mantle suggest that at least 60 to 90 per cent of the radioactive heat sources lie above 400 km. If we assume the chondritic model for the earth, then essentially all heat sources must be in the outer 600 km. A marked differentiation of potassium, uranium, and thorium would strongly suggest a similar concentration of other elements normally associated with potassium. Such a concentration requires that the material of the upper mantle under the ocean have a bulk composition intermediate between that of basalts and dunites.

A further consequence of the upward concentration of radioactivity is that the melting temperature is most closely approached in the region 100 to 600 km. The effect of the concentration of radioactivity on the temperature gradient is further enhanced by the contribution of radiation to the thermal conductivity. At depths greater than a few hundred kilometers, the increased conductivity markedly lowers the rate of increase of temperature with depth, with the result that the steady-state temperature is considerably lower than the melting temperature at depths below 400 to 600 km.

Summary

The abundances of the major metals in the solar atmosphere agree remarkably well with the abundance of the metals in chondritic meteorites. The only metals that appear to differ significantly are iron and potassium, and it is not certain whether these discrepancies can be attributed to uncertainties in the interpretation of the solar spectra. The present rate of heat loss from the earth is consistent with the hypothesis that a major portion of the earth is of chondritic material. The data do not allow a distinction between an earth composed of an iron core plus chondritic mantle and an earth consisting wholly of chondritic material. The observed ratio of iron to stony meteorites and the abundance of iron in the sun favor the second interpretation. If the earth as a whole is of chondritic composition, then the earth's core probably contains major amounts of silicon alloyed with iron. An iron-silicon core is consistent with seismic observation interpreted in terms of high-pressure equations of state. On the chondritic model, the mantle must be chemically differentiated, with the heat-producing elements concentrated within the upper 600 to 700 km. Since the concentration of heat-producing elements in dunites is apparently much lower than in chondritic materials, a material intermediate in chemical composition between dunite and basalt would be required for the upper mantle under the oceans. A similar but somewhat less stringent requirement on the composition of the mantle, independent of the chondritic hypothesis, is set by the solid nature of the mantle.

Acknowledgments

I have had the advantage of discussing the problems treated in this paper with a number of individuals, principally Francis Birch, Jesse Greenstein, Harry Hess, and A. E. Ringwood. They are, of course, not to be held in any way responsible for errors of fact or judgment. I am in particular debt to Professor Greenstein for his guidance in matters astronomical. Sydney Clark, Jr., critically reviewed the manuscript, and his many suggestions are gratefully acknowledged.

Calculations on the steady-state temperature distribution in the earth were carried out at the Massachusetts Institute of Technology I. B. M. 704 Computation Center. Norman Ness aided in these calculations. A full report of the steady-state and time-dependent temperature of an earth having radiative conductivity will be published elsewhere.

References

Aller, L. 1958. The abundances of the elements in the sun and stars, *Handbuch der Physik,* Part X, vol. 2.

Bate, G. L., J. R. Huizenga, and H. A. Potratz. 1957. Thorium content of stone meteorites, *Science, 126,* 612–614.

Birch, F. 1952. Elasticity and constitution of the earth's interior, *J. Geophys. Research, 57,* 227–286.

Birch, F. 1954. Heat from radioactivity, in *Nuclear Geology,* pp. 148–174 (H. Faul, ed.), John Wiley & Sons, New York.

Birch, F. 1958. Differentiation of the mantle, *Bull. Geol. Soc. Am., 69,* 483–486.

Bullard, E. C. 1954. The interior of the earth, in *The Earth as a Planet,* pp. 57–137 (G. Kuiper, ed.), University of Chicago Press.

Bullard, E. C., A. E. Maxwell, and R. Revelle. 1956. Heat flow through the deep ocean floor, *Advances in Geophys., III,* 153–181, Academic Press, New York.

Bundy, F. P., H. T. Hall, H. M. Strong, and R. H. Wentorf. 1955. Man-made diamonds, *Nature, 176,* 51–55.

Byerly, P. 1956. Subcontinental structure in light of seismological evidence, *Advances in Geophys., III,* 105–152, Academic Press, New York.

Clark, S. P. 1956. Effect of radiative transfer on temperatures in the earth, *Bull. Geol. Soc. Am., 67,* 1123–1124.

Clark, S. P. 1957*a*. Radiative transfer in the earth's mantle, *Trans. Am. Geophys. Union, 38,* 931–938.

Clark, S. P. 1957*b*. Absorption spectra of some silicates in the visible and near infrared, *Am. Mineralogist, 42,* 732–742.

Clarke, F. W., and H. S. Washington. 1924. The composition of the earth's crust, *U. S. Geol. Survey, Profess. Paper 127.*

Daly, R. A. 1933. *Igneous Rocks and the Depths of the Earth,* McGraw-Hill Book Company, New York.

Edwards, G. 1955. Sodium and potassium in meteorites, *Geochim. et Cosmochim. Acta, 8,* 285–294.

Ewing, M., and F. Press. 1956. Structure of the earth's crust, *Handbuch der Physik, 47,* 246–257.

Geiss, J., and D. C. Hess. 1958. Argon-potassium ages and the isotopic composition of argon from meteorites, *Astrophys. J., 127,* 224–236.

Goldschmidt, V. M. 1954. *Geochemistry,* Clarendon Press, Oxford.

Greenstein, J. L. 1956. The abundances of the chemical elements in the galaxy and the theory of their origin, *Publs. Astron. Soc. Pacific, 68,* 185–203.

Greenstein, J. L., and R. S. Richardson. 1951. Lithium and the internal circulation of the sun, *Astrophys. J., 113,* 536–546.

Greenstein, J. L., and E. Tandberg-Hanssen. 1954. The abundance of beryllium in the sun, *Astrophys. J., 119,* 113–119.

Hamaguchi, H., G. W. Reed, and A. Turkevich. 1957. Uranium and barium in stone meteorites, *Geochim. et Cosmochim. Acta, 12,* 337–347.

MacDonald, G. J. F. 1956. Quartz-coesite stability relations at high temperatures and pressures, *Am. J. Sci., 254,* 713–721.

MacDonald, G. J. F., and L. Knopoff. 1958. The chemical composition of the outer core (in press).

Masuda, A. 1958. Isotopic composition of primeval lead of the earth, *Geochim. et Cosmochim. Acta, 13,* 143–152.

Patterson, C. 1955. The Pb^{207}/Pb^{206} ages of some stone meteorites, *Geochim. et Cosmochim. Acta, 7,* 151–153.

Patterson, C., G. Tilton, and M. Inghram. 1955. Age of the earth, *Science, 121,* 69.

Rankama, K., and T. G. Sahama. 1950. *Geochemistry,* University of Chicago Press.

Reed, G. W., and A. Turkevich. 1955. Uranium content of two iron meteorites, *Nature, 176,* 794–795.

Reed, G. W., H. Hamaguchi, and A. Turkevich. 1958. The uranium contents of iron meteorites, *Geochim. et Cosmochim. Acta, 13,* 248–255.

Ross, C. S., M. D. Foster, and A. T. Myers. 1954. Origin of dunite and olivine rich inclusions in basaltic rocks, *Am. Mineralogist, 39,* 693–757.

Runcorn, S. K., and D. C. Tozer. 1955. The electrical conductivity of olivine at high temperatures and pressures, *Ann. géophys., 11,* 98–102.

Schumacher, E. 1956*a*. Allerbestimmung von Steinmeteoriten mit der Rubidium-Strontium Methode, *Z. Naturforsch., 11a,* 206.

Schumacher, E., 1956*b*. Isolierung von K, Rb, Sr, Ba und seltenen Erden aus Steinmeteoriten, *Helv. Chim. Acta, 39,* 531–537.

Schwarzschild, M., R. Howard, and R. Harm. 1957. Inhomogeneous stellar models, V, A solar model with convective envelope and inhomogeneous interior, *Astrophys. J., 125,* 233–241.

Simon, F. E. 1953. The melting of iron at high pressures, *Nature, 172,* 746.

Suess, H. E., and H. C. Urey. 1956. Abundance of the elements, *Revs. Modern Phys., 28,* 53–74.

Tilton, G. 1956. Geochemistry of lead and its parents, *Carnegie Inst. Wash. Year Book 55,* 167–168.

Urey, H. C. 1952. *The Planets,* Yale University Press, New Haven.

Urey, H. C. 1954. On the dissipation of gas and volatilized elements from protoplanets, *Astrophys. J. Suppl. 1,* 147–173.

Urey, H. C., and H. Craig. 1953. The composition of the stone meteorites and the origin of meteorites, *Geochim. et Cosmochim. Acta, 4,* 36–82.

Verhoogen, J. 1956. Temperatures within the earth, in *Physics and Chemistry of the Earth, I,* 17–43 (Ahrens et al., eds.), Pergamon Press, London.

Vinogradov, A. P. 1956. The regularity in distribution of chemical elements in the earth's crust, *Akad. Nauk Soyosa S.S.R., Geokhimiya, 1,* 1–52.

Wasserburg, G. J., and R. J. Hayden. 1955*a*. Age of meteorites by the A^{40}-K^{40} method, *Phys. Rev., 97,* 86–87.

Wasserburg, G. J., and R. J. Hayden. 1955*b*. A^{40}-K^{40} dating, *Geochim. et Cosmochim. Acta, 7,* 51–60.

Watson, F. G. 1956. *Between the Planets,* Harvard University Press, Cambridge, Massachusetts.

Wiik, H. B. 1956. Chemical composition of some stony meteorites, *Geochim. et Cosmochim. Acta, 9,* 279–289.

Williams, A. F. 1932. *The Genesis of the Diamond,* vol. I, E. F. Benn, London.

Yoder, H. S. 1952. Change of melting point of diopside with pressure, *J. Geol., 60,* 364–374.

Equations of State and Polymorphism at High Pressures

SYDNEY P. CLARK, JR.

Geophysical Laboratory
Carnegie Institution of Washington

Pressures near the surface of the earth have little influence on the chemical and physical properties of rocks and minerals. But the pressures below the earth's crust are sufficient to affect chemical equilibria and to cause phase transitions to denser polymorphs. At the very high pressures of the earth's core, the electronic structure of atoms may be altered.

In addition to these chemical effects, pressure influences the physical properties of homogeneous phases. Two conspicuous changes are the increase in density and the decrease in compressibility caused by high pressures. These affect the density and seismic velocities in the earth.

The discussion of phase changes and equations of state that follows is of necessity qualitative and general. Theoretical and experimental results from the field of high-pressure physics have been used freely; they lead to generalizations that can usefully be applied to the earth. Since the pressures deep in the earth are beyond the present range of experiment, theoretical predictions of high-pressure effects are of interest. Therefore reviews of Thomas-Fermi theory and of the present status of quantum-mechanical equations of state of simple substances have been included.

Results of studies of equations of state and polymorphism can be related to the earth through seismic velocities. The ratio of bulk modulus to density (elastic ratio) at various depths in the earth is known from the velocities of elastic waves. It can also be obtained from the equation of state, and comparison of these two sets of data yields the most important body of information about the internal constitution of the earth.

Information about the homogeneity of the earth can also be derived from the elastic ratio. Expected changes in this quantity with pressure, or depth, derived from the equation of state, are much less than those observed at several depths in the earth. These departures occur at the Mohorovičić discontinuity, the "20° discontinuity" between 350 and 1000 km, and the boundaries of the outer and inner core. Present information is inadequate to disclose whether these anomalous regions arise from changes of composition, phase, or both, but equations of state suggest that none of the discontinuities could result from compression of homogeneous material.

Changes of Crystal Structure

We begin by considering the familiar type of phase transition arising from a change in crystal structure. It is exemplified by the polymorphism of SiO_2, TiO_2, Al_2SiO_5, and ice. Under pressure, polymorphs of this type arise from lattice rearrangements which result in denser phases; interatomic distances and the structures of the atoms themselves are little affected. We shall consider transitions involving important changes in electronic structure in the next section.

Interest in phase transitions has been stimulated by the possibility that they may be invoked to explain the Mohorovičić and 20° discontinuities in the earth. The former may result in part from the transition of basalt to eclogite, and the latter may be related to the appearance of a cubic form of olivine (Robertson, Birch, and MacDonald, 1957; Ringwood, 1958). These suggestions must be regarded as tentative, but the following arguments show them to be plausible in the sense that high-pressure polymorphs of common silicates are to be expected in the earth.

A large number of phase transitions in silicates can be produced by heating at low pressure. But melting limits the amount of thermal energy that can be supplied to a crystal lattice; there is no such limit to the amount of strain energy that can be produced by compression. The volume change associated with the formation of high-pressure phases is commonly between 0.5 and 1 cm^3/g atom. At a pressure of 10^5 bars, $P\Delta V$ is a few kilocalories per gram atom, which is of the same order of magnitude as the heat of formation of silicates from their oxides. Hence ample energy is available to produce important chemical effects.

The chemical and structural complexity of many silicates implies the possibility of a wide variety of crystal structures. Many hypothetical polymorphs would be denser than the ones actually observed and would thus be favored by pressure. A great many polymorphs of chemically simple materials have been discovered by Bridgman (1952*a*) at high pressures. It would be surprising if the same were not true of silicates.

These arguments suggesting the probability of polymorphism of silicates at high pressure are supported by observations up to 5×10^4 bars. Several minerals that are found in nature but have not been made in the laboratory at low pressure have been synthesized at high pressure. Examples are jadeite, kyanite, sillimanite, and pyrope (Clark, Robertson, and Birch, 1957; Coes, 1955; Griggs and Kennedy, 1956; Robertson, Birch, and MacDonald, 1957). Moreover, phases unknown in nature, such as coesite (a polymorph of silica), $Al_2Si_3O_9$, and $Mg_3Fe_2Si_3O_{12}$ (a garnet), have been synthesized.

Fields of stability of some of the phases mentioned above have been outlined in the laboratory; the original papers should be consulted for details. The important point for present purposes is that high-pressure polymorphs of common minerals are expected, and they have been found experimentally. As the range of experimental pressures is extended, additional transitions are likely to be found.

The present state of our knowledge does not enable us to make precise statements about the transitions produced by pressure in complex systems. Simply demonstrating the existence of an assemblage, identical in composition and denser than one that is observed, does not prove that the hypothetical assemblage is ever stable. For example, enstatite and anorthite are known to coexist at low pressure, but a mixture of kyanite and diopside is denser. Nevertheless it is not demonstrated that they can coexist at high pressure, since enstatite and anorthite might invert directly to an even denser mixture of garnets and aluminosilicates. This does not exhaust the possibilities, and the observed coexistence of omphacite and kyanite in eclogites, although suggestive, may be possible only because of jadeite and acmite in solid solution in the pyroxene.

Only a few of the known examples of polymorphism in silicates can be considered to take place in one-component systems. Reactions such as the breakdown of albite to jadeite plus quartz, or the reaction of forsterite, cordierite, and spinel to form pyrope, must be regarded as taking place in binary or ternary systems. The appearance of these and other high-pressure phases will profoundly affect phase diagrams;

joins and tie lines will be shifted. Because of the chemical complexity of most rocks, these effects of pressure on heterogeneous equilibria may be more important than the appearance of new phases *per se*.

Consider, for example, some effects of pressure on melting relations, applied to the compositions of basalts. There is reason to believe that basalts originate by partial fusion of the outer part of the mantle; the material that melts is likely to be eclogitic rather than gabbroic in phase. If an eclogite is melted at high pressure, the composition of the first liquid to appear will be different from that of the first liquid in equilibrium with a gabbro of identical bulk composition, partly because pressure is likely to affect the melting points of the constituent minerals differently, and partly because of drastic changes in the appearance of the phase diagram as new phases become stable.

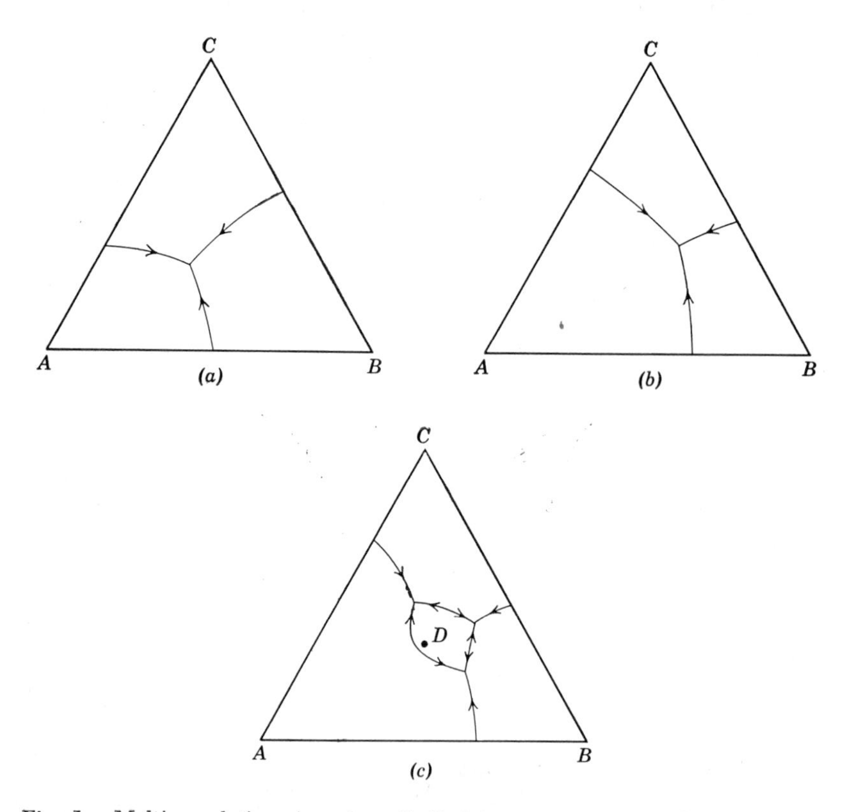

Fig. 1. Melting relations in a hypothetical ternary system at three pressures. Diagrams *a*, *b*, and *c* represent increasingly high pressures. The ternary compound, *D*, exists only at high pressures.

The hypothetical phase diagrams of figure 1 illustrate these melting relations. A ternary system is shown for simplicity, but similar considerations apply to more complex systems. At low pressures (fig. 1*a*) the only stable solid phases at high temperatures are the three end members. At higher pressures (fig. 1*b*) this is still true, but the melting point of phase *A* has increased more than that of the other end members. As a result the composition of the ternary eutectic has changed. At the highest pressure shown, a ternary compound has appeared (fig. 1*c*), and there are now three ternary eutectics, none of which has the composition of the eutectic at low pressure. The first liquid to appear must have the composition of one of these eutectics.

Thus we may expect the composition of basalts to depend on their depth of origin. It cannot be asserted, however, that this is the only cause of their chemical heterogeneity, since partial pressures of volatile components and the bulk composition of the parent material also affect the composition of the product. But the pressure effect must be included with the other factors.

Electronic Transitions

At sufficiently high pressure, phenomena basically different from the lattice rearrangements discussed above may take place. They result from the breakdown of the electronic shells of the atoms of which the crystal is composed, and they may be accompanied by marked changes in the electrical properties of the solid. Only a few such transitions are known, but they may be expected to become increasingly common as the range of experimentation expands.

The dependence of electronic energy levels in a solid on interatomic distance is shown schematically in figure 2. The discrete energy levels of the isolated atoms are broadened into bands by interactions with other atoms as the interatomic distance is decreased, but regions of forbidden energy are preserved in the solid at normal interatomic distances. Under these conditions, it may happen that one band (the valence band) is completely filled with electrons, and the next higher band (the conduction band) is empty. This will strictly be true only at 0° K, but in any event a solid in this state is a semiconductor or insulator, depending on the width of the zone of forbidden energy. If the valence band is not fully occupied, the substance is a metal; the following argument is restricted to nonmetals.

At some interatomic distance, the valence and conduction bands

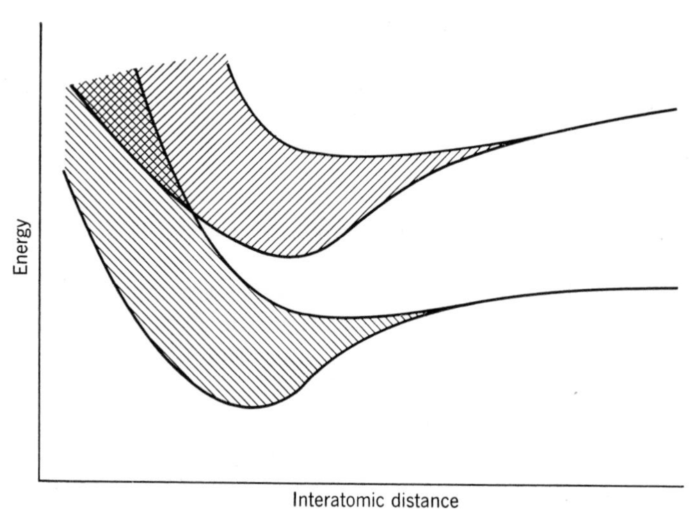

Fig. 2. Schematic diagram of two of the electronic energy bands in a solid, illustrating band overlap.

will overlap. When this happens, a state of slightly higher energy becomes accessible to the electrons at the top of the conduction band, and they can move in an applied potential. The solid has then become a metal. Such a transition to a metallic phase will presumably be shown by any insulator at high enough pressure.

Detailed knowledge of the Helmholtz free energy as a function of volume is necessary before the nature of this type of transition can be determined. Two possible cases are shown in figure 3. Curve A applies when there is no first-order phase transition, i.e. no discontinuity in volume or entropy. It has no point of inflection and no two points lying on a common tangent. At normal temperatures the material represented by it would show a gradual increase in electrical conductivity under pressure, with a high limiting value corresponding to that of a metal.

Curve B represents a first-order transition. The points a and b lie on a common tangent; at volumes between those represented by these points, two phases will be present, and the slope of the line tangent to the free-energy curve at these points is equal to the negative of the equilibrium pressure. The electrical conductivity will jump discontinuously at this pressure. It appears that curve B would represent most transitions resulting from band overlap (see also Mott,

1957), but accurate knowledge of the Helmholtz free energy is necessary before the question can be answered for any particular case.

Experimentally this question is also open, although most known examples of transition to a metallic state follow curve *B*. Tellurium may be an exception, but experimental data are somewhat conflicting and the matter is not yet settled (Bridgman, 1952*b*). Some interesting new metallic transitions have been discovered through experimentation with shock waves (Alder and Christian, 1956). In an interval of pressure below 250,000 bars the electrical conductivity of CsBr and CsI increased a million-fold; that of NaCl did not. It is not yet known whether the transitions in the cesium salts are first-order.

The most familiar transition to a metallic phase, the tin transition, involves a major structural reorganization as well as band overlap. Gray tin, the low-temperature, low-pressure form, has a diamond structure, whereas white tin is nearly a close-packed metal; the volume change at the transition is more than 20 per cent.

There is reason to think that the phase boundaries between metallic and nonmetallic forms of the same substance will in many cases have negative slopes on the *P*-*T* plane, as in the tin transition. The fact that the Debye temperatures of metals are usually lower than those of nonmetals implies that metallic modifications will have the

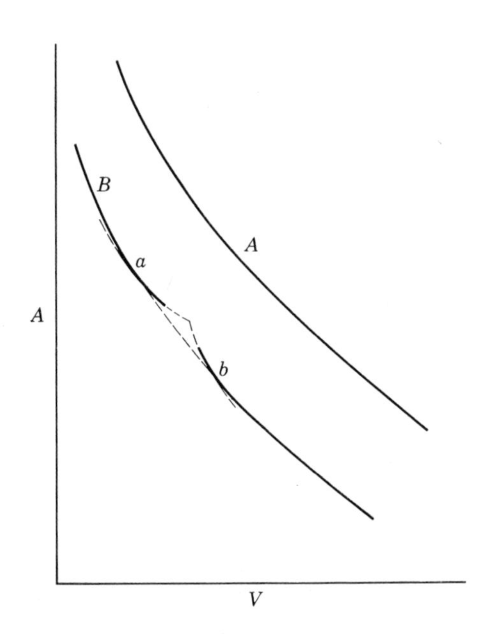

Fig. 3. Helmholtz free energy as a function of volume for a substance that does not have a first-order phase transition (curve *A*), and for one that does (curve *B*).

higher entropies. In addition, there is a contribution to the specific heat of a metal arising from the conduction electrons. The magnitude of this effect is small as far as it affects the specific heat, but its effect on the entropy at high temperature may be important. Both these considerations suggest that the metallic modification will be the high-temperature as well as the high-pressure form.

It has been suggested that the metallic nature of the earth's core might be explained by a transition to a metallic form in silicates (Ramsey, 1949). This idea, however, encounters difficulties (Birch, 1952), and the older notion that the core is composed predominately of nickel-iron is preferable in many ways. The possibility that silicates could alloy with iron at the pressure of the core is not excluded, however.

A related type of electronic transition has been recognized in two metals. The energy band corresponding to an unoccupied electronic subshell with principal quantum number less than that of the outermost occupied shell may cross the band representing the conduction electrons. The conduction electrons will then jump to the lower subshell; this transition corresponds physically to their moving closer to the nucleus, on the average, and leads to a contraction of the atom. A transition of this sort may occur without change in lattice type.

The transition in cerium at 7000 bars takes place without change in space group, and it probably represents such an electronic rearrangement (Lawson and Tang, cited by Bridgman, 1954). The transition in cesium at 45,000 bars is believed to result from the shifting of electrons from the 6*s* to the 5*d* bands; no change in lattice type is believed to accompany it (Sternheimer, 1950). Transitions of this type are also possible in liquids and glasses. They are likely in any substance containing atoms with unoccupied subshells.

A Thermodynamic Equation of State

The only successful equations of state of wide applicability at low pressures are thermodynamic. We shall discuss only the equation proposed by Birch (1952); its range of applicability has been extended by Gilvarry (1957), and a more general equation, of which Birch's is a special case, has also been proposed by Gilvarry. All equations of this nature contain adjustable parameters which must be fixed by experiment. Furthermore, their validity is assured only over the range of conditions for which data are available; considerable uncertainty is attached to their use as formulas for extrapolation of experimental results, especially since phase transitions may take place outside the range of experiment.

Interest in the thermodynamic approach to the equation of state of solids arises from its ability to predict the results of measurements of compression of a single phase with high accuracy and to correlate experimental results and express them in analytical form. In particular, it shows that the amount of compression, rather than the pressure, is the quantity that should be taken as independent variable in comparing experimental observations on different substances; this point is sometimes overlooked.

Murnaghan (1937) proved that

$$v_0/v = \rho/\rho_0 = (1 + 2f)^{3/2} \tag{1}$$

where v is volume, ρ is density, f is the negative of the elastic strain, and the subscripts 0 refer to zero pressure. This result is strictly applicable only in the special case of hydrostatic compression of an isotropic or cubic material, but the theory described below seems to describe results obtained with materials of lower symmetry with good precision.

Birch's (1952) fundamental results are

$$P = 3K_0 f(1 + 2f)^{5/2}(1 - 2\xi f) \tag{2}$$

and

$$K = K_0(1 + 2f)^{5/2}[1 + 7f - 2\xi f(2 + 9f)] \tag{3}$$

In these expressions, P is pressure, K is bulk modulus, K_0 is bulk modulus at zero pressure, and ξ is a dimensionless constant. These results are obtained by expanding the Helmholtz free energy, A, in the form

$$A = a(T)f^2 + b(T)f^3 \tag{4}$$

This demands that v_0, K_0, and ξ be functions of T, the temperature, and that f vanish when P vanishes at all temperatures. In terms of a and b, $K_0 = 2a/9v_0$ and $\xi = -3b/4a$; ξ represents the effect of the third-order term in the expansion. In this form, (2) and (3) refer to isothermal compression, but if (4) is replaced by the analogous expression

$$U = a(S)f^2 + b(S)f^3 \tag{5}$$

where U is internal energy and S is entropy, equations identical in form to (2) and (3) result. Now, however, v_0, K_0, and ξ are functions of S, and the equations refer to adiabatic compression. Derivation from (4) is most useful when measurements of static compression are to be interpreted, and derivation from (5) applies to the interpretation of dynamic measurements in the laboratory or to seismic results.

This theory does not give numerical values of K_0 and ξ; these must be found from experiment. A limit on admissible values of ξ may, however, be set by consideration of (3). Positive values lead eventually to negative K, which is impossible. K vanishes at $f = 1/3$ if $\xi = 1$, and at $f = 0.71$ if $\xi = 1/2$. Hence a material can satisfy (2) with positive ξ only over a limited range of compression. Experimentally, ξ is usually found to be negative (Birch, 1952; Swenson, 1955; Stewart, 1955).

Frequently $2\xi f$ is negligible compared with unity, and then (2) predicts that P/K_0 is a universal function of f for all substances. This law of corresponding states is evidently most stringently tested by those measurements that have produced the largest values of f rather than those that have subjected a relatively incompressible material to the highest pressures. The term in ξ, and neglected terms involving higher powers of f, become important only when f is large, which is not necessarily the same as having P large.

In an exhaustive discussion of the constitution of the earth's interior, Birch (1952) used (1), with $\xi = 0$, to deduce the elastic ratio that the materials of the mantle would have at zero pressure. Comparison of these results with laboratory measurements led to several conclusions about the constitution of the mantle. Between the Mohorovičić discontinuity and a depth of about 350 km the elastic ratio was found to be compatible with the values found for ultrabasic rock like dunite or eclogite. Between 1000 km and the core boundary, the elastic ratio is higher than the values expected for any of the common silicates. Oxides such as periclase, corundum, or spinel have the required elasticity, and Birch therefore inferred that high-pressure phases are the dominant constituents of the lower mantle. He suggested that a polymorph of olivine with a spinel structure might be abundant in this region, and the idea has received a measure of confirmation in the work of Ringwood (1958). In this view, the 20° discontinuity is interpreted as a region of gradual transition from low- to high-pressure phases, perhaps superimposed on a change in composition.

Some of the strongest evidence for the existence of high-pressure phases in the earth is contained in Birch's work. Rather large extrapolations of experimental data were required, however, and the method may be capable of greater sensitivity when further data are available. It may even prove possible to limit the composition and temperature of the high-pressure phases.

The Thomas-Fermi Approximation

Overlap of the valence and conduction bands will take place in any substance at high enough pressure, as stated above. As the substance is further compressed, overlap will affect electrons lying closer to the nuclei. Eventually even the K electrons will be thus affected, and all trace of atomic structure will be wiped out. In this limit of extreme compression a simple statistical model, the Thomas-Fermi (TF) approximation, may be used. It is not valid unless the pressure is so high that the effects of atomic and crystal structure can be neglected.

Only a bare outline of TF theory can be given here; the reader is referred to the excellent review by March (1957) for details. Numerical results of the theory are given by Feynman, Metropolis, and Teller (1949), and a more complete and accurate set of solutions has been published by Latter (1955, 1956).

The central feature of the TF approximation is the neglect of atomic structure. The distinct electronic energy bands of solids at low pressure are assumed to be broadened into a continuum. From preceding discussions it appears that such a model is plausible at high enough pressure, but if it is to lead to definite numerical results further approximations are necessary. Those adopted in TF theory are, first, to neglect the fact that the electrons themselves are discrete and, second, to focus attention on a single "cell" within the solid, containing a nucleus and sufficient electrons to maintain electrical neutrality. Individual electrons are thus assumed to move in the field of a degenerate gas of "smeared out" electrons and of the nuclei.

Hence the TF approximation suffers from all the defects of a one-electron model. Neither exchange nor correlation is included, although account is taken of exchange in an extension of the method known as Thomas-Fermi-Dirac (TFD) theory. But unless correlation is considered, it seems best to neglect exchange as well, since the two effects tend to cancel each other. This has been emphasized by Latter (1955), and although the TFD theory is the more complete, it may be the less accurate.

The validity of using the devices of smeared-out electrons and the cellular approximation for purposes of calculation is uncertain; the former is particularly suspect for light elements. Hence the numerical results of TF theory are in doubt even if the neglect of atomic structure is valid. Since the range of pressure over which the atomic structure can be neglected cannot be specified, it is all but impossible to subject the theory to experimental test.

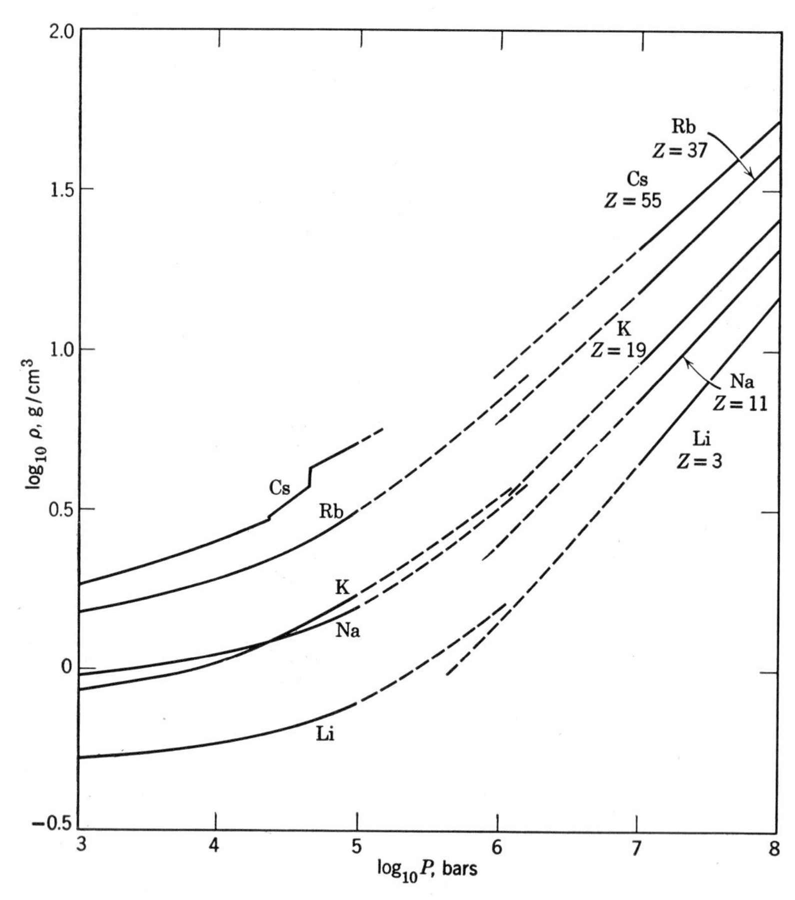

Fig. 4. Pressure-density relations for the alkali metals at low temperature. The low-pressure data are from Bridgman (1952*a*), extrapolated with the aid of equation 1. The high-pressure data are from TF theory (Latter, 1956).

Some results of TF theory are compared with experiment in figures 4 and 5. Experimentally determined pressure-density relations of the alkali metals (fig. 4) can be smoothly joined to the corresponding TF curves, given sufficient freedom as to the pressure at which the connection is made. Clearly there is too much latitude to permit the use of such extrapolations to test the correctness of the TF curves. Special difficulties are raised by the polymorphism of cesium, and undiscovered polymorphs of some of the other alkali metals may become stable at high pressures.

Figure 5 shows some data for iron and raises additional questions. The experimental data agree best with the TFD curve (curve 1), although they may approach the TF curve (curve 2) most closely above 10^8 bars. Again polymorphism makes extrapolation of experimental data hazardous; it is believed that the α-γ inversion in iron takes place at about 0.13 megabar at room temperature (Bancroft, Peterson, and Minshall, 1956).

The coincidence of the two branches of curve 2 (corresponding to temperatures of 0 and roughly 5000° K) over most of the pressure range is of special interest, since it implies that the thermal expansion tends asymptotically to zero at high pressure. Experiment shows that

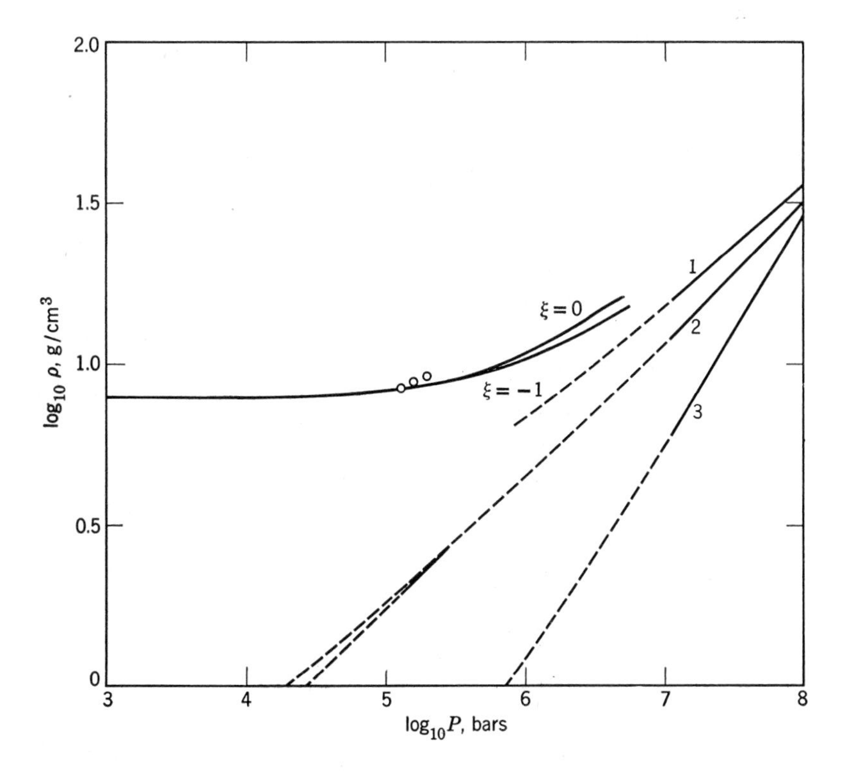

Fig. 5. Pressure-density relations for iron. Curve 1 is the TFD curve at 0° K (Jensen, 1938). Curve 2 is the TF curve at temperatures of 0° and roughly 5000° K, and curve 3 is the TF curve at constant entropy (Latter, 1955; 1956) corresponding to a temperature of about 4000° K at zero pressure. Birch-Murnaghan curves are given for two values of ξ, and the open circles represent data from shock waves (Bancroft, Peterson, and Minshall, 1956).

this quantity decreases with pressure, and equation 1 predicts that it passes through zero at a finite pressure (Birch, 1952). This result is uncertain because the pressure may be outside of the range of validity of (1), and the interesting prediction of TF theory cannot at present be checked.

A further point concerning the application of these results to the earth arises from the large difference between the curve for adiabiatic compression (curve 3) and curves 1 and 2. Although the entropy of iron along this curve is high (it corresponds to a temperature of about 4000° K at zero pressure), the discrepancy illustrates the danger of using TF theory to predict the mean atomic number of the earth's core. Had a much lower entropy been selected for curve 3, it would have been indistinguishable from curve 2.

The crux of the difficulty in applying TF theory lies in the uncertainty in the low-pressure limit of the region in which neglect of atomic structure is valid. If a limit could be set, the validity of the other approximations of TF theory could at least be roughly assessed; lacking such a limit, the quantitative predictions of TF theory must be accepted with reservations.

Theoretical Equations of State

It is possible, in principle, to compute the equation of state of any solid from quantum theory, but the calculations are so complicated that they have been carried out for only the simplest substances. Reasonably complete predictions have been made for hydrogen (Wigner and Huntington, 1935; Kronig, de Boer, and Korringa, 1946; Ramsey, 1954; March, 1956), and for "metallic ammonium" (Bernal and Massey, 1954). "Metallic ammonium" has the composition NH_4; at low pressure it would have the molecular composition $NH_3 + \frac{1}{2}H_2$.

Data for hydrogen at 0° K are shown in figure 6. Extrapolation of Stewart's (1955) results at low temperatures leads to densities considerably higher than those predicted for solid molecular hydrogen. The theoretical values should be most accurate for the metallic phase of hydrogen, which is predicted to be stable above 0.8 megabar. Densities of this phase are compared with results of TF theory in the figure; the results are purely formal, since "smearing out" the electron in hydrogen cannot be expected to be valid. Nevertheless the agreement with quantum theory is striking, although perhaps fortuitous.

Bernal and Massey (1954) found that the metallic modification of ammonium would become stable at a pressure that was not likely to

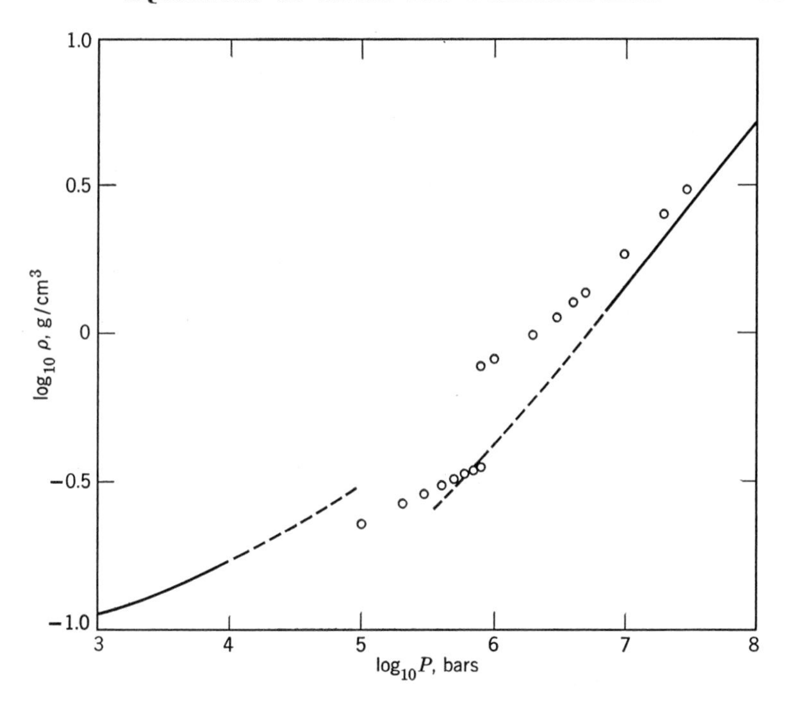

Fig. 6. Pressure-density relations for hydrogen at 0° K. Low-pressure data are from Stewart (1955), extrapolated with the aid of equation 1. High-pressure data are from TF theory (Latter, 1956), and the open circles represent quantum-mechanical calculations (Ramsey, 1950).

exceed 250,000 bars, and a pressure less than 60,000 bars is not excluded by their results. Calculations of density for this substance are less accurate than those for hydrogen.

Rough calculations pertaining to a metallic transition in helium are also available (ten Seldam, 1957). The volume at which band overlap commences was computed from several models. Pressures were obtained from TF theory; they were found to range between about 30 and 220 megabars, depending on the particular model adopted.

Clearly the quantum theory of equations of state and polymorphism of solids is in its infancy. Simplifying assumptions must be made in order to arrive at any solution at all, and the results are of quantitative value for only the simplest substances.

Nevertheless, this approach to the problem will become increasingly important. At present there is no satisfactory way of bridging the gap between experiment and the domain of TF breakdown. Refined theories may accomplish this, and as the range of pressure accessible to the experimenter is expanded, such theories can be stringently tested.

Conclusion

Two approaches to equations of state of solids have been considered. The thermodynamic approach, exemplified by the Birch-Murnaghan equation, is applicable at low pressure where experimental data are available. The theory is useful in correlating experimental results and expressing them accurately in analytical form; with due reservation, it may also be used for extrapolation. At very high pressure the Thomas-Fermi statistical model is available, but the low-pressure limit of its applicability is poorly defined and its accuracy is untested. At pressures between these two limits there is no satisfactory general way to determine the equation of state.

Polymorphism may result mainly from rearrangement of crystal structure, or it may be associated with breakdown of the electronic structure of the solid. Both types of phase transition are exceedingly difficult to predict, but it is highly likely that both will be shown by complex substances. The second type of transition is uncommon within the present range of experiment, but it is likely to be a common precursor of complete TF breakdown at higher pressures.

Polymorphism further complicates the problem of predicting equations of state. Much investigation, both experimental and theoretical, must be carried out before these fundamental problems are solved.

References

Alder, B. J., and R. H. Christian. 1956. Metallic transitions in ionic and molecular crystals, *Phys. Rev., 104,* 550–551.

Bancroft, D., E. L. Peterson, and S. Minshall. 1956. Polymorphism of iron at high pressure, *J. Appl. Phys., 27,* 291–298.

Bernal, M. J. M., and H. S. W. Massey. 1954. Metallic ammonium, *Monthly Notices Roy. Astron. Soc., 114,* 172–179.

Birch, F. 1952. Elasticity and constitution of the earth's interior, *J. Geophys. Research, 57,* 227–286.

Bridgman, P. W. 1952*a*. *The Physics of High Pressure,* G. Bell and Sons, London, 445 pp.

Bridgman, P. W. 1952*b*. The resistance of 72 elements, alloys and compounds to 100,000 kg/cm², *Proc. Am. Acad. Arts Sci., 81,* 165–251.

Bridgman, P. W. 1954. Certain effects of pressure on seven rare earth metals, *Proc. Am. Acad. Arts Sci., 83,* 1–22.

Clark, S. P., E. C. Robertson, and F. Birch. 1957. Experimental determination of kyanite-sillimanite equilibrium relations at high temperatures and pressures, *Am. J. Sci., 255,* 628–640.

Coes, L. 1955. High pressure minerals, *J. Am. Ceram. Soc., 38,* 298.

Feynman, R. P., N. Metropolis, and E. Teller. 1949. Equations of state of elements based on the generalized Fermi-Thomas theory, *Phys. Rev., 75,* 1561–1573.

Gilvarry, J. J. 1957. Temperature-dependent equations of state of solids, *J. Appl. Phys., 28,* 1253–1261.

Griggs, D. T., and G. C. Kennedy. 1956. A simple apparatus for high pressures and temperatures, *Am. J. Sci., 254,* 722–735.

Jensen, H. 1938. Das Druck-Dichte-Diagramm der Elemente bei höheren Drucken am Temperaturnullpunkt, *Z. Physik, 111,* 373–385.

Kronig, R., J. de Boer, and J. Korringa. 1946. On the internal constitution of the earth, *Physica, 12,* 245–256.

Latter, R. 1955. Temperature behavior of the Thomas-Fermi statistical model for atoms, *Phys. Rev., 99,* 1854–1870.

Latter, R. 1956. Thomas-Fermi model of compressed atoms, *J. Chem. Phys., 24,* 280–292.

March, N. H. 1956. On metallic hydrogen, *Physica, 22,* 311–314.

March, N. H. 1957. The Thomas-Fermi approximation in quantum mechanics, *Advances in Physics, 6,* 1–101.

Mott, N. F. 1957. On the transition to metallic conduction in semiconductors, *Report of Meeting on Semiconductors,* London, The Physical Society, pp. 5–13.

Murnaghan, F. D. 1937. Finite deformations of an elastic solid, *Am. J. Math., 59,* 235–260.

Ramsey, W. H. 1949. On the nature of the earth's core, *Monthly Notices Roy. Astron. Soc., Geophys. Suppl., 5,* 409–426.

Ramsey, W. H. 1950. The planets and the white dwarfs, *Monthly Notices Roy. Astron. Soc., 110,* 444–454.

Ramsey, W. H. 1954. Transitions to metallic phases, *Occasional Notes, Roy. Astron. Soc., 3,* 87–95.

Ringwood, A. E. 1958. Olivine-spinel transition in fayalite, *Bull. Geol. Soc. Am., 69,* 129.

Robertson, E. C., F. Birch, and G. J. F. MacDonald. 1957. Experimental determination of jadeite stability relations to 25,000 bars, *Am. J. Sci., 255,* 115–137.

ten Seldam, C. A. 1957. Calculation of the interatomic distance at which a model of compressed solid helium becomes a metal, *Proc. Phys. Soc. (London), A, 70,* 97–109.

Sternheimer, R. 1950. On the compressibility of metallic cesium, *Phys. Rev., 78,* 235–243.

Stewart, J. W. 1955. Compressibilities of some solidified gases at low temperature, *Phys. Rev., 97,* 578–582.

Swenson, C. A. 1955. Compression of the alkali metals to 10,000 atmospheres at low temperature, *Phys. Rev., 99,* 423–430.

Wigner, E. P., and H. B. Huntington. 1935. On the possibility of a metallic modification of hydrogen, *J. Chem. Phys., 3,* 764–770.